PLANS FOR DREAM HOMES

Introduced and selected by

Murray Armor

PRISM PRESS
BRIDPORT, DORSET

PLANS FOR DREAM HOMES
First published in the United Kingdom in 1986 by
PRISM PRESS
2 South Street,
Bridport,
Dorset DT6 3NO

Second edition 1988
Third edition 1991

ISBN 1 85327 069 5

Text copyright 1991 - Murray Armor

ACKNOWLEDGEMENTS
Drawings by Derrick Spence
Cover Design by Wren Art and Design

Front cover: Courtesy of Potton Limited

Typeset by RTS, Worksop
Printed in Singapore

Contents

Foreword

By Martin Cruttenden, Director of Sales, British Coal.

This new British Coal edition of *Plans for Dream Homes* is the first major book to be published in the 90s for those choosing a design for — and then building — their own new home, and naturally we are delighted to be associated with its publication.

It reflects the tremendous changes in domestic architecture over the last few years, not least the return by public demand towards providing chimneys in new home designs, especially those with traditional real coal fires at their base.

The move back to chimneys and the new, efficient family of coal and smokeless fuel-fired heating appliances are two important reasons why British Coal is sponsoring this year's edition.

We are at the very heart of making modern homes energy efficient, and we fully appreciate that new houses have to be cost effective structures for families to live in. We've been in the energy business on a grand scale far longer than anyone else and have a total commitment to meeting the need for modern, efficient and economical home heating systems in the 1990s and beyond.

As the principal player in providing quality-controlled Real British Coal to fuel these systems, our involvement in meeting an increasing demand for smokeless fuels sees us at the forefront of technology designed to protect the environment. And when it comes to running costs, the enormous improvements in efficiency in British mines in fact means that coal and smokeless fuel fires have not moved up in line with inflation — making solid fuel an excellent buy.

Today, with the emergence of Coal and Energy Services, the new consultancy arm of British Coal, we can also offer a highly practical and professional heating design service to self builders, and our own contribution to these pages details what is available.

This publication features more than 400 homes built in recent years around the UK in all price brackets. It describes how the designs themselves are related to the living requirements of the families who commissioned them, to their surroundings and, most importantly, to their budgets.

These are not showhomes, or architectural concepts but the real homes of people who had freedom of choice — and knew what they wanted. And when it comes to external design and internal warmth, our market research shows that people want a chimney on their next home, a chimney capable of providing natural ventilation and, combined with a real coal fire, serving as the biggest house-warming radiator of all.

I hope that this publication, and British Coal's contribution to it, will help give those looking to build new homes for themselves a useful insight into the potential for energy concious design and energy effective home heating installations.

If readers are simply browsing through the book to find ready-made design ideas, I hope that the competent design of an energy system is one suggestion they will remember. If they are actually choosing a heating system for their new home, our CES nationwide design service is at their disposal.

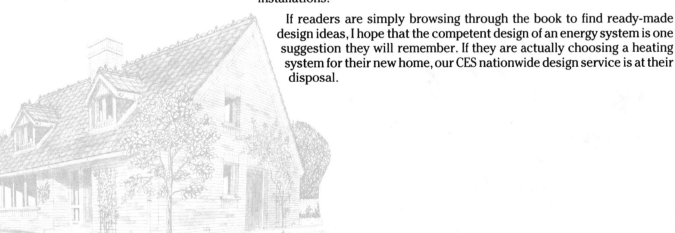

Choosing a Design

The Choices

Houses are for people. Unfortunately most of the people get little say in the design of the house that they live in, and their choice of a new property is limited to buildings already designed by others. However, every year about 30,000 families move into newly built homes where they have some say in the design, and this book presents 400 typical homes for which they commissioned the plans. How did they decide what they wanted, and how did they set about getting it? Of course, they all had professional advice from the designers who prepared the drawings, but they all had to make up their own minds what sort of home they wanted before the first pencil line was drawn.

The decisions are best made by considering the three functions of any new dwelling. First of all it is a contribution to the landscape. It will affect the appearance of the place where it is to be built, will require services ranging from the obvious water supply, to the less obvious medical services that we also expect to be on tap, and it will still be there in two hundred years time. Forty years ago it was decided that, because of this, all development should be regulated and controlled, and the planning acts were born. Today everyone agrees that planning controls are necessary, and just about everyone building a new home finds them an intolerable restriction of their desire to do their own thing. Whatever you may feel about this, the blunt fact is that whether or not you can build a new home at all, and if so every detail of its size, appearance and materials is controlled from the Town Hall. Every choice that you make in these matters is going to be subject to the approval of others, and it is essential to understand what is likely to be approved, and what is not.

The second function of a new home was described by the French architect Corbusier as a house being a machine for living in. This is a very convenient description of the part of the design for a new home where the individual and not the planner makes the decisions. Open plan living, or separate rooms? A small kitchen with an adjoining utility room, or a big family kitchen? A fireplace or not? All these are decisions that you will make to suit your own particular pattern of living, and it is easy to assume that you will decide to specify exactly what appeals to you, and that the interior of the home will be designed to meet your families specific requirements.

In practice this is rarely the case, as when the decisions have to be made a third consideration has to be taken into account — the home as an investment. This is not simply a matter of the cost, but of how worthwhile an investment you are making in bricks and mortar. At some stage of the decision making process virtually every home builder stops to ask himself what the resale value of the property will be, and starts considering how he can be sure that it always remains at the top of the market for its size and position. Invariably this aspect of the whole business comes to play a larger and larger part in his attitude to the alternatives, and tends to become the most important consideration.

When these three factors are put together the question to be answered can usually be expressed as "what design shall I choose which is:

★ the best investment for my money,

★ will be acceptable to the planners,

★ and will suit my family's living requirements."

It is very unusual to find anyone arranging their priorities differently, although there are a few, and they add a little variety to the architect's life and to the sort of houses and bungalows that get built. Apart from these rare exceptions, all the pressures are to conform to the conventional, which is why avant garde new homes are more often seen illustrated in magazines than on the ground.

Fortunately, conventional houses and bungalows these days are better designed and better looking than ever before, largely because consumer choice has returned to the housing market after three decades of housing shortages. (Now it is money to buy houses or to pay for mortgages that is short). Today's new homes are built in a wide variety of styles, and only the 'modern' homes of twenty years ago are out of fashion. All are represented among the four hundred designs in this book, and the following pages describe in greater detail the factors that you will have to consider when choosing between them.

Choosing a Design

The Planners

Planning consent for a new home is a subject dealt with at length in the other books in this series, and here we only look at the way that the Planning Acts control the design and the materials for a new home. However, it is important to remember that the regulations also determine whether or not any building of any sort can be erected at all, and if so what the access arrangements shall be, and how it will inter-relate with the environment in every possible way. Planning consents may also impose conditions, such as saying that the garden gates must be set back a certain distance from the road, or even requiring that in rural areas the householder must be employed locally. Consents often have a whole list of 'reserved matters' that require further approval at an appropriate stage.

All this can sound very frightening, particularly when one hears or reads of other people's adventures with planning appeals or other confrontations with the planners, but in practice all is quite simple. First of all, discover what sort of a building the planners would like to approve. Invariably this will be in the style and materials that are typical of the other new homes in the local area. Consideration of the investment value of the new property will usually lead to you wanting a house or bungalow in the same style, and presumably you want to build there because you like the local style anyway. It is probable that your view and the official view will coincide. In this case all that is required is for your plans to be presented in a way that makes it clear that your proposals meet the usual requirements, and deserve automatic approval!

If your understanding of the local planning scene leads you to suspect that your plans are not exactly what the planners are going to be looking for, then it is essential that your application is submitted in a way that gives it the best chance of success. The arguments for your proposals must be put forward properly, seeking a meeting to discuss the proposals on site, perhaps lobbying the local councillors, and certainly setting up the original application in a way that gives you the best opening for an appeal if it is refused.

All this requires that your application should be handled by a professional unless you are very sure of what you are doing, and the professional should be someone who has handled hundreds of planning applications like yours, not just someone who knows how to fill in the forms. In practice it is usual for the person who prepares your plans to submit your planning application on your behalf, so the initial choice of designer has to be made with this in mind. You will certainly want to discuss the pros and cons of the planning application with him, and reading the other two books in this series will help you to know what questions to ask.

In matters of design and the approval of materials there has been some relaxation of a very authoritarian approach adopted by planning authorities in the early 1980's, and successive planning appeal findings and Department of the Environment directives have emphasised that the approval must be of what is acceptable, and not of an ideal which a planning officer may consider desirable. Nevertheless, the system operates in a way that makes it very difficult to get consent for buildings or materials which do not conform to an established local style, and a key element in this is the time factor. The overwhelming majority of people who want to build are in a hurry, and they are usually prepared to compromise on design details in order to hurry up the paperwork. In theory a decision has to be given on a planning application in eight weeks, but the national average decision time on an application is nearly twice this time. Those who have borrowed money to buy a building plot, and who do not wish to lose a prospective purchaser for their existing house, will usually agree to changing a window or the style of the new home if this cuts through an argument and hastens the start of the work on site.

The rigour with which the planning acts are used to control the design of new home varies enormously in different parts of the country. In attractive rural areas and picture book villages the design of a new home may be reported on by three or four different experts before it ever reaches the planning committee, and it is not unusual for drawings to be revised half a dozen times before consent is obtained. By this time the applicant will be convinced that the pace of the deliberations is related to keeping the deliberators in employment. Be that as it may, the accepted routine is discussion, compromise, and redraw the plans until honour is satisfied all round. To adopt other tactics will probably involve even more lengthy delays, and if you want to force issues you must be sure that you have the time to spare.

Virtually every county has a published design guide of some sort, and these are readily available at District Planning Offices. An alternative way of understanding the sort of styles which the planners regard with favour is to look at the new homes being built on plots like yours in the local area. This means buildings actually under construction following a recent planning approval, and not properties built a year or two ago. Planning fashions change, and do not make the popular error of assuming that a planning consent in the past is a precedent for other similar applications. For instance, full bar or 'Georgian' windows are quickly moving out of fashion and in some rural areas the planners will suggest that they are inappropriate to the surroundings. The fact that three years ago they gave consent for windows of this sort in a house across the road is no precedent at all. You will be told that the house across the road merely 'demonstrates the way in which this type of window is adversely affecting the street scene' and this becomes an argument used against you. All of this has a jargon of its own — find out enough about it to be able to discuss it with your own expert, and make sure that he really is an expert.

Choosing a Design

The Local Scene

Fifteen years ago the local architectural styles in different parts of the country were as dead as the dodo as far as 99% of new homes were concerned. The national developers were using the same standard design types from one end of Britain to the other, and virtually everyone else was following suit. Bungalows had flat pitched roofs, picture windows, and were advertised as being 'ranch style' to cash in on vogue for anything American. Dormer bungalows with flat roofs to the dormer windows had the ugliest profile of any home ever built in Britain. Houses were as box-like as possible, and were invariably built in cheap walling materials with panels of contrasting materials to 'add interest'.

Fortunately these homes were built for a race of gardeners, and the splendid front gardens of our suburbs largely distract from the shortcomings of a million of these stereotyped homes. At the time that they were built a few architects were still designing homes in other styles, and a few local authorities built council housing using traditional materials, particularly in stone areas, but all the attention was focused on 'functional' designs that cut costs and often seemed to use new materials simply because they were new.

In the mid 1970's all this started to change. Once the housing shortage was replaced with a shortage of cash to buy houses, the building industry started to listen to their customers for the first time in as long as anyone could remember. The result was a dramatic return to both regional and 1930's styles. Neo-georgian homes took the lead, followed by a surprising return to mock-tudor designs. In the town halls the strong new planning departments formed after the local authority reorganisation of the early seventies got into their stride and promoted regional styles with enthusiasm. The result has been a remarkable revival of a whole range of different house styles, all of them conforming to either a traditional or a regional theme, and all as concerned with the materials of a new home as with its shape.

Today the emphasis is on traditional proportions, traditional roof shapes, and local materials. Roof pitches are up, flat roofs are out, and new building regulations have reduced windows to a maximum 24% of wall area. By 1985 the Ideal Home Exhibition had a mock Elizabethan thatched home as the house of the year. In 1975 this would have been unthinkable. On a wider stage, public disillusion with tower blocks and the other buildings of the 1960's make it fairly certain that it will be a very long time before any significant number of new homes will be built with new and non-traditional design themes. The result of all this is that those building for themselves are building in a wide range of styles, although, as explained on the opposite page these are all subject to the influences of the planning acts. Let us look at some of these styles.

'Georgian' homes led the movement away from modernism at a popular level, and the name covers a whole range of architectural styles and excesses. At its best it describes homes that are accurately in the style and proportions of domestic architecture in the late 18th and early 19th centuries, but this is usually in town houses built on high value sites. In the suburbs the name is attached to any house with a hip roof, full bar windows and a centrally placed front door. If the doorway has a fibreglass portico and the windows are of the sash type the house will command a premium price and will be much admired, even though the Georgians never built detached homes at six to the acre. They also kept their carriages at the back, not behind 'Georgian panelled' up and over garage doors. But it is inappropriate to make fun of this style: it is much admired by homebuyers, and lends itself to well proportioned comfortable rooms. In peri-urban areas where the style is well established it will usually be acceptable to the planners.

The regional style home arrived very soon after the Georgian home, and is much more significant. It is difficult to define, and easy to identify. The name is used to describe any house which demonstrates as many as practicable of the pre-Victorian architectural features of the area. This

means half hip roofs in Hampshire, complex clusters of gable roofs of different spans in the West country, tile hanging in Kent, colour washed brick in Essex, and the use of interesting local materials everywhere. Casement windows without top lights are de rigeur, although they are often made in hardwood and are stained, which would have been a novelty to those who originated the styles. Even the ubiquitous up and over garage door is increasingly found with chevron boarding, so that it looks something like a pair of coach house doors. All this is matched by a renewed interest in detailing: brick corbels at eaves, stone laid in the appropriate way to suit the grain and texture of the material, chimneys that once more seek to be decorative as well as functional. It is all a splendid revival, and examples of it all are to be found in the pages that follow.

Tudor style homes are the latest development. They have little in common with houses built in the 16th century, which incidentally had the timber framing covered with plaster, or if not, brightly painted, but they are a cheerful return to one of the most popular styles of Edwardian England, which is where our version of the Tudor style originated. They are pretty houses, and with their elaborate front doors and leaded lights they make a centre piece for the Englishmans pretty garden, which for far too long has only served to disguise an ugly, functional home.

Bungalows are a special case. The word is Hindi, brought home from India by tea planters in the last century, and the whole concept is wholly alien. Certainly the Welsh long house and the Scottish bothy have a long history, but in most parts of the country the yeomans home was two storeys high just as soon as he could afford more than a hovel. However, the convenience and utility of the bungalow have now given it its own place in our domestic architecture, and it is here to stay. In many areas, particularly in Wales and the South West, bungalows are now well established and accepted without question by the planners. Everywhere else the rule is that unless you are building among other bungalows you must assume that you will have to argue your case. The number of bungalows built every year show that it is often a perfectly good case.

Choosing a Design

The Layout

So far we have discussed the factors that are likely to affect your choice of the style of a new home, and the way in which the site will influence your decisions. The internal layout gives you far more scope for having exactly what you and your family want, although as already explained, it is likely that you will be very concerned that you build a property that is the best possible investment, and this will put a brake on flights of fancy that are too exuberant. How do you make sure that you get what you want?

First of all, the council of perfection. This is that you should think hard about your pattern of living and your likes and dislikes, and write them down in the form of concise notes. Look carefully at the designs in this book, and make notes of the features in some of them that particularly appeal to you. Then explain all this to the architect or designer who is to prepare your plans, give him your notes, and wait to see what his draft design looks like. Avoid giving him your own design drawn up on pages from a pad of graph paper that you have bought specially from the local stationers. In this way you will benefit from his professional training and experience, and will not let him slide into the easy course of simply drawing up the client's sketch. If you have drawn your own sketch — and why not — keep it to yourself so that you can compare it with his proposals in due course. You will probably find that he has approached the design in a different and interesting way, and the odds are that you will recognise that it is a better way. The first draft is only for discussion anyway, and two alternatives to look at are better than one.

I have described this course as a counsel of perfection because it is unlikely that you will take this advice. Although you have a lifetime's experience of communicating with words, and very little experience of drawing plans, most clients approach architects with the inevitable sheet of squared paper in their hands. The choice is yours. Whether you are going to brief a designer and leave him to work out a layout for you, or whether you are going to initiate the design concept yourself, the rest of this chapter should help you.

The best way to make a start is to consider each room of your dream house in turn and to decide what sort of a room you want it to be, what features you want in it, and what features you do not want. Once you have a clear idea of all these ideal rooms you can think about fitting them in a shell of the right shape and size. Start with the hall. Do you think a hall is a very important feature of a home, or is it not very important? If the former, would you accept that all the other rooms should be slightly smaller so that the hall can be really imposing, perhaps with room for a circular table in the centre of the room for a super flower arrangement? Or does the size not matter at all, and you see the only job of the hall to be to connect up the different rooms in the house? Should the front door open directly into the hall, or via a storm porch? Should the hall give access to the lounge through imposing double doors in the centre of a wall, or through a discreet door at one side?

Any staircase is likely to be in the hall; should this be as imposing as practicable, with a half landing and elaborate balustrades, or should it be an unobtrusive and functional single flight? Should the space under the stairs be boxed in, or left open as somewhere to put the pram? Do not worry how all the features that you want can be fitted into the design as the purpose of the exercise is not only to list everything that you hope can be arranged, but also to convey to your designer the feel of the sort of home that you want.

If you carry on like this through all the rooms you will cover a fair number of pages. Remember that you should also think about views from windows, about whether you want to enjoy the best view from your own bedroom window, or whether this is immaterial. Decide whether you want any particular view from the kitchen. And so on. If two members of a family draw up their own list separately, the debate when they compare them will go on for days. All to the good: the whole point of this is to make sure that you are getting exactly what you want, and to make sure that nothing is built without being carefully considered.

Kitchens and bathrooms are areas where it is particularly important to think carefully about the essentials of what you require, and not to get tied down with detail. These rooms have in common that the fittings can be specified in detail when the house is actually being built, but the basic decisions have to be made at an early stage. Starting with the kitchen area, ignore the relative merits of oak versus melamine cupboard fronts and instead think what size and shape of room you need. Kitchens can be divided into three types: 'farmhouse kitchens' with room for a free standing table and space for other activities, 'breakfast kitchens' with room for a breakfast bar or a table in an alcove, and 'cooks workshop' kitchens with space for nothing but food technology. Your view on which will suit your own living pattern can be complicated by consideration of whether you want a separate utility room, or no utility room and the washing machine and chest freezer in the kitchen. And if the latter, where will the dog sleep? Identify the essential concepts, make decisions on them, and only then move onto the detail.

Bathrooms offer a similar series of options. Fashions change: until a few years ago the w.c. tended to be in a cubicle of its own if space permitted. Now it is invariably back in the bathroom, and the five fittings bathroom with bath, basin, bidet, separate shower and w.c. is usual in larger homes. The latest trend is for this luxury bathroom to be built as the private bathroom of the master suite, with a simpler bathroom for the family and guests. Big en suite bathrooms like this are often associated with small dressing rooms, or a dressing alcove. These are a throwback to Victorian living, and are also somewhere to put fitted cupboards so that the bedroom looks as little like a hotel bedroom as possible. On the other hand, fitted cupboard manufacturers now promote built-in furniture that fits all round the bed-head with a wealth of bedside cupboards, shelves, lights and other supposed aids to a night's sleep. Which approach do you favour?

Both of the other books in this series carry a check list for use in making these decisions, but neither have the number of actual layouts that are shown in the design pages of this book. These are all the actual plans drawn to meet the real requirements of real clients, and looking through them should give a very good idea of the different approaches to all of this. The plans vary from the bungalow with a double sunken bath set in a mirrored alcove in the bedroom which appears on page 311 to the most conventional of designs, and the details can be as useful a source of design ideas as the overall concepts.

Choosing a Design

To Suit Your Site

Any new home has to suit the site on which it is to be built, and this is why any serious choice of a design can only be made after considering where it is going to be built. This may sound obvious, but it is surprising how many people run around looking for land on which to build a specific home for which they have already chosen the design. Daydreaming about a specific design irrespective of where it is to be built is fine, and daydreams keep up morale while you are searching for the right plot, but the real world is rather different.

A site for a new home will have its own fixed characteristics — the position of the access, the direction of the principal views, the path of the sun at different times of the day, and the slope of the land.

To these must be added the fixed requirements of the new building, and the need to meet them at an acceptable cost. The drains must flow downhill. The drive must have a maximum slope of one in seven. Regulations specify clearances between the buildings and the boundaries, and the distances between foundations and established trees. All of these factors and fixed requirements are unchanged whether you build a house or bungalow in any particular shape, style or material. Let us look at some of them in detail.

First of all, do not be too surprised or disappointed if your dream site for your dream home has a major problem, particularly if it is an isolated infill plot in a rural area. If you think about it, there has to be some reason why any plot with the potential to get outline planning consent has not been built on. Perhaps it is because the owner simply did not want it developed, or because there was no demand for it to be developed, but very often it is because there is a snag of some sort. The access may involve a deep cutting into a bank at the roadside, or the drains may have to be pumped, or there are foundation difficulties. All these are engineering problems which can be overcome, and it will be possible to estimate the cost involved. The price of the land should reflect the special cost of building on it, but obviously the problems should be examined in detail at an early stage. It is a useful rule always to ask yourself why a building plot with outline planning consent has not yet been developed by others.

One characteristic of every plot that is self evident is its orientation in relation to the sun, and the views that it enjoys. A generation ago a 'south facing site' where the sun would warm the principal rooms was considered very important, but today, with central heating and double glazing, this is given a far lower priority. Most people consider that the views are far more important — the nice views to be enjoyed and the unfortunate views to be obscured. Remember too that the views from the first floor rooms are often as important as those through ground floor windows, and that many housewives consider the view through the kitchen window to be at least as important as any other.

The role of any existing trees on the site has got to be settled at an early stage. If they are the subject of a tree preservation order they become part of your negotiations with the planning authority. If you do not know if there is a tree preservation order, remember that enquiries at the town hall may lead to an order being issued straight away. A nice catch twenty two situation which you will have to play by ear. At any rate, if existing trees are retained they are going to be a major factor in your design as they will affect the views from the windows as well as possibly complicating the foundations. They will certainly also affect your landscaping, limiting what will grow beneath them, providing huge areas of shade, and giving barrow loads of leaves to be swept up in the autumn. In spite of all this, few attributes of a site are more pleasing than mature trees of the right species.

Would suit the suburbs anywhere.

Rural areas, South East England.

Rural areas, the West of England.

17

Choosing a Design

To Suit the Slope

If a site slopes significantly, you must consider your approach to building on the slope as a first stage in establishing the design concept

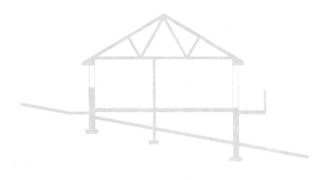

Option One. Build up above the slope. Involves suspended floors, some additional foundation costs, and the need for very careful landscaping to conceal the large area of brickwork below floor level. Will improve the view, especially from the balcony.

Option Two. Build into the slope. Permits a cost effective solid floor on natural ground, but may require a retaining wall or steep garden to the rear. Excavated material will have to be carted away unless it can be used for landscaping on site.

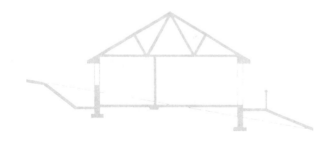

Option Three. 'Cut and Fill'. This is the usual approach, combining the minimum foundation costs with the look of being built into the hillside. Care required with landscaping.

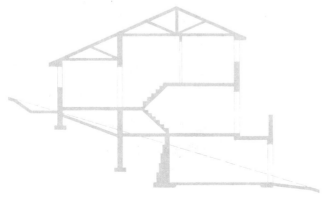

Option Four. Multi level. Garage below with living accommodation above, following the slope. Gives interesting layouts with opportunities for balconies to take advantage of views, but construction costs will be high. Inevitable steps outside and changes of level inside may limit resale potential.

The next consideration is the slope of the land. Here again, regional practice is paramount. In the West Riding of Yorkshire, homes are commonly built on sites with one in five slopes, and local styles and local building practice are geared to this. In other parts of the country any slope at all is deemed to merit special consideration. Wherever you build, there are two approaches to be considered; should you arrange to remove the slope, or design a home to make use of the slope?

If the site permits it is invariably cheaper to excavate a level plinth for a new home, adjusting the levels and spreading the surplus soil as part of your landscaping. This involves either digging into the slope or else digging out part of the plinth and using the excavated material to raise the level of the other part. This is called "cut and fill" and the sketch shows what is involved, as do many of the plans on the design pages.

Digging out a level plinth is not always possible, sometimes because the site is too steep or the ground too rocky, but usually because the plot is too small to allow for the necessary changes of level. Remember that you cannot excavate close up to your neighbour's fence: in law his land is entitled to support from your land. In this case you have to consider a building designed to make use of the slope, and sometimes those who like this style of home will deliberately alter the ground levels on their land to be able to do this. An example is on page 356.

Invariably a multi-level home of this sort is more expensive to construct than providing the same living accommodation on a level plinth, and changes of a level in a home are more attractive to the younger generation than to the elderly. This may affect the re-sale potential, and it is generally true that while split level homes are often exceptionally attractive and lend themselves to exciting decor, they often have a limited re-sale market. There are many examples of multi-level homes in the design section of this book.

The slope also affects the drains. Ideally drains should slope down to the sewer or septic tank at a regular slope of one in forty, about two feet below the ground, and should all leave the house at one convenient point. This is the ideal: lots of new homes have drains emerging at various points, with a pump to move the effluent up-hill to a private septic tank, which itself requires special sub-soil drainage. All things are possible, and all the solutions cost money.

If the slope is at all steep it will also involve the design of a drive. This is always a more complicated issue than it seems to be. First of all the local authority will want a visibility splay at the point where the drive joins the road, and will insist that any gates are set back a car's length from the road. They will probably want your drive laid out so that a car can turn round in it, and will insist that rain water from your drive should not cascade across the pavement. There is obviously a maximum slope that your car can negotiate, but long before you reach this limit, problems will arrive in designing the drive so that your car does not 'hang up' when making the change of gradients as it gets onto the road, or into the garage. Finally, the appearance of the drive is important. It will almost certainly be the largest feature in your front garden, and has to be designed with your landscaping proposals in mind.

The actual ground conditions as far as the foundations are concerned are usually less important than many other considerations, as long as they are understood by all concerned at an early stage. The value of a new house has now risen to a point where the additional cost of specially reinforced raft foundations is not a prohibitively expensive element in the total cost. Even complicated piled foundations are often cost-effective in the overall scheme, particularly if the purchase price of the land reflects the potential foundation difficulties.

All these considerations are discussed at length in the other books in this series. As set out briefly here they should help you to identify the characteristics of any building plot which you need to have in mind when thinking about a home to be built on it.

Choosing a Design

House or Bungalow?

In spite of the rude things written about bungalows on an earlier page, and although some county design guides refer to there being 'a presumption against single storey construction', the inescapable fact is that bungalows are an established part of our housing scene and are very popular with home buyers. What are the pros and cons of the house versus bungalow options?

To start with, you will only have this choice of homes on a relatively small proportion of building plots. In most situations it is obvious that planning consent is only going to be granted for a house. In a few other areas only a single storey design will be acceptable. Again, only a small proportion of building plots on the market have the frontage for a large bungalow, so if you want four bedrooms it is likely that you will be obliged to build a house unless you find a plot at least sixty feet wide. Even so, there are plenty of situations where the option is available, and these are the facts to consider.

- ★ A bungalow is likely to cost marginally more to build than a house of the same floor area.

- ★ In most parts of the country a bungalow is usually worth rather more than a house of the same size. If this is an important factor you should check this out with a local estate agent.

- ★ A bungalow will take up more of the plot area than a house, and this can lead to it looking cramped between the boundaries. If your frontage is limited, a bungalow may not have the feel of gracious living that comes with a bigger garden around a home.

- ★ Bungalows usually have less waste space than a house, — if you regard the staircase well as waste space.

- ★ Bungalows generally permit more flexible layouts as fewer walls have to be loadbearing.

- ★ Split level and multi level homes are more easily arranged as bungalows. So are changes in ceiling height and sloping ceilings.

- ★ If provision is to be made for a home to be extended at a later date, the ease with which this can be arranged, and how much room on the site is available for it, is often a key factor in deciding whether to build a house or a bungalow.

- ★ Routine maintenance work like painting and cleaning gutters is more easily dealt with by the average householder if he is working on a bungalow. This often appears to be a major consideration to those faced with making a choice.

- ★ Finally, the 'no stairs' factor is enormously important to many elderly persons.

Reproduced by kind permission of Cala Homes (Essex) Limited.

Consideration of this house/bungalow option invariably leads to discussion of dormer bungalows, and of building a bungalow that is designed for extra rooms to be put in the roof at a later date. This is rarely as straightforward as it may seem to be.

The rectangular dormer bungalow with first floor windows in the gable walls and a flat roofed dormer window in one roof slope had a enormous vogue twenty years ago, and a typical example is illustrated on page 255. At that time statutory requirements and low labour costs combined to make this a particularly cheap way to provide four bedrooms on a narrow plot. Besides this bungalows commanded premium prices over houses, and the functional shape was fashionable. All of these circumstances have changed, and unless a building with dormer windows and low eaves relates to a traditional style it will invariably be better in every way to build a conventional house. Incidentally, flat roof dormers are now very unusual. Unless covered with lead they present maintenance problems, and they rarely look attractive. Pitched roof dormers appear in many places in the design pages, and are often discussed in the descriptions of the designs. A bungalow which is designed so that rooms can be put in the roof at a later date does make sense in some circumstances. It must be realised that this must be a design requirement from the start, and that it is not possible to ask for arrangements to be made for rooms in the roof while the building work is under way — and this is a common request! Provision has to be made for a stairwell, and current building regulations require heavy ceiling joists and other features that will not be used until the first floor rooms are fitted out. An example is on page 268.

Choosing a Design

Garages

If you consider only the basic economics of building a home, a garage is a very expensive luxury. It costs a great deal, probably as much as the kitchen, and is only used to accommodate a car which is itself perfectly weatherproof, and which will not depreciate in value any faster if kept out of doors. Looked at in this way, you are paying a large sum of money so that your car is marginally warmer to get into in the mornings, and so that you can unload groceries from the car under cover when it is raining. None of this is likely to dissuade you from having a garage, but it is interesting to consider just how much a luxury it is. If you have a tight budget this may encourage you to build a larger house and leave the garage until later.

However, there is more to this than the simple utilitarian view. A garage adds another element to the building, or if it is detached, it turns one building into a group of buildings. This adds to the complexity and interest that we look for today in the design of a new home, makes it all look more impressive, and probably a better investment. A garage can also be built large enough to provide storage space for garden equipment and other things, or if you wish it can be further extended into a workshop. If you build a detached double garage, with a roof pitch of over 45° there will be space for a room in the roof, which can be anything from a simple loft to a self-contained flat.

The pros and cons of detached versus integral garages are often irrelevant, as the size and shape of your site may make the choice for you. Given the option, remember that a detached garage can be positioned in relation to the house so that each complements the other, perhaps with link wall to give a courtyard effect. It will be cheaper to build a detached rather than an integral garage as it will not require complex foundations, a fire proof ceiling or other expensive features, and it can be built after the house is completed if this is more convenient. On the other hand it is more expensive to provide electricity, water, or an outside W.C. in a detached garage. An integral garage provides somewhere to put a central heating boiler or an extra freezer, and in many ways is useful simply because it is part of the main building. Finally, an overwhelming advantage of an integral garage for the elderly or infirm is the opportunity to get in or out of a car 'out of the weather'.

Virtually all new garages are built with up-and-over garage doors, and these are now available in a very wide variety of styles and materials, including wooden doors that look like traditional coach house doors. If you want a double garage it is preferable to have two single doors with a masonry pillar between them rather than one double door, although this will take up a little more space. It looks better, is more convenient, and gives more room for car doors to be opened. Electric door openers with remote control arrangements which enable up-and-over doors to be opened from inside a car are now well established and very reliable. They are also addictive: once you are used to them you will not readily go back to opening a garage door by hand. There is something very satisfying to the ego in pressing a button in your car as you drive in the gate and seeing the light come on and the garage door open, and this becomes even more important than practical considerations.

A double garage with a 45° roof pitch has space for rooms in the roof.

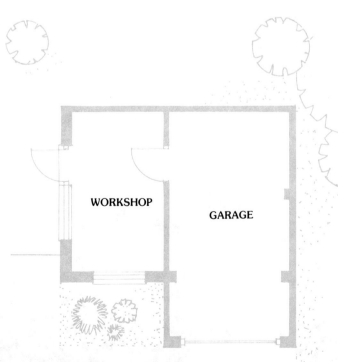

WORKSHOP

GARAGE

If you want to have a garden store or workshop as part of your garage, you have an opportunity to get away from the conventional garage shape.

Building a Home

Landscaping

This chapter is not about designing a garden, or about gardening, but looks at some of the basic considerations involved in relating the house or bungalow to its garden. If you are an experienced and enthusiastic gardener you have probably always thought of your new home in relation to its garden, and you are looking for the right design for a house to suit the dream garden which you can visualise. Most people put things the other way round, and choose a dream house first, and then think about a garden to occupy the space around it. It is important that those in this second group find a little time to give the same careful, analytical thought to the garden that they will give to considering room sizes, window positions and the colour of the bathroom suite.

First of all, how much time are you going to want to give to looking after your garden? At one end of the scale you may think that the less bother the garden is, the better it will suit you. Fine — carefully chosen shrubs, the right grass, no borders, no edges, paths set flush in the grass, and you will have a minimum maintenance garden which can look very attractive indeed. At the other extreme, you may intend that the garden will be a very important part of your life. If so, it is even more important that you analyse what you are going to be able to do, and plan accordingly. If you are fortunate enough to be able to afford to pay someone to look after your garden for you, careful consideration of the labour requirement is just as important, as you will want a perfect garden for your money, and an acre can be laid out either to need only half a day a week to maintain, or to occupy someone nearly full time.

The next thing to consider is your timetable. This is important, and is often overlooked. Do you look forward to watching the garden slowly taking shape, and hope to see your dreams come true in three of four years, or do you want visitors to be admiring it in six months' time? Remember a wisteria will take seven years before it makes a show but a cherry will be in flower next spring. This can be an important issue if your life style is such that you might move at any time, and need your home always to be a good resale prospect. An established garden may or may not add to the value of a property but it certainly always makes it more saleable.

This leads on to the next consideration, which is that of cost. It used to be said that anyone building a house should be prepared to spend at least 10% of its value on its surroundings. The cost of building is now so high that this would require a large plot on which to spend the sum involved, but the principle that the garden deserves its place in the budget is important. This may be a cash budget if you intend to have a landscaping contractor to do all the work, or a budget for your own labour plus some cash if you intend to do all the work yourself. In this latter case, beware of over-estimating your own capacity or the time that you will have available, particularly if you are going to do much earth moving by hand.

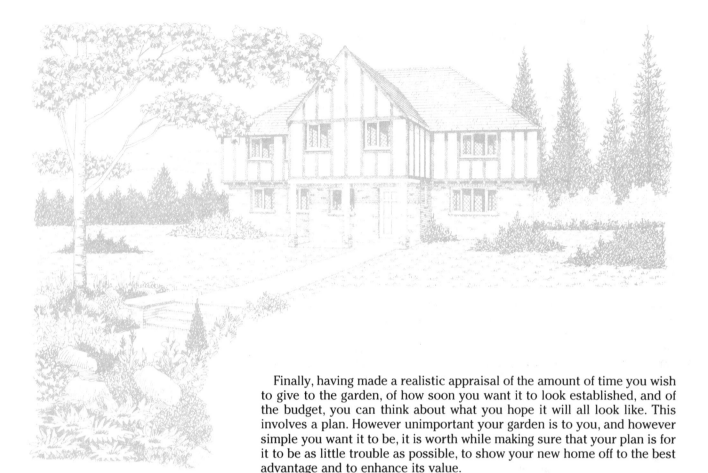

Finally, having made a realistic appraisal of the amount of time you wish to give to the garden, of how soon you want it to look established, and of the budget, you can think about what you hope it will all look like. This involves a plan. However unimportant your garden is to you, and however simple you want it to be, it is worth while making sure that your plan is for it to be as little trouble as possible, to show your new home off to the best advantage and to enhance its value.

If you are building on an eighth of an acre in a built-up area, your choices are limited, and you will almost certainly have a marvellous opportunity to look at all your options by simply going for a walk to see what all your neighbours have done with their own plots. Look at their gardens in winter as well as in summer, take local advice on what takes time and trouble, and what is easily looked after, sort out your own masterplan, and away you go. Your garden can set off your house very well, but its size will dictate a limit to what you can do.

With anything over a quarter of an acre the challenge is much more complicated. At this size your garden can be given a distinct character, and house and garden can complement each other in a very special way. If you have this opportunity, then you need to be a very experienced gardener to be confident that you can design a garden like this. Even if you are, it is worth spending a relatively small sum in buying someone else's ideas as well, if only so that you can be absolutely sure that your own are the best. Unfortunately, the right garden designers are as hard to find as the right people to design the house itself.

Local landscaping contractors, nurserymen and garden centres usually offer to design gardens, but this is inevitably linked to their own services. If you are wanting to place a single order at a lump sum price for all the work, materials and plants involved, then contacting them is one obvious way to make a start. Ask for a detailed quotation, which should come with an attractive lay-out plan, lists of plants, details of how the ground will be prepared and of any top soil to be provided, arrangements to replace trees and shrubs that do not take, and proposals to maintain lawns for a fixed period. Everything should be as detailed as possible, so that you can get friends who are keen gardeners to advise you on the proposals.

However, landscaping is one area where the cost of a package service is likely to be far more than the cost of the component parts, and where many people prefer to make their own arrangements for all the various elements involved. If this is what you are likely to want you can ask your local landscaper if he will provide you with a design for a fee, with the option to use his services or not as you wish. Keep in mind that all landscaping contractors make their livings from supplying plants and making gardens and not from designing gardens. There are pressures on them to design what they would find it most profitable to handle, and your only safeguard in this is their local reputation. It is well worthwhile going out of your way to find out what this is, and to look at other gardens that they have made. Do not just visit the one "show garden" that they suggest to you.

An alternative is to use the services of a garden designer. This makes the whole business more complicated, but need not cost very much in relation to the total cost of the garden, and you will know that the advice that you are getting is free of commercial pressure. A garden designer's proposals can be used to get competing quotations from landscaping contractors, or will be your blueprint for managing the job yourself. The problem is to find a designer.

Personal recommendations are invaluable but most people will have to resort to the yellow pages or similar directories. The best initial approach is made by letter, explaining that you are wanting a new garden designed on a plot of xxxx sq. yds. (or x acres) and will be interested to know what the designer can do for you and the costs involved. After that, leave them to sell their services to you and evaluate the proposals very carefully. Again, ask to be put in touch with previous clients. Finally, in explaining your requirements to a designer, make sure he or she understands your own situation with regard to maintenance, timetable and budget.

Some gardening magazines offer a garden design service and these are usually so cheap that it is fun to sign up for one or two of them anyway. The proposals are invariably for an enthusiast's garden with something of everything — lots of quarts in a pint pot. This will give you plenty of ideas, and if you have explained your maintenance/timetable/budget proposals firmly you may even find that they have been given consideration.

All of this needs to be done at an early stage, just as soon as you have settled on the house or bungalow plans themselves. Certainly you want to know exactly the shape and contours of your new garden whilst the builder still has earth moving plant on site, so that you can get him to dump soil where it will be required and to leave the site with the ground at levels that will suit the landscaping work. If you have a large site it is a very good idea to fence off the builder's theatre of operations and to start making the garden on the rest of the land while the house is being built. In this way you will almost certainly be able to get one season ahead, and having part of the garden finished will encourage you to make a start on the area left by the builder as soon as you move in.

To be realistic, if you are managing the building of a new home yourself, it is unlikely that you will have the time or energy to spare to give any of this the attention it deserves, but even so it is important that you do have a landscaping scheme and try to give it consideration, in spite of the over-riding priority to be given to getting the roof tiled on schedule. On the other hand, if you have placed a contract with a builder, then involvement with planning the garden will serve as an outlet for all your frustrations whilst the building work proceeds so slowly. You will have time for visits to garden exhibitions, garden centres, and a great deal of reading and can even venture to plant trees amid the builders confusion if you protect them properly! However much time you have for this, or however little, the important thing is to have a plan at an early stage, and to ensure that it is suited to the long-term relationship between you and the garden which is going to be outside your window for as long as you live in the house.

Given the determination to make an effective plan for the new garden, preferably before the builder moves his earth-moving equipment away from the site, what are the features to be considered? Many of them are the physical characteristics of the ground from the gardener's viewpoint, such as the soil type, the aspect, and the local climate. These are specialist matters, but others are common to all gardens everywhere. Among the more important are the following.

THE DRIVE. Unless you have a very large garden indeed, the drive is the largest single feature at the front of the house, and once it is built it is very difficult to move. It is likely that your planning consent will require that the gates, if any, are set back a fixed distance from the road, that the slope for the first few yards should not exceed a certain gradient, and that there is provision for a car to be able to turn on the drive without backing out into the road. If you can meet all these requirements and still have alternative alignments for the drive, do consider how they will look, and the feel that they will give to the garden, as well as thinking about them simply as a way of getting the car to the garage. If you have a very large garden you may wish to consider a bend in the drive to slow down vehicles using it, but make sure that the oil tanker and the council refuse vehicle can negotiate it.

A tarmac surface drive is expensive, and how long it lasts without costly repairs will depend on how the edges are retained to stop it spreading sideways. If it is only to take cars it can be edged with 8" x 2" path edging set in concrete, but if it will be used by heavy delivery vehicles it is well worthwhile using road curbing. The specifications for the construction of the drive itself should be drawn up by your architect, or should be a standard specification from a source that you trust, and should certainly not be left to the tarmacadam contractor. If the cost of a tarmac drive is beyond your budget, then have the curbing installed to retain gravel or chippings and let your car act as a roller for a year or two until it suits you to lay tarmac.

TREES. If you are lucky enough to have mature trees on your site you are probably determined to retain them if this is possible. There are a lot of factors involved in this. Tree preservation orders are mentioned on an earlier page, but it is also likely that steps will have to be taken to preserve the house from being damaged by the trees. Tree roots affect foundations in a number of ways, and precautions against damage can involve deepening the foundations or digging a deep trench between the building and any trees, and filling it with concrete. Conversely the building work may have an effect on the trees by altering the sub-surface drainage as well as by interfering with the roots. If a tree is a key element in your landscaping, or is subject to a tree preservation order, it is a good idea to get it surveyed by a qualified tree surgeon. He should be able to advise on the size it will reach, its probable life, and any work necessary to keep it healthy and safe.

If you are planting trees that will grow to any size it is important to take advice on the appropriate clearance from your buildings to avoid problems in the future. This only applies to trees of forest species like beech, cedar, and particularly poplar, and not to fruit trees or ornamentals like flowering cherries or weeping willows.

HEDGES. If you have an existing field hedge on a boundary of your land you are very lucky, but it may need a great deal of work to put it in good order. First of all, check with your solicitor whether it belongs to you, or to your neighbour. If the latter, all that you can do to it without his agreement is to keep it trimmed from your side 'in accordance with good practice'. If it is not regularly trimmed on the other side it is worth considering whether you want to try to arrange to take on this work, because a hedge that is regularly cut on one side only will soon become mis-shapen and unattractive. Again, this is a matter on which to get expert advice, particularly if your hedge is of mixed species.

Planting a new hedge always presents a difficult choice of exactly what to plant. Fast growing hedges like privet and leylandii require frequent trimming, and are very greedy, starving neighbouring plants of nutrients. More attractive hedges, like beech and yew, which require little maintenance, take some years to become established. If you can take the long term view and plant a slow growing hedge you will probably never regret it.

WALLS. Old walls around a garden are invariably very attractive, a good wind break, and splendid for climbing plants of all sorts. They also have a tendency to start to fall down the moment that you assume responsibility for them, especially if the ground is higher on one side than on the other. The worst potential problem is in the foundations. If a wall leans at all you should consider finding old bricks or stone to match the original material, and have a buttress or buttresses built to support the wall before it becomes unstable. This is cheaper than rebuilding, and if the buttress is really massive and in character, and quickly clothed with climbing shrubs, no one will know it is not original.

The stone coping or coping brickwork is another weak point: fortunately it is easily replaced and it is important to get this done before rain gets down into the masonry. Repointing is less essential than dealing with water getting in at the top, but if it needs to be done, make sure that the work is carried out in exactly the style of the original, with mortar made from the same sand so that the colour matches. If the original wall was built with lime mortar, use lime mortar for the repairs. Walls are a lot of work, but if you are lucky enough to have one, it is worth it.

FENCES. The only type of fence which is in any way suited to today's regional architectural styles is a timber post and rail fence. This is attractive, lasts a very long time, and can be fitted with wire mesh at a low level to keep your dog at home. All that can be said about close boarded or chain link fences is that the sooner they are hidden by creepers, climbers, and appropriately planted shrubs the better. If they are unavoidable, and they sometimes are, consider if you can arrange for garden features to give them additional support. A brick built cold frame or compost bay half way along the fence, firmly fastened to it, will help it to still be standing up to the wind long after it would otherwise have needed replacing.

PATHS, PATIOS AND FEATURE WALLING. There are many garden books with lengthy chapters on the design and construction of masonry garden features and garden paving, and they are well worth reading. However, they are written by enthusiasts for enthusiasts, so let us look at the snags. Starting with paths, keep in mind that all types need maintenance to some extent or other, and that if they are not laid on properly made foundations they will become uneven and dangerous. Some stone flags become very slippery in wet weather, particularly if they are in the shade, and if you intend to walk around your garden paths at all times of the year it is important to ask about the non-slip characteristics of the surface.

Patios are features that need to be as large as possible, as they invariably manage to look mean and skimpy unless they are big enough to set off the building to which they relate. Unless a paved area has a diagonal dimension of at least a third of any adjacent building it is unlikely to look attractive. It is also important to consider carefully the use to which the patio will be put. If it is principally a feature to be seen and admired, but not used, then the slabs can have gaps to be filled with alpine plants, dwarf walls can be of a height to suit the outlook, and everything arranged for the visual effect. If it will be used for sitting out, or for parties with lots of guests, it is important that there are no gaps to trap high heels, and it will help informal gatherings if any walls are at a convenient height for sitting down.

Masonry features, from simple low walls through to flights of steps and pergolas, are all subject to one over-riding design rule: they must look substantial. Single skin brick walls and nine inch pillars may be structurally satisfactory, and will save on materials, but will always look flimsy and cheap. The same walls at thirteen inches and pillars that are twice as thick as they need to be, will look solid, dignified and established. This is particulary true of any timber used in a garden feature as in a pergola.

Many people take a great deal of pleasure in carrying out this sort of building work themselves, and it is a very good way to exercise a talent for D.I.Y. bricklaying. What is poor workmanship in a building becomes charming rustic brickwork in a surround to a raised flowerbed! However, foundations, drainage holes and damp courses are all important, and not all types of bricks or stone are suited to garden use, as some are affected by damp and frost. Marshalls of Halifax, who sell cast stone for landscaping have an excellent free booklet about all of this.

POOLS. Water in a garden involves a maintenance commitment and if you intend to swim in it you can expect to spend as much time looking after the pool as you are likely to spend actually in the water. If you are an enthusiast you already know this, and will enjoy it. On the other hand, a pool as a status symbol requires careful consideration of the long term commitment, and of the effect on the value of the property. Except in a few areas where high value properties are expected to have pools, they can make a house difficult to sell.

If this does not discourage you, then make your plans for your pool at an early stage. If it is to be built at the same time as your house, it is up to the pool contractor to arrange an effective liaison with your builder. If it is to be built later, then it is important to ensure that an excavator will be able to get round to the site of the pool in due course. You will probably want to retain the excavated soil in your garden, piling it up as a bank to be planted as a shrubbery, so you should allow for this in your landscaping plan. It is probably a good idea to make all the arrangements for pipe runs for a future swimming pool while the house is being built, particularly if the pool is to be heated using your domestic boiler.

ELECTRICITY. Electrical sockets in the garden can be very convenient for electric garden tools, garden lighting, and barbecue accessories, and if they are arranged when the contract is placed for wiring the house the cost will be very reasonable. Special circuit breakers and weather-proof sockets will make everything safe. Garden lighting, and any lighting or pumps used with an ornamental pool usually operate at a safe low voltage, and the transformers and cable for this are supplied by the manufacturers of the lights used. Security flood lighting, which is becoming quite common these days, invariably requires mains voltages. All of this requires discussion with an electrician, and it is important to remember that the work involved is little trouble at the time the house is being built, but will be a nuisance to carry out afterwards.

Making it Happen

Placing a Contract

There are two ways of building a house or bungalow on your own land, and it is important to distinguish clearly between them. The first is to place a single contract with a builder for the construction of the building. The contract will make it clear that he is responsible for everything from site insurances and arranging the water connection before he moves onto the plot, through to cleaning the finished building before he hands it over to you. You are responsible for paying him in stages as work progresses and warrant to him that the land belongs to you and that the appropriate planning consents have been granted. The contract may or may not provide for him to be supervised by your architect and may or may not involve special arrangements for matters like you buying the kitchen units yourself, or employing your firm's electrician for the wiring, but essentially the responsibility for managing the job rest with the builder.

The alternative is to manage the job yourself, employing firms or individual craftsmen as sub-contractors. In this case you have the final responsibility for the work on site, the liaison between the different trades, and a thousand and one things like services, insurances, contracts with the authorities and much else. If you manage the job this way, whether or not you actually do any of the work yourself, you are what is called a 'self-builder'. The distinction becomes very clear when you look at the VAT position, as a self builder reclaims the VAT paid on materials by filling in forms and receiving a cheque from the VAT authorities, even though he is not VAT registered, while a builder who has a contract to build a house reclaims the VAT himself and has to be registered. The difference is very fundamental. Everything in this chapter is for those who wish to place a contract with a builder, and some of it is reproduced from *Home Plans* which deals with this subject in far greater detail.

USING AN ARCHITECT. An architect in private practice will prepare plans to your instructions, obtain all the consents you require on your behalf, find you a builder, prepare a contract for you to sign, supervise the work and approve bills before sending them on for you to pay. He will be concerned to see that you get good value for your money, but he does operate at the top end of the market. His fee will be around 9% of the cost of the work, plus expenses. He should have professional indemnity insurances. Find an architect by personal recommendation, or by asking the R.I.B.A. to recommend a practice in your local area which specializes in individual houses of the size which you propose to build.

USING A LOCAL DESIGN CONSULTANT. A design consultant may offer the same services as a registered architect, or a more limited and informal service. His fees are negotiable and he may not carry insurances — both are something to check in advance. Reach him by personal recommendation or through yellow pages, and make sure that he has the experience you require.

USING A 'PACKAGE COMPANY'. Various national companies offer comprehensive services for those building on their own, and the five design practices whose plans are featured in this book will all provide whatever assistance their clients may require, from site appraisals and preliminary design studies, to involvement with the actual building contract and supply of materials. As the size and scope of this book demonstrates, their strength is their enormous experience. All work is done against fixed quotations, which many find reassuring. There are many package companies and with any of them check on their resources and ask to see other homes under construction, particularly when they are agents for imported kit houses.

USING A BUILDER. Another way of having a house built is to approach a builder, who you already know, and whose work you particularly admire and to ask him to handle everything for you including the design. With the right existing personal relationships this can be a very good way of doing things, but make sure that you have the right contract.

QUOTATIONS, SPECIFICATIONS AND PRIME COST SUMS. An architect, designer or package company will obtain competing quotations from builders for you, and will know the builders who they should approach. However, there are probably one or two builders known to you who you would like approached as well and you should not hesitate to ask for this to be arranged. A builder who is invited to quote to build a house is sent a set of drawings and a specification. The specification sets out exactly the materials to be used, the standards of workmanship required and who is responsible for what while the work is being done. It is a lengthy and complex document, but there are ways in which it can be condensed and Building Your Own Home has a whole section about this including a specimen contract which is essential reading before you start negotiating a contract.

A builder will not want to quote for the particular fixtures and fittings that you require and so will allow a 'prime cost sum' for the items concerned. A p.c. sum of £1,200 for a kitchen means that the builder has allowed for kitchen fittings to this value: if you want to spend less than this the contract price will be reduced; if more, it will be increased. Typical features covered by p.c. sums are kitchens, bathrooms, central heating, fitted furniture, fireplaces, feature staircases, wall tiling and floor tiling. It is a very useful arrangement but make sure you know the basis on which p.c. sums are calculated — list price, trade price, special offers or what.

THE NATIONAL HOUSE BUILDERS COUNCIL. Virtually all house builders belong to the N.H.B.C. which issues ten year warranties on new houses built by its members. An N.H.B.C. warranty is normally required by banks and building societies as a condition of granting a mortgage, but is not generally available to selfbuilders, who have other alternatives set out in Building Your Own Home. The usual alternative for them is the similar Foundation 15 warranty from the Municipal Mutual Insurance Company

CONTRACTS. Whoever is handling your design is the best person to advise you on a contract with a builder. An architect will write a formal contract for you. Make sure it is a fixed price contract, without inflation escalation clauses and that any extras to be charged have to be authorised by you as well as by the architect before the expenditure is incurred.

If you are using a large building firm, they may present you with one of the various standard forms of contract used in the building industry. You will quickly see that 90% of the clauses protect the builder and not the client and it is important to take advice before signing one of these contracts.

A quotation from a small local builder may well be hand written on one side of a piece of lined paper. This may seem to you to be casual in the extreme, but if the price is right, and the builder is right, it can be the basis of an excellent contract. What you do is send him a letter accepting his offer which *refers to an attached specification and drawing.*

In any arrangement to build a new home it is essential never to pay in advance for any work. Progress payments should always be for rather less than the actual value of the work done, and usually there are retention arrangements in the contract or in the specification to allow for this. Work that is extra to the contract should be costed and authorised in writing before it is put in hand. If these rules are followed you will always be in control of the contract. 99% of disputes on contracts arise from situations where clients have lost control of the contracts by ignoring the terms in them!

Making it Happen

Managing the Job Yourself

In 1990 the VAT authorities made refunds of the VAT on the cost of building materials to 9,817 people who had built new homes for themselves on their own, without using a builder. Another two thousand had moved into homes that they had built for themselves as members of selfbuild housing associations, and at least another thousand added to the total as they were in business in some way on their own and could reclaim the VAT through their business accounts. Nearly thirteen thousand families in all.

This accounts for one in sixteen of all new private sector houses built, and nearly everyone knows someone who has either built a house for themselves, or is planning to do so. They do not necessarily do any of the physical work themselves, and they need not have any building skills or experience, but they have to manage the whole project, engaging sub-contractors to do the work and buying all the materials. Essentially they have to manage the job, although nearly all get involved in some of the actual building work at some stage or another.

What has caused this boom in DIY housebuilding? It has a lot to do with encouragement from both banks and building societies, which are now much more helpful than they uséd to be to those who want to do without a builder. Provided that you can persuade them that you have a viable proposition, and that you are the sort of person who will make it all happen, they will readily help with bridging finance, and will give you a mortgage when the new home is finished. They will want you to arrange architects progress certificates and special insurances, but this is all part of managing the job.

No-one ever pretends that building for yourself is easy, or that it does not involve an enormous amount of hard work, but the advantages are really impressive. First of all, the saving, expressed as the difference between the open market value of the finished property and what you have spent on land and building work, is usually at least 25%, and it is sometimes nearly 50%. Besides this, you make sure that you get exactly the home that you and your family want, and you will certainly find the whole project challenging and exciting. How do those who want the challenge set about things?

There are two different ways of being a self builder, and they are quite different — you either join a self-build housing association or else you build on your own. The essential difference between them is that the individuals who go it alone have either got a building plot to start with, or manage to borrow the money to buy a plot (which is not easy), or else they find a plot sold by a council or a development corporation on a 'build now, pay later' basis. They use the title to the plot as security to borrow the money for the building, and when the home is finished they get an ordinary mortgage to repay the loan. In order to arrange this finance it is essential that they really know what to ask for, know what the bank or building society will be expecting of them, and manage to convince all concerned that they really understand what they are doing.

If you have ambition to be a solo self builder, the key to all of this is to make yourself an expert on the subject before you raise the matter with your bank manager or with anyone else whose support you will need. You will have to know something about what it will cost to build your dream home on any particular site, what the optimum ratio of plot cost to building cost should be, and on what basis finance is usually made available. You must be able to discuss the certificates that you will be expected to provide, the insurances that you will be expected to arrange, and to have worked out the costings. There are books that you can read about all of this, and some companies offer special services to help you, but essentially your management of the job starts with you learning everything that you are going to need to know. All on your own.

Being on their own is one problem that the group self builders certainly do not have. They start by finding between twelve to twenty people to form an association to build as many homes as there are members, all working together under an elected foreman, with all the arrangements made by an elected committee. They get loan funds from the Housing Corporation or from a commercial bank to pay for the site and all the building work, and when all the houses are finished they take up ordinary mortgages that have already been arranged for the new homes, use the mortgage money to pay off the loans, and then wind up the association. Unlike individual self builders who usually employ others to do most or all of the building work, group members do a very high proportion of the work themselves, and tend to be involved for rather longer periods than the individuals. Eighteen months to finish a scheme is considered good going for an Association, while most people who build on their own have everything buttoned up in less than a year.

And the risks in all of this? Strangely, virtually none. It is very difficult to get started at all, and to do so you need the assistance of a great many other people. All of them come to have a stake in your success in one way or another, and between them they will make sure that you never get to start unless you have set everything up in a way that makes sure you cannot fail. Among them are the bank, the building society, the inspecting architect, building inspectors, electricity board inspectors, the water board, the planning authority — you will have a host of others involved. Their bureaucratic requirements will seem to hold you back at every stage until you actually get started. From that point on they all have a vested interest in making sure that you finish, and everything then works to urge you on. In some ways building on your own is like pushing a wheel up a steep hill. Everything conspires against you until you are able to start, but when you do start the job gains its own momentum that pulls you along as if the wheel is running down the other side of the hill. The result is that there are virtually no self builders' disaster stories. Even if you die while you are building there are special insurances to enable your executors to hire a contractor to finish the job!

How do you find out more about all of this? The best way to start is with the companion volume to this book, which is called *Building Your Own Home* and which is up-dated each year. It is not concerned with laying brick on brick but with the infrastructure of the world of self building, and deals with finding a site, choosing designs, planning, finance, costings, using sub-contractors, joining associations and making it all happen. There are 24 case histories with photos, plans, the actual cost of the jobs, and the values of the completed homes. Details of where to get it are at the back of this book.

Other sources of advice and help are the package companies, who offer a special range of services to self builders. Involvement with them enables you to go it alone with access to the advice of professionals, and if they supply you with a complete kit of structural materials it takes the whole business of placing orders, and arranging deliveries off your hands.

The Designers

The designers of the plans in this book are from one or the other of Britain's five leading home plan design specialists, and are examples of both their standard designs and of plans that they have drawn to meet their clients individual requirements. All of the design companies offer special services of different sorts, and work for both housebuilders and for private individuals who wish to build on their own land. They all have access to all of the plans in this book, and will prepare plans based on design concepts illustrated here, or will draw plans specially to clients requirements after careful discussion and appropriate site visits.

The five design companies whose work is illustrated are

PRESTOPLAN HOMES LIMITED

Britain's leading timber frame specialists, with offices and regionally based staff covering the whole of Great Britain. Prestoplan will advise clients on every aspect of building either an individual new home or a whole development of speculative housing, will provide comprehensive architectural services, and supply material packages for timber frame construction which are carefully geared to clients requirements. Whatever sort of home you may want to build, and wherever you want to build it, Prestoplan have the experience, technical resources and back up to meet your requirements and have been doing just that for 20 years.

DESIGN AND MATERIALS LIMITED

Established in 1972, D & M have built a national reputation for their architectural and material supply services for homes of traditional construction, and specialise in working for those intending to build a new home on their own land. They usually arrange for clients to place contracts with NHBC registered builders, but also have a special service for those building on their own using sub contractors. Much of their work is with farmers and a 'D & M Farmhouse' has become accepted in the farming world as describing good design and first class construction.

POTTON LIMITED

Potton are a well known company with a range of distinctive homes built using a heavy timber aisled frame. They appear for the first time in this new edition of Plans for Dream Homes with twenty four of their designs in a special supplement. Their houses can only be built using their own service, and these plans are only available from the company.

R.B.S. LTD.

Established for twenty years and based in South Wales, RBS provide made to measure services for either traditional or timber frame construction. Their wide experience of the housing scene in Wales and the South West of England enables them to give a personal service in this area where the planners requirements and local conditions are often very different from those in the rest of the country.

PLAN SALES SERVICES LTD.

Unlike the other four companies, which provide support and services at all stages of a building project, PSS specialise in selling home plans for a wide range of standard designs to builders and others who are able to handle their own planning applications. By special arrangement they are able to supply plans for all the designs in this book except those in the two special collections, and can alter them to individual requirements.

Further details of the services offered by these designers will be found on pages 408 to 414 of this book, and experienced staff at any of their offices are always pleased to deal with enquiries either by letter or telephone.

Index

We apologise for the complex system of reference numbers. These enable any of the design practices who contributed drawings to this book to refer to the original drawings and discuss them with new clients.

FRONT ELEVATION

REAR ELEVATION

vert tile hanging to dormer heads + cheeks

stepped flashing + tray dpc

marley modern smooth grey roof tiles

tile hanging to dormer cheeks + over windows

bradstone colour to be approved

stepped flashing + tray dpc

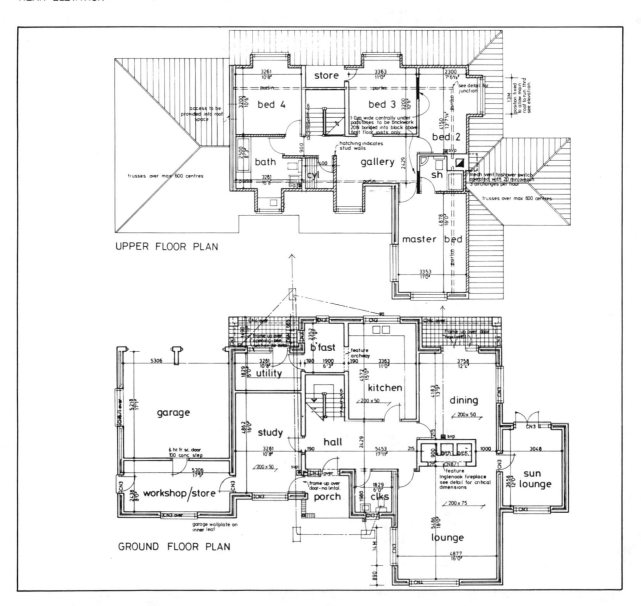

UPPER FLOOR PLAN

store

bed 4

bed 3

bed 2

bath

cyl

gallery

sh

master bed

access to be provided into roof space

trusses over max 600 centres

hatching indicates stud walls

1.0m wide centrally under padstones to be brickwork 20N bonded into block above half floor posts only

mech vent to shower switch operated with 2D min overall air changes per hour

trusses over max 600 centres

see detail for junction

position fixed to allow main roof to run thro see elevation

GROUND FLOOR PLAN

garage

utility

b'fast

kitchen

dining

study

hall

sun lounge

workshop/store

porch

clks

lounge

feature archway

feature inglenook fireplace see detail for critical dimensions

frame up over door - no lintol.

garage wallplate on inner leaf

½ hr. fr. sc. door 100 conc step

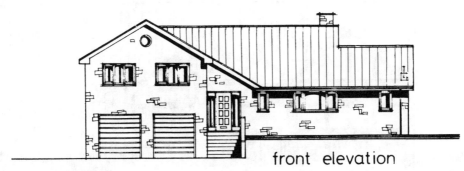

front elevation

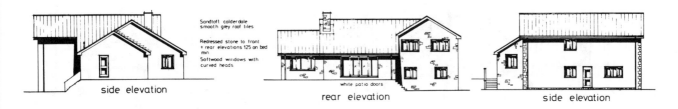

side elevation

Sandtoft calderdale
smooth grey roof tiles

Redressed stone to front
+ rear elevations 125 on bed
min

Softwood windows with
curved heads

rear elevation

white patio doors

side elevation

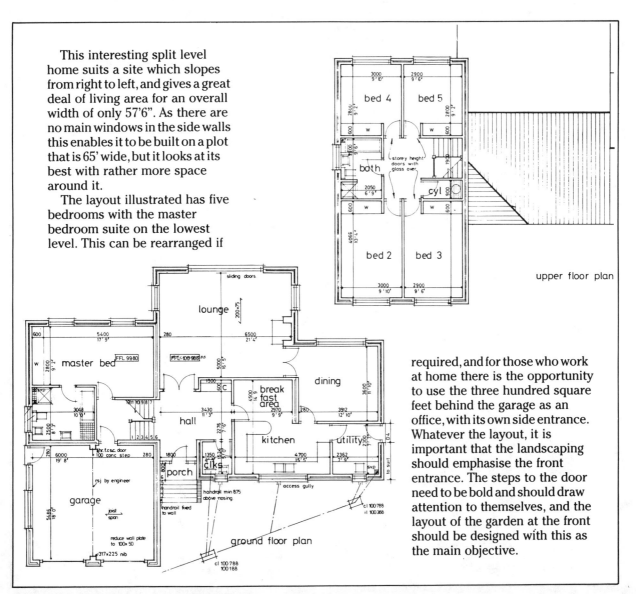

This interesting split level home suits a site which slopes from right to left, and gives a great deal of living area for an overall width of only 57'6". As there are no main windows in the side walls this enables it to be built on a plot that is 65' wide, but it looks at its best with rather more space around it.

The layout illustrated has five bedrooms with the master bedroom suite on the lowest level. This can be rearranged if

required, and for those who work at home there is the opportunity to use the three hundred square feet behind the garage as an office, with its own side entrance. Whatever the layout, it is important that the landscaping should emphasise the front entrance. The steps to the door need to be bold and should draw attention to themselves, and the layout of the garden at the front should be designed with this as the main objective.

upper floor plan

ground floor plan

This large family home has a self contained flat over the garage which can be used in many ways. As shewn in the plan there are four bedrooms in the main part of the house, and two very large first floor rooms to the flat. However, the lounge to the flat is quite large enough to be a bed-sitting room, and with some rearrangement of doors bedroom 5 can be part of the principal accommodation. The WC in the lobby to the side entrance is then extended to become a shower room for the flat ... but the permutations are endless! The design concept is a splendid start for a large home which can exactly suit any requirements.

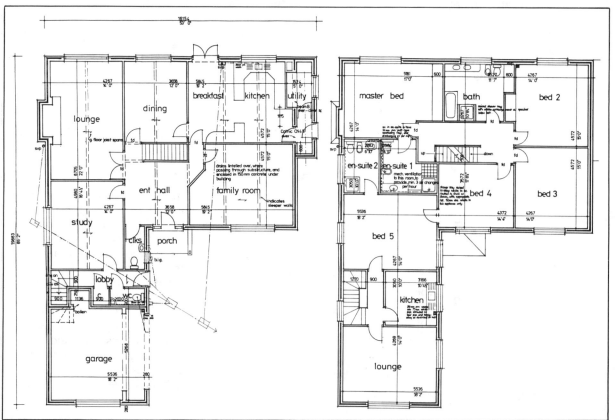

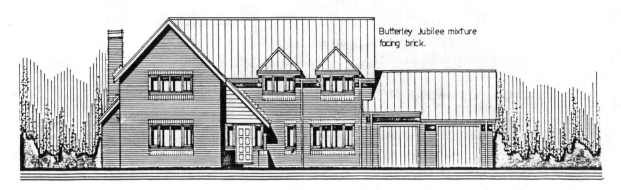

Butterley Jubilee mixture
facing brick.

all windows double-
glazed in aluminium frames

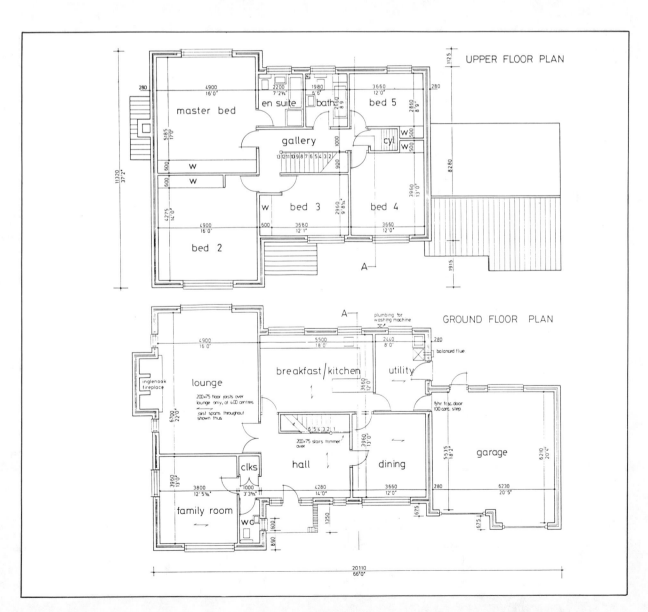

UPPER FLOOR PLAN

master bed

en suite

bath

bed 5

gallery

cyl

w

w

w

bed 3

bed 4

bed 2

GROUND FLOOR PLAN

plumbing for washing machine

balanced flue

inglenook fireplace

lounge

breakfast/kitchen

utility

200x75 floor joists over lounge only, at 400 centres

joist spans throughout shown thus

½ hr. fr.sc. door
100 conc. step

200x75 stairs trimmer over

clks

hall

dining

garage

family room

wc

FRONT ELEVATION

stepped lead flashing and tray d.p.c.

s.v.p fitted durable cage. and weathering slate.

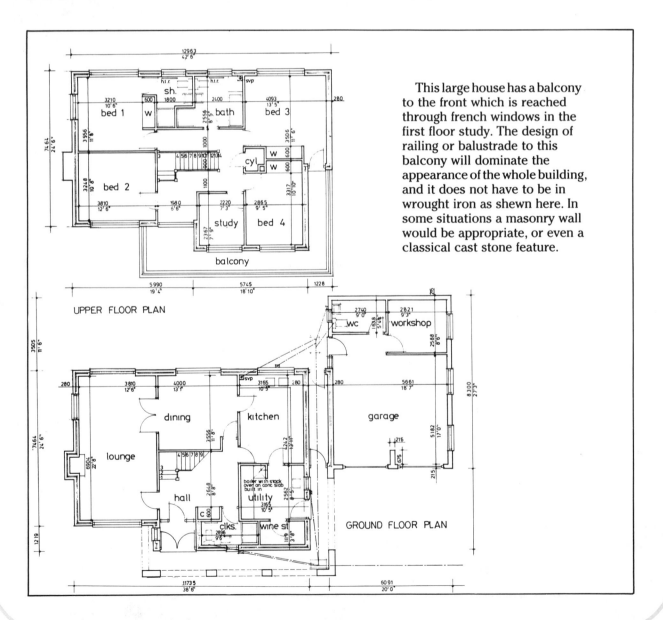

UPPER FLOOR PLAN

bed 1

bed 2

sh.

bath

cyl

bed 3

study

bed 4

balcony

GROUND FLOOR PLAN

lounge

dining

kitchen

garage

hall

utility

clks.

wine st

wc

workshop

boiler with stack over on conc slab built in

This large house has a balcony to the front which is reached through french windows in the first floor study. The design of railing or balustrade to this balcony will dominate the appearance of the whole building, and it does not have to be in wrought iron as shewn here. In some situations a masonry wall would be appropriate, or even a classical cast stone feature.

FRONT ELEVATION

REAR ELEVATION

Hardrow old-stone
standard sizing.

Butterley jubilee mixture brickwork
to ground floor.

Cement render painted off-white
timber to be stained to match
hardwood joinery.

Hardwood casement joinery

SIDE ELEVATION

SIDE ELEVATION

A tudor style house. The notes on the drawing shew how much thought was given to the materials. The bricks are Butterley Jubilee Mixture from South Yorkshire, and are a mottled colour like the soft clamp-fired bricks used in Tudor times, although in fact they are very hard semi-engineering bricks. The render is off-white, and the timber framing is to be stained to match the hardwood joinery. The roof tiles are Hardrow slates, which look like old stone slates, and which can be laid in diminishing courses with larger slates at the bottom and smaller ones above. All of this will have been debated at length with the planners.

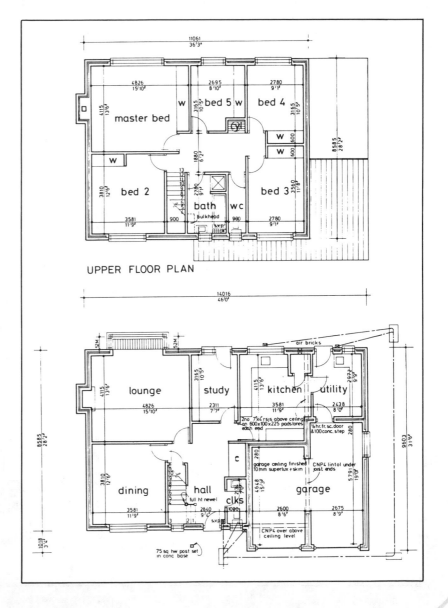

UPPER FLOOR PLAN

FRONT ELEVATION

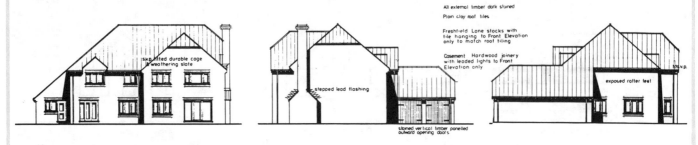

All external timber dark stained

Plain clay roof tiles

Freshfield Lane stocks with tile hanging to Front Elevation only to match roof tiling

Casement Hardwood joinery with leaded lights to Front Elevation only

s.v.p. fitted durable cage & weathering slate

stepped lead flashing

exposed rafter feet

stained vertical timber panelled outward opening doors

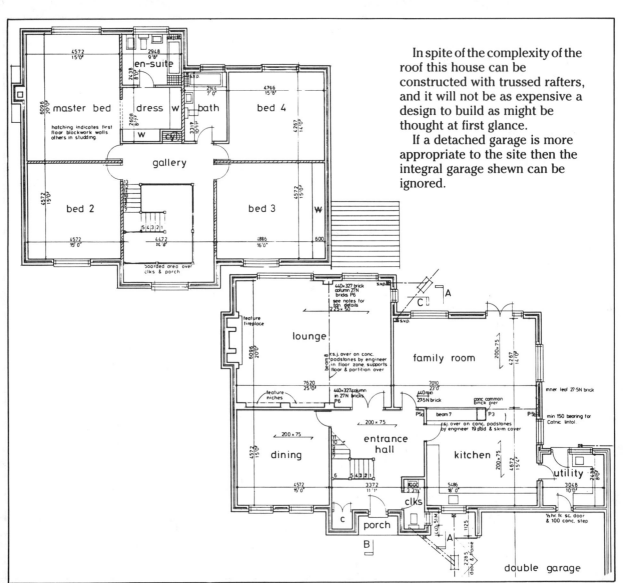

In spite of the complexity of the roof this house can be constructed with trussed rafters, and it will not be as expensive a design to build as might be thought at first glance.

If a detached garage is more appropriate to the site then the integral garage shewn can be ignored.

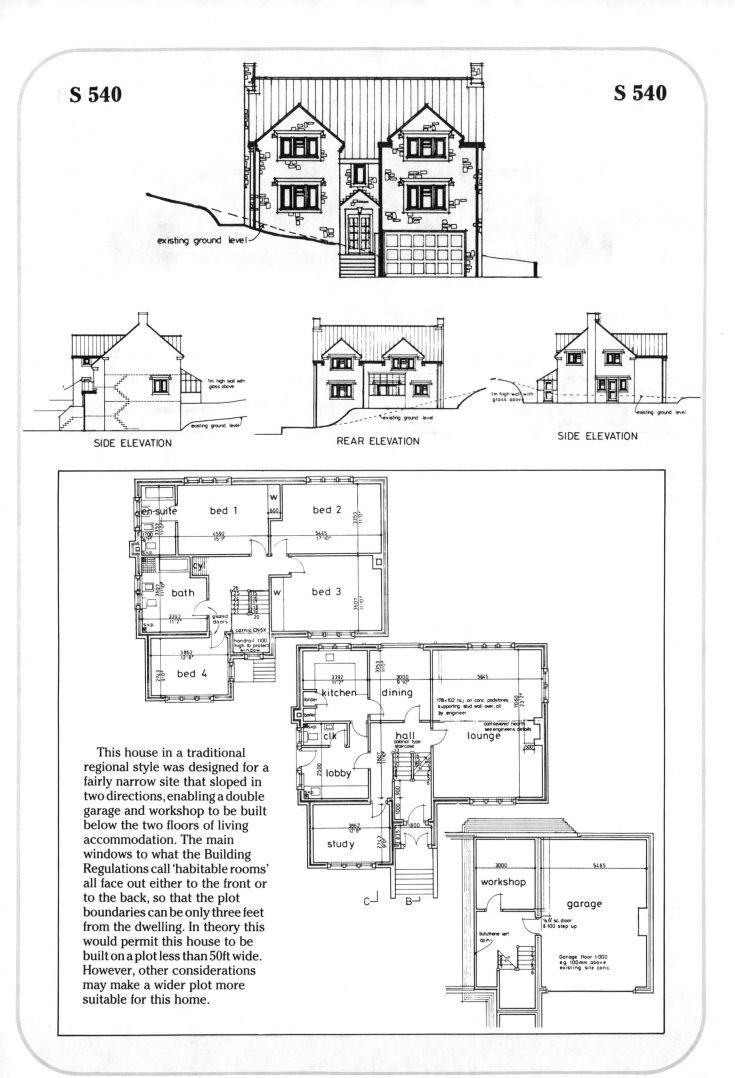

existing ground level

SIDE ELEVATION

REAR ELEVATION

SIDE ELEVATION

This house in a traditional regional style was designed for a fairly narrow site that sloped in two directions, enabling a double garage and workshop to be built below the two floors of living accommodation. The main windows to what the Building Regulations call 'habitable rooms' all face out either to the front or to the back, so that the plot boundaries can be only three feet from the dwelling. In theory this would permit this house to be built on a plot less than 50ft wide. However, other considerations may make a wider plot more suitable for this home.

FRONT ELEVATION

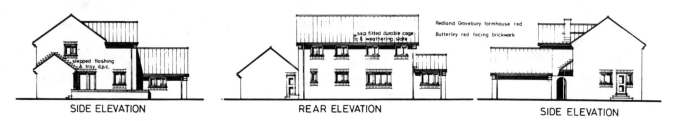

SIDE ELEVATION

REAR ELEVATION

SIDE ELEVATION

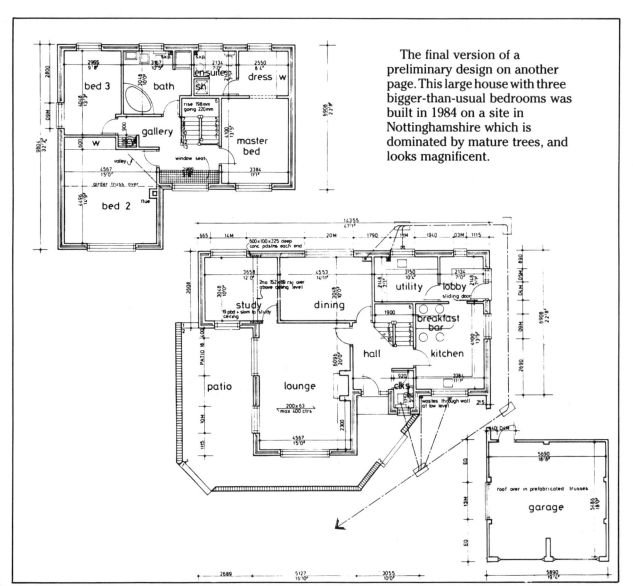

The final version of a preliminary design on another page. This large house with three bigger-than-usual bedrooms was built in 1984 on a site in Nottinghamshire which is dominated by mature trees, and looks magnificent.

FRONT ELEVATION

REAR ELEVATION

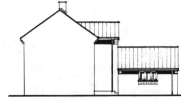

SIDE ELEVATION

SIDE ELEVATION

This was the original proposal for the design number W1193 which appears elsewhere in this book, and by comparing the two you can see how the design developed from this relatively simple building into a more complex structure.

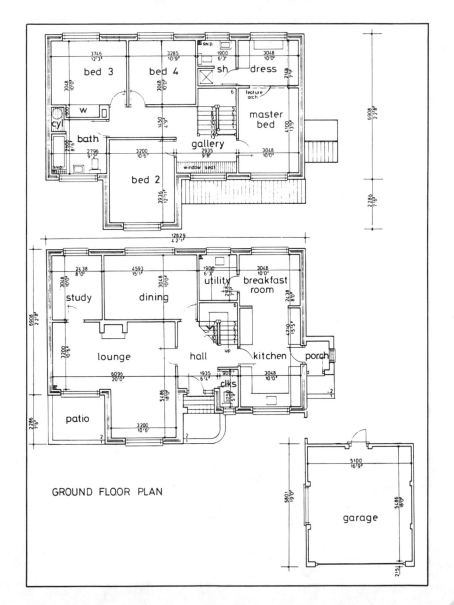

GROUND FLOOR PLAN

Marley Modern Smooth Grey roof tiles

svp.

stepped flashing & tray dpc

Render with stone quoins

stone plinth

SIDE ELEVATION

lead flashing & tray dpc

REAR ELEVATION

stepped flashing & tray dpc

SIDE ELEVATION

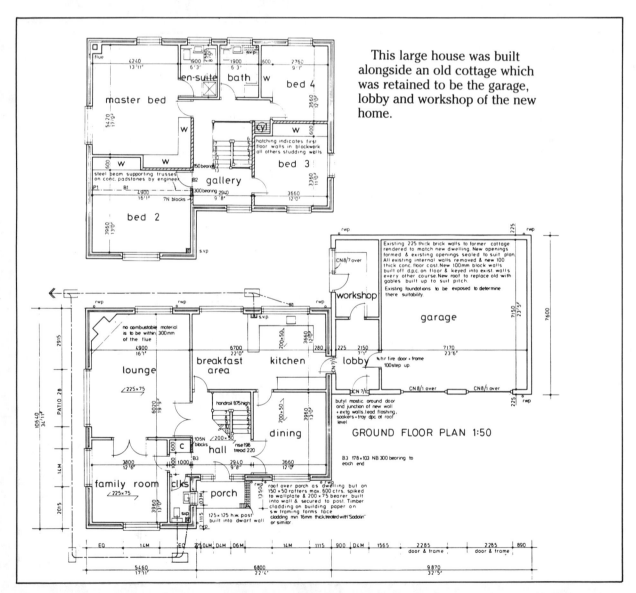

This large house was built alongside an old cottage which was retained to be the garage, lobby and workshop of the new home.

GROUND FLOOR PLAN 1:50

Existing 225 thick brick walls to former cottage rendered to match new dwelling. New openings formed & existing openings sealed to suit plan. All existing internal walls removed & new 100 thick conc. floor cast. New 100mm block walls built off d.p.c. on floor & keyed into exist. walls every other course. New roof to replace old with gables built up to suit pitch.

Existing foundations to be exposed to determine there suitability.

squint bricks
at cills

front elevation 1·100

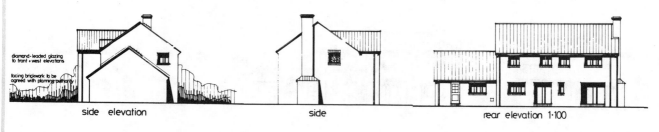

diamond-leaded glazing
to front + west elevations

facing brickwork to be
agreed with planning authority

side elevation   side   rear elevation 1·100

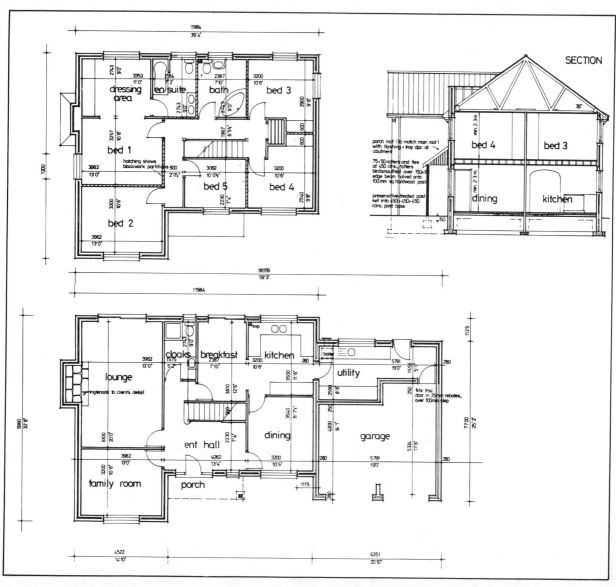

SECTION

dressing area · en suite · bath · bed 3
bed 1 · hatching shows blockwork partitions 900 · bed 5 · bed 4
bed 2

bed 4 · bed 3
dining · kitchen

lounge · cloaks · breakfast · kitchen · utility
inglenook to clients detail
ent hall · dining · garage
family room · porch

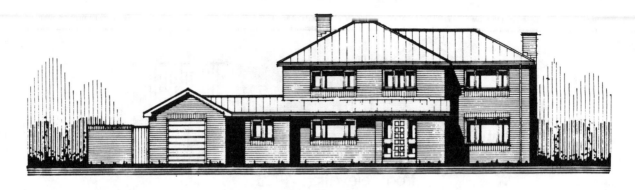

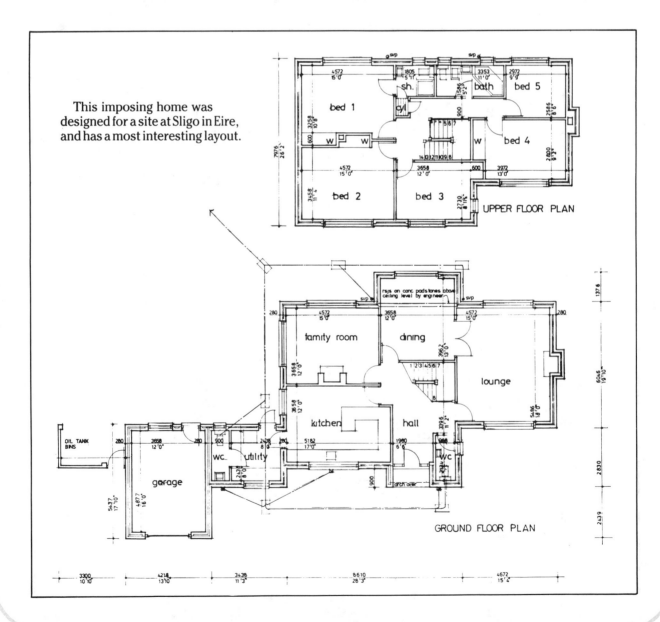

This imposing home was designed for a site at Sligo in Eire, and has a most interesting layout.

UPPER FLOOR PLAN

bed 1
bed 2
bed 3
bed 4
bed 5
sh.
bath
cyl

GROUND FLOOR PLAN

family room
dining
lounge
kitchen
hall
garage
wc
utility
wc
OIL TANK
BINS

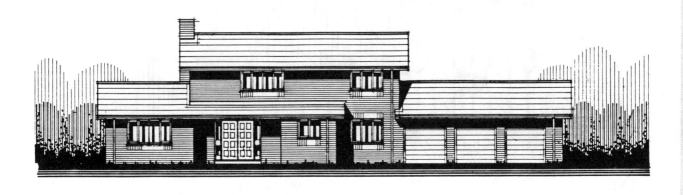

REAR ELEVATION

GABLE ELEVATION

GABLE ELEVATION

GROUND FLOOR PLAN

UPPER FLOOR PLAN

11268
37' 0"

890 · 19M · 1340 · 13M · 13M · 890

3581
11' 9"   3034
10' 0"   600   3353
11' 0"

bed 2   bed 3   w   bed 4

cyl.

bath

sh   master bed   bed 5

2353
7' 9"

1524
5' 0"   4691
15' 5"   3353
11' 0"

2690   19M   13M   890

GROUND FLOOR PLAN

4517
14' 10"   11268
37' 0"   8850
29' 0"

dining   kitchen / breakfast   utility/workshop

3658
12' 0"   7010
23' 0"   8600
28' 3"

lounge   hall   study   garage

8600
28' 3"

4267
14' 0"   clks

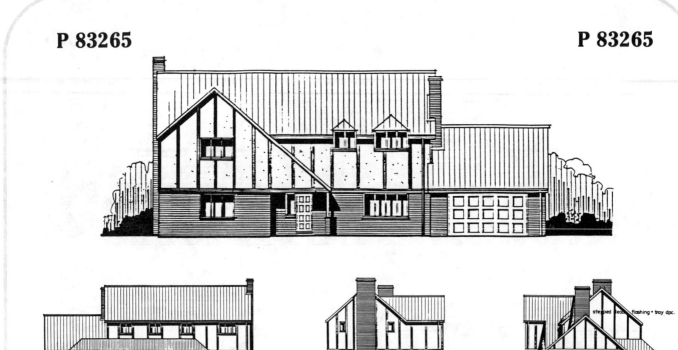

rear elevation   side elevation   garage end elevation

UPPER FLOOR

bed 2   bath   bed 5   bed 4

en-suite

master bed

GROUND FLOOR

verandah   porch

utility   WC

dining   breakfast kitchen

lounge

family room   garage

hall

study   porch

This large house is based on the P.S.S. Avonmere design, which is certainly their most popular large house type. The success of this design concept demonstrates clearly how those of us with a chance to choose the appearance of our homes are reaching back to traditional values, and a good thing too!

P.S.S. and D & M Ltd have literally dozens of variants of this design, with a wide choice of layouts while retaining the external appearance.

front elevation

side elevation

rear elevation

side elevation

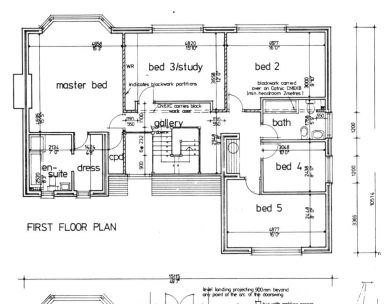

FIRST FLOOR PLAN

master bed

bed 3/study

indicates blockwork partitions

WR

bed 2

blockwork carried over on Catnic CN6XB (min. headroom 2 metres)

CN6XC carries blockwork cover

gallery

bath

en-suite

dress

cpd

bed 4

bed 5

Five bedrooms on an upper floor always means a great deal of room down below, and in this house the extra space is utilised as a large family room at the same end of the home as the kitchen. The stairs are centrally placed in the hall, with a twelve foot high window on one side. This provides a most striking feature at the expense of a cramped front entrance: an alternative would be to move the stairs along and have an eight foot window from the stair landing. As with all these designs, the client takes his or her choice.

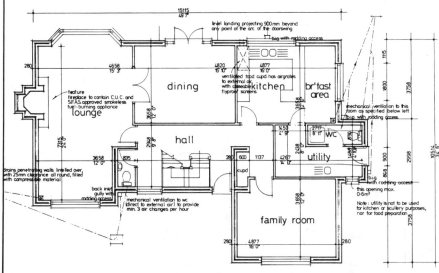

level landing projecting 900mm beyond any point of the arc of the doorswing

feature fireplace to contain C.U.C. and S.F.A.S. approved smokeless fuel-burning appliance

lounge

dining

ventilated food cupd. has airgrates to external air, with closeable flyproof screens

kitchen

br'fast area

mechanical ventilation to this room as specified below left

hall

WC

utility

drains penetrating walls linelled over, with 25mm clearance all round, filled with compressible material

back inlet gully with rodding access

mechanical ventilation to wc (direct to external air) to provide min. 3 air changes per hour

cupd

rodding access this opening max. 0·6m³

Note: utility is not to be used for kitchen or scullery purposes, nor for food preparation

family room

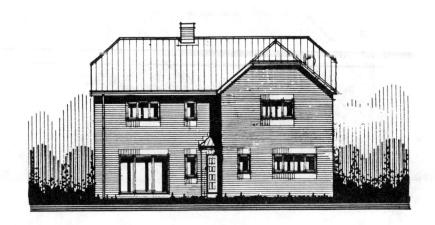

REAR ELEVATION

SIDE ELEVATION

A front door set across the angle between two wings of a house looks far more striking than it appears in these 'architects elevations' drawings. It adds an extra dimension to the hall, and in this case helps to set off a feature staircase. This design concept has been used in many different guises by D & M over the years, and is particularly effective with the half-hip roof shewn here.

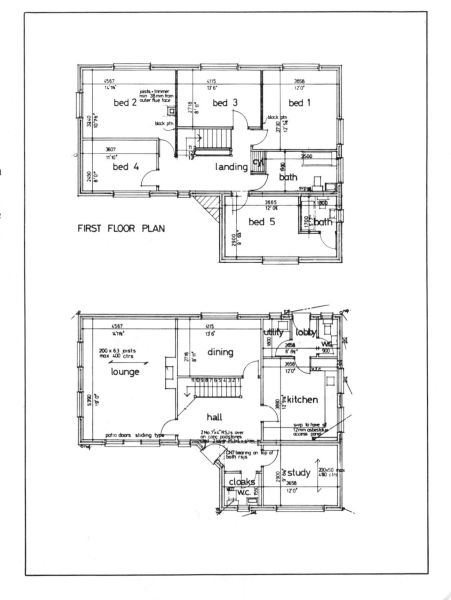

FIRST FLOOR PLAN

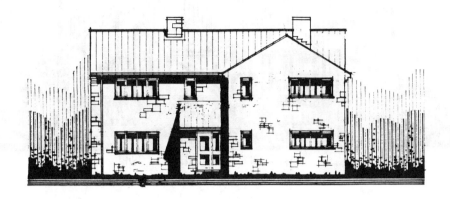

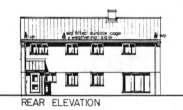

REAR ELEVATION

SIDE ELEVATION

A large farmhouse built on a farm in South Yorkshire. The planning consent was unusual, being obtained on a "one for one" basis, on condition that an older farmhouse was demolished as soon as the new one was completed.

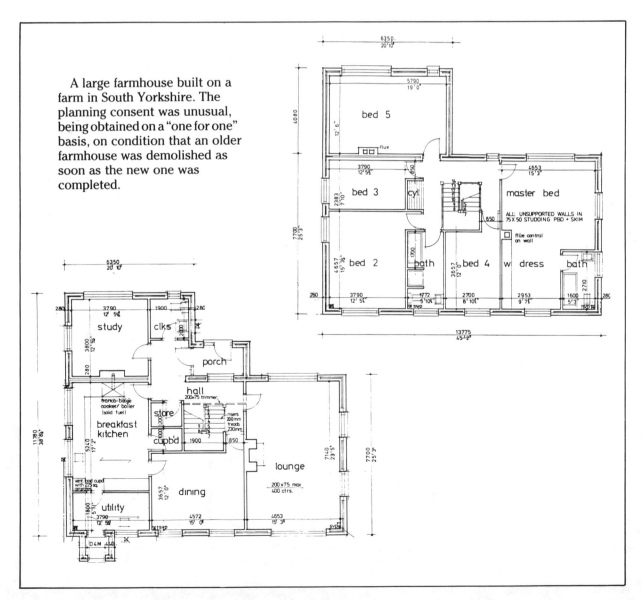

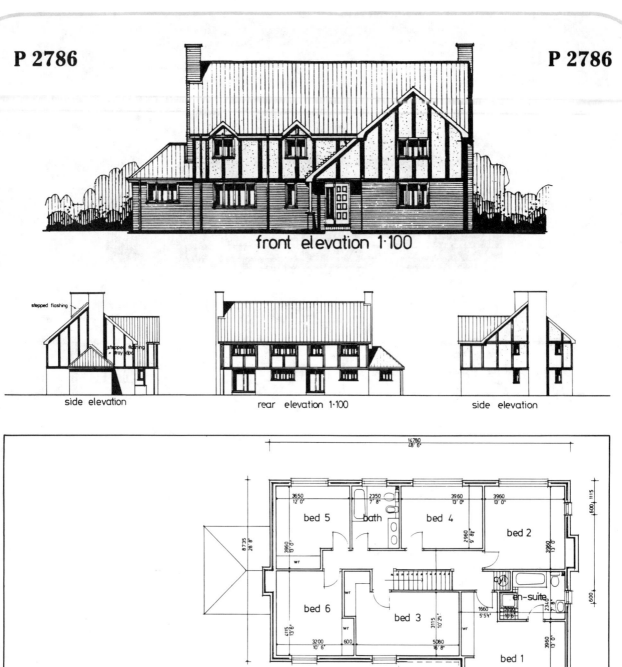

front elevation 1·100

side elevation   rear elevation 1·100   side elevation

FIRST FLOOR PLAN

bed 5
bed 4
bed 2
bath
bed 6
bed 3
en-suite
bed 1

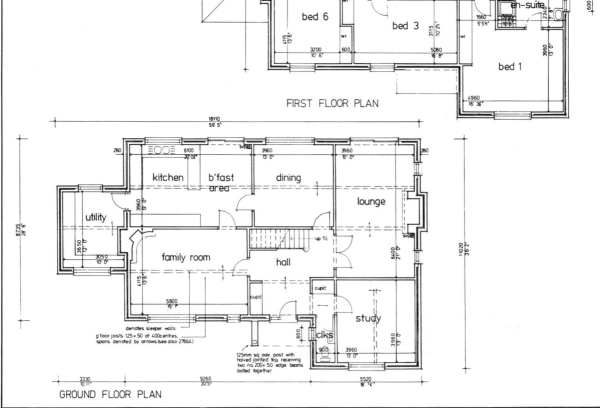

GROUND FLOOR PLAN

kitchen
b'fast area
dining
lounge
utility
family room
hall
study
cupd
clks

denotes sleeper walls.
g'floor joists 125 × 50 at 400centres,
spans denoted by arrows (see also 2786/4)

125mm sq. oak post with
halved jointed top, receiving
two no 200 × 50 edge beams
bolted together.

FRONT ELEVATION

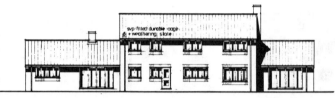

This very large house has a self contained granny flat as one wing, and at nearly a hundred feet long is a well balanced and most impressive home. The granny flat is completely self contained with two bedrooms, its own kitchen, and, what is most important with a granny flat, its own front door. The connecting door into the main house is through a two skin cavity wall, so there is excellent sound insulation between the two parts of the building.

Sound insulation has also been a major consideration in planning the rest of the building, with all the walls between bedrooms lining up with the walls between rooms below: this means that the first floor walls can be in 4" solid blockwork, giving 40db sound reduction.

The big lounge has windows in three walls and the fireplace and other features in the fourth. This gives a marvellously light and airy room, but careful consideration has to be given to whether there is room left for radiators and furniture that has to stand against walls. Generally speaking, the larger the room the easier this is.

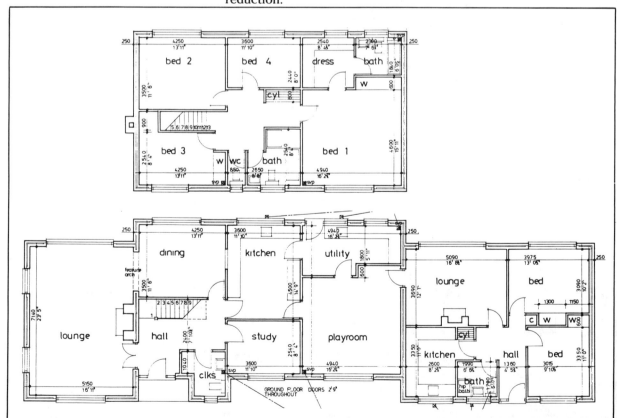

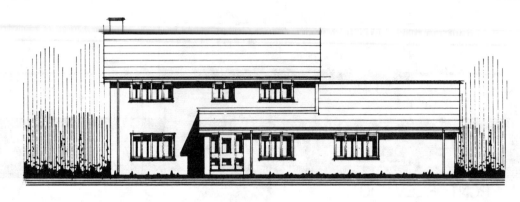

REAR ELEVATION

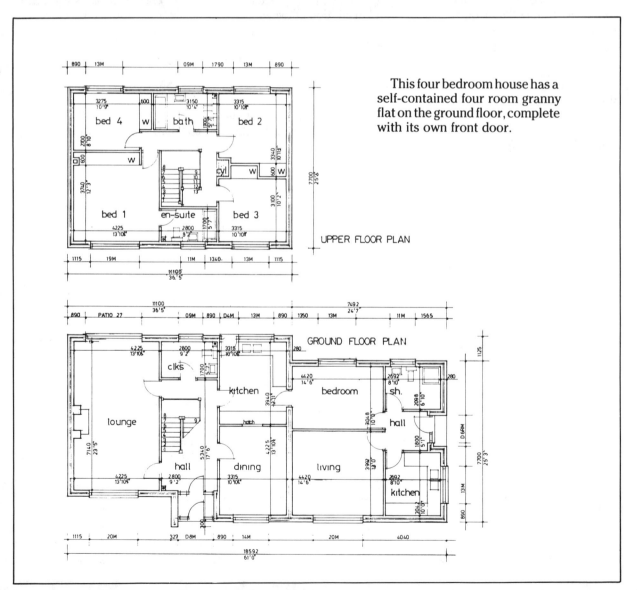

This four bedroom house has a self-contained four room granny flat on the ground floor, complete with its own front door.

UPPER FLOOR PLAN

GROUND FLOOR PLAN

REAR ELEVATION

stepped lead flashing
& tray dpc

Slate roof 24 x 12 x¾" thick.

Natural stone
with Stone lintols
(supplied by client.)

Hardwood casement joinery

SIDE ELEVATION

SIDE ELEVATION

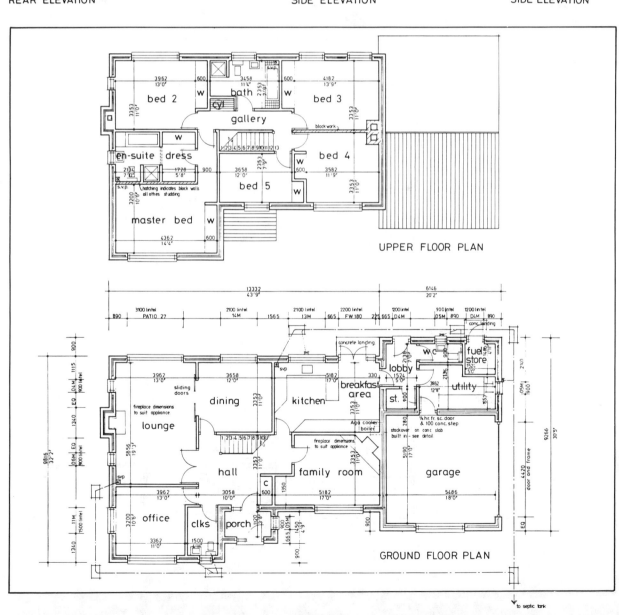

UPPER FLOOR PLAN

bed 2 — 3962 / 13'0" — 3353 / 11'0"
bath — 3458 / 11'4" — 2353 / 7'8"
bed 3 — 4182 / 13'9" — 3353 / 11'0"
cyl
gallery
block work
en-suite — 2134 / 7'0"
dress — 1728 / 5'8"
bed 5 — 3658 / 12'0" — 2353 / 7'9"
bed 4 — 3582 / 11'9" — 3353 / 11'0"
s.v.p. hatching indicates block walls all other studding
master bed — 4362 / 14'4" — 3200 / 10'6"

GROUND FLOOR PLAN

13332 / 43'9"   6146 / 20'2"

3100 lintel PATIO 27 14M 2100 lintel 1565 2100 lintel 13M 665 2200 lintel FW 180 225 665 1200 lintel D4M 05M 900 lintel 05M 1200 lintel D4M 890 conc.landing

concrete landing
lobby
fuel store — 1524 / 5'0"
w.c.
utility — 3962 / 12'8"
st.
breakfast area — 330 — 1524 / 5'0"
dining — 3658 / 12'0" — 3353 / 11'0"
kitchen — 5182 / 17'0"
Aga cooker boiler
½ hr. fr. sc. door & 100 conc. step stackover on conc slab built in - see detail
lounge — 3962 / 13'0"
sliding doors
fireplace dimensions to suit appliance
hall — 3962 / 13'0" — 3058 / 10'0"
family room — 5182 / 17'0" — 3353 / 11'0"
fireplace dimensions to suit appliance
garage — 5190 — 5486 / 18'0"
office — 3362 / 11'0" — 3200 / 10'6"
clks
porch
1500

9816 / 32'2"   door and frame   9266 / 30'5"

to septic tank

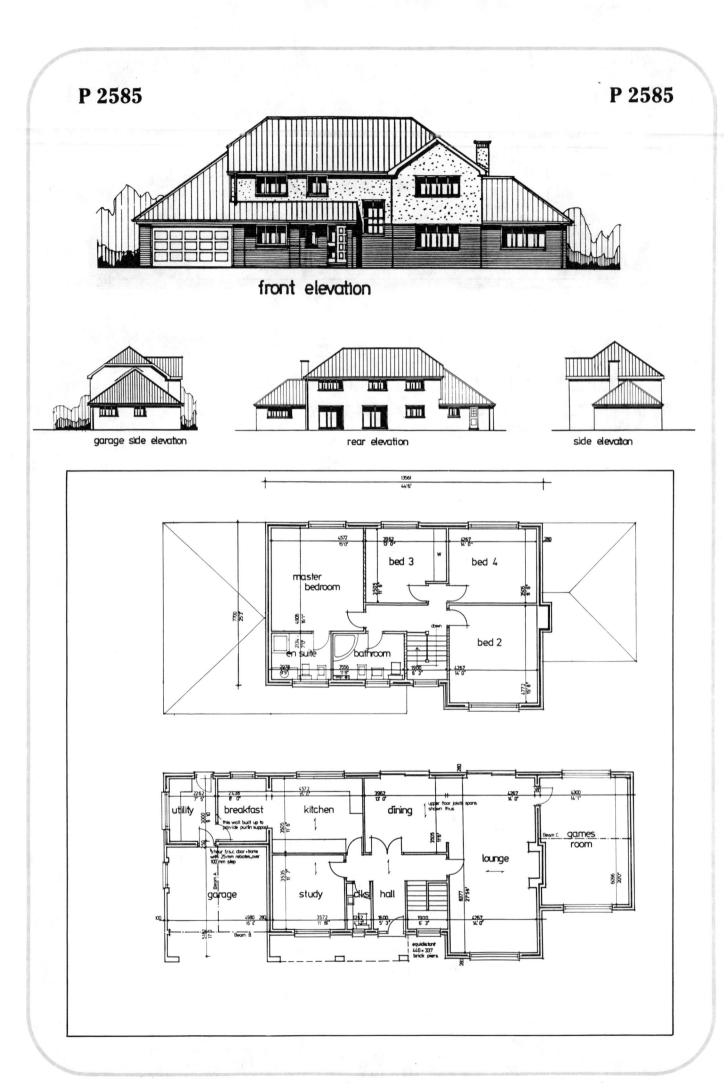

front elevation

garage side elevation

rear elevation

side elevation

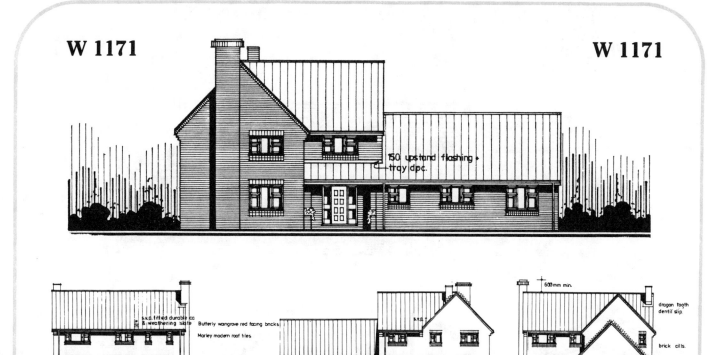

150 upstand flashing →
tray dpc.

s.v.p. fitted durable ca
& weathering slate

Butterly wangrove red facing bricks.

Marley modern roof tiles.

600 mm min.

dragon tooth
dentil slip.

brick cills.

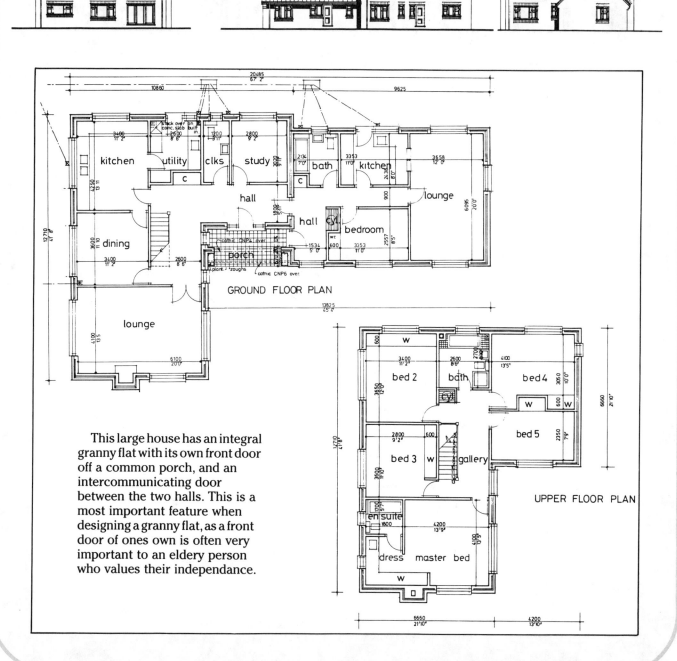

GROUND FLOOR PLAN

kitchen utility clks study bath kitchen lounge

hall

hall cyl bedroom

porch

dining

lounge

UPPER FLOOR PLAN

bed 2 bath bed 4

bed 3 gallery bed 5

en suite

dress master bed

This large house has an integral granny flat with its own front door off a common porch, and an intercommunicating door between the two halls. This is a most important feature when designing a granny flat, as a front door of ones own is often very important to an eldery person who values their independance.

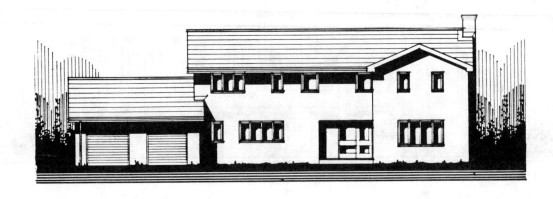

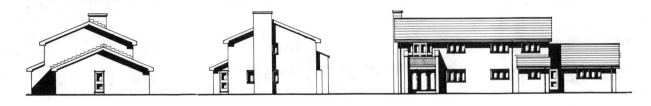

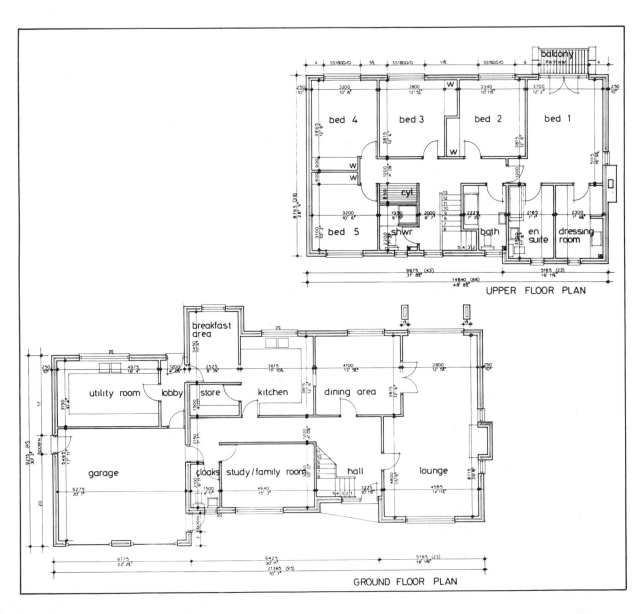

bed 4

bed 3

bed 2

bed 1

bed 5

cyl

shwr

bath

en suite

dressing room

balcony

UPPER FLOOR PLAN

breakfast area

utility room

lobby

store

kitchen

dining area

garage

cloaks

study/family room

hall

lounge

GROUND FLOOR PLAN

FRONT ELEVATION

GABLE ELEVATION REAR ELEVATION GABLE ELEVATION

This large home was designed for a site in Ireland, and is typical of the use made of the large building plots found in the Republic.

However, it would be equally acceptable in many parts of the South and West of England, and particularly in Wales. Whether a big enough plot for it can be found is a different matter!

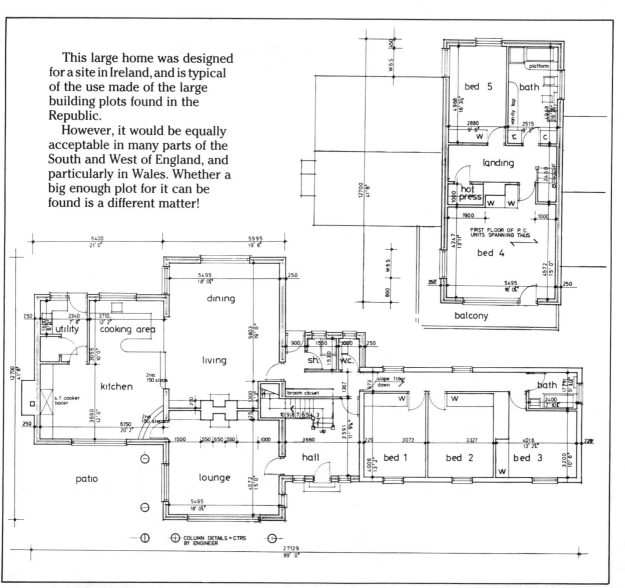

FRONT ELEVATION

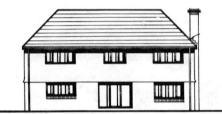

REAR ELEVATION

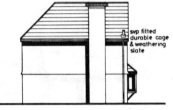

SIDE ELEVATIONS

svp fitted durable cage & weathering slate

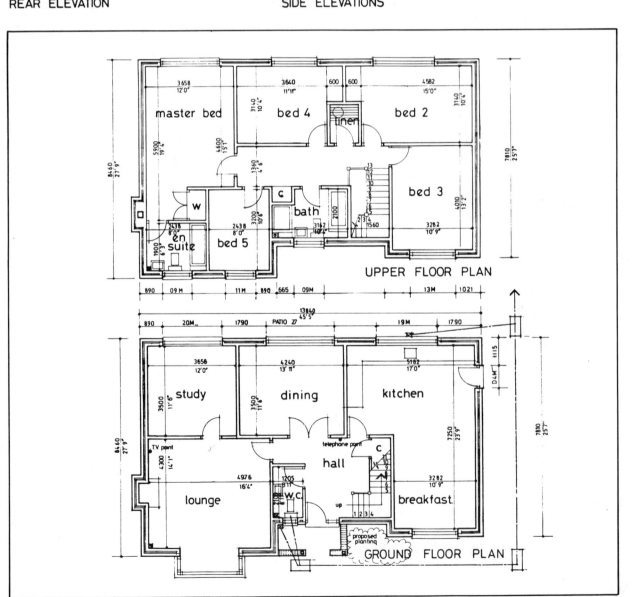

UPPER FLOOR PLAN

master bed — 3658 / 12'0"
bed 4 — 3640 / 11'11"
600 600
bed 2 — 4582 / 15'0"
linen
3140 / 10'4"
3140 / 10'4"
8460 / 27'9"
7810 / 25'7"
5900 / 19'4"
4600 / 15'1"
1360 / 4'6"
w
c
bath
bed 3 — 4010 / 13'2"
3200 / 10'6"
2100
en suite
1900 / 6'3"
bed 5
2438 / 8'0"
2438 / 8'0"
3162 / 10'4"
1560
3282 / 10'9"

890 09M 11M 890 665 09M 13M 1021

GROUND FLOOR PLAN

13840 / 45'5"
890 20M 1790 PATIO 27 19M 1790
4115
study — 3658 / 12'0"
dining — 4240 / 13'11"
kitchen — 5182 / 17'0"
D4M
3500 / 11'6"
3500 / 11'8"
8460 / 27'9"
7250 / 23'9"
7810 / 25'7"
T.V. point
4300 / 14'1"
telephone point
c
hall
lounge — 4976 / 16'4"
1205 / 3'11"
w.c.
3282 / 10'9"
up 1 2 3 4
breakfast
proposed planting

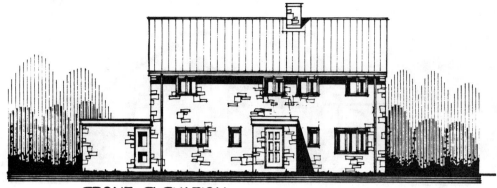

FRONT ELEVATION

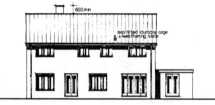

This five bedroom house has a simple shape making it very cost effective to build with an interesting and unusual internal layout making it a very attractive house to live in. The lounge is very large with two sets of double doors leading into the dining room and the hall, while at the other end of its twenty eight foot length there is a door through to the study. The kitchen is linked to what is shewn as a breakfast room, but which would probably become a living room where there are children in the family.

There are five bedrooms, and if required the two bathrooms can be changed over, so that the master bedroom suite has the corner bath!

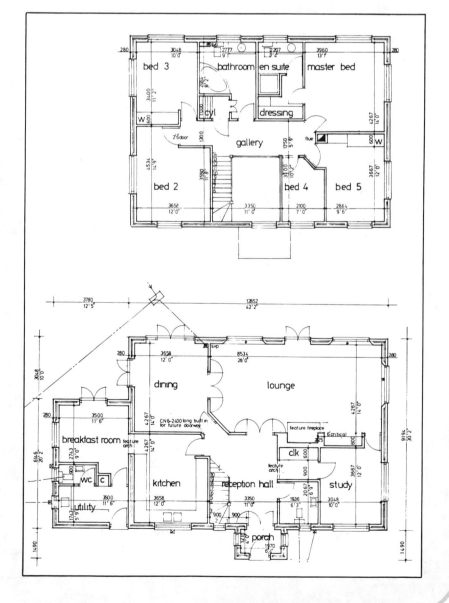

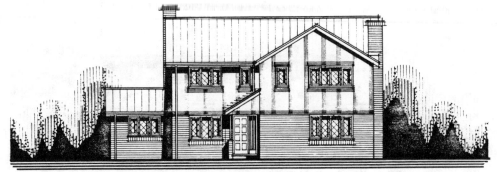

FRONT ELEVATION

REAR ELEVATION   SIDE ELEVATION   SIDE ELEVATION

1000mm min

redland stonewold grey
roof tiles

windows
with diamond leaded lights

butterley darley grey
facing brickwork

A very pretty, very well laid out house in a style that is currently enormously popular. In only 1900 sq.ft. it has just about every feature for a dream home: five bedrooms, huge kitchen with breakfast alcove, impressive study, luxury bathroom to the master suite and a sensible "dirty boots" lobby at the back door. The deeply recessed porch and feature stairs in the large hall give this home a really prestigous feel.

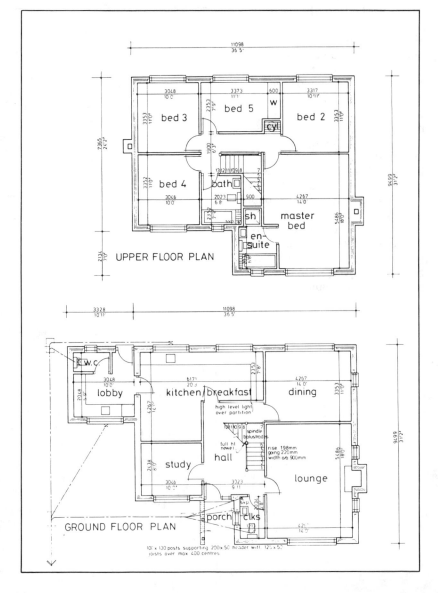

UPPER FLOOR PLAN

GROUND FLOOR PLAN

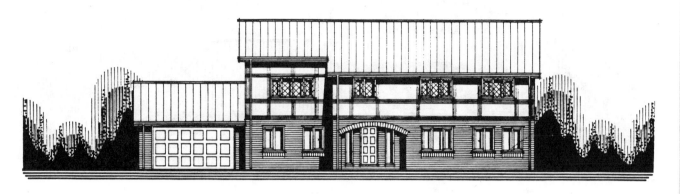

SIDE ELEVATION   REAR ELEVATION   SIDE ELEVATION

leaded lights to first floor windows only

s.v.p fitted durable cage & weathering slate

lead flashing

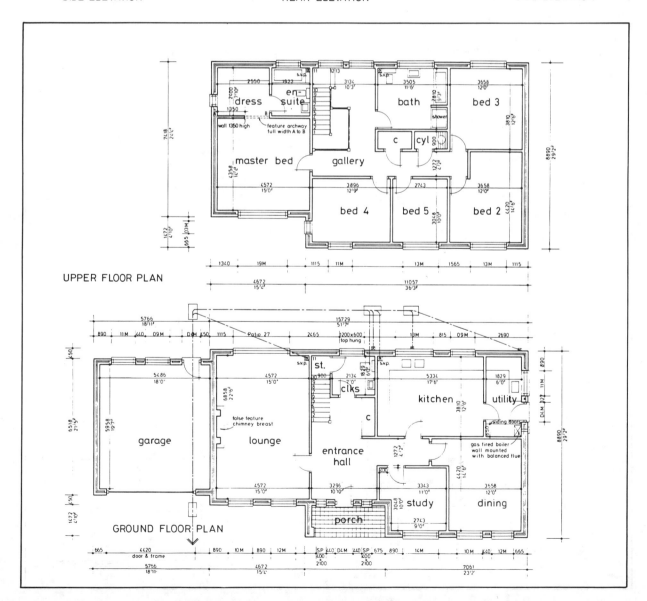

UPPER FLOOR PLAN

GROUND FLOOR PLAN

DRIVE ELEVATION

GABLE ELEVATIONS

FIRST FLOOR PLAN

SECOND FLOOR PLAN

This is one of a pair of large three storey homes designed for an infill plot in a West Country town, and it had to be very much in the local style.

DRIVE ELEVATION

GABLE ELEVATIONS

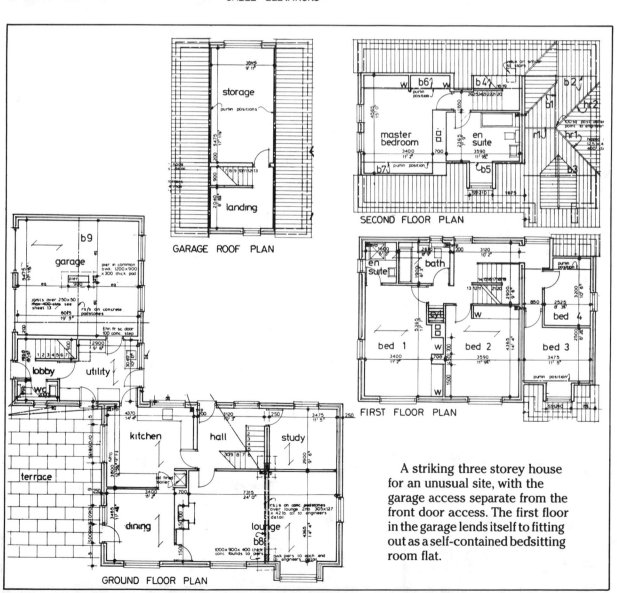

GARAGE ROOF PLAN

SECOND FLOOR PLAN

FIRST FLOOR PLAN

GROUND FLOOR PLAN

A striking three storey house for an unusual site, with the garage access separate from the front door access. The first floor in the garage lends itself to fitting out as a self-contained bedsitting room flat.

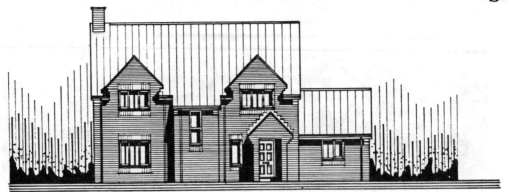

front elevation

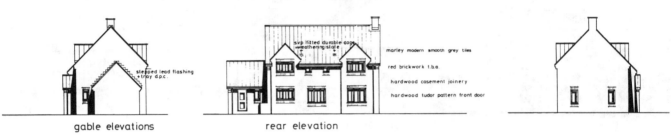

gable elevations

rear elevation

svp lfitted durable dac
+weathering slate

marley modern smooth grey tiles

red brickwork t.b.a.

hardwood casement joinery

hardwood tudor pattern front door

stepped lead flashing
+ tray d.p.c.

This house with the dormers in the roof is from Design & Materials Ltd and has been built so many times that they have designed a trussed rafter roof to suit the dormers, even though they are above the wall plate. Normally this can only be done for a design that is to be built many times, and to some extent the house has to be designed around the roof. In this case five separate types of truss are required.

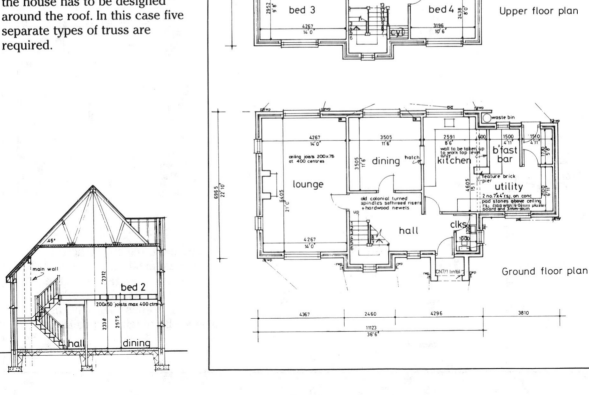

Upper floor plan

master bed — 3667 12'0"
en-suite
bath
bed 2 — 3196 10'6"
3353 11'0"
3867 12'8"
gallery
bed 3 — 2952 9'8"
bed 4 — 2438 8'0"
4267 14'0"
cyl
3196 10'6"
6965 22'10"
11123 36'6"

Ground floor plan

lounge
dining — 3505 11'6"
kitchen — 2591 8'6"
b'fast bar — 1500 4'11" / 1510 4'11"
ceiling joists 200x75 at 400 centres
4267 14'0"
hatch
wall to be taken up to work top level only
waste bin
feature brick pier
utility
2 no.7x4 r.s.j. on conc pad stones above ceiling f'sj. clad with 9.5mm plaster board and 3mm skum
old colonial turned spindles softwood risers + hardwood newels
hall
clks
CN7/1 lintol
6965 22'10"
6965 22'10"
4367 / 2460 / 4296 / 3810
11123 36'6"

main wall
bed 2
45°
2312
2338
2575
200x50 joists max 400 ctrs
hall
dining

FRONT ELEVATION

Another variant of the popular Cotswold design home by Design & Materials Ltd. In this instance the overall length of the building is sixty two feet, making this a really imposing building.

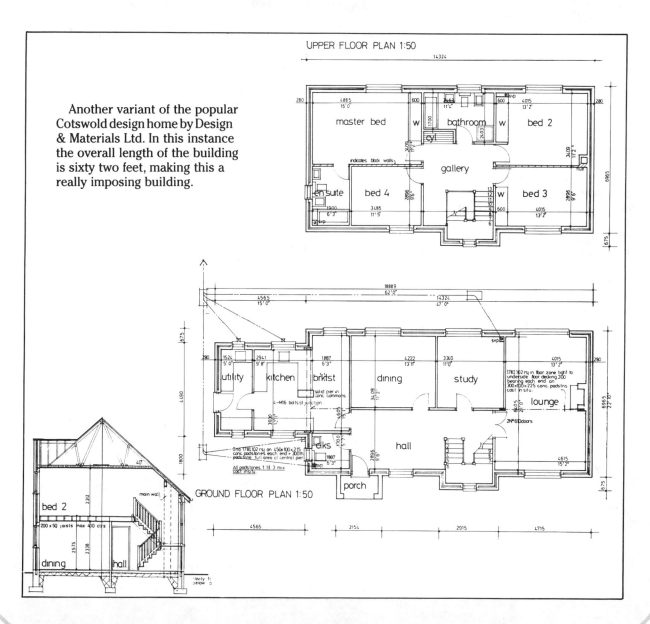

UPPER FLOOR PLAN 1:50

GROUND FLOOR PLAN 1:50

FRONT ELEVATION

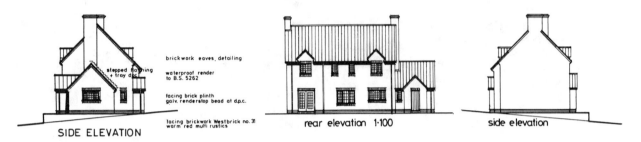

SIDE ELEVATION

brickwork eaves detailing

waterproof render
to B.S. 5262

facing brick plinth
galv. renderstop bead at d.p.c.

facing brickwork Westbrick no. 31
warm red multi rustics

stepped flashing
+ tray d.p.c.

rear elevation 1·100

side elevation

A house in the Cotswold style. The kitchen is interesting, with an 'island' stove. A stove in this position does not meet the NHBC requirement that there should be a work surface on either side of the cooker, so that pans of boiling water do not have to be lifted over the floor in case they spill and scald any cat, baby or comatose husband who may be down there. For this reason the plan shows one work surface extended round to the stove, and it should really be shewn on the other side as well. This rather defeats the object of having a feature cooker like this, but, as your new house is not being built speculatively by a developer, the NHBC inspector is unlikely to be too strict about this.

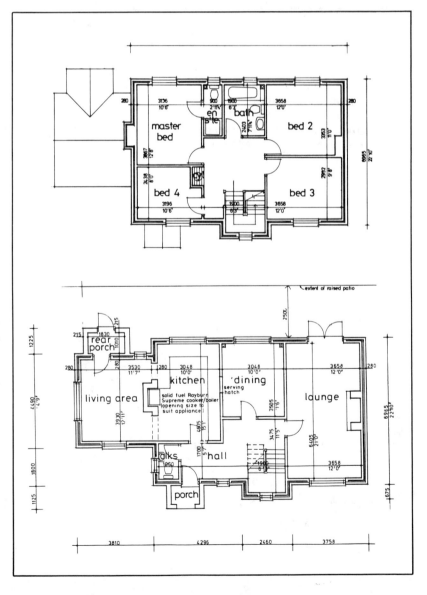

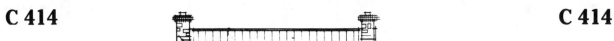

FRONT ELEVATION

stepped lead flashing & tray d.p.c.

stepped flashing + tray dpc

Redland Grovebury Tiles Farmhouse Red

Bradstone Trad walling Weathered Ham

Hardwood Casement joinery

SIDE ELEVATION

REAR ELEVATION

SIDE ELEVATION

Another 'Cotswold' style home from D & M with their special roof trusses that were designed for this type of roof, which is usually built with purlins. The section shows how trusses with an extended ceiling tie bearing on the dormer lintols alternate with trusses with extended rafters bearing on the wall plate. This arrangement has to be very carefully engineered, but gives useful cost savings.

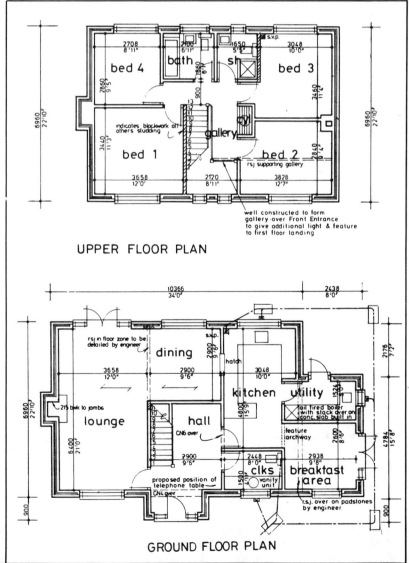

2708 / 8'11"   1650   3048 / 10'0"

bed 4   bath   sh   bed 3

2850 / 9'5"   3450 / 11'2"

900   6960 / 22'10"

6960 / 22'10"

indicates blockwork others studding

gallery

3440 / 11'3"

bed 1   bed 2

rsj supporting gallery

3658 / 12'0"   2120 / 8'11"   3828 / 12'7"

well constructed to form gallery over Front Entrance to give additional light & feature to first floor landing

UPPER FLOOR PLAN

10366 / 34'0"   2438 / 8'0"

rsj in floor zone to be detailed by engineer

dining   s.v.p.

2900 / 9'6"   hatch

2176 / 7'2"

3658 / 12'0"   2900 / 9'6"   3048 / 10'0"

kitchen   utility

215 bwk to jambs   4800 / 15'9"   oil fired boiler with stack over on conc. slab built in

6960 / 22'10"

lounge   hall   CN6 over

feature archway   2600 / 8'6"   4784 / 15'8"

6400 / 21'0"   2900 / 9'6"

2448 / 8'0"   clks   2938 / 9'8"

vanity unit   breakfast area

proposed position of telephone table   CN4 over   1500

r.s.j. over on padstones by engineer

900   900

GROUND FLOOR PLAN

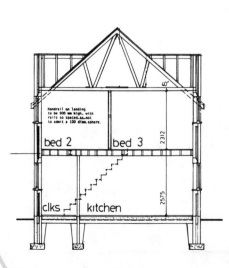

Handrail on landing to be 900 mm high, with rails so spaced as not to admit a 100 diam. sphere.

bed 2   bed 3   2312

clks   kitchen   2575

This country home was built on a very special site in the Peak District of Derbyshire in 1985, and the design incorporates all the stone features that are typical of the area, and which the planners require.

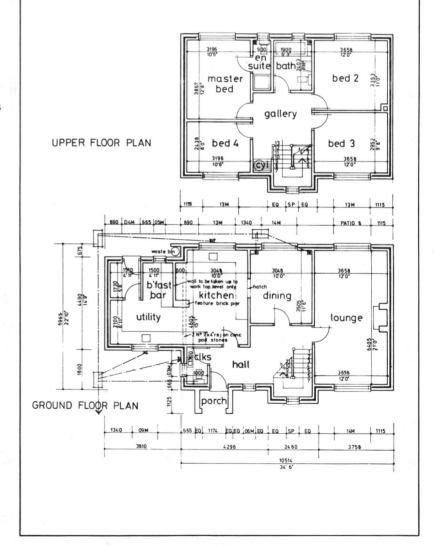

UPPER FLOOR PLAN

GROUND FLOOR PLAN

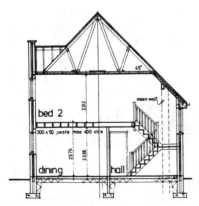

FRONT ELEVATION

GABLE ELEVATION

Concrete interlocking tiles double pantile colour & sample to be agreed with planners

Render with Random stone features

Hardwood casement joinery

REAR ELEVATION

GABLE ELEVATION

stepped lead flashing & tray d.p.c.

A house in the Cotswold style with a mix of render and natural stone for the walls. A note on the drawing says that the tile type and colour were to be agreed with the planners, and the choice will have had to be made very carefully to suit the walling style. The dormer gables are shewn with timber infill panels, but they could have been built in masonry if required as they rise directly from loadbearing walls. This would have needed a narrow pillar of masonry at the side of each window. See design C 414 for an example of this.

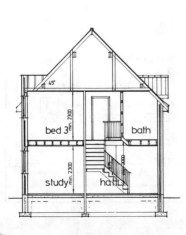

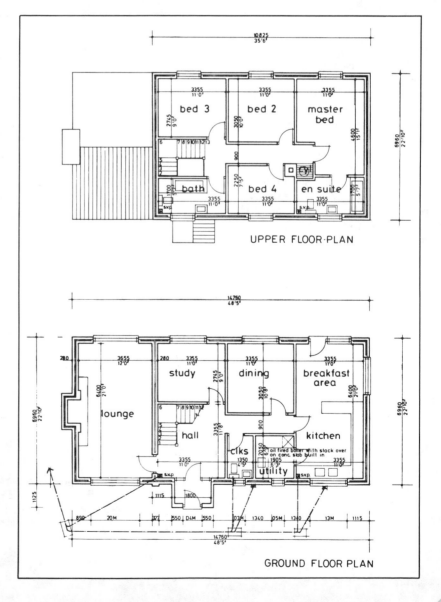

UPPER FLOOR PLAN

GROUND FLOOR PLAN

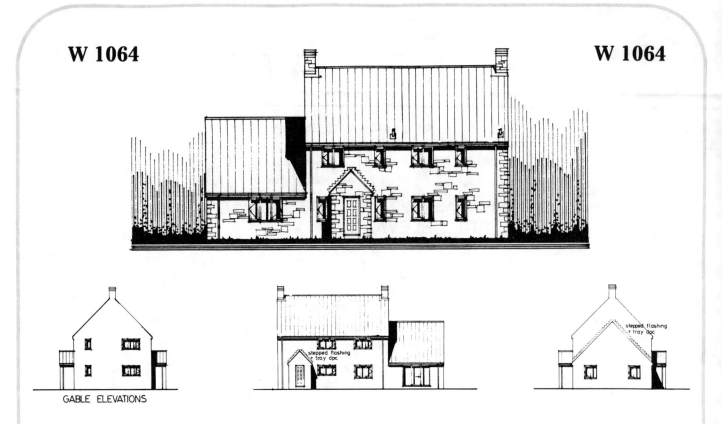

GABLE ELEVATIONS

This north country farmhouse has very big rooms: the lounge and dining room alone are nearly as big as a small retirement bungalow. The severe style, with small entrance porches, small windows and a high gable roof looks severe when viewed with a suburban eye. In the setting for which it was designed it is exactly right — you have to imagine dry stone walls to the garden, sheep in the fields, and the fells beyond.

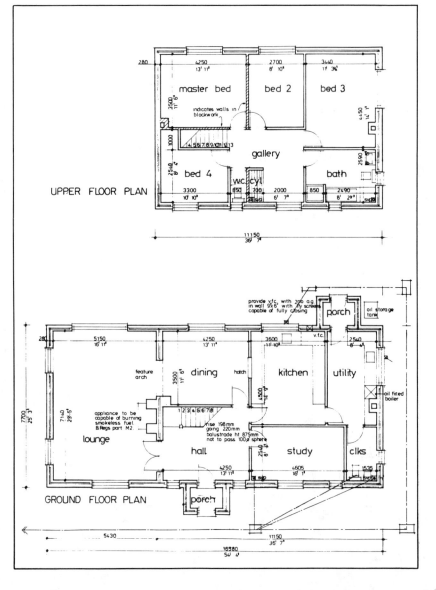

UPPER FLOOR PLAN

GROUND FLOOR PLAN

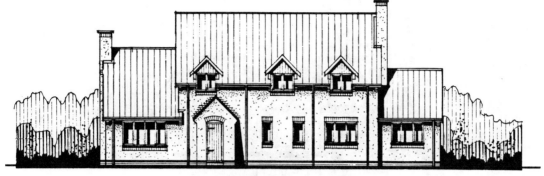

front elevation 1·100

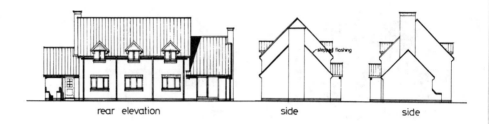

rear elevation   side   side

With its farmhouse kitchen and big utility room this is a splendid house for the country, shewn here with two chimneys, one for a fire in the lounge and the other for a solid fuel stove in the kitchen. These stoves are becoming very popular for big homes in rural areas, and most of them are properly described as "multi-fuel" stoves as they can burn a wide range of fuels.

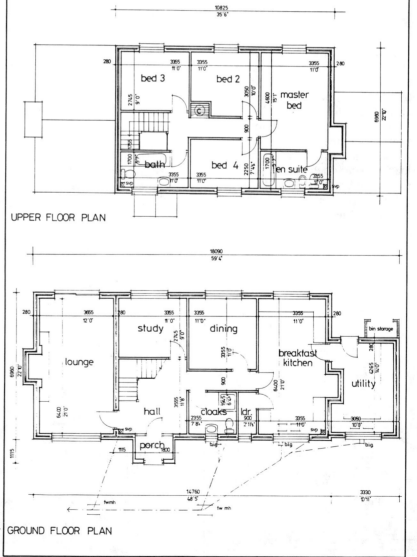

UPPER FLOOR PLAN

GROUND FLOOR PLAN

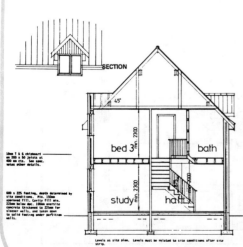

SECTION

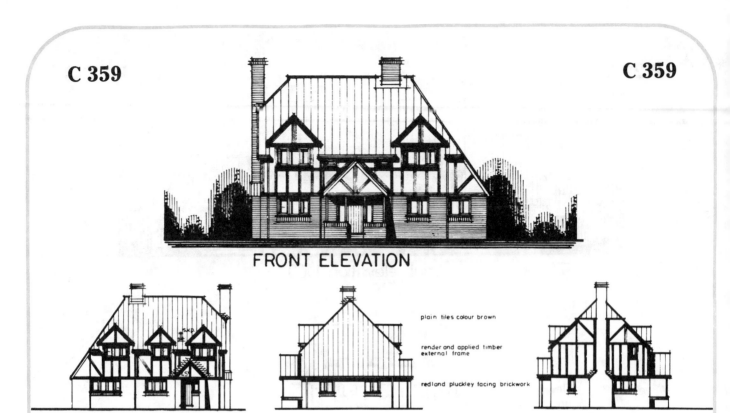

FRONT ELEVATION

REAR ELEVATION

SIDE ELEVATION

SIDE ELEVATION

plain tiles colour brown

render and applied timber external frame

redland pluckley facing brickwork

This heavily timbered neo-tudor house has some interesting features, including porches at the front and back doors that are very appropriate to the style. The inglenook fireplace in the lounge shares a chimney with the corner fireplace in the hall: an unusual feature which helps to make this such an interesting home. The big gable chimney is for a solid fuel cooker in the kitchen.

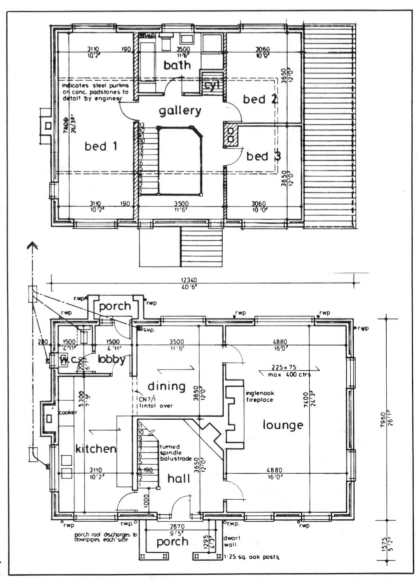

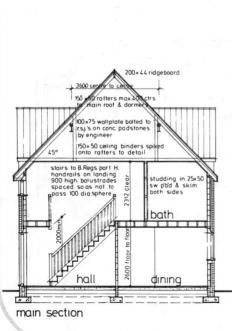

main section

A half-timbered house with the inglenook fireplace and huge outside chimney breast that matches the period style. The hall and first floor landing are very large and give an air of distinction to the interior. Double doors from the hall into the lounge add to this.

The house is shewn with no division at all between the kitchen and the dining room, and the arrangement of the floor joists to the first floor above enables any sort of non-structural divider to be used to separate the two areas - or a conventional wall can be built! The choice is yours.

The details of the staircase are always important in a house of this style, especially when there is room on the landing for furniture and a window seat. In recent years the staircase manufacturers have revived many of the Victorian newel and balustrade designs, and there is now a wide choice of both modern and period options. Of course, if you want a Tudor staircase to match your Tudor style home this will be something of a challenge, but it can be done!

rear elevation 1·100   side

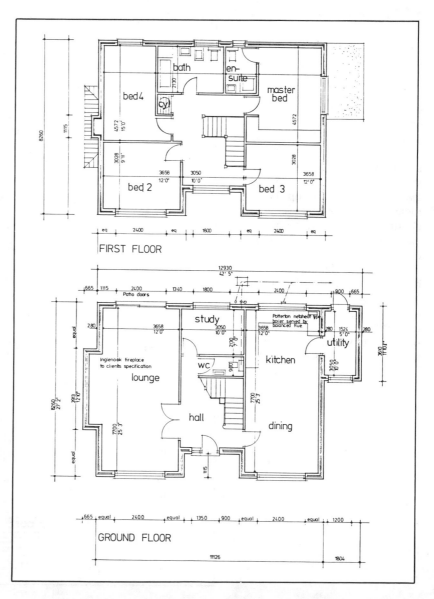

FIRST FLOOR

GROUND FLOOR

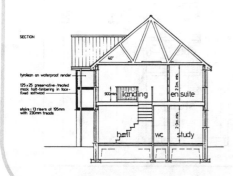

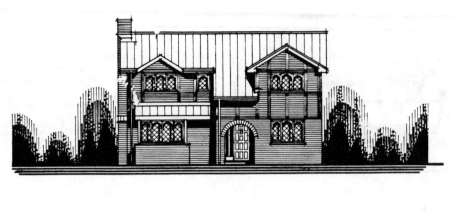

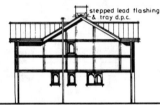
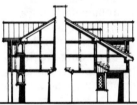

A mock-tudor design with arched window heads matching an arch over the porch to the front entrance. These arches to windows are becoming very popular, and windows in this style are available from all the manufacturers. They are not specially made, and are usually standard windows with arched glazing beads at the top. This means that if you ever want to change the style any competant carpenter can easily take them out.

The double glazing has diamond pattern leading. There are various ways of doing this, and if you want leaded lights it is important to ask to see a sample of the actual leading system proposed. Some look contrived but the best are excellent.

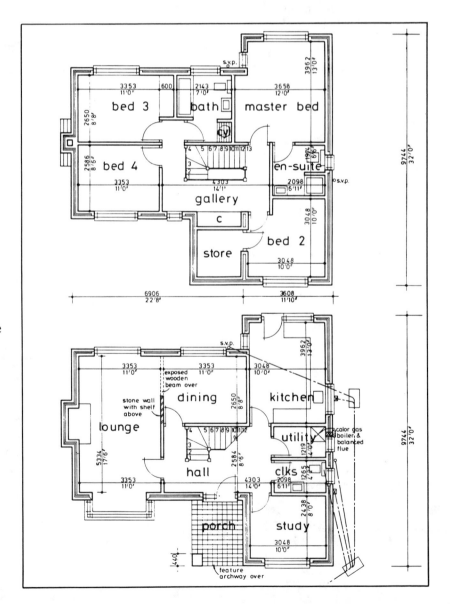

FRONT ELEVATION

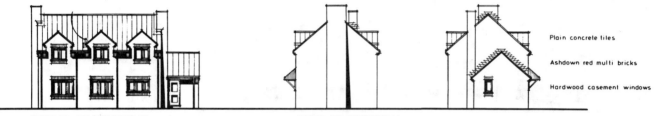

REAR ELEVATION   SIDE ELEVATION   SIDE ELEVATION

Plain concrete tiles

Ashdown red multi bricks

Hardwood casement windows

With six dormers and a chimney up each gable, this is just the house for a Cotswold village, although in the Cotswolds it would probably be built in stone. The style is now very fashionable on "village street" plots, and looks well with leaded lights to the windows.

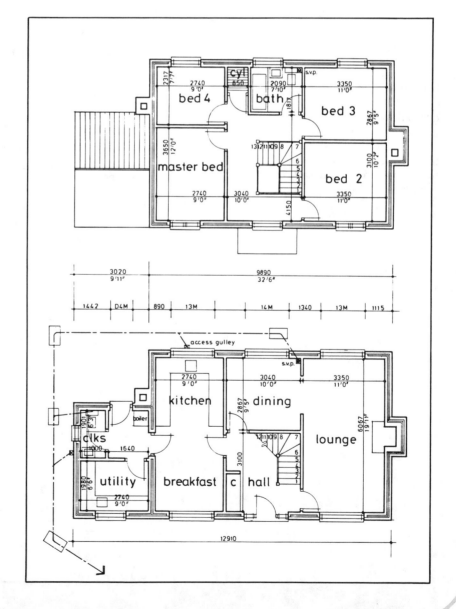

FRONT ELEVATION

pitch to suit gables
over lounge

stepped lead flashing
& tray d.p.c.

s.v.p. fitted durable cage
& weathering slate

Redland slate grey-plain clay
tiles+valley tiles

Bradstone traditional walling
in weathered cotswold with
concrete cills

Hardwood casement joinery
with hardwood arch formes to
window heads & concrete cills

SIDE ELEVATION   REAR ELEVATION   SIDE ELEVATION

A four bedroom house with a
two room granny flat that has its
own bathroom. It is unusual to
find a new home of this size and
character with only one
bathroom for four bedrooms, but
the dressing room can easily be
turned into an en-suite bathroom
if required.

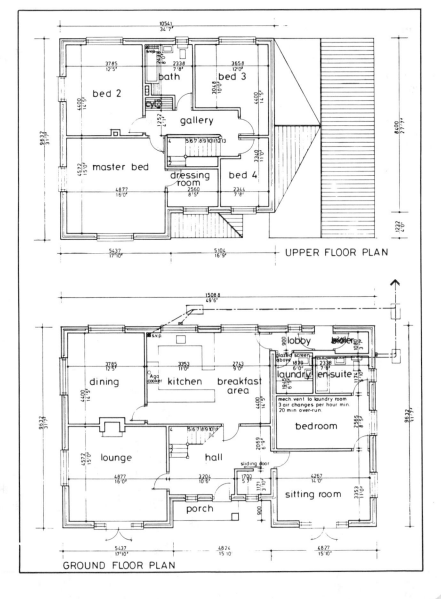

UPPER FLOOR PLAN

GROUND FLOOR PLAN

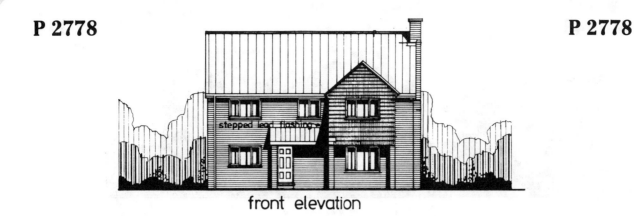

front elevation

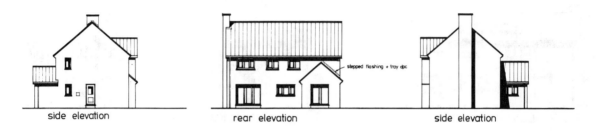

side elevation

rear elevation

side elevation

A house in an Essex style with a tile hung projecting bay to one of the front bedrooms. The study at the rear is really quite separate from the rest of the house, giving the privacy from everyday living that is needed by many people who work at home.

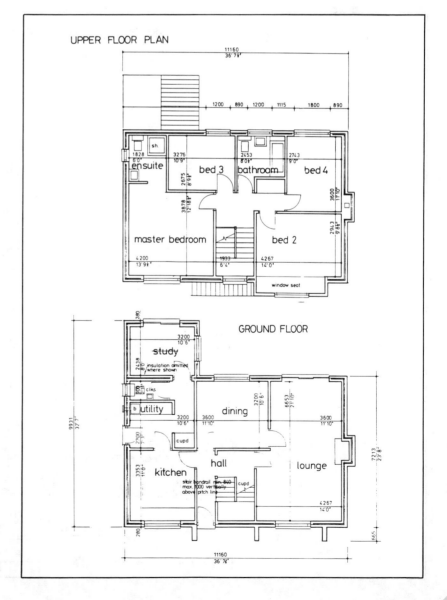

UPPER FLOOR PLAN

GROUND FLOOR

FRONT ELEVATION

s.v.p. fitted durable edge
& weathering slate

REAR ELEVATION

stepped lead flashing
& tray d.p.c.

SIDE ELEVATIONS

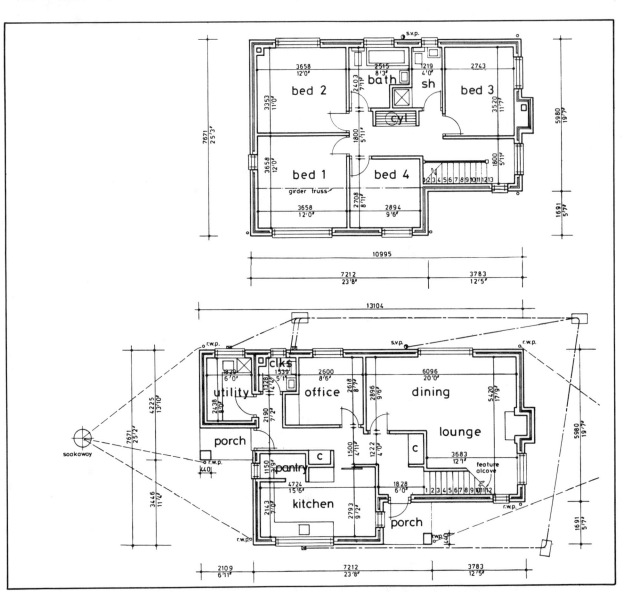

s.v.p.

3658 12'0"	2515 8'3"	1219 4'0"	2743
bed 2	bath	sh	bed 3

3353 11'0"

2403 7'11"

cyl

3520 11'7"

5980 19'7"

1800 5'11"

bed 1

bed 4

1800 5'11"

3658 12'0"

girder truss

3658 12'0"

2708 8'11"

2894 9'6"

7671 25'3"

1691 5'7"

1 2 3 4 5 6 7 8 9 10 11 12 13

10995

7212 23'8"

3783 12'5"

13104

r.w.p.

s.v.p.

r.w.p.

clks 1539 5'11"

1820 6'0"

1328 4'4"

2600 8'6"

2618 8'7"

6096 20'0"

r.w.p.

2438

utility

office

2896 9'6"

dining

5420 17'9"

4225 13'10"

2190 7'2"

5980 19'7"

7671 25'2"

porch

1500 4'11"

1222 4'0"

lounge

c

soakaway

r.w.p. 440

1150 3'9"

pantry

c

c

3683 12'1"

feature alcove

3446 11'4"

4724 15'6"

1828 6'0"

2143 7'0"

kitchen

2793 9'2"

1 2 3 4 5 6 7 8 9 10 11 12

porch

1691 5'7"

r.w.p.

r.w.p.

r.w.p. 440

2109 6'11"

7212 23'8"

3783 12'5"

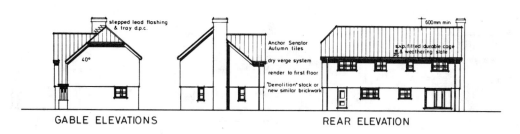

stepped lead flashing
& tray d.p.c.

40°

dry verge system

render to first floor

"Demolition" stock or
new similar brickwork

Anchor Senator
Autumn tiles

600mm min

s.v.p. fitted durable cage
& weathering slate

GABLE ELEVATIONS

REAR ELEVATION

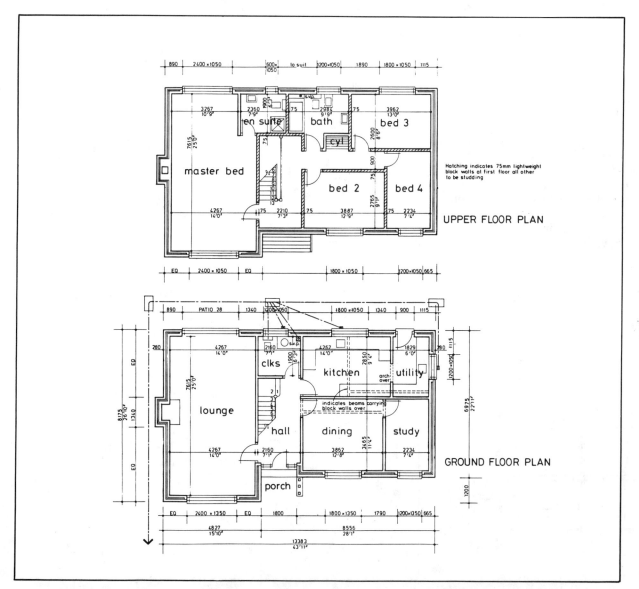

Hatching indicates 75mm lightweight
block walls at first floor all other
to be studding

UPPER FLOOR PLAN

en suite

bath

bed 3

cyl

master bed

bed 2

bed 4

indicates beams carrying
block walls over

clks

kitchen

utility

arch
over

lounge

hall

dining

study

porch

GROUND FLOOR PLAN

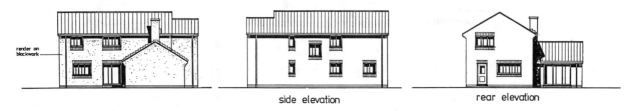

side elevation

rear elevation

render on blockwork

This house is an interesting shape and has a complex roof line, but the structure is simple to build and the roof construction is based on trussed rafters and quite cost effective. The large study and the cloakroom are quite separate from the rest of the living accommodation, making it popular as a vicarage or doctors home where visitors can be interviewed away from family activities.

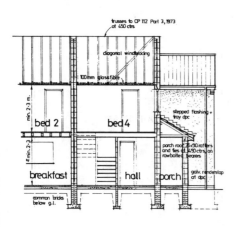

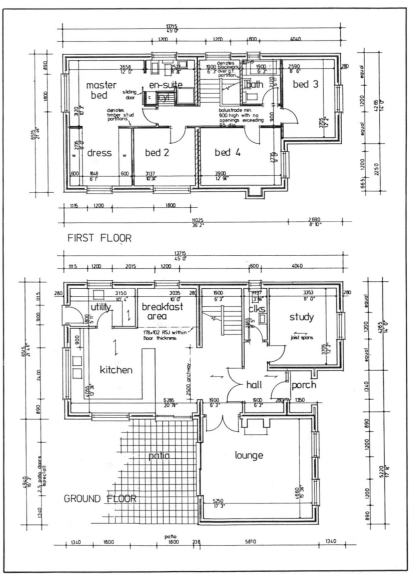

FIRST FLOOR

GROUND FLOOR

FRONT ELEVATION

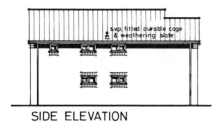

s.v.p. fitted durable cope & weathering slate

SIDE ELEVATION

REAR ELEVATION

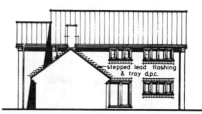

stepped lead flashing & tray d.p.c.

SIDE ELEVATION

A big house that can just fit in a forty two foot plot if space is at a premium.

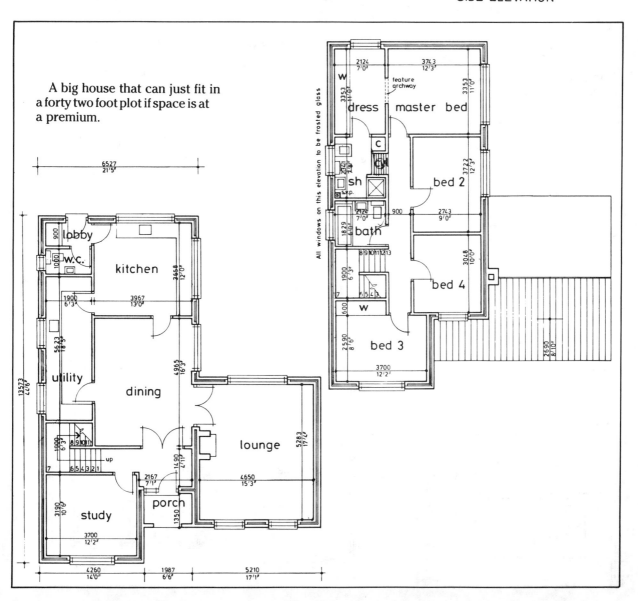

front elevation

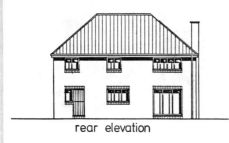

rear elevation

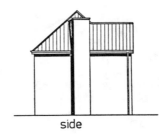

side

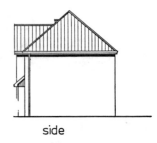

side

A four bedroom house with large rooms and enough room on the landing for a desk or sewing table below the window. The bedrooms can be rearranged to give a small en-suite bathroom if required.

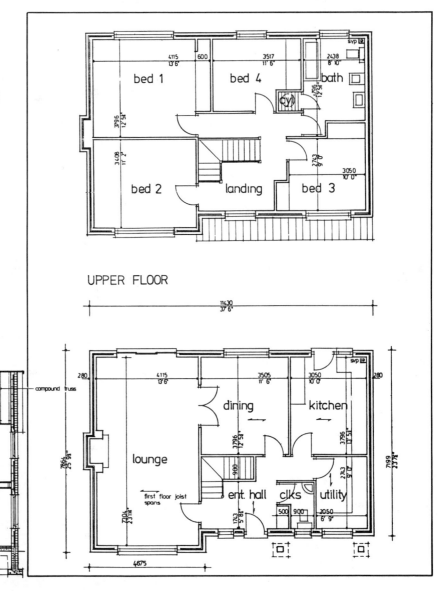

UPPER FLOOR

FRONT ELEVATION

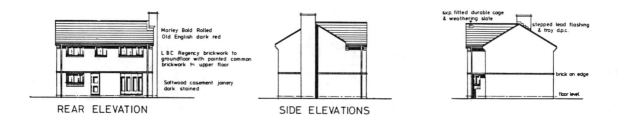

REAR ELEVATION

Marley Bold Rolled
Old English dark red

LBC Regency brickwork to
groundfloor with painted common
brickwork to upper floor

Softwood casement joinery
dark stained

SIDE ELEVATIONS

s.v.p. fitted durable cage
& weathering slate

stepped lead flashing
& tray d.p.c.

brick on edge

floor level

A compact home with the crisp
feel that comes from the
combination of brick, render and
a gable roof.

The drainage arrangements
have been left on the plans, as
there is a special combined
system with both rainwater and
foul drainage taken into the same
main drain. The usual
arrangement is for rainwater —
called surface water — to be
taken to soakaways or into a
completely separate drain. The
local authority advises on what is
required in any particular area.

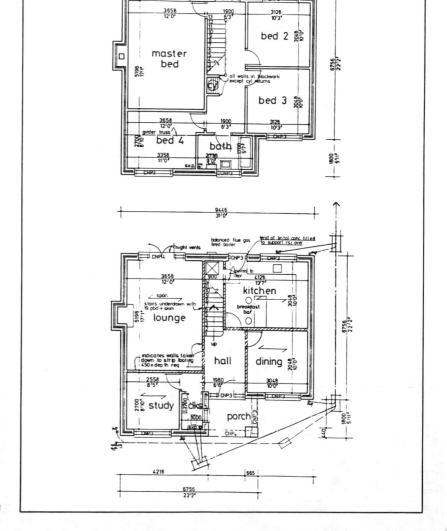

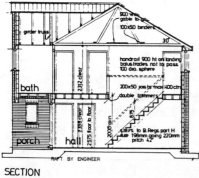

SECTION

REAR ELEVATION   SIDE ELEVATIONS

The section drawing of this four bedroom house shews how the complex looking roof of this house is based on a simple rectangle of trussed rafters, with the dormer above the wall plate. If this can be arranged easily then the cost savings are significant, and the money saved can either be used to reduce the total budget or else spent on more expensive features elsewhere.

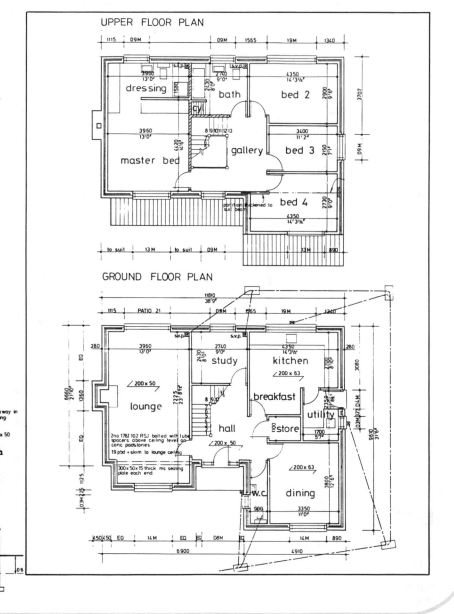

UPPER FLOOR PLAN

dressing
bath
bed 2
cyl
master bed
gallery
bed 3
bed 4
partition thickened to suit bath

GROUND FLOOR PLAN

study
kitchen
lounge
breakfast
hall
store
utility
w.c
dining

100 x 50 ridge binder
900 wide walkway in t.& g. boarding
100 x 50
unsupported f.f. walls in 75 x 50 stridding on double joists
18 mm decking on 200x 50 or 200 x 63 joists max. 400 ctrs.
40°
r.s.j.
2 N° 225 x 75 joists under dormer
perimeter wall position
50 screed on reinforced concrete detailed by engineer
selected fill in compacted layers

GROUND LEVEL BUILT UP TO ALLOW CONNECTION TO
EXISTING M.H. AT ENTRANCE

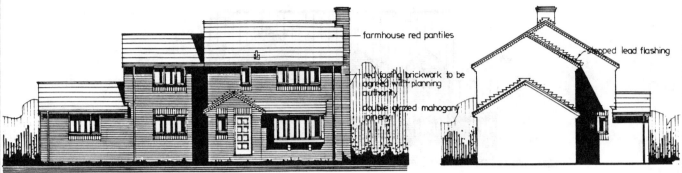

front elevation   side

— farmhouse red pantiles

— stepped lead flashing

red facing brickwork to be
agreed with planning
authority

double glazed mahogany
joinery

side   rear elevation

There is more room in this cottage style home than one anticipates at first glance, and the large 'spare' room next to the kitchen obviously has many roles. If built with an outside door it will make a very convenient office for a farmer or anyone else who works from home, or, if built in a village street, would be an excellent small shop.

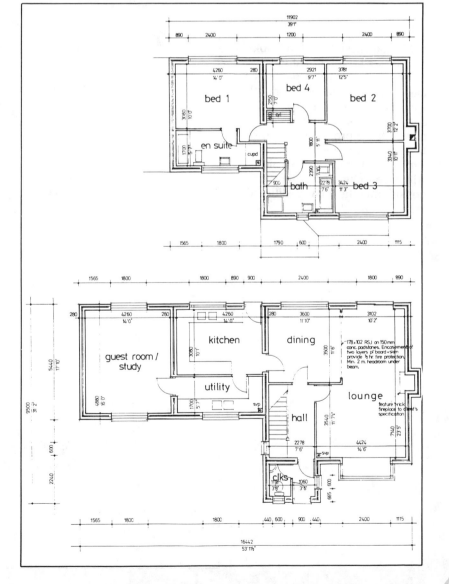

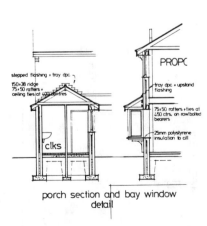

PROPO

stepped flashing + tray dpc

150×38 ridge
75×50 rafters +
ceiling ties at 400 centres

tray dpc + upstand
flashing

75×50 rafters + ties at
450 ctrs. on rawlbolted
bearers

25mm polystyrene
insulation to cill

clks

porch section and bay window
detail

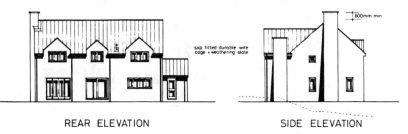

REAR ELEVATION   SIDE ELEVATION   SIDE ELEVATION

A home in a style that will look equally well if built in stone. However, in this case the timber cladding to the end of the porch would not be appropriate, and some changes would have to be made. One approach would be to leave this gable open, with heavy exposed rafters, but a decision will have to be made after considering the local traditional architectural style.

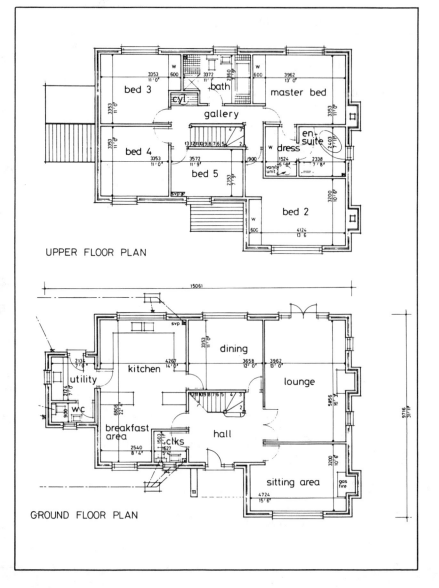

UPPER FLOOR PLAN

GROUND FLOOR PLAN

FRONT ELEVATION

REAR ELEVATION

Dark Brown roof tiles T.B.A.

Red brickwork T.B.A.

Hardwood casement joinery

SIDE ELEVATION

SIDE ELEVATION

This farmhouse has everything the farmers wife asks for: a WC and plenty of dirty boot space at the back door, direct access to the farm office without going through the kitchen, and well laid out living accommodation well away from the back door and the kitchen.

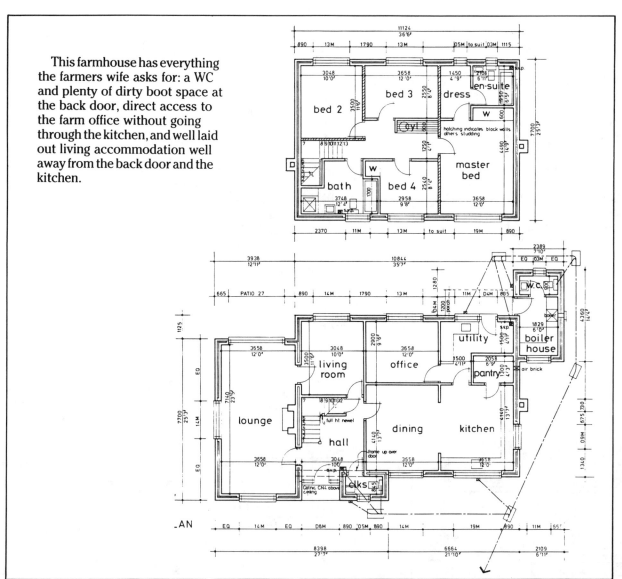

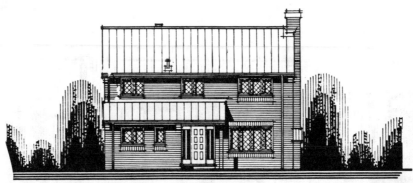

FRONT ELEVATION

REAR ELEVATION

Ludlow dark brown roofing tiles

facing brickwork to be approved

diamond leaded lights throughout

GABLE ELEVATIONS

stained vertical weatherboarding

Diamond leaded lights throughout are a feature of this 3/4 bedroom home, which has a first floor layout that enables a fourth bedroom to be used as a dressing room if desired. I always thought the point of a dressing room was that it could be as untidy as you wish, while the bedroom remains immaculate! Once you get used to this it must be difficult to dispense with the dressing room and have to keep the bedroom tidy.

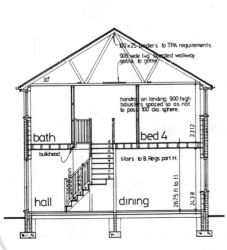

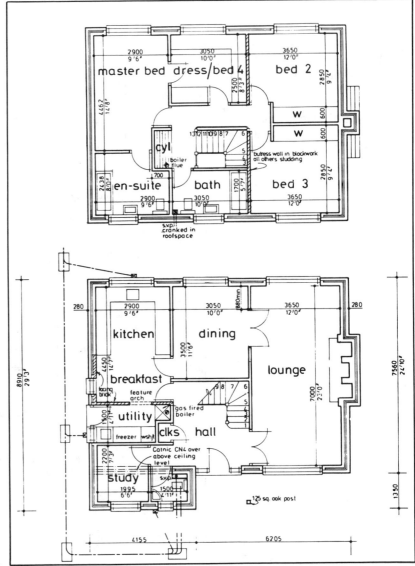

FRONT ELEVATION

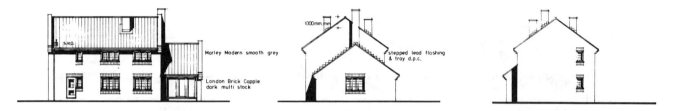

Marley Modern smooth grey

London Brick Capple dark multi stock

1000 mm. min

stepped lead flashing & tray d.p.c.

A house with four fireplaces and a solid fuel Aga cooker — a record for grates to clean out in a new home as far as anyone connected with this book can remember. What a jolly house it must be on a cold day though, with a fire in every downstairs room.

The walls are in a London stock brick, which is irregular in shape and multi-coloured. The use of stone tabling (or coping stones) to the gable walls is unusual above brick walls, and this was a local feature to which the new building conformed.

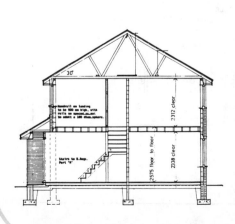

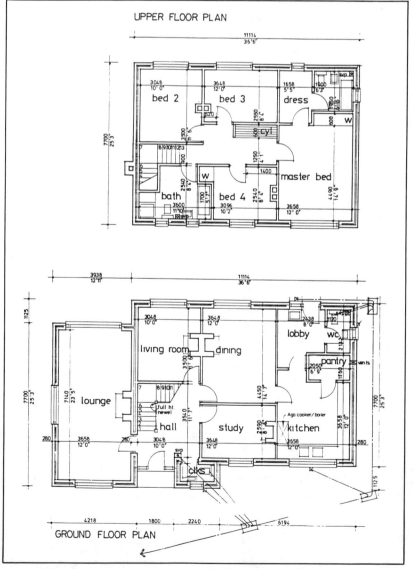

FRONT ELEVATION

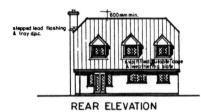

stepped lead flashing & tray d.p.c.

600mm min.

hanging tiled gable face & weathering plate

REAR ELEVATION

velux window

SIDE ELEVATION

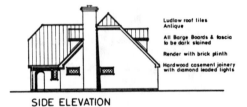

Ludlow roof tiles Antique

All Barge Boards & fascia to be dark stained

Render with brick plinth

Hardwood casement joinery with diamond leaded lights

SIDE ELEVATION

This dormer bungalow will not be exactly economical to build, but what a lot of character it has. For many people this is the ideal 'home in the country', and it would suit me very nicely, except that I would want to replace the Velux window to the en-suite bathroom with a very small dormer.

study · kitchen · dining · reception hall · lounge · utility · en-suite · bed 4 · clks · lobby · porch

bed 3 · dressing room · bed 2 · bath · en-suite · bed 1

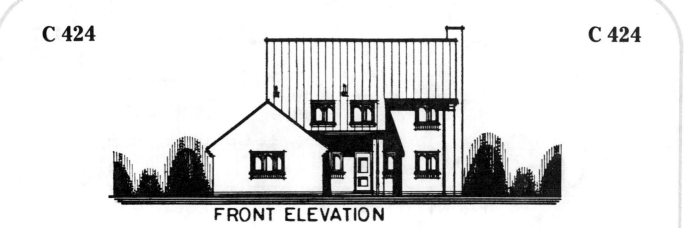

FRONT ELEVATION

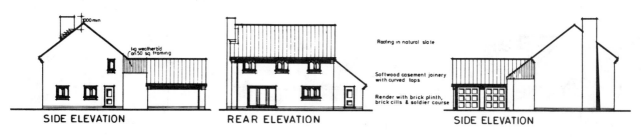

SIDE ELEVATION

REAR ELEVATION

Roofing in natural slate

Softwood casement joinery
with curved tops

Render with brick plinth,
brick cills & soldier course

SIDE ELEVATION

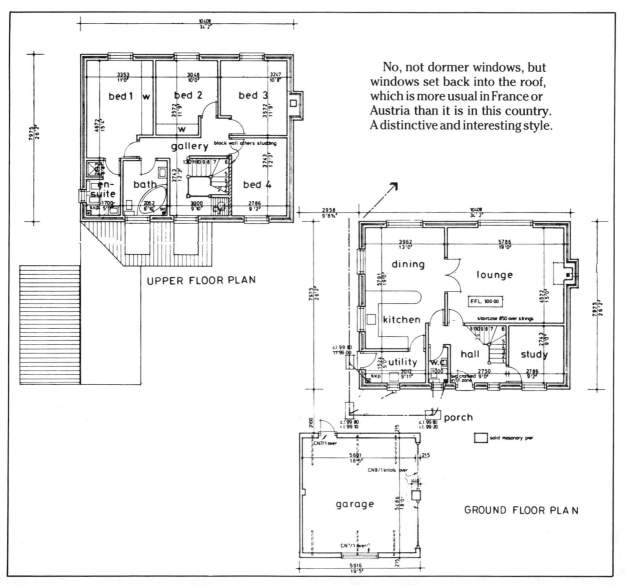

No, not dormer windows, but
windows set back into the roof,
which is more usual in France or
Austria than it is in this country.
A distinctive and interesting style.

UPPER FLOOR PLAN

GROUND FLOOR PLAN

97

FRONT ELEVATION

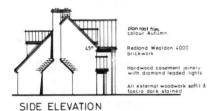

plain roof tiles
colour Autumn

Redland Wealdon 4000
brickwork

Hardwood casement joinery
with diamond leaded lights

All external woodwork soffit &
fascia dark stained

SIDE ELEVATION

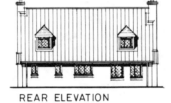

REAR ELEVATION

Hunter Regency rainwater
goods in brown

SIDE ELEVATION

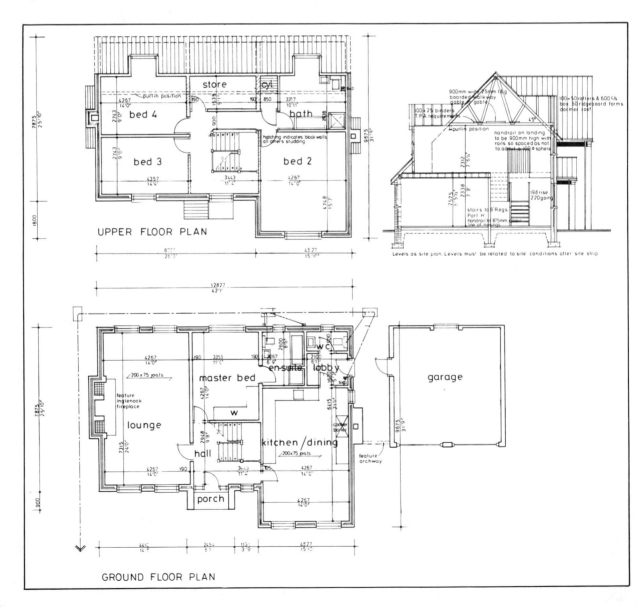

UPPER FLOOR PLAN

GROUND FLOOR PLAN

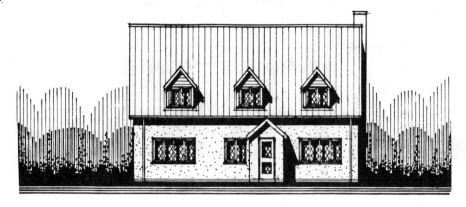

REAR ELEVATION

GABLE ELEVATIONS

What a lot of room in this friendly dormer bungalow. The purlin roof construction prevents moving internal walls to suit your individual requirements, but the layout is very well planned anyway, and the home has lots of character.

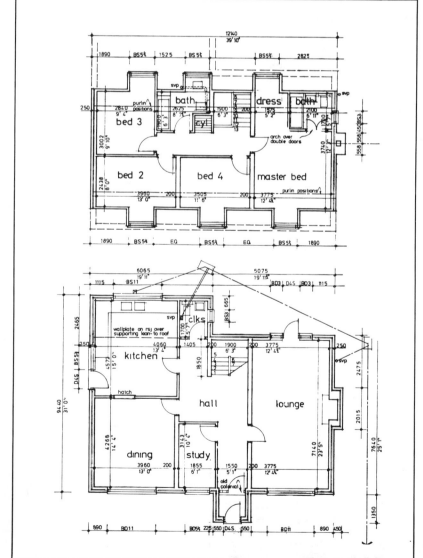

W 960

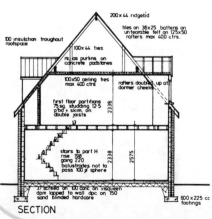

SECTION

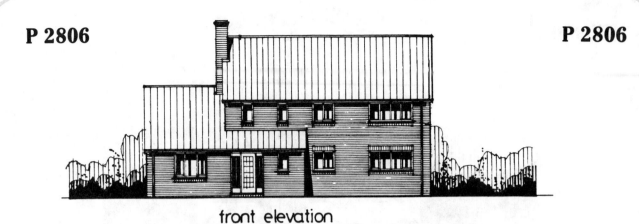

front elevation

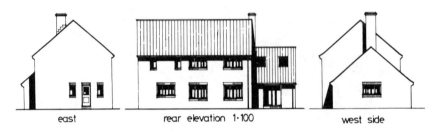

east   rear elevation 1·100   west side

A house with a cost-effective trussed rafter roof to the main two storey part and a purlin roof over the lounge with a childrens play room under the tiles. This is lit by Velux windows set in the sloping ceiling, but a window can be set in the gable end wall if required.

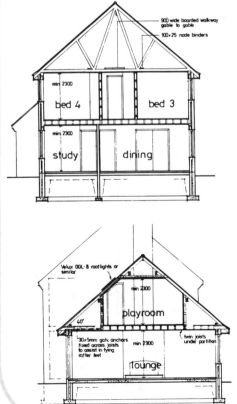

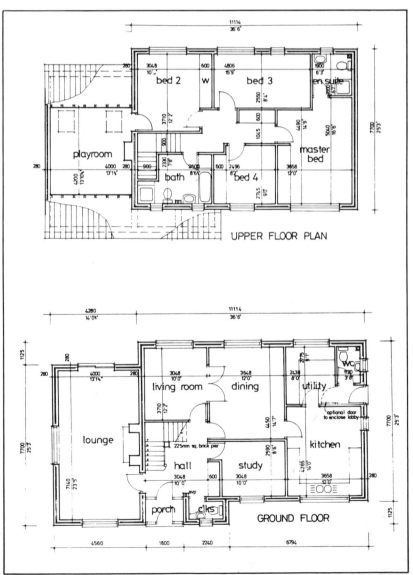

UPPER FLOOR PLAN

GROUND FLOOR

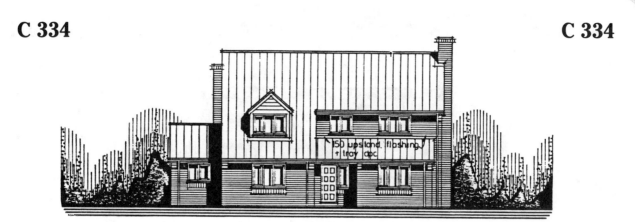

FRONT ELEVATION

REAR ELEVATION

swp fitted durable cage
+ weathering slate

SIDE ELEVATION

lead soakers to cheeks
lead apron to cill

stepped flashing + tray dpc

Marley Wessex tiles
in antique brown

Butterley Old English Rose
brickwork

SIDE ELEVATION

150 upstand flashing
+ tray dpc

The drainage arrangements shewn on this plan demonstrate just how involved the pipe runs below ground can become when the local authority requires two separate systems for foul and surface drainage. It is more usual for surface water to be discharged into simple soakaways, but it should never be taken for granted that this will be acceptable.

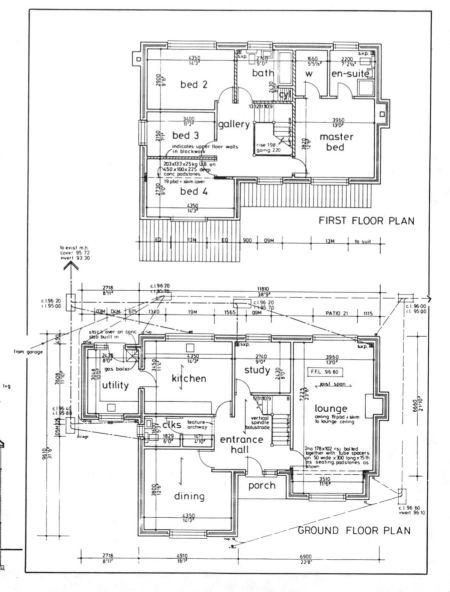

FIRST FLOOR PLAN

bed 2

bath

w

en-suite

gallery

bed 3

indicates upper floor walls
in blockwork

203x133 x25kg UB. on
450 x 100 x 225 deep
conc padstones

19 pbd + skim cover

bed 4

rise 198
going 220

master bed

GROUND FLOOR PLAN

utility

gas boiler

kitchen

study

F.F.L. 96 80

joist span

clks

feature
archway

lounge
ceiling 19 pbd + skim
to lounge ceiling

vertical
spindle
balustrade

entrance
hall

dining

porch

2no 178x102 rsj bolted
together with tube spacers
on 50 wide x 300 long x 15 th
ms. seating padstones as
shown.

from garage

to exist m.h.
cover 95 72
invert 93 30

SECTION

900 wide walkway in t+g
bding

100 x 25 binders

75x50 studding pbd + skim

18 t+g chipboard on 200 x 50
joists max 400 ctrs.

37 screed on 100 conc on
1000g dpm lapped to inner
leaf wall dpc on 150 sand
blinded hardcore

cavity fill min 225 below dpc

600 x 225 footing

Levels as site plan. Levels must be related to site conditions after site strip.

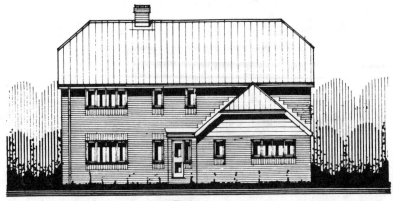

FRONT ELEVATION

This is a variant of a popular D & M design, and it has been built very many times in one form or another. The angled front door helps the hall to seem far larger than it really is, and it provides a doorway into every ground floor room in a very convenient way. The first floor layout is dominated by the large landing with the central stair well, and personally I would prefer larger windows to the landing.

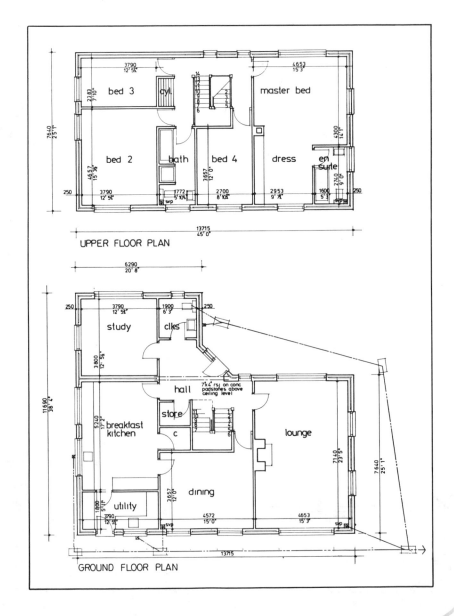

UPPER FLOOR PLAN

GROUND FLOOR PLAN

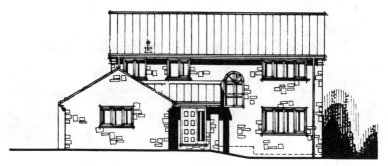

FRONT ELEVATION

SIDE ELEVATION

Marley Modern roof tiles

Stone with rendered gables

render

REAR ELEVATION

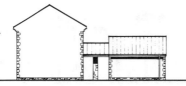

SIDE ELEVATION

A nice stone house in a north country style with a big hall and a step down into the lounge. The Building Regulations require that a door may not open onto the top of a step, and in this design it has been easy to set it back beside the stairs.

The covered way between the house and the garage needs careful thought, perhaps being paved with stone slabs, with a stone flower trough or similar feature.

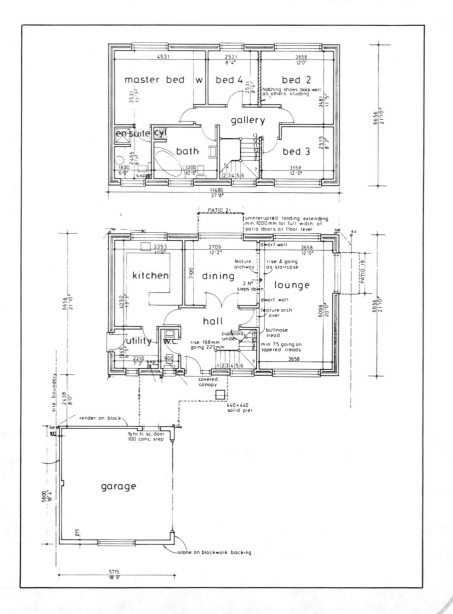

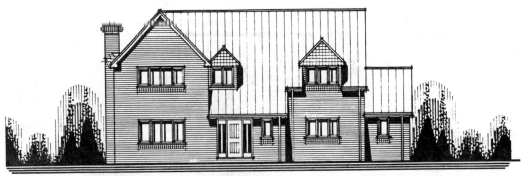

FRONT ELEVATION

Marley Modern
Antique tiles

Butterley Blaby Golden
Handmade brickwork
with feature brick cills

Hardwood casement
joinery

SIDE ELEVATION   REAR ELEVATION   SIDE ELEVATION

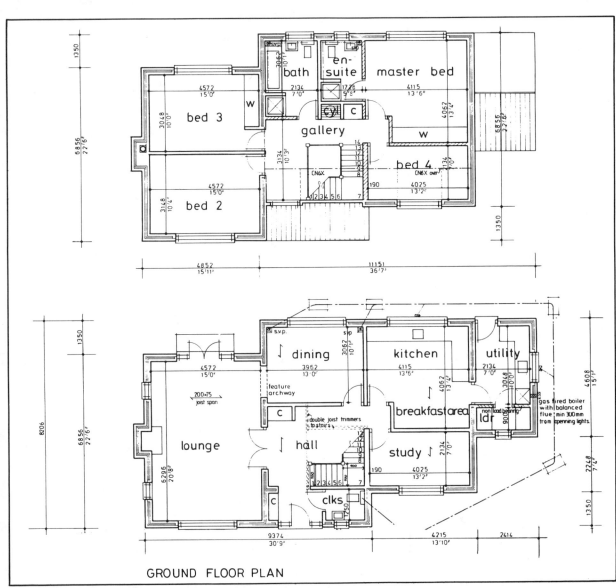

GROUND FLOOR PLAN

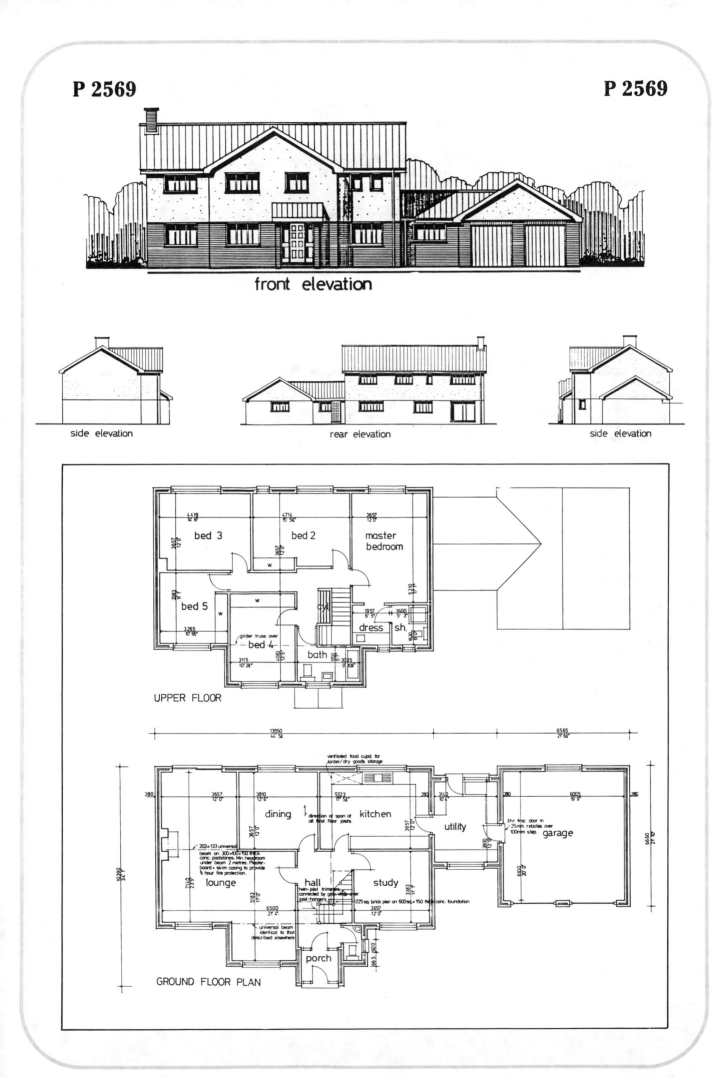

front elevation

side elevation

rear elevation

side elevation

UPPER FLOOR

bed 3

bed 2

master bedroom

bed 5

bed 4

cyl

dress

sh.

bath

girder truss over

GROUND FLOOR PLAN

dining

kitchen

utility

garage

lounge

hall

study

porch

ventilated food cupd. for larder/dry goods storage

direction of span of all first floor joists

203 × 133 universal beam on 300 ×100 × 150 thick conc. padstones. Min. headroom under beam 2 metres. Plaster-board + skim casing to provide ½ hour fire protection.

½ hr fire door in 25mm. rebates over 100mm step.

twin-joist trimmers connected by gang-nail or joist-hangers.

225 sq. brick pier on 600sq.× 150 thick conc. foundation

universal beam identical to that described elsewhere

stepped lead flashing
+ tray d.p.c.

tray dpc to parapet
walls

Marley mendip roof tiles
colour smooth brown.

L.B.C. georgian red-multi
brickwork.

Boulton + Paul doublehung
sash windows. all bar

Fibreglass portico + columns
to clients supply.

gable elevation

s.v.p. fitted durable edge
+ weathering slab

rear elevation

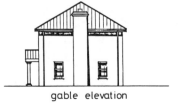

gable elevation

A family room which is quite separate from the lounge is becoming very popular these days, and must be a boon when different generations of a family want different television programmes.

Note that the flat roof over the kitchen, utility and family room has no access from the first floor, and cannot be used as a balcony. If it is likely that anyone building to this design will want to use it as a balcony at any time in the future, then a lintel for the necessary door can be built into the first floor wall, and the specification for the flat roof should be up-rated.

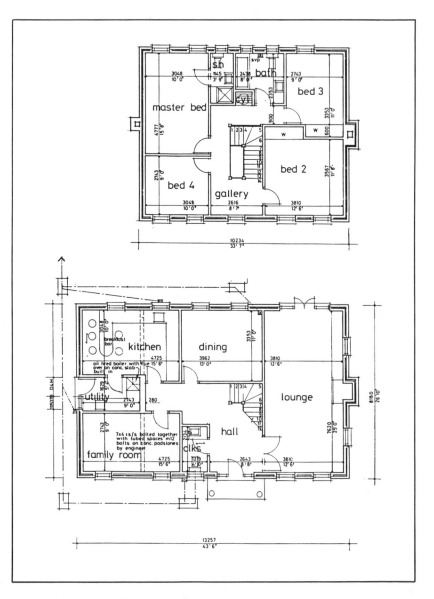

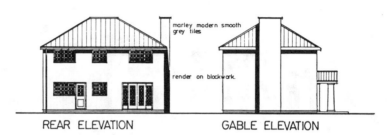

REAR ELEVATION   GABLE ELEVATION

marley modern smooth grey tiles

render on blockwork.

This is an example of the sort of Georgian style houses that suddenly became popular in the mid 1970s, and heralded the return to regional and period style homes after thirty years of functional 'modern design'. Although they are not now built in such numbers as a few years ago, they retain their popularity and are always easily sold. Perhaps this is as much to do with the convenience of the layout as with the appearance.

In this particular design the utility room can have its door moved to become either a study or a cloakroom.

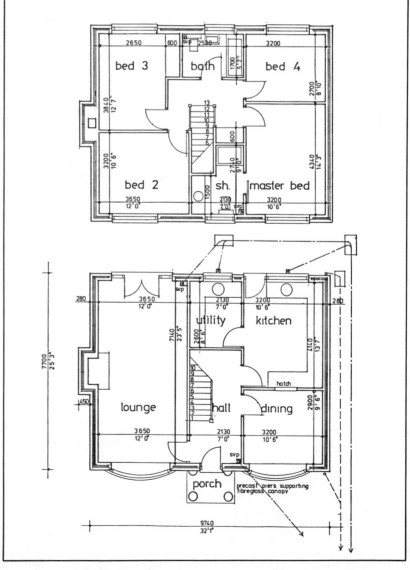

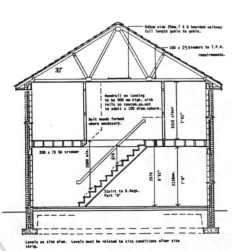

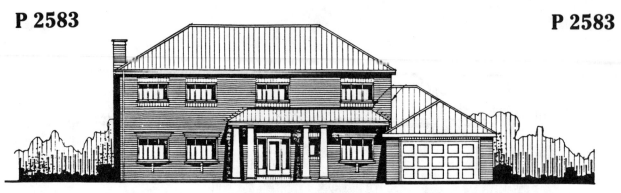

front elevation

rear elevation   side elevation

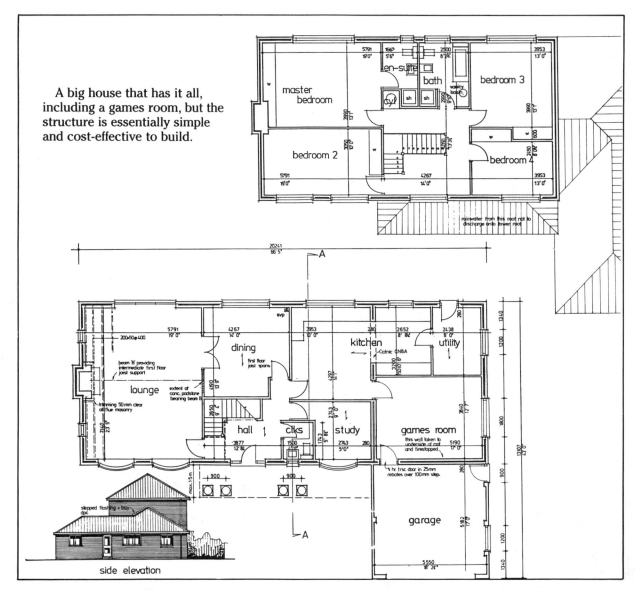

A big house that has it all,
including a games room, but the
structure is essentially simple
and cost-effective to build.

rear elevation

elevation

side elevation

This pleasant home with its Georgian style entrance will fit in well in the suburbs of most large towns, and in some villages in the South of England. It will almost certainly look best built in the stock bricks which are typical of the south, which are mottled in colour and irregular in shape compared with the less interesting bricks from brickyards in the midlands and north. The tiles should be small plain tiles or clay pantiles in a colour chosen carefully to complement the bricks

As the entrance is such a key feature of this design when viewed from the outside, the hall deserves to be given a similar emphasis inside, and calls for a prestige staircase with great care taken in the choice of newels and balustrading.

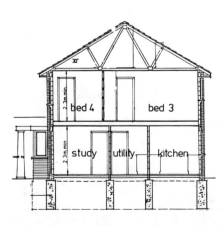

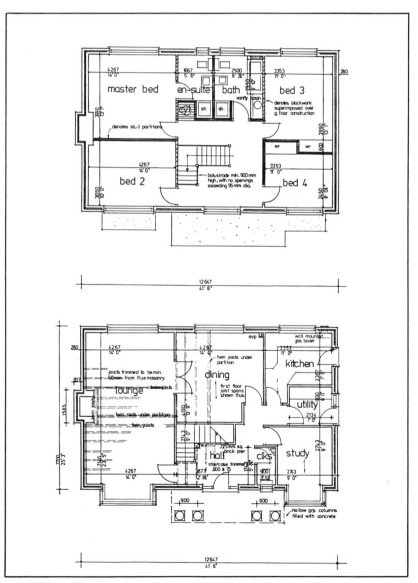

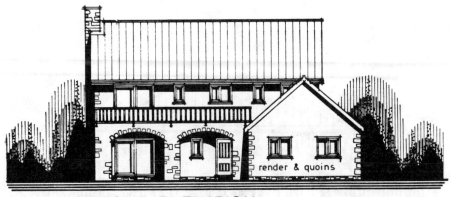

FRONT ELEVATION

SIDE ELEVATION

W.I. gate to clients choice

REAR ELEVATION

SIDE ELEVATION

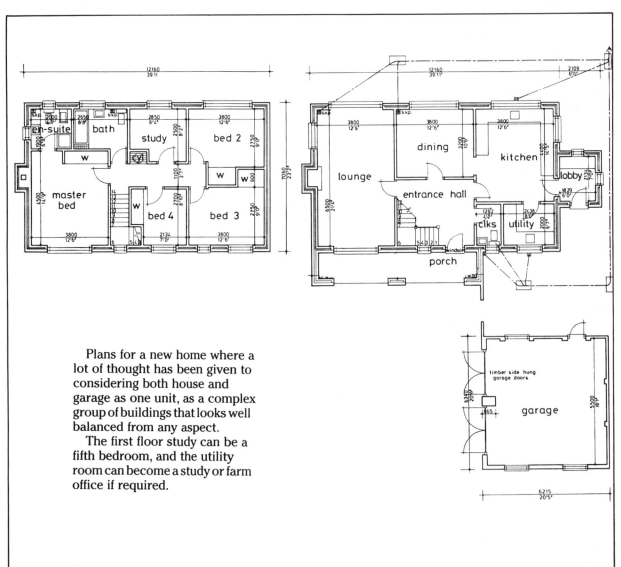

Plans for a new home where a lot of thought has been given to considering both house and garage as one unit, as a complex group of buildings that looks well balanced from any aspect.

The first floor study can be a fifth bedroom, and the utility room can become a study or farm office if required.

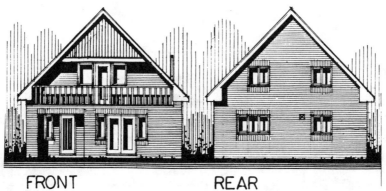

FRONT   REAR

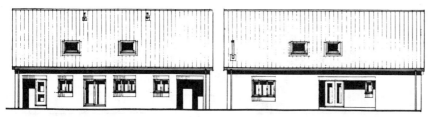

SIDE ELEVATIONS

A design with many unusual features, including the Swedish style balcony to the master bedroom, a gallery over the dining area, and much else. Study the plans - they are full of ideas.

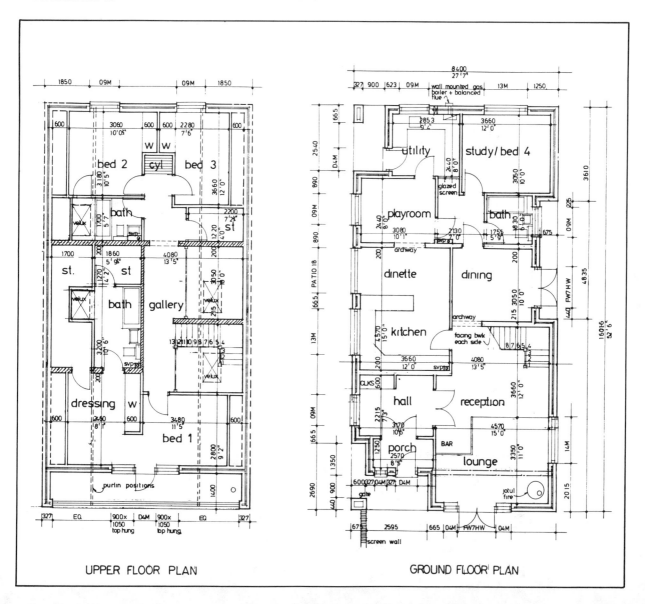

UPPER FLOOR PLAN

GROUND FLOOR PLAN

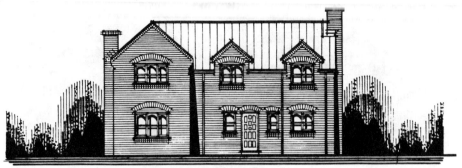

FRONT ELEVATION

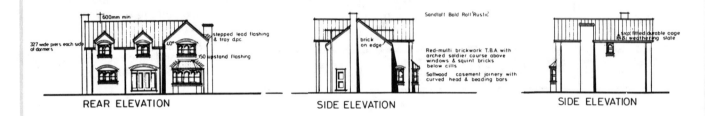

REAR ELEVATION

600mm min
327 wide piers each side of dormers
stepped lead flashing & tray d.p.c.
150 upstand flashing

SIDE ELEVATION

Sandtoft Bold Roll 'Rustic'
brick on edge
Red-multi brickwork T.B.A. with arched soldier course above windows & squint bricks below cills
Softwood casement joinery with curved head & beading bars

SIDE ELEVATION

sxp fitted durable cage & weathering slate

There is a fashionably Victorian feel to this house, and to the long lounge with its big 'walk-in' bay window. The choice of the right brick is very important for a design like this, and so is the selection of the right roof tiles.

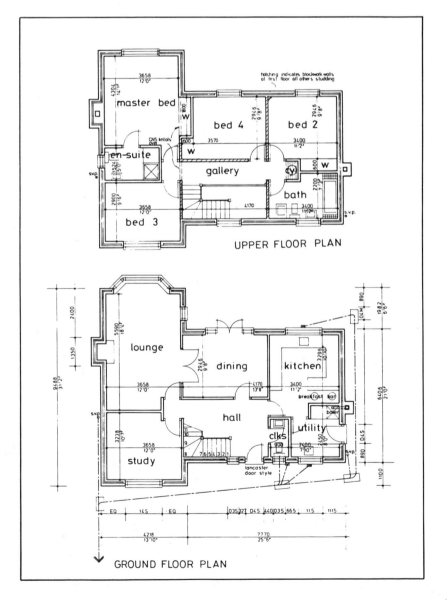

UPPER FLOOR PLAN

master bed
en-suite
bed 4
bed 2
gallery
cyl
bath
bed 3

hatching indicates blockwork walls at first floor all others studding

GROUND FLOOR PLAN

lounge
dining
kitchen
breakfast bar
hall
utility
clks
study
lancaster door style

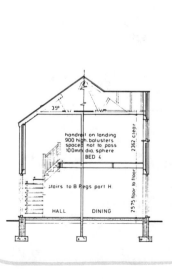

35°
handrail on landing 900 high balusters spaced not to pass 100mm dia. sphere
BED 4
2362 clear
stairs to B Regs part H
2575 floor to floor
HALL   DINING

The D & M Collection

Design and Materials Limited has nearly twenty years experience of designing homes to their clients' requirements and have a library of many thousand drawings, all stored in rows and rows of plan cabinets. Unlike the standard houses offered by builders and developers, which are drawn to suit their own commercial interests, these drawings are for homes which were commissioned to meet the particular requirements of individual families. They were the houses and bungalows that people really wanted to live in, and how they have changed, very significantly over the years.

In the 70's the ranch style held sway, with 22½ degree pitched roofs and picture windows. Then Georgian homes arrived, uncertainly at first with full bar windows simply put into the old box shapes, but quickly evolving into the well proportioned Georgian style homes that are still often built today, and which now have more and more attention paid to the real period design characteristics.

The next development was the concern for homes in regional styles appropriate to different parts of the country. Whether this stemmed from the publication of the County Design Guides, or whether it followed from a growing public awareness that local traditional architecture was important is uncertain, but they arrived, and are here to stay.

The mid 80's saw the return of the Tudor home for the first time since the 30's, and it was immediately hugely popular. As a result the 1988 edition of this book had a Tudor Homes Section which is still here in this 1991 edition. Copies of the books in public libraries carry more thumb prints on these pages than any others and they account for a large proportion of houses for which D & M have supplied material over the last four years.

More recently Post-Modernist styles have arrived, together with some Victorian style homes, but what is interesting is not so much the arrrival of new styles as the fact that all of them are now being built at the same time. The 90's are going to be the decade of consumer choice in housing, and companies which can provide designs to meet the aspirations of families able to build for themselves will flourish as never before.

Design and Materials are specialists in designing homes to peoples own requirements and for this new edition of Plans For Dream Homes they have provided a collection of thirty one of the designs which were most typical of the homes which they designed for their clients' in 1990. They are in different styles. Some are developments of well established design concepts from earlier years, most are new. They are examples of the homes which people are choosing for themselves all over the country. Consumer choice in housing arrived in the 80's; these are the options for the 90's.

The plans for the 31 homes on the following pages are the copyright of D & M Ltd and are only available as part of the companies package service.

The Kegworth design from the D & M Collection.

A four bedroom house designed to the detailed requirements of a doctor in the East Midlands.

The D & M Collection

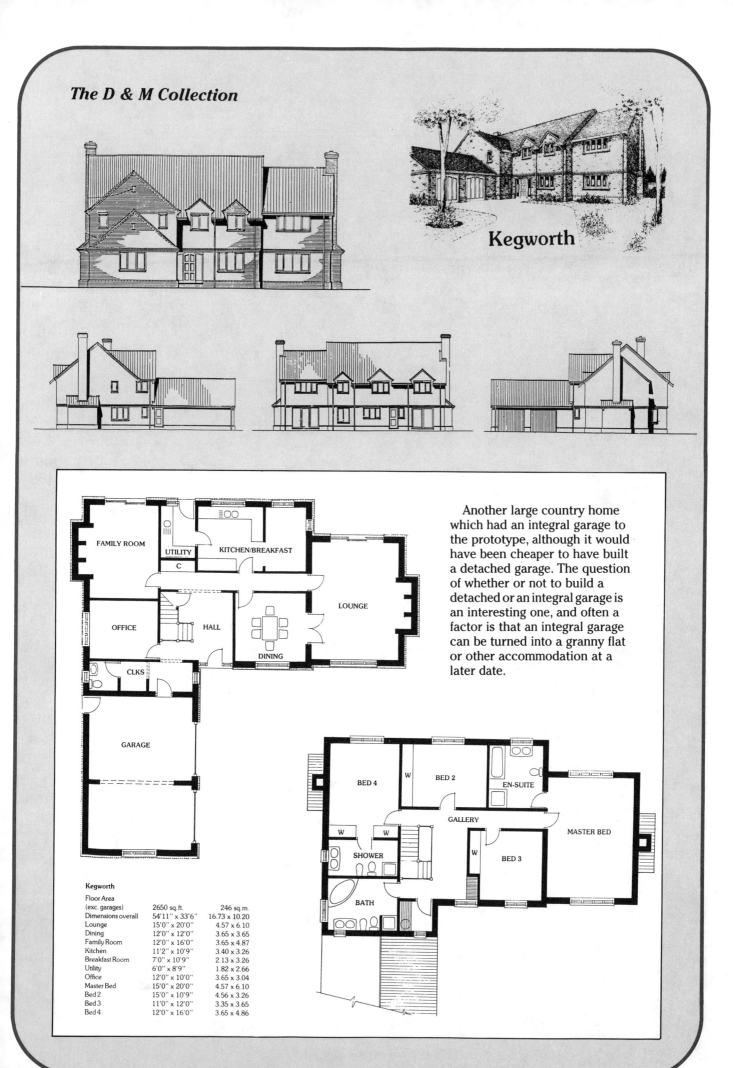

Kegworth

FAMILY ROOM

UTILITY

KITCHEN/BREAKFAST

C

OFFICE

HALL

LOUNGE

DINING

CLKS

GARAGE

Another large country home which had an integral garage to the prototype, although it would have been cheaper to have built a detached garage. The question of whether or not to build a detached or an integral garage is an interesting one, and often a factor is that an integral garage can be turned into a granny flat or other accommodation at a later date.

BED 4

W

BED 2

EN-SUITE

GALLERY

W

W

MASTER BED

SHOWER

W

BED 3

BATH

Kegworth

Floor Area

(exc. garages)	2650 sq.ft.	246 sq.m.
Dimensions overall	54'11" x 33'6"	16.73 x 10.20
Lounge	15'0" x 20'0"	4.57 x 6.10
Dining	12'0" x 12'0"	3.65 x 3.65
Family Room	12'0" x 16'0"	3.65 x 4.87
Kitchen	11'2" x 10'9"	3.40 x 3.26
Breakfast Room	7'0" x 10'9"	2.13 x 3.26
Utility	6'0" x 8'9"	1.82 x 2.66
Office	12'0" x 10'0"	3.65 x 3.04
Master Bed	15'0" x 20'0"	4.57 x 6.10
Bed 2	15'0" x 10'9"	4.56 x 3.26
Bed 3	11'0" x 12'0"	3.35 x 3.65
Bed 4	12'0" x 16'0"	3.65 x 4.86

Cranbrook

SIDE ELEVATION

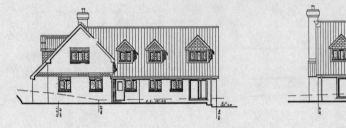

This large family house of over 2700 square feet has the ground floor accommodation arranged with a family room quite separate from the lounge and study. The dining room is integral with the kitchen, but all of this can be rearranged for someone requiring a formal dining room.

A lobby at the back door is a popular feature in rural areas, providing somewhere for wellingtons and for the dogs to sleep! On the first floor all four bedrooms have their own bathrooms, which is an American concept that has recently arrived in this country, and which surely is due to become a standard feature in large houses. More traditional is the window to the gallery above the stairs, which provides light for the hallway below. With the deeply recessed porch the hall would otherwise be rather dark; with the light from above the feature staircase is emphasised

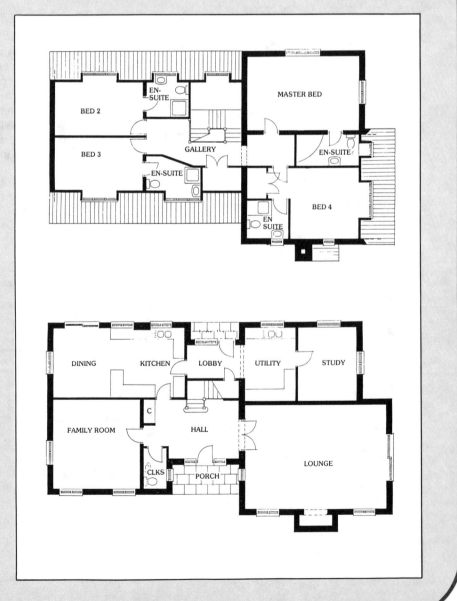

Cranbrook		
Floor Area	2739 sq.ft.	254 sq.m.
Dimensions overall	59'2" x 32'10"	18.04 x 10.01
Lounge	24'5" x 17'6"	7.44 x 5.33
Family Room	15'0" x 15'0"	4.57 x 4.57
Dining/Kitchen	22'7" x 12'0"	6.89 x 3.65
Utility	8'11" x 12'11"	2.72 x 3.93
Computer Room	10'0" x 12'11"	3.04 x 3.93
Master Bed	19'3" x 12'11"	5.87 x 3.93
Bed 2	15'0" x 9'0"	4.57 x 2.74
Bed 3	15'0" x 9'0"	4.57 x 2.74
Bed 4	11'11" x 12'0"	3.64 x 3.65

The D & M Collection

Alvechurch

This house of 2100 square feet has a very practical ground floor layout with four bedrooms and three bathrooms above. The stairs lead into a gallery which has its own window, which is a feature very much to be desired where this can be arranged.

The Alvechurch house shown here with a mock timber framing and herringbone brickwork. These Tudor features can be built very easily using traditional construction.

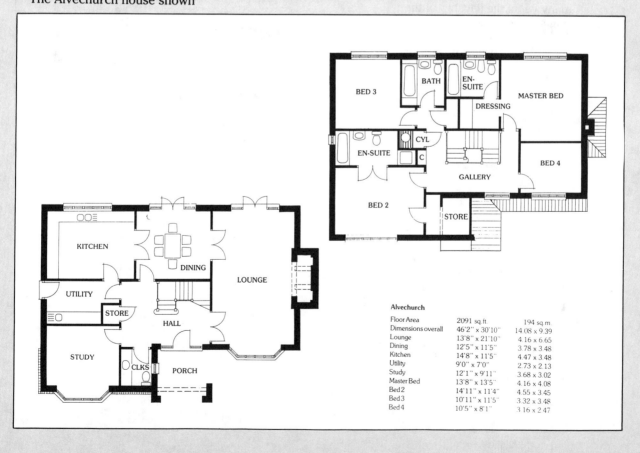

Alvechurch

Floor Area	2091 sq.ft.	194 sq.m.
Dimensions overall	46'2" x 30'10"	14.08 x 9.39
Lounge	13'8" x 21'10"	4.16 x 6.65
Dining	12'5" x 11'5"	3.78 x 3.48
Kitchen	14'8" x 11'5"	4.47 x 3.48
Utility	9'0" x 7'0"	2.73 x 2.13
Study	12'1" x 9'11"	3.68 x 3.02
Master Bed	13'8" x 13'5"	4.16 x 4.08
Bed 2	14'11" x 11'4"	4.55 x 3.45
Bed 3	10'11" x 11'5"	3.32 x 3.48
Bed 4	10'5" x 8'1"	3.16 x 2.47

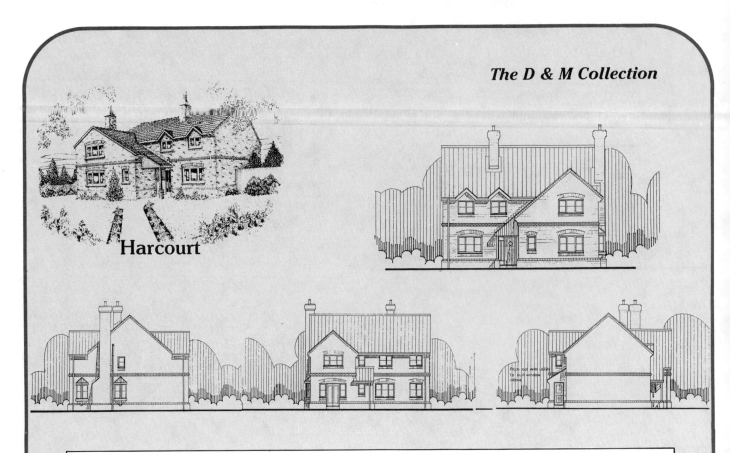

Harcourt

This is another modification of a popular D & M design of the 80's, in this case a condensed version of the Avonmere design. The original Avonmere, for so many years the flagship of the D & M range of luxury homes, required a very wide plot. This version of it can be built on a site of suburban dimensions, while retaining many of the characteristics of the original.

The layout as shown is sometimes criticised as there is no direct access between the kitchen and the family room. A view of this depends on the age of the family concerned, but it can be arranged, although at the cost of breaking the continuous work surface which extends around three sides of the kitchen as shown.

Harcourt

Floor Area	2079 sq.ft.	193 sq.m.
Dimensions overall	37'2" x 37'4"	11.32 x 11.37
Drawing Room	13'0" x 18'0"	3.96 x 5.48
Family Room	12'0" x 14'0"	3.65 x 4.26
Dining	12'0" x 17'2"	3.65 x 5.23
Study	7'0" x 10'0"	2.13 x 3.04
Kitchen (max)	12'8" x 12'0"	4.76 x 3.65
Utility	5'3" x 6'10"	1.60 x 2.07
Master Bed	12'0" x 17'2"	3.65 x 5.23
Bed 2	13'0" x 11'0"	3.96 x 3.35
Bed 3	10'0" x 13'0"	3.05 x 3.65
Bed 4	8'1" x 12'0"	2.46 x 3.65
Bed 5	8'0" x 8'9"	2.43 x 2.65

The D & M Collection

Rushbury

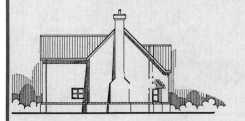

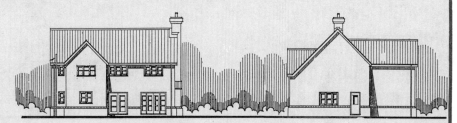

Originally built in Staffordshire, one of the requirements for this house was that it should have a really large family room, four double bedrooms, and two large bathrooms. This would normally need a house of over 2000 square feet, and at 1829 square feet the Rushbury offers a very cost effective way of meeting these requirements.

It is shown here built with facing bricks and flat Hardrow roof tiles. These large roof tiles are particularly well suited to the lean to porch over the front door.

Rushbury

Floor Area	1829 sq.ft.	170 sq.m.
Dimensions overall	39'0" x 40'4"	11.88 x 12.28
Lounge	12'6" x 18'6"	3.81 x 5.63
Family Room	12'0" x 16'1"	3.65 x 4.91
Dining	12'0" x 9'8"	3.65 x 2.95
Kitchen	11'0" x 14'6"	3.35 x 4.40
Utility	8'5" x 7'3"	2.55 x 2.20
Master Bed	11'0" x 14'6"	3.34 x 4.40
Bed 2	11'3" x 15'2"	3.43 x 4.61
Bed 3	12'6" x 10'0"	3.81 x 3.04
Bed 4	12'10" x 9'8"	3.90 x 2.95

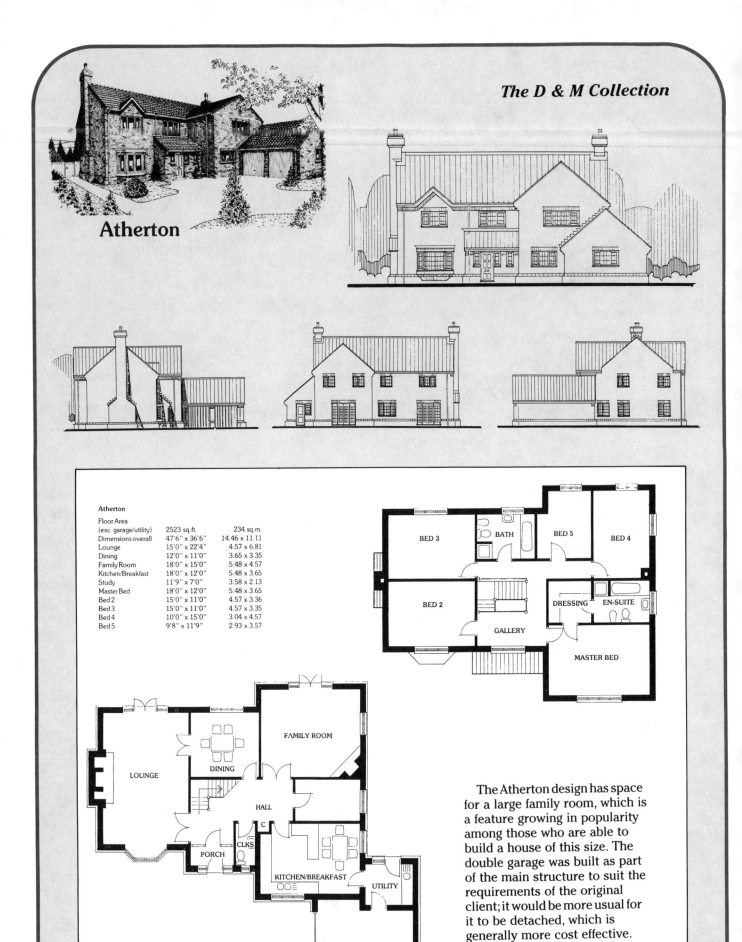

Atherton

Atherton

Floor Area

(exc. garage/utility)	2523 sq.ft.	234 sq.m.
Dimensions overall	47'6" x 36'6"	14.46 x 11.11
Lounge	15'0" x 22'4"	4.57 x 6.81
Dining	12'0" x 11'0"	3.65 x 3.35
Family Room	18'0" x 15'0"	5.48 x 4.57
Kitchen/Breakfast	18'0" x 12'0"	5.48 x 3.65
Study	11'9" x 7'0"	3.58 x 2.13
Master Bed	18'0" x 12'0"	5.48 x 3.65
Bed 2	15'0" x 11'0"	4.57 x 3.36
Bed 3	15'0" x 11'0"	4.57 x 3.35
Bed 4	10'0" x 15'0"	3.04 x 4.57
Bed 5	9'8" x 11'9"	2.93 x 3.57

The Atherton design has space for a large family room, which is a feature growing in popularity among those who are able to build a house of this size. The double garage was built as part of the main structure to suit the requirements of the original client; it would be more usual for it to be detached, which is generally more cost effective.

The D & M Collection

Wanborough

This large family house of over 2500 square feet has a fashionable raised plinth to window sill level. Above the eaves a bell moulding marks the start of the rendered finish to the first storey, while above there are three separate levels to the eaves, achieved by having dormer windows to one wing. In this way a large house, which a few years ago would have been an uncompromising functional block, is given the complex shape and appeal of a period farmhouse.

The first floor layout illustrated here has a very large games room on the first floor. Most families would probably prefer a four or five bedroom layout, and if the games room becomes the master bedroom suite it can be of very generous proportions.

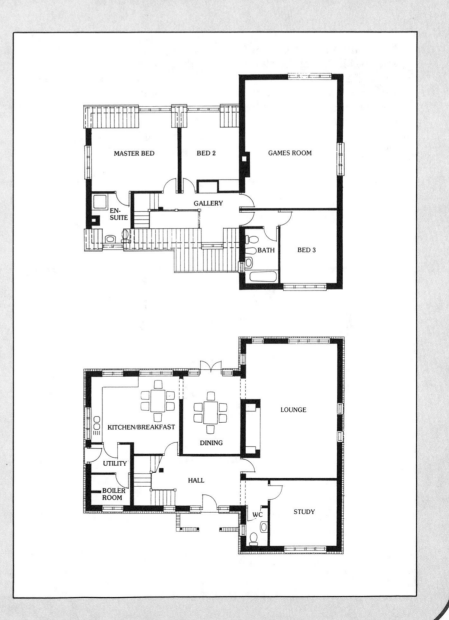

Wanborough

Floor Area	2595 sq.ft.	241 sq.m.
Dimensions overall	47'7" x 38'6"	14.50 x 11.73
Lounge	17'2" x 24'0"	5.24 x 7.31
Dining	10'7" x 14'0"	3.23 x 4.26
Kitchen/Breakfast	16'4" x 14'0"	4.98 x 4.26
Utility	7'3" x 5'0"	2.21 x 1.52
Study	12'10" x 12'0"	3.92 x 3.65
Master Bedroom	16'4" x 14'0"	4.98 x 4.26
Bedroom 2	10'7" x 14'0"	3.23 x 4.26
Bedroom 3	10'7" x 13'4"	3.24 x 4.05
Games Room	17'2" x 23'0"	5.24 x 7.01

Mistley

This is an updated version of the successful D & M Brierley design, and is shown here with the first floor cantilevered out from the ground floor walls in the style of a Tudor jettied house. This can be achieved very easily with traditional construction, although it is usually associated with timber framing.

The imposing flight of winding stairs leading to the large gallery with its own window gives this the feel of a home much larger than the actual 1675 square feet. The office on the first floor can of course be used as a fourth bedroom.

Mistley

Floor Area	1675 sq.ft.	155 sq.m.
Dimensions overall	36'7" x 33'0"	11.15 x 10.05
Lounge	12'6" x 19'4"	3.81 x 5.89
Dining	14'6" x 11'6"	4.41 x 3.50
Kitchen/Breakfast	11'5" x 19'4"	3.49 x 5.89
Master Bed	12'6" x 19'4"	3.81 x 5.89
Bed 2	14'6" x 11'6"	4.41 x 3.50
Bed 3	11'5" x 10'6"	3.49 x 3.19
Office/Bed 4	8'0" x 8'6"	2.43 x 2.60

Malton

The Malton is a straight forward 1600 square foot design which includes nearly all of the design features which have made D & M Designs so popular among those building on their own land in the 70's and 80's.

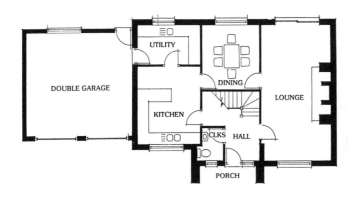

Malton

Floor Area (exc. garage) 1600 sq.ft.		148 sq.m.
Dimensions overall	35'11'' x 25'3''	10.95 x 7.70
Lounge	12'6'' x 23'5''	3.80 x 7.14
Dining	10'0'' x 11'0''	3.04 x 3.34
Kitchen	11'0'' x 13'2''	3.34 x 4.01
Utility	11'0'' x 7'0''	3.34 x 2.12
Master Bed	11'0'' x 10'4''	3.34 x 3.16
Bed 2	12'6'' x 12'2''	3.80 x 3.70
Bed 3	11'0'' x 13'0''	3.34 x 3.94
Bed 4	12'6'' x 11'0''	3.80 x 3.34

Abbotsbury

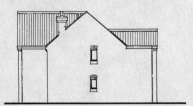

This is another large house for a narrow plot, but which is sufficiently complex to stand on its own in a rural situation. It was built in the Derbyshire Dales, where the planners required traditional brick arches over windows, stone sills, and side hung garage doors. However, consent was obtained for it to be built under cost effective pantiles, effecting a satisfactory compromise between cost effective construction and regional styling.

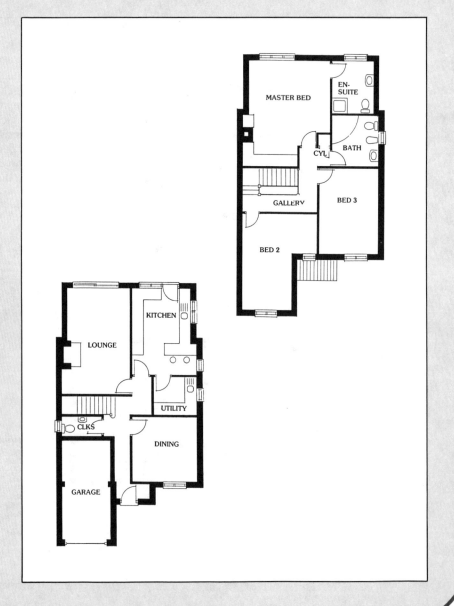

Abbotsbury

Floor Area (inc. garage)	1667 sq.ft.	154 sq.m.
Dimensions overall	25'5" x 44'5"	7.74 x 13.55
Lounge	11'8" x 18'1"	3.55 x 5.52
Dining	10'6" x 10'10"	3.19 x 3.31
Kitchen	9'5" x 14'10"	2.86 x 4.52
Utility	6'4" x 6'3"	1.93 x 1.90
Garage	8'7" x 16'8"	2.60 x 5.09
Bed 1	14'9" x 18'1"	4.50 x 5.52
Bed 2 (max)	12'9" x 17'3"	3.88 x 5.26
Bed 3	10'6" x 14'2"	3.20 x 4.31

The D & M Collection

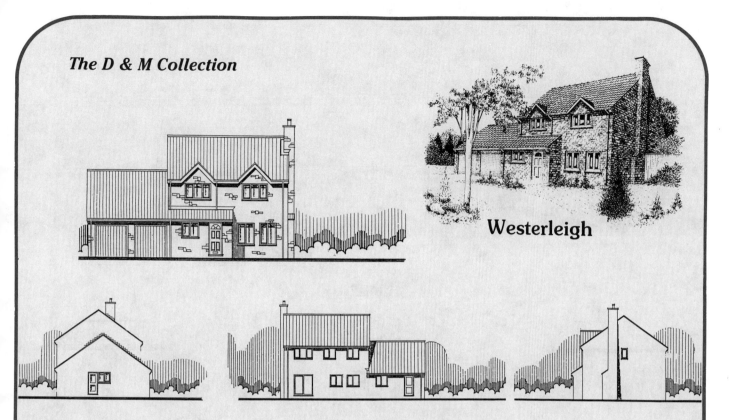

Westerleigh

A straight forward design for a four bedroom house under 1300 square feet. It can be built on its own with a detached garage, or with a single or double garage as shown. The latter option provides an opportunity for a large utility room, and if required the kitchen can be extended into the utility room area to give it an interesting L shape.

The two gables over the front bedrooms are above the window lintels, and are simply planted onto a standard trussed rafter roof, giving significant cost savings over gables which are set into the roof structure itself.

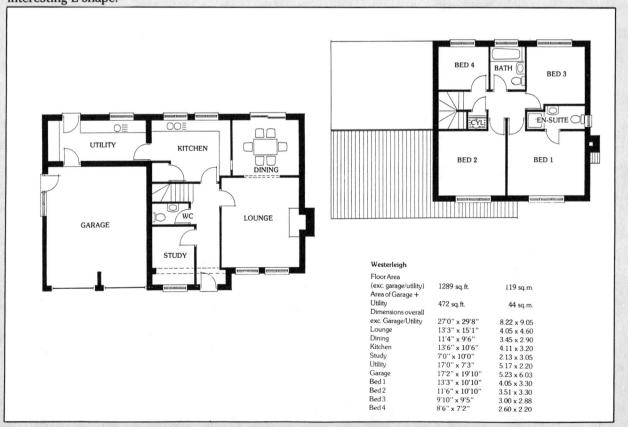

Westerleigh

Floor Area		
(exc. garage/utility)	1289 sq.ft.	119 sq.m.
Area of Garage +		
Utility	472 sq.ft.	44 sq.m.
Dimensions overall		
exc. Garage/Utility	27'0" x 29'8"	8.22 x 9.05
Lounge	13'3" x 15'1"	4.05 x 4.60
Dining	11'4" x 9'6"	3.45 x 2.90
Kitchen	13'6" x 10'6"	4.11 x 3.20
Study	7'0" x 10'0"	2.13 x 3.05
Utility	17'0" x 7'3"	5.17 x 2.20
Garage	17'2" x 19'10"	5.23 x 6.03
Bed 1	13'3" x 10'10"	4.05 x 3.30
Bed 2	11'6" x 10'10"	3.51 x 3.30
Bed 3	9'10" x 9'5"	3.00 x 2.88
Bed 4	8'6" x 7'2"	2.60 x 2.20

Maybush

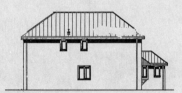

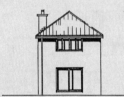

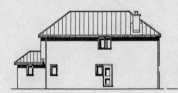

Rising land prices lead to the sub division of suburban building sites and there is an increasing demand for narrow houses for narrow plots in prestige residential areas. The Maybush house of 1258 square feet can be built on a plot only 34 feet wide with garage at the side, or if car parking can be arranged elsewhere it will fit on a plot only 26 feet wide.

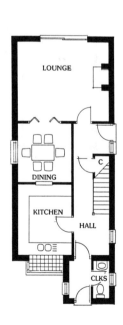

Maybush

Floor Area	1258 sq.ft.	117 sq. m.
Dimensions overall	17'10" x 45'6"	5.43 x 13.86
Lounge	16'0" x 13'6"	4.87 x 4.12
Dining	9'5" x 10'0"	2.87 x 3.04
Kitchen	9'5" x 12'0"	2.87 x 3.65
Master Bed (inc. en suite)	16'0" x 13'6"	4.87 x 4.12
Bed 2	9'1" x 12'0"	2.77 x 3.65
Bed 3	6'7" x 8'9"	2.00 x 2.65

The D & M Collection

Rushwick

The Rushwick design house has been included in the D & M collection as an example of a large split level house to suit a sloping site. The accommodation was also designed to meet the special requirements of the family so that on entering the front door you find a hall giving access to a study, guest room suite and gymnasium with a sauna. Going up a flight of steps leads to the main living accommodation, from which a further flight of steps lead to the main bedrooms.

This house was designed to suit the magnificent views from the site on which it was built, and the terrace on the intermediate level is perhaps the key feature to the whole design. It is included here as an example of how D & M can work to meet a clients particular requirements, and also as a source of design ideas for others.

Rushwick

Floor Area	2627 sq.ft.	244 sq.m.
Dimensions overall	39'6" x 64'3"	12.03 x 19.57
Lounge	20'0" x 17'7"	6.10 x 5.36
Dining	11'0" x 14'6"	3.35 x 4.42
Kitchen	8'2" x 11'6"	2.50 x 3.50
Utility	11'6" x 6'0"	3.50 x 1.83
Breakfast Room	11'0" x 11'6"	3.35 x 3.50
Study	16'2" x 11'0"	4.93 x 3.35
Training Room (max)	13'0" x 15'0"	3.96 x 4.57
Guest Room	12'11" x 13'6"	3.94 x 4.10
Master Bed	16'5" x 11'0"	5.00 x 3.35
Bed 2	12'11" x 11'6"	3.94 x 3.50
Bed 3	14'5" x 9'5"	4.39 x 2.86

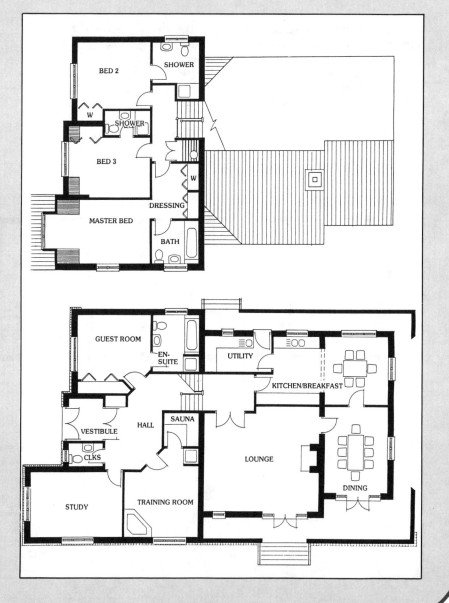

Hatfield

  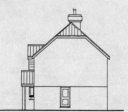

The Hatfield design house is shown here with a rendered finish above brickwork and a projecting timber clad bay on the front elevation, which is very much the traditional style in Essex where the prototype was built.

The kitchen layout is illustrated with a separate utility room, although this can be dispensed with if required, and perhaps an external porch built at the kitchen door. The master bedroom is shown with separate doors to the dressing room and

to the en suite bathroom. This was to suit the clients for whom the original house was designed. A more usual arrangement would be to have the bathroom leading off the dressing room.

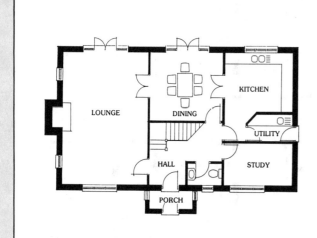

Hatfield

Floor Area	1800 sq.ft.	167 sq.m.
Dimensions overall	42'6" x 23'10"	12.95 x 7.26
Lounge	15'0" x 22'0"	4.57 x 6.70
Dining	13'0" x 11'6"	3.96 x 3.50
Kitchen	12'0" x 9'2"	3.65 x 2.80
Study	12'0" x 6'11"	3.65 x 2.10
Master Bed	15'0" x 15'5"	4.57 x 4.70
Bed 2	12'0" x 11'6"	3.65 x 3.50
Bed 3	12'0" x 10'2"	3.65 x 3.10
Bed 4	13'0" x 8'2"	3.96 x 2.50

The D & M Collection

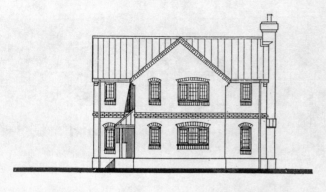

Swannington

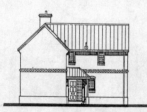

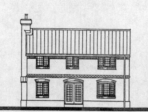

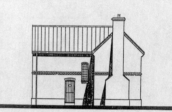

The Swannington house was drawn for a rural site in the North Country, where a property such as this is said to 'stand square' and is not expected to blend into a gentle landscape. Very carefully considered brick features are essential to this style, and here we have the house built on a high plinth, brick arches over the windows, a stringer course at first floor level and elaborate feature brickwork under the tiles.

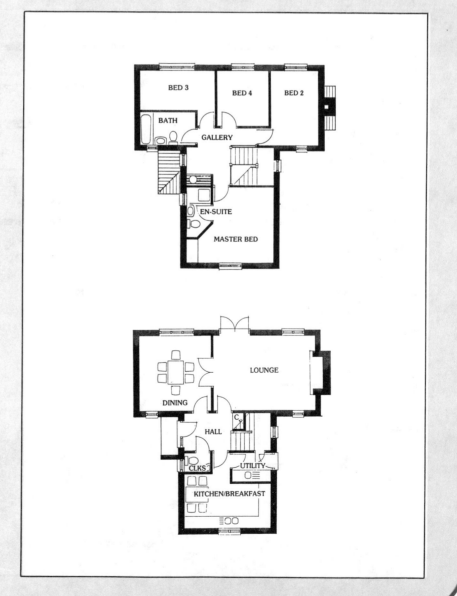

Swannington

Floor Area	1438 sq.ft.	133 sq.m
Dimensions overall	32'8" x 34'8"	9.94 x 10.5t
Lounge	18'0" x 13'0"	5.48 x 3.9t
Dining	12'6" x 13'0"	3.81 x 3.9t
Kitchen/Breakfast	15'0" x 7'9"	4.57 x 2.35
Master Bed	15'0" x 13'0"	4.57 x 3.95
Bed 2	8'4" x 13'0"	2.54 x 3.9t
Bed 3	13'0" x 7'1"	3.96 x 2.1t
Bed 4	8'10" x 9'9"	2.69 x 2.9t

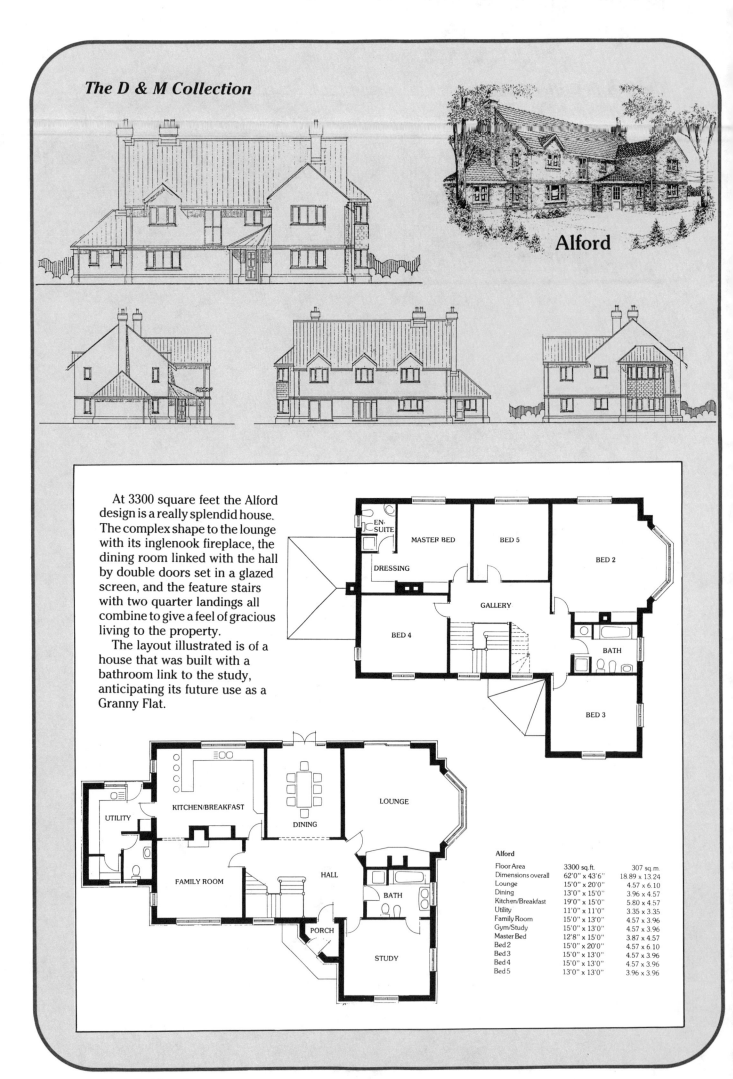

Alford

At 3300 square feet the Alford design is a really splendid house. The complex shape to the lounge with its inglenook fireplace, the dining room linked with the hall by double doors set in a glazed screen, and the feature stairs with two quarter landings all combine to give a feel of gracious living to the property.

The layout illustrated is of a house that was built with a bathroom link to the study, anticipating its future use as a Granny Flat.

EN-SUITE

MASTER BED

BED 5

BED 2

DRESSING

GALLERY

BED 4

BATH

BED 3

UTILITY

KITCHEN/BREAKFAST

DINING

LOUNGE

FAMILY ROOM

HALL

BATH

PORCH

STUDY

Alford

Floor Area	3300 sq.ft.	307 sq. m.
Dimensions overall	62'0" x 43'6"	18.89 x 13.24
Lounge	15'0" x 20'0"	4.57 x 6.10
Dining	13'0" x 15'0"	3.96 x 4.57
Kitchen/Breakfast	19'0" x 15'0"	5.80 x 4.57
Utility	11'0" x 11'0"	3.35 x 3.35
Family Room	15'0" x 13'0"	4.57 x 3.96
Gym/Study	15'0" x 13'0"	4.57 x 3.96
Master Bed	12'8" x 15'0"	3.87 x 4.57
Bed 2	15'0" x 20'0"	4.57 x 6.10
Bed 3	15'0" x 13'0"	4.57 x 3.96
Bed 4	15'0" x 13'0"	4.57 x 3.96
Bed 5	13'0" x 13'0"	3.96 x 3.96

The D & M Collection

Wyrevale

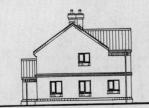

Wyrevale		
Floor Area	2345 sq.ft.	218 sq.m.
Dimensions overall	46'3" x 37'9"	14.09 x 11.49
Drawing Room	14'9" x 22'11"	4.49 x 6.99
Farmhouse Kitchen	16'0" x 20'0"	4.87 x 6.10
Dining	13'0" x 12'0"	3.96 x 3.65
Office	7'0" x 10'7"	2.13 x 3.23
Master Bed	14'9" x 22'11"	4.49 x 6.99
Bed 2	16'0" x 13'0"	4.87 x 3.96
Bed 3	15'7" x 10'7"	4.74 x 3.23
Bed 4	8'2" x 12'0"	2.49 x 3.65

This is an interesting design for a farmhouse in a situation where the door into the kitchen is to be the most important entrance.

Note the farm office. The finances of building a farmhouse need to be carefully planned to suit the possibility of capital allowances on part of the cost. Designating one room as a farm office can sometimes enable part of the cost to be written off in the accounts in a very convenient way. This requires careful consideration at an early stage.

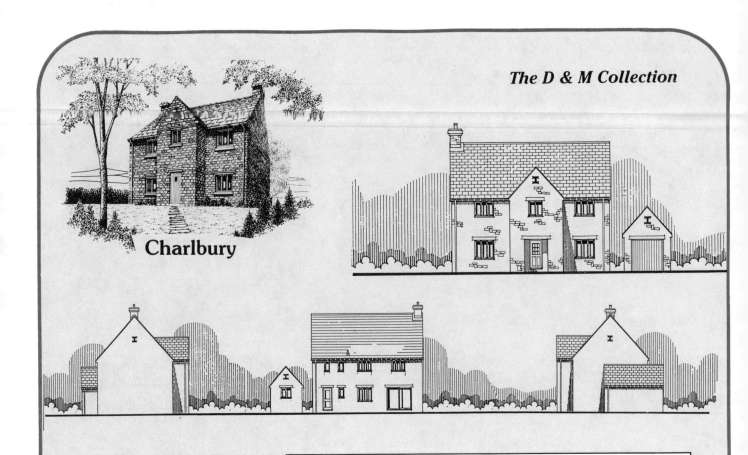

The D & M Collection

Charlbury

Another house that stands 'Four square to the wind' and which was originally built in the Cotswolds. This accounts for the stone heads and sills to the windows, as well as the exposed rafter feet under the eaves.

Again a design where there is room on the first floor landing for a desk and filing cabinet or perhaps for a sewing table.

It is shown here with the chimney breast wholly within the gable wall: if the planners will permit it to be moved outside it will give much more room in the lounge.

Charlbury

Floor Area	1582 sq.ft.	147 sq.m.
Dimensions overall	35'4" x 28'10"	10.78 x 8.79
Lounge	13'0" x 22'0"	3.96 x 6.70
Dining	10'0" x 11'6"	3.04 x 3.50
Kitchen/Breakfast	10'0" x 14'6"	3.04 x 4.45
Master Bed	10'0" x 13'0"	3.04 x 3.96
Bed 2	13'0" x 10'6"	3.96 x 3.20
Bed 3	13'0" x 9'6"	3.96 x 2.90

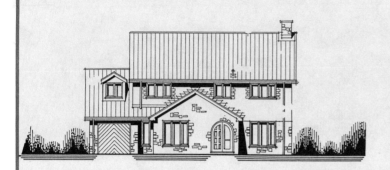

Penarth

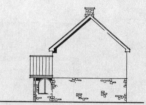

The Penarth house was designed for a site in South Wales, and has a number of interesting features. The angled walls to the study enable a very comprehensive ground floor accommodation to be provided in a modest area, and there are five bedrooms, an en suite bathroom and a large family bathroom on the first floor.

Note that the large window to the floor in the side wall of the porch enables a solid front door to be used. This which suits the appearance of the house when it is built in stone as illustrated, and gives plenty of light for the porch and the hall.

Penarth

Floor Area (inc. garage)	1861 sq.ft.	172 sq.m.
Dimensions overall	45'9" x 29'10"	13.94 x 9.10
Lounge	12'0" x 22'0"	3.65 x 6.70
Sitting Room	10'8" x 11'0"	3.25 x 3.35
Kitchen/Dining	10'8" x 22'0"	3.25 x 6.70
Utility	9'0" x 5'7"	2.74 x 1.70
Study	8'0" x 9'0"	2.43 x 2.74
Garage	9'0" x 17'0"	2.74 x 5.19
Master Bed	12'0" x 10'8"	3.65 x 3.24
Bed 2	12'0" x 9'0"	3.65 x 2.75
Bed 3	10'8" x 9'2"	3.25 x 2.80
Bed 4	10'8" x 9'2"	3.25 x 2.80
Bed 5	10'8" x 7'9"	3.25 x 2.35

Harbourne

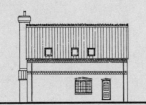

This house was designed to meet a requirement for a Victorian style town house with three bedrooms, each with its own bathroom, a lounge to the rear and a single garage. It is illustrated with many Victorian features and suitable Victorian materials for them are now once again available in builders merchants. In this case these included crested ridge tiles and special bricks. Tile hanging to the small dormer window adds to the effect, and the design of the chimney is also important. Incidentally, the fireplace is shown in the garden wall of the lounge but it can easily be moved into any of the other walls if required.

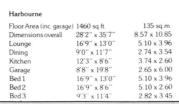

Harbourne

Floor Area (inc. garage)	1460 sq.ft.	135 sq.m.
Dimensions overall	28'2" x 35'7"	8.57 x 10.85
Lounge	16'9" x 13'0"	5.10 x 3.96
Dining	9'0" x 11'7"	2.74 x 3.54
Kitchen	12'3" x 8'6"	3.74 x 2.60
Garage	8'8" x 19'8"	2.65 x 6.00
Bed 1	16'9" x 13'0"	5.10 x 3.96
Bed 2	16'9" x 8'6"	5.10 x 2.60
Bed 3	9'3" x 11'4"	2.82 x 3.45

The D & M Collection

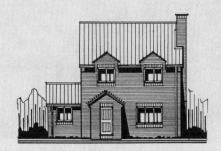

Hedgefield

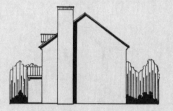

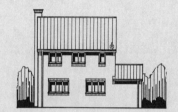

The Hedgefield house, nearly square with porches to the front and back doors, is almost the standard farm cottage in rural areas of the Home Counties. Illustrated here with a stable door, it provides practical accommodation for those who work in the country with a well balanced and traditional appearance.

The sketch above shows a gable porch to the front door and a lean-to porch to the back door, while the architects drawing show both as gable porches. A choice in this depends on local regional design features on other small cottages.

For some reason this design has been drawn with the plan to a different hand to the elevations, which served to remind readers that all the designs in this book can be built to either hand.

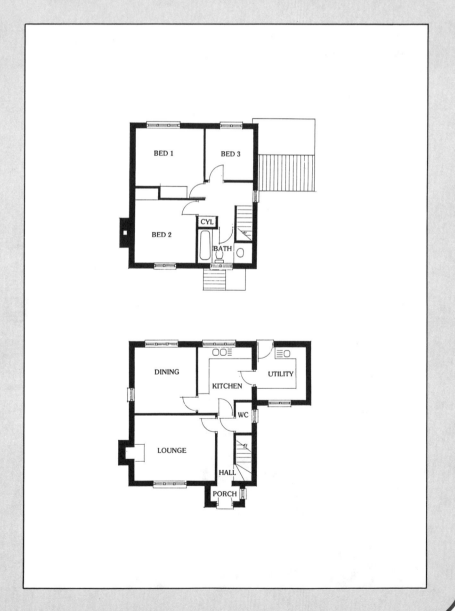

Hedgefield

Floor Area (exc. utility)	1058 sq.ft.	98 sq.m.
Dimensions overall		
(exc. utility)	24'1" x 25'3"	7.33 x 7.70
Lounge	14'5" x 11'6"	4.40 x 3.51
Dining	10'1" x 11'6"	3.07 x 3.50
Kitchen	12'0" x 11'6"	3.60 x 3.50
Bed 1	13'5" x 12'4"	4.08 x 3.75
Bed 2	12'4" x 10'8"	3.75 x 3.26
Bed 3	8'6" x 9'0"	2.59 x 2.75

Bedale

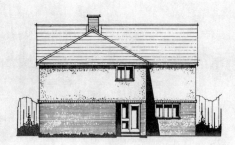

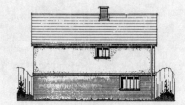

The Bedale design is very popular on corner plots, particularly those where the garage is approached from one side of the house with a separate path from the road to the front door at right angles to it.

The windows in this design can be moved around to suit the constraints of a narrow site, and it has been built on plots as narrow as 29 feet.

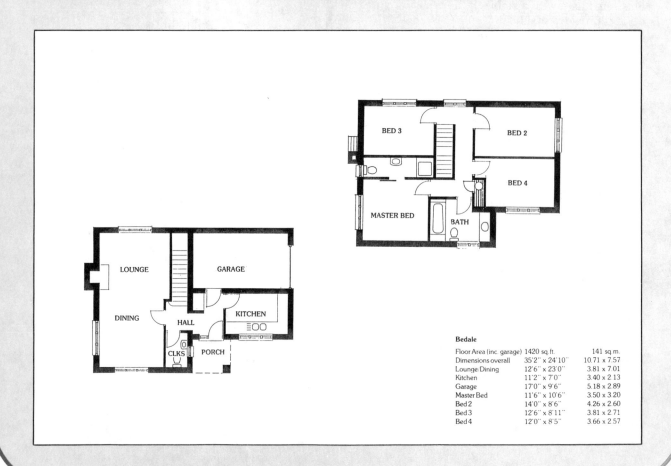

Bedale

Floor Area (inc. garage)	1420 sq.ft.	141 sq.m.
Dimensions overall	35'2" x 24'10"	10.71 x 7.57
Lounge/Dining	12'6" x 23'0"	3.81 x 7.01
Kitchen	11'2" x 7'0"	3.40 x 2.13
Garage	17'0" x 9'6"	5.18 x 2.89
Master Bed	11'6" x 10'6"	3.50 x 3.20
Bed 2	14'0" x 8'6"	4.26 x 2.60
Bed 3	12'6" x 8'11"	3.81 x 2.71
Bed 4	12'0" x 8'5"	3.66 x 2.57

The D & M Collection

Beechfield

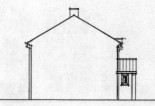

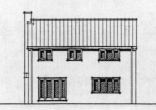

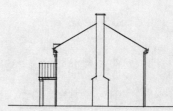

This design for the 90's is an update of the D & M Westbury design, which has been built in large numbers in all parts of the country. It is a most cost effective design, and the layout represents one of the standard ways of getting a quart into a pint pot!

The character of this house comes from the non structural features. As illustrated, this starts with a plinth that extends well above the damp course, feature brickwork below the ground floor windows, and render to the first floor projecting beyond the brickwork. The dormers over the first floor window are false, being simply planted onto a trussed rafter roof. Attention to detail with the chimney, including some tiling to the chimney breast, completes an interesting approach to building a very cost effective home.

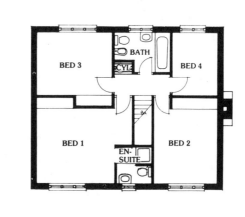

Beechfield

Floor Area (inc. porch)	1421 sq.ft.	132 sq.m.
Dimensions overall	31'2" x 30'2"	9.50 x 9.20
Lounge	13'7" x 23'5"	4.15 x 7.14
Dining	9'10" x 12'0"	2.99 x 3.65
Kitchen	12'1" x 11'1"	3.69 x 3.38
Utility	5'3" x 12'0"	1.60 x 3.65
Bed 1	12'1" x 11'7"	3.69 x 3.54
Bed 2	10'4" x 11'7"	3.15 x 3.54
Bed 3	12'1" x 9'6"	3.69 x 2.90
Bed 4	7'1" x 9'6"	2.15 x 2.90

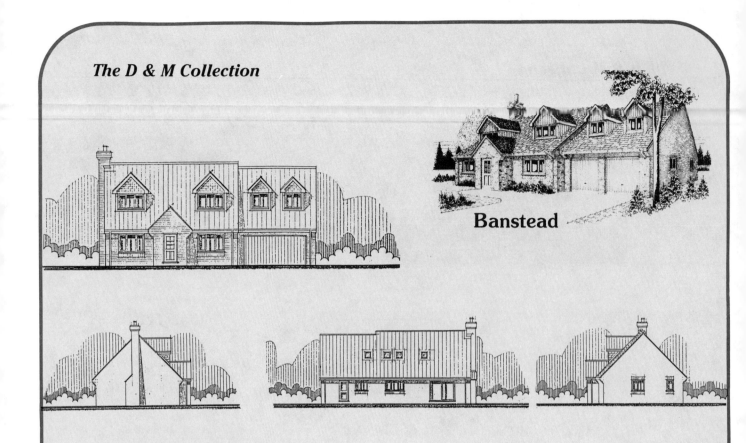

Banstead

The Banstead design cottage has developed over the years to be the ideal solution to meeting the planners requirements in many rural situations. It can be built either with a double garage and four bedroom accommodation as shown, with a single garage and three bedroom accommodation, or simply as a compact cottage which will have a separate garage or parking arrangements.

If the cottage is to be built with the intention of adding on a garage at a later date then lintels should be built into the gable wall at the points where openings will be required in due course.

Banstead

Floor Area (inc. garage)	1800 sq.ft.	167 sq.m.
Dimensions overall	48'0" x 26'9"	14.63 x 8.15
Lounge	16'10" x 13'0"	5.13 x 3.96
Family Room	10'0" x 11'7"	3.04 x 3.52
Dining	10'9" x 11'0"	3.27 x 3.35
Kitchen	10'9" x 13'7"	3.27 x 4.13
Lobby	12'8" x 5'10"	3.87 x 1.76
Garage	17'0" x 17'0"	5.19 x 5.18
Master Bed	10'0" x 16'1"	3.04 x 4.89
Bed 2	9'8" x 14'7"	2.95 x 4.44
Bed 3	10'9" x 6'10"	3.27 x 2.09
Bed 4	7'0" x 7'7"	2.13 x 2.30

The D & M Collection

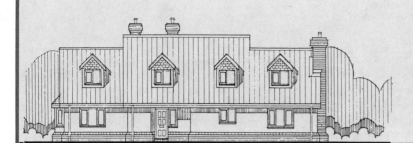

Oakington

The Oakington house of 2085 square feet is for sun lovers, with a large conservatory, huge bay windows to the lounge, and a covered porch to the family room at the other end of the house.

As shown here neither of the bathrooms have a window, and will require forced ventilation. However, it may be possible to incorporate either small dormers on the rear elevation or velux roof lights. There are plenty of options: what is important is not to detract from the cottage feel of this large and interesting property.

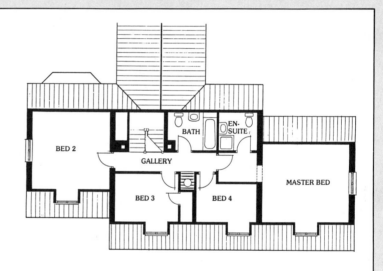

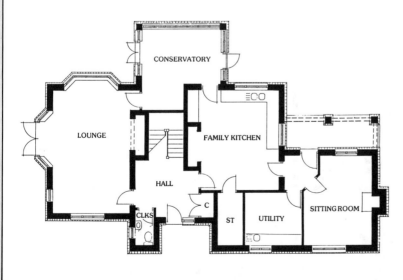

Oakington		
Floor Area		
(exc. conservatory)	2085 sq. ft.	193 sq.m.
Dimensions overall	58'4" x 28'2"	17.78 x 8.57
Lounge	14'0" x 21'0"	4.26 x 6.40
Family Kitchen	16'0" x 17'0"	4.87 x 5.18
Sitting Room	12'0" x 15'4"	3.65 x 4.67
Utility	10'3" x 9'0"	3.12 x 2.74
Master Bed	15'8" x 13'3"	4.76 x 4.05
Bed 2	14'0" x 13'3"	4.26 x 4.05
Bed 3	11'1" x 8'5"	3.37 x 2.57
Bed 4	10'10" x 6'7"	3.29 x 2.00

Newhaven

There is always a demand for
L shaped bungalows of under
1200 square feet, and this is the
new addition to the large range
of such designs available from
D & M.

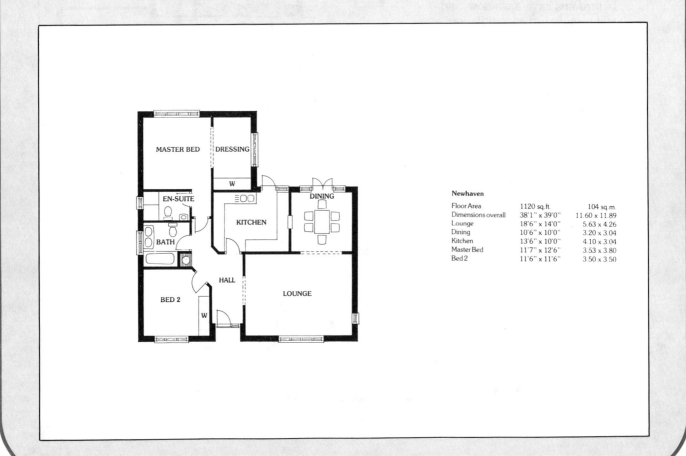

Newhaven

Floor Area	1120 sq.ft.	104 sq.m.
Dimensions overall	38'1" x 39'0"	11.60 x 11.89
Lounge	18'6" x 14'0"	5.63 x 4.26
Dining	10'6" x 10'0"	3.20 x 3.04
Kitchen	13'6" x 10'0"	4.10 x 3.04
Master Bed	11'7" x 12'6"	3.53 x 3.80
Bed 2	11'6" x 11'6"	3.50 x 3.50

The D & M Collection

Kingsford

This bungalow can be built with or without the garage, which gives the option of moving the window in bedroom 2 into the front elevation.

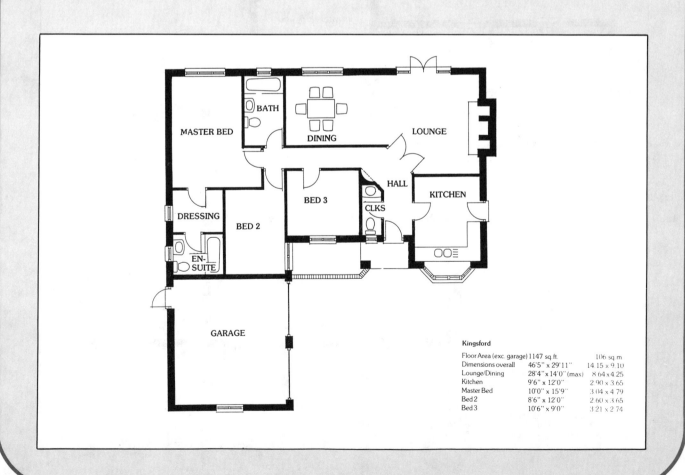

Kingsford

Floor Area (exc. garage)	1147 sq.ft.	106 sq m
Dimensions overall	46'5" x 29'11"	14.15 x 9.10
Lounge/Dining	28'4" x 14'0" (max)	8.64 x 4.25
Kitchen	9'6" x 12'0"	2.90 x 3.65
Master Bed	10'0" x 15'9"	3.04 x 4.79
Bed 2	8'6" x 12'0"	2.60 x 3.65
Bed 3	10'6" x 9'0"	3.21 x 2.74

The D & M Collection

Givendale

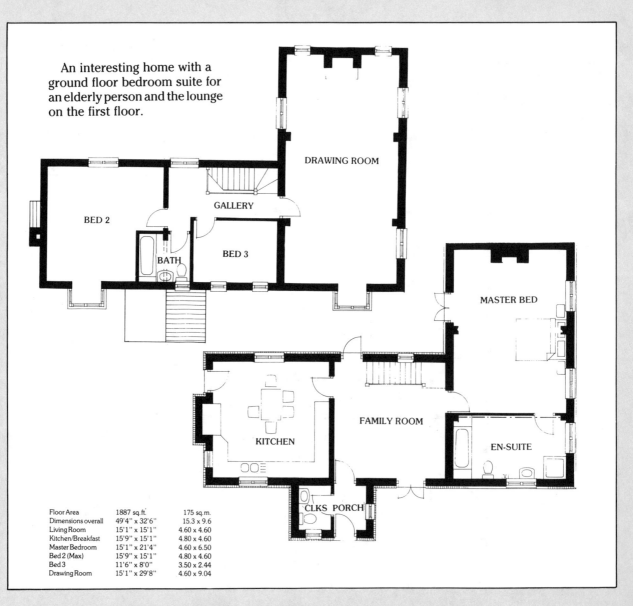

An interesting home with a
ground floor bedroom suite for
an elderly person and the lounge
on the first floor.

DRAWING ROOM

GALLERY

BED 2

BATH

BED 3

MASTER BED

KITCHEN

FAMILY ROOM

EN-SUITE

CLKS PORCH

Floor Area	1887 sq.ft.	175 sq.m.
Dimensions overall	49'4" x 32'6"	15.3 x 9.6
Living Room	15'1" x 15'1"	4.60 x 4.60
Kitchen/Breakfast	15'9" x 15'1"	4.80 x 4.60
Master Bedroom	15'1" x 21'4"	4.60 x 6.50
Bed 2 (Max)	15'9" x 15'1"	4.80 x 4.60
Bed 3	11'6" x 8'0"	3.50 x 2.44
Drawing Room	15'1" x 29'8"	4.60 x 9.04

The D & M Collection

Churchgate

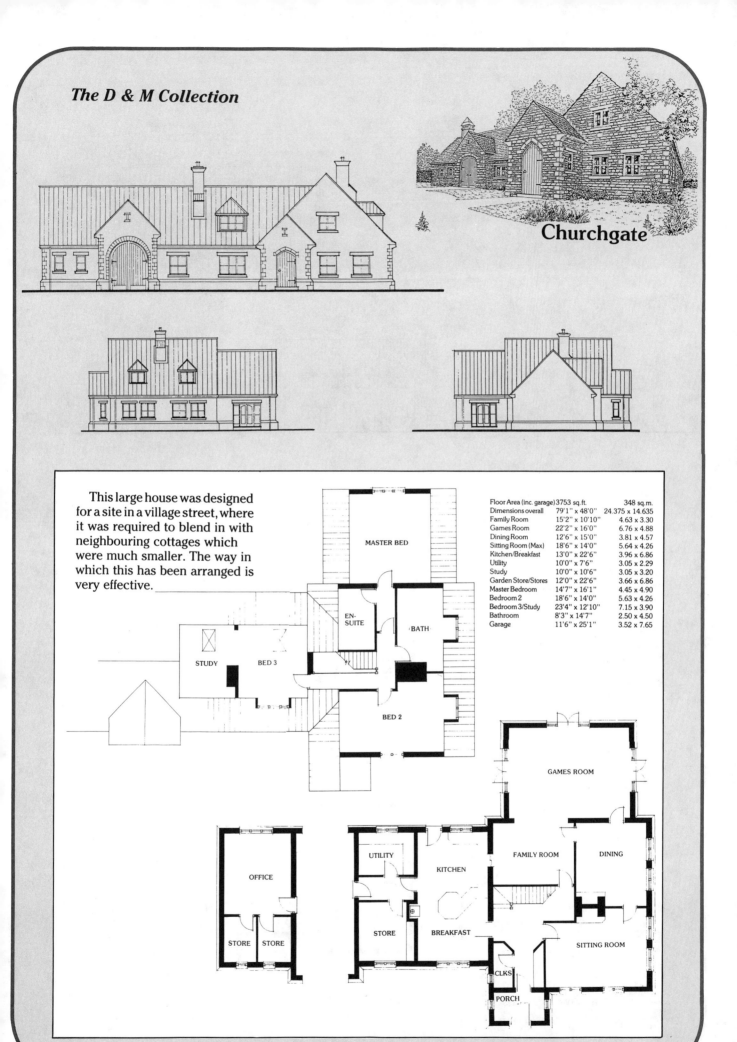

This large house was designed for a site in a village street, where it was required to blend in with neighbouring cottages which were much smaller. The way in which this has been arranged is very effective.

Floor Area (inc. garage)	3753 sq.ft.	348 sq.m.
Dimensions overall	79'1" x 48'0"	24.375 x 14.635
Family Room	15'2" x 10'10"	4.63 x 3.30
Games Room	22'2" x 16'0"	6.76 x 4.88
Dining Room	12'6" x 15'0"	3.81 x 4.57
Sitting Room (Max)	18'6" x 14'0"	5.64 x 4.26
Kitchen/Breakfast	13'0" x 22'6"	3.96 x 6.86
Utility	10'0" x 7'6"	3.05 x 2.29
Study	10'0" x 10'6"	3.05 x 3.20
Garden Store/Stores	12'0" x 22'6"	3.66 x 6.86
Master Bedroom	14'7" x 16'1"	4.45 x 4.90
Bedroom 2	18'6" x 14'0"	5.63 x 4.26
Bedroom 3/Study	23'4" x 12'10"	7.15 x 3.90
Bathroom	8'3" x 14'7"	2.50 x 4.50
Garage	11'6" x 25'1"	3.52 x 7.65

MASTER BED

EN-SUITE

BATH

STUDY

BED 3

BED 2

GAMES ROOM

OFFICE

UTILITY

KITCHEN

FAMILY ROOM

DINING

STORE

STORE

STORE

BREAKFAST

SITTING ROOM

CLKS

PORCH

Nocton

This is a re-design of the
D & M Cotswold house of which
so many were built in the 80's. It
incorporates all the alterations
that clients asked for in the
earlier design, and at under 2200
square feet has every feature of a
large country home on a cost
effective scale.

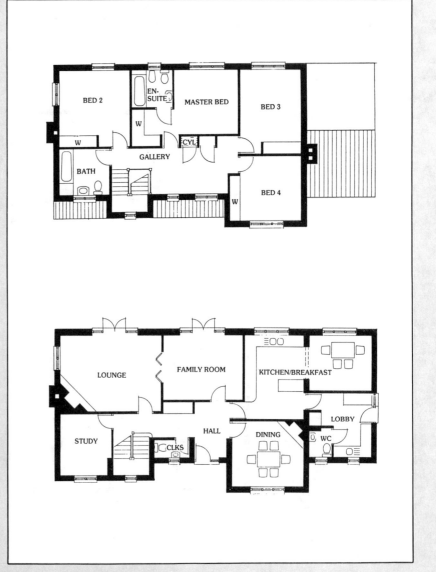

Nocton		
Floor Area	2194 sq.ft.	204 sq.m.
Dimensions overall	56'5" x 25'10"	17.18 x 7.86
Lounge	17'6" x 13'0"	5.33 x 3.96
Family Room	14'0" x 11'0"	4.26 x 3.35
Study	9'0" x 10'8"	2.74 x 3.25
Dining	12'6" x 11'8"	3.81 x 3.55
Kitchen	10'6" x 14'3"	3.21 x 4.35
Breakfast Room	11'0" x 9'8"	3.35 x 2.95
Lobby/Utility	11'0" x 11'0"	3.35 x 3.35
Master Bed	11'8" x 11'0"	3.55 x 3.35
Bed 2	12'6" x 13'0"	3.81 x 3.96
Bed 3	10'6" x 14'3"	3.21 x 4.35
Bed 4	12'6" x 11'8"	3.81 x 3.55

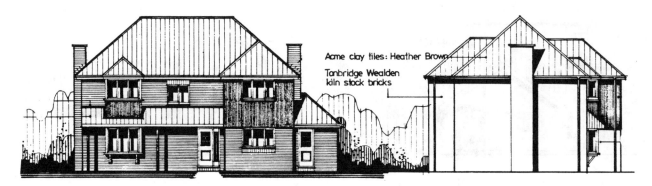

Acme clay tiles: Heather Brown

Tonbridge Wealden
kiln stock bricks

rear elevation　　　　　　　　　side elevation

A modern home with a very 1930s feel to it: one that will fit in very well on an infill plot in a well established up-market suburb.

It is a house with an extraordinary amount of cupboard space: there are six large built in wardrobes upstairs, as well as a large linen cupboard. The walk-in wardrobe alcoves in the two larger bedrooms are a novel feature, and if required they could easily be turned into small dressing rooms.

Note that the internal walls which are hatched are to be built in 4" blockwork, which gives a very high level of sound insulation. This benefits the larger bedrooms: if a block partition is required between bedrooms 3 and 4 this could be arranged by providing a steel joist in the ceiling above the lounge.

The study by the front door with the adjacent WC makes this design of home well suited to doctors and others who see the public in their own homes, and if required the study door can be moved closer to the front door, and an internal screen and door provided to keep this part of the house separate from the rest.

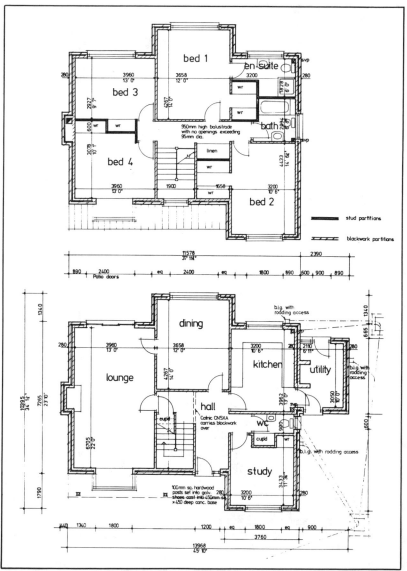

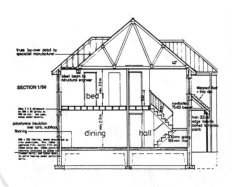

SECTION 1/50

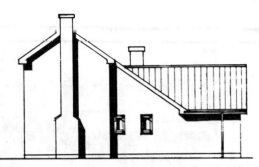

front elevation

A home with the appearance of a bungalow from one side, but uncompromisingly two storeys at the other. This arrangement is very useful where outline planning consent for a dwelling on a narrow plot is for a "single storey structure", and you want to negotiate for detail consent for a house!

rear elevation

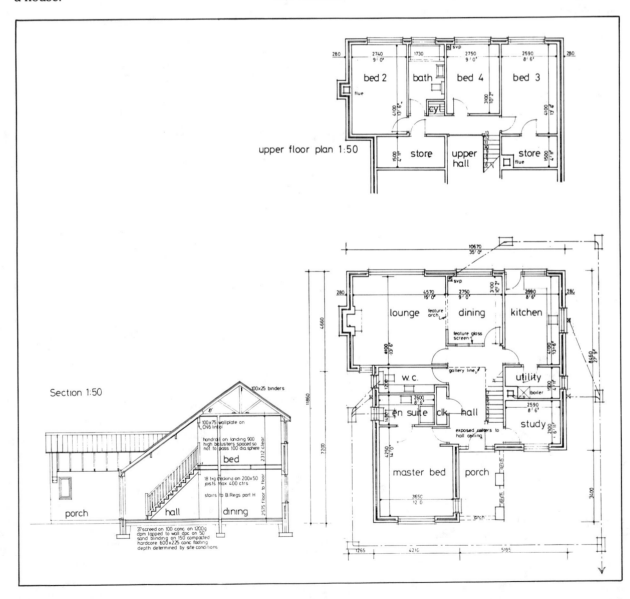

upper floor plan 1:50

Section 1:50

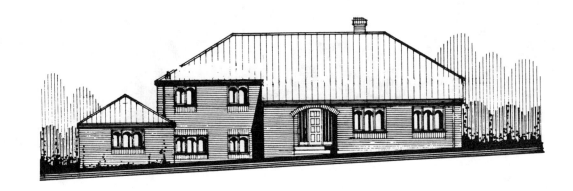

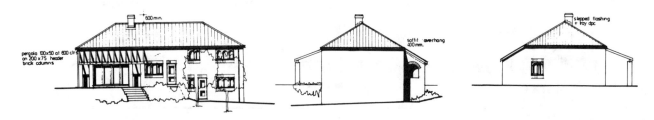

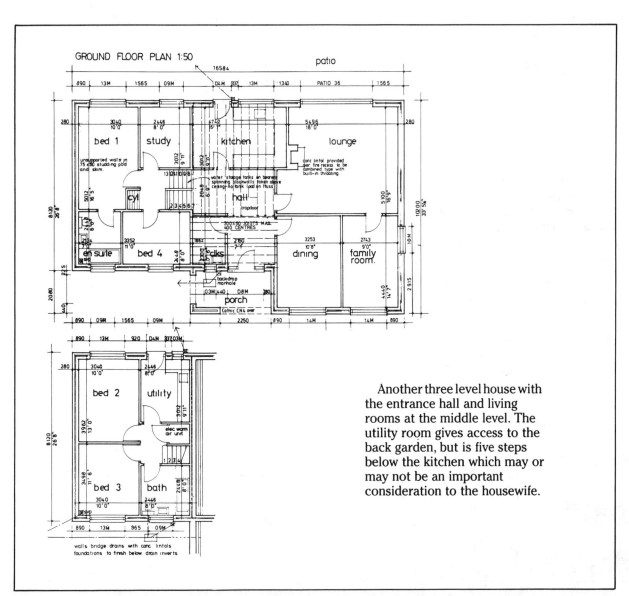

GROUND FLOOR PLAN 1:50

Another three level house with the entrance hall and living rooms at the middle level. The utility room gives access to the back garden, but is five steps below the kitchen which may or may not be an important consideration to the housewife.

FRONT ELEVATION

REAR ELEVATION   SIDE ELEVATION   SIDE ELEVATION

This is a home with many features of a baronial hall in a very compact building. When you go in through the front door the first thing to be seen is an exceptionally wide bottom quarter landing to the stairs, and in the lounge there is an inglenook fireplace and a patio window nearly twelve feet wide. French windows to the master bedroom lead onto a balcony. You will see that no details are shewn of the balcony railings, except for a note that they will conform to the Building Regulations. If you can get Planning Consent for a 'blank cheque' specification like this it is very useful, as a decision on the balustrade can be postponed until you are actually standing on the balcony and can make up your mind what you want when you have got the feel of it all.

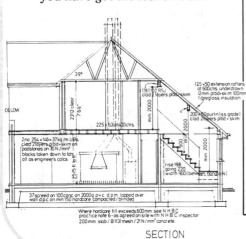

SECTION

FRONT ELEVATION

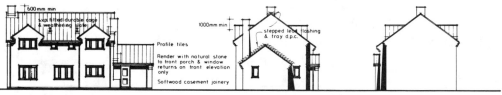

REAR ELEVATION GABLE ELEVATIONS

Another variant of a popular design for rural areas. The large and well lit hall gives this house a very spacious feel, and the kitchen end of the house can be rearranged in many different ways providing that the brick pier between the kitchen and utility room is retained, as this supports the joists which support the bedroom external walls above.

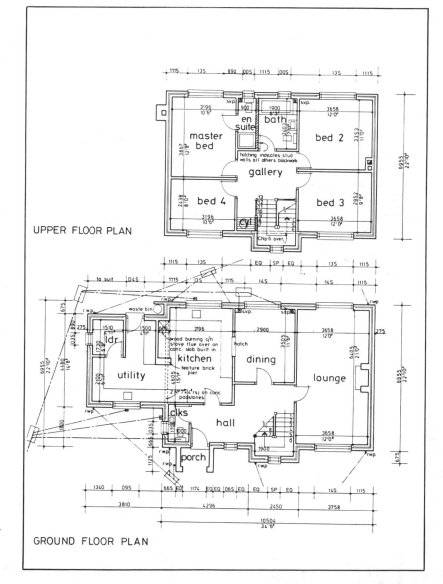

UPPER FLOOR PLAN

GROUND FLOOR PLAN

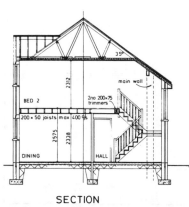

SECTION

REAR ELEVATION

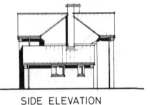

SIDE ELEVATION

SIDE ELEVATION

This interesting house in stone has some unusual features, including a large cloakroom off the hall that has been fitted out as a shower room, an unusually shaped lounge, and a study/playroom that leads off the lounge instead of the hall, which would be more usual.

The use in the lounge of two 4' windows adjacent to each other instead of one larger window is in character when building in stone, and big openings in stone walls should be avoided, or at least given careful consideration. This rule is broken with the large patio window in the rear elevation, but this side of the house is unlikely to be overlooked, and anyway patio windows are such a tremendous amenity that they are accepted in the back of period style homes as a necessary anachronism.

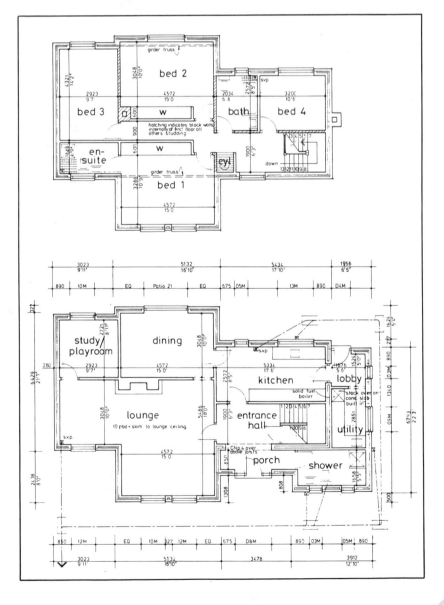

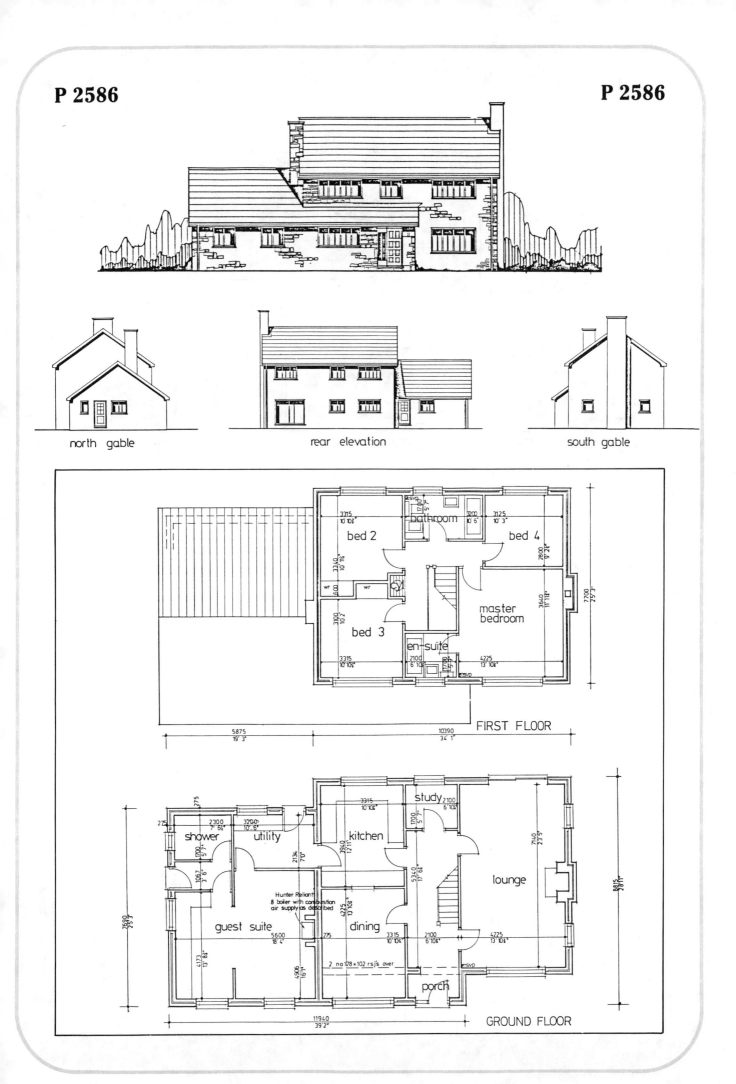

north gable

rear elevation

south gable

FIRST FLOOR

bed 2

bathroom

bed 4

master bedroom

en-suite

bed 3

GROUND FLOOR

shower

utility

study

kitchen

lounge

guest suite

dining

porch

Hunter Reliant 8 boiler with combustion air supply as described

2 no 178 x 102 rsj's over

Marley Modern tiles
dark grey

Steetley Mellow Durham
stock bricks

natural ground

f.f.l.

SIDE ELEVATION

bay window on
gallows brackets

REAR ELEVATION

f.f.l.

bay window on
gallows brackets

kitchen f.f. level

line of natural ground

SIDE ELEVATION

The main part of this house is less than twenty feet wide, and this is sometimes called for when building on an infill plot in a village of small scale cottages. Note the steps up into the kitchen to make use of the rise of the land to the rear of the building plot.

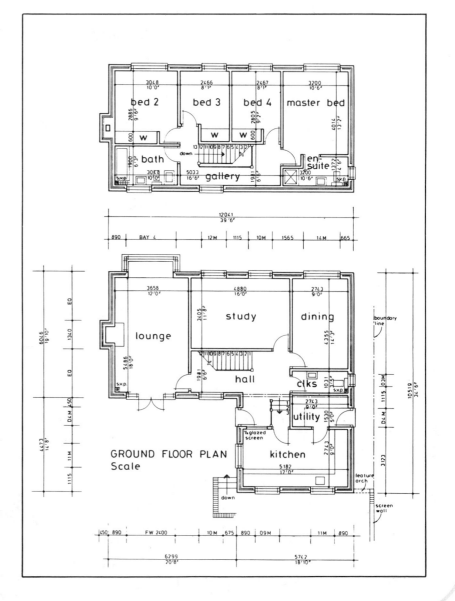

GROUND FLOOR PLAN
Scale

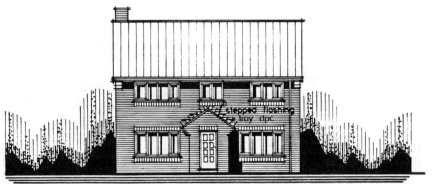

MAIN ENTRANCE ELEVATION

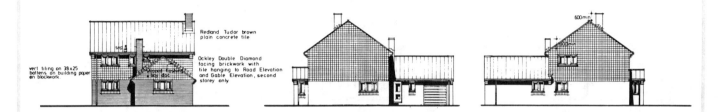

Redland Tudor brown
plain concrete tile

Ockley Double Diamond
facing brickwork with
tile hanging to Road Elevation
and Gable Elevation, second
storey only

vert tiling on 38x25
battens on building paper
on blockwork

This house is unusual in having tile hanging to the first floor walls at the sides and back only. Tiling like this was originally a cheap way of having a weatherproof wall, but today it is an expensive and fashionable regional feature, and is usually used on the front of a new home where it will be seen and admired.

This is a farmhouse design, with a farm office and WC at the back door, but the layout will appeal to others living in rural areas.

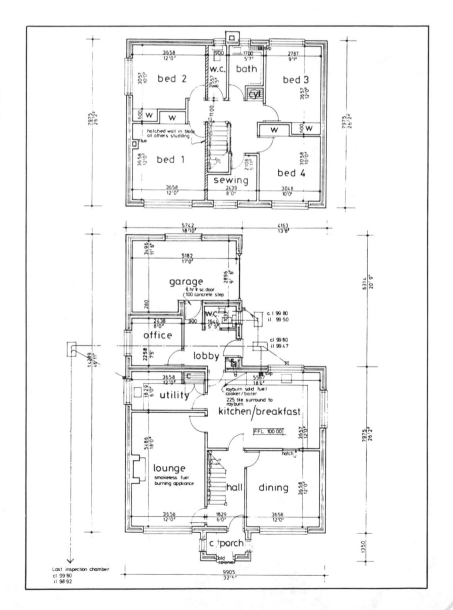

FRONT ELEVATION

SIDE ELEVATION

REAR ELEVATION

SIDE ELEVATION

This is an interesting example of a house built on a site that slopes both from front to back and from one side to the other. It is usually far more economical to cut a level plinth into the slope for a conventional home than to build a split level dwelling, even though this may involve complex retaining walls as in this instance.

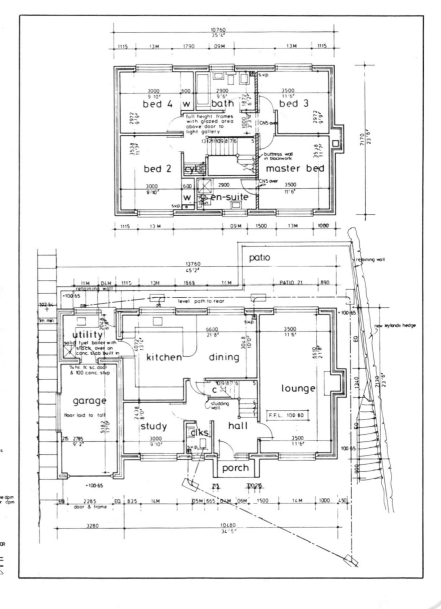

Section B-B   Section A-A

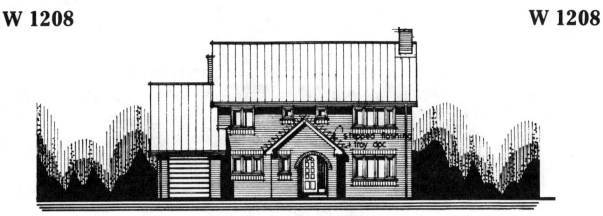

FRONT ELEVATION

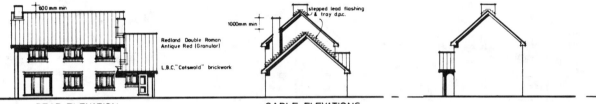

REAR ELEVATION   GABLE ELEVATIONS

Quite a modestly sized home, but with lots of interest and character. The garage is large enough to be divided into a garage and utility room if you wish, with the entrance to the kitchen through the utility room.

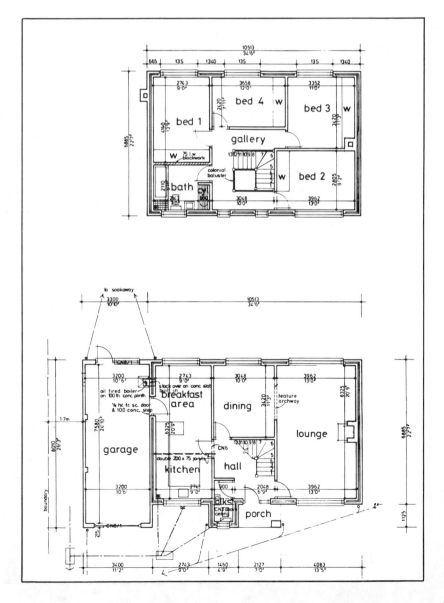

FRONT ELEVATION

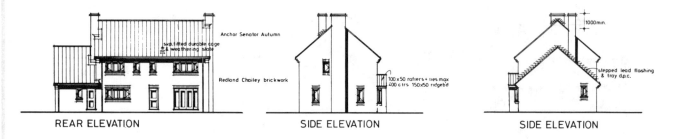

REAR ELEVATION   SIDE ELEVATION   SIDE ELEVATION

An imposing house to be built
in Redland Chailey bricks under
Anchor Senator tiles. The choice
of the right brick and tile for any
particular site and for a particular
design, is so important. The initial
choice can be made from
catalogues or from a display of
bricks and tiles at a Builders
Merchants, but you should always
try to see a house built from the
materials you choose before you
finally make up your mind.

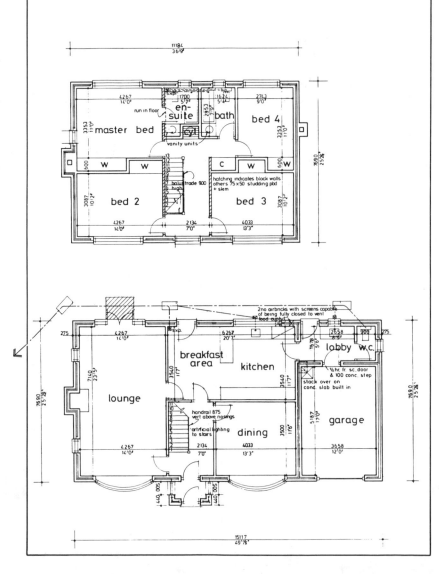

FRONT ELEVATION

REAR ELEVATION

SIDE ELEVATION

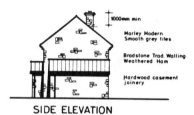

SIDE ELEVATION

stepped lead flashing
& tray d.p.c.

1000mm min

Marley Modern
Smooth grey tiles

Bradstone Trad. Walling
Weathered Ham

Hardwood casement
joinery

A house for the country with an office leading off the kitchen. This can easily have an outside door in its side wall if required, and this would suit farmers and others who work from home. Note that the stairs take off from the back of the hall, which is an unusual and rather old fashioned arrangement.

The lounge fireplace is on an inside wall where it can share a flue with a multi-fuel stove in the kitchen. If a stove of this type is not required then it is worth considering whether the fireplace should be moved to the gable wall.

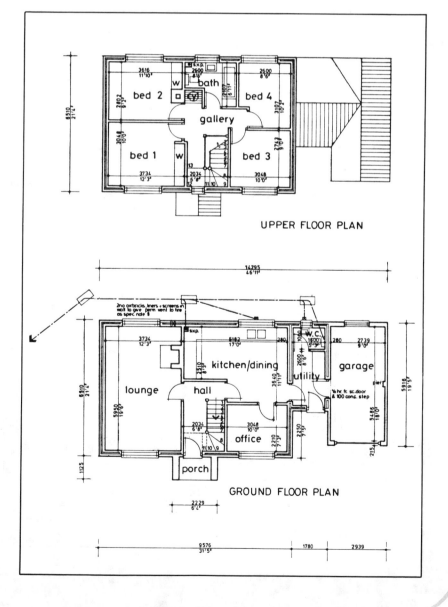

UPPER FLOOR PLAN

GROUND FLOOR PLAN

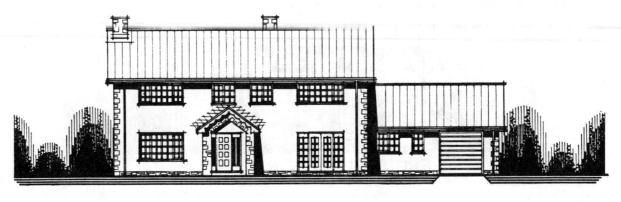

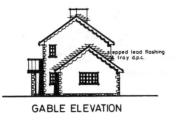

GABLE ELEVATION

Asbestos cement tiles

Scalloped barge boards

Render with natural stone
plinth quoins & chimneys

u.P.V.C. white georgian windows

REAR ELEVATION

GABLE ELEVATION

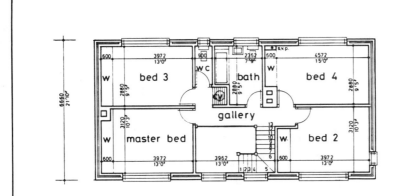

This very pretty farmhouse is
less than 22ft wide overall, but
has all the farmhouse features
which are usually found in a
much larger home. The Victorian
scalloped barge boards are to
match similar features on an
adjacent building.

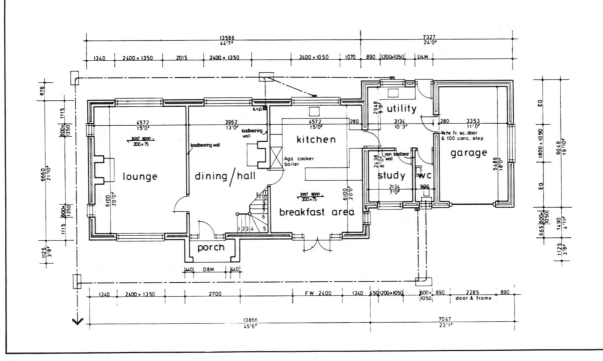

600mm min

REAR ELEVATION

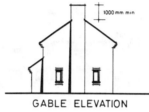

1000 mm min

GABLE ELEVATION

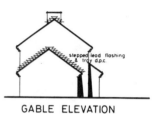

stepped lead flashing & tray d.p.c.

GABLE ELEVATION

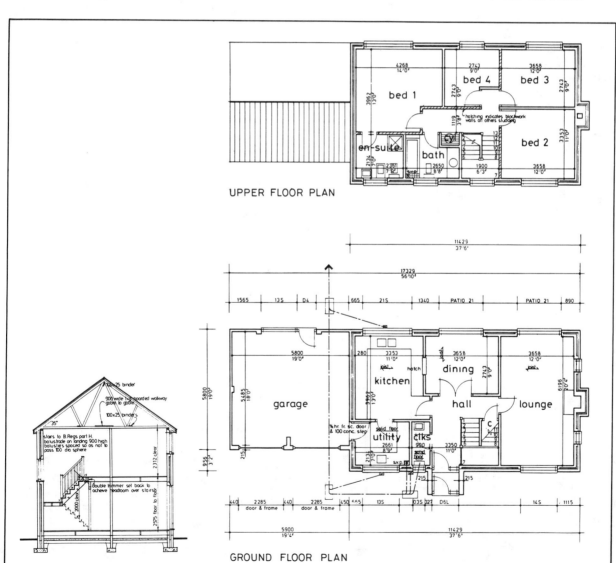

UPPER FLOOR PLAN

bed 1

bed 4

bed 3

bed 2

en-suite

bath

hatching indicates blockwork walls all others studding

GROUND FLOOR PLAN

garage

kitchen

dining

hall

lounge

utility

clks

stairs to B.Regs part H.
balustrade on landing 900 high
balusters spaced so as not to
pass 100 dia sphere

double trimmer set back to
achieve headroom over stairs

900 wide half-boarded walkway
gable to gable

Levels as site plan. Levels must be related to site conditions after site strip.

Redland Regent Mk II tiles
or similar; colour to be agreed

retaining wall

original ground level

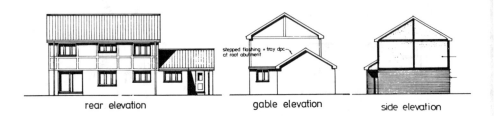

rear elevation

stepped flashing + tray dpc
at roof abutment

gable elevation

side elevation

Half timbering comes in many styles, and it is important to make sure that the style adopted for a new home is in what is called the "local architectural idiom". The half timbering shewn in the drawing would not suit every situation, but can be adapted if required. The local planners will readily advise on the characteristics of the traditional style, and this is easily arranged.

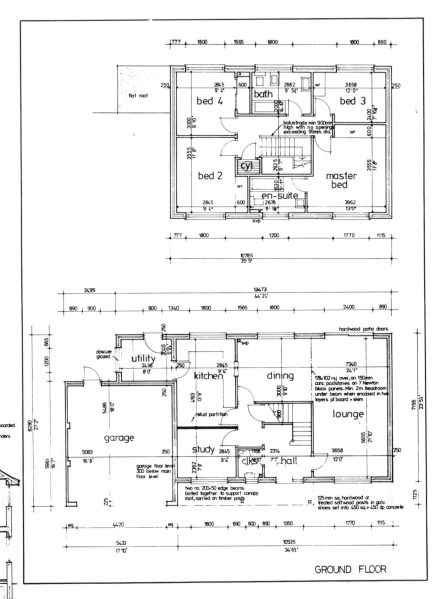

GROUND FLOOR

SECTION

900 wide boarded

100×25 binders

30°

2350

tray dpc

75×50 rafters + ties at 450 ctrs,
underdrawn in t.+g. boarding

en suite

bath

edge beam halved onto
timber posts

hall

dining

2350

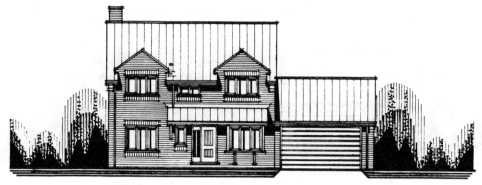

FRONT ELEVATION

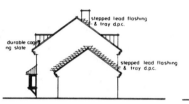

SIDE ELEVATION

REAR ELEVATION   SIDE ELEVATION

A straightforward no-nonsense layout inside this four bedroom home, with plenty of features to give character outside. If space on the plot permits, then another eighteen inches of garage width would enable it to be fitted with two single garage doors, which would look even better.

You will see from the section that the house was built using trench fill foundations. This has many advantages when a house is to be constructed on an isolated plot and if a mixer lorry can reach all corners of the foundations.

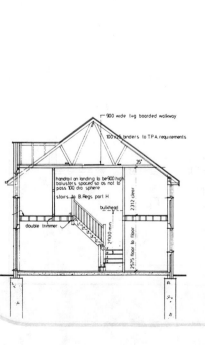

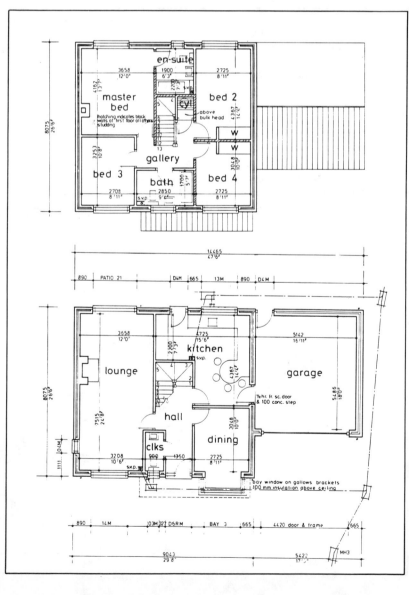

FRONT ELEVATION

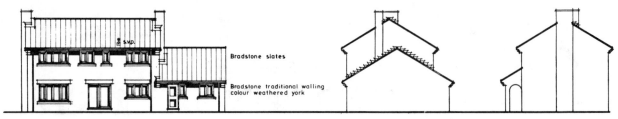

REAR ELEVATION

GABLE ELEVATIONS

Bradstone slates

Bradstone traditional walling colour weathered york

The utility room/garage arrangement in this large home is interesting, giving a balance between room for two cars, a garage alcove as a workshop or garden tools store, and the largest possible utility room. I wonder why the door into the garage is positioned where it is, opening so that it can swing into the parked car? Most people would prefer it to open into the garage alcove. This sort of detail is very much the architects clients choice.

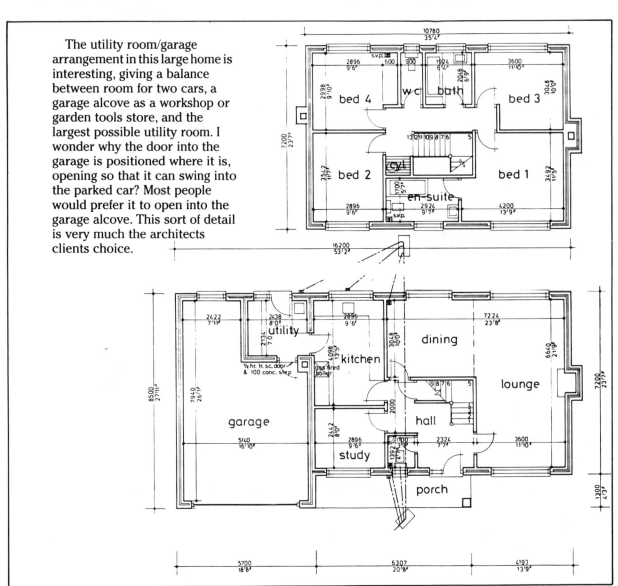

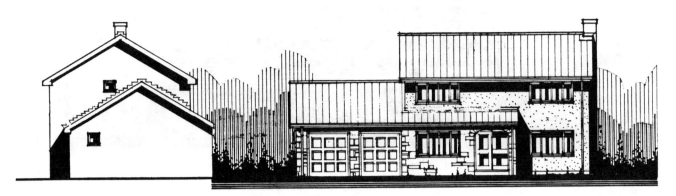

The master bedroom suite in this four bedroom home has a very large 'walk in' wardrobe, and this is a feature which is gaining in popularity.

The garage is 18'4" wide, which just permits two single garage doors instead of one double door. How much better this looks!

REAR ELEVATION

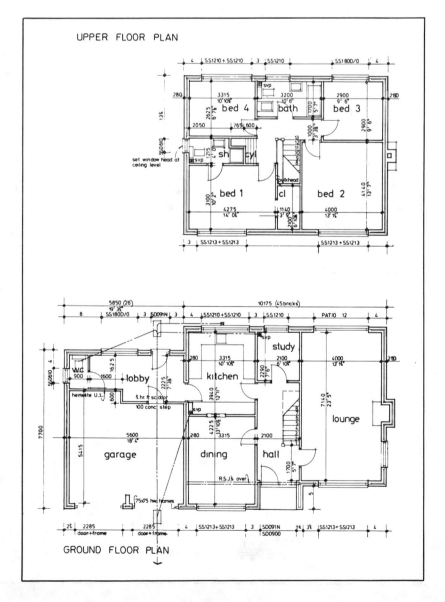

UPPER FLOOR PLAN

GROUND FLOOR PLAN

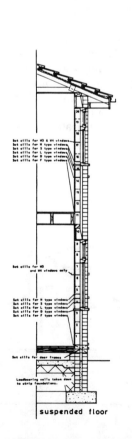

suspended floor

FRONT ELEVATION

REAR ELEVATION

Marley Bold Roll
colour to be approved

Alpine render with
stone features

SIDE ELEVATION

stepped lead flashing
& tray d.p.c.

SIDE ELEVATION

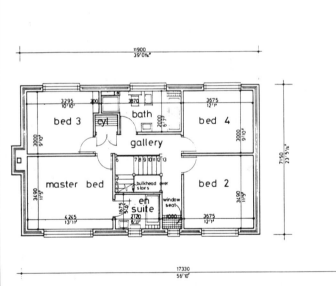

11900
39'0¼"

7150
23'5¼"

bed 3
3295
10'10"

cyl

bath

bed 4
3675
12'1"

gallery

master bed

bulkhead over
stairs

en suite

bed 2

4245
13'11"

3675
12'1"

A modern home with most of
the features that home builders
look for today. To start with there
is an imposing hall with a feature
staircase, big enough for one or
two pieces of furniture and in
every way a room in its own right.
The era of considering halls
'wasted space' is definitely gone,
and this hall with a stair well to
suit turned balustrading is right
in fashion.

There are two living rooms:
one a formal lounge and the other
variously a family room, snug,
television room — call it what
you will, it is very much what
todays homebuilders want. The
kitchen has a separate breakfast
alcove.

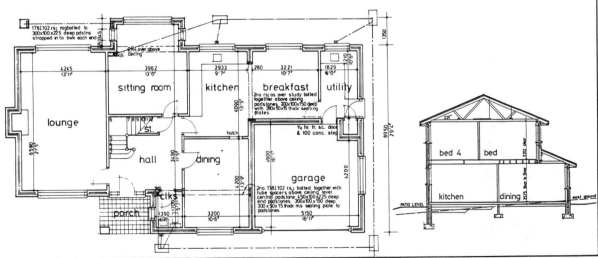

17330
56'10"

sitting room
3962
13'0"

kitchen
2933
9'7"

breakfast
3221
10'7"

utility
1829
6'0"

lounge

hall

dining

garage

porch

bed 4

bed

kitchen

dining

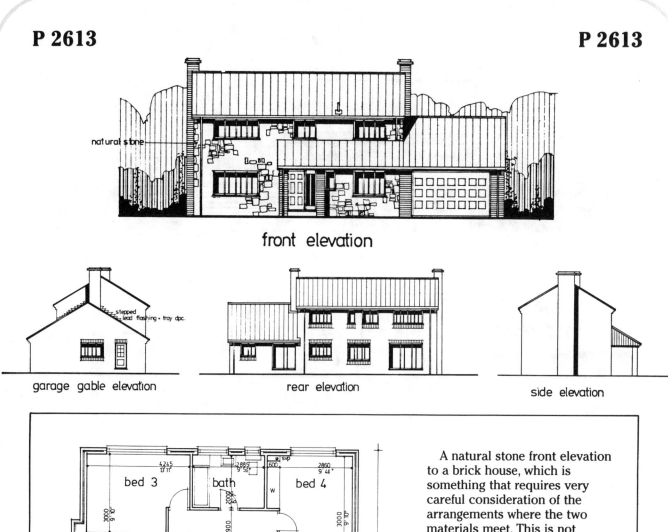

front elevation

garage gable elevation   rear elevation   side elevation

natural stone

stepped
lead flashing + tray dpc.

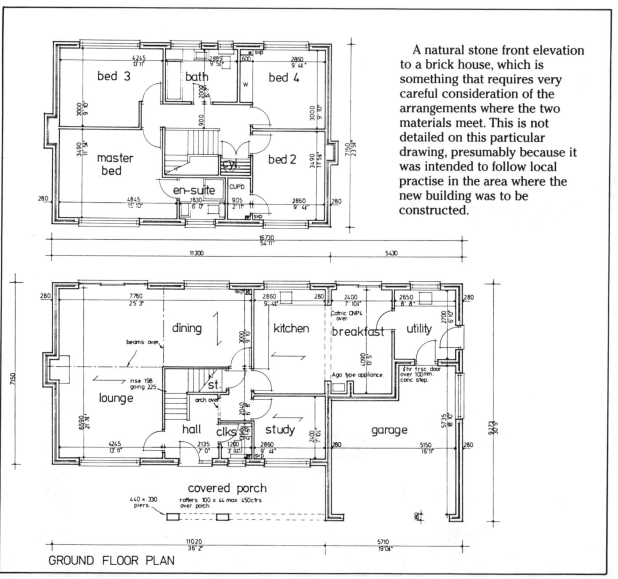

A natural stone front elevation to a brick house, which is something that requires very careful consideration of the arrangements where the two materials meet. This is not detailed on this particular drawing, presumably because it was intended to follow local practise in the area where the new building was to be constructed.

bed 3   bath   bed 4

master
bed

en-suite   cyl.   bed 2

CUPD.

dining   kitchen   breakfast   utility

lounge

st.

hall   clks   study   garage

covered porch

GROUND FLOOR PLAN

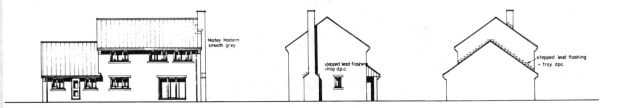

The storey height window to the stair well is a key feature in this house, which has an interesting layout. Besides having a bathroom that is bigger than the smaller bedrooms, it also has the only access to the dining room through the kitchen. If required it would be simple to turn one bathroom into two, one en suite and one for the family and guests, and a door can easily be provided between the dining room and the hall.

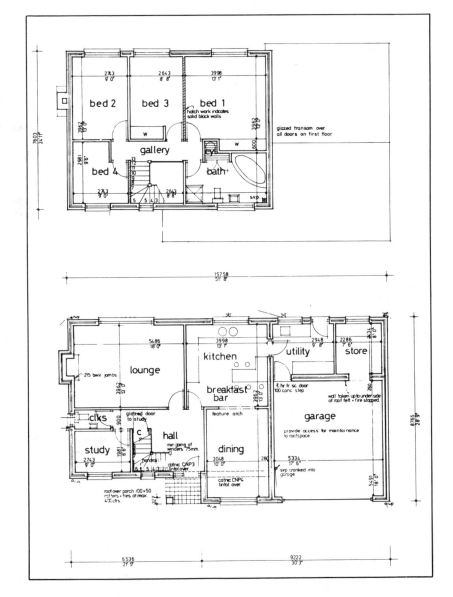

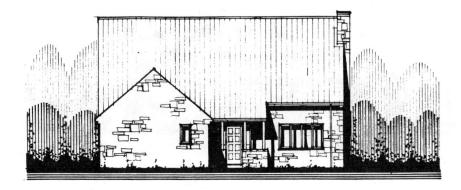

Lots of character in this interesting house which has all the first floor windows at the back or to the sides. An arrangement like this gives a lot of storage space in the eaves.

The choice of tile has to be exactly right for a home where the roof is as dominant a feature as it is here, and as the roof seems to be supported by the timber posts of the porch - which is an illusion - then these posts must be really massive.

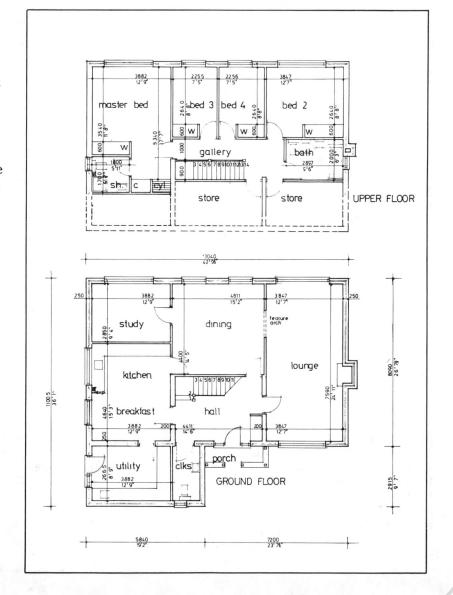

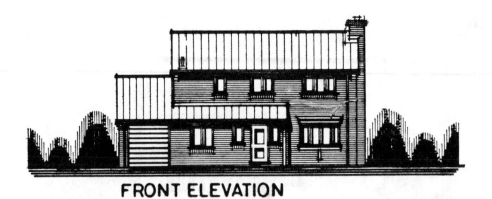

FRONT ELEVATION

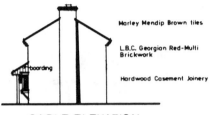

Marley Mendip Brown tiles

L.B.C. Georgian Red-Multi Brickwork

Hardwood Casement Joinery

boarding

GABLE ELEVATION

REAR ELEVATION

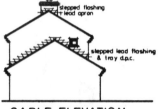

stepped flashing & lead apron

stepped lead flashing & tray d.p.c.

GABLE ELEVATION

This is a plan for a four bedroom house to a design concept that is very popular, shewn here at the minimum practicable width from front to back.

A house in this style has usually got a span for the main roof of about twenty four feet. Here it has been reduced to just under twenty feet internally, which permits two double bedrooms within the width. Part of the front wall to the ground floor is pulled forward to give room for a garage and utility room, and a larger study, but the limit on this is the need for the roof over the study window to be below the cill of the window above. This limits this projection to three feet, permitting a garage of 16'4" and a narrow utility room of 4'11". Another two feet of roof span would have made it all much easier.

Incidentally, there are penalties for going *over* the usual twenty four foot span for this style of house, starting with an expensive increase in the size of the roof truss timbers. Whoever is going to draw the plans for your new home should be able to explain all this to you.

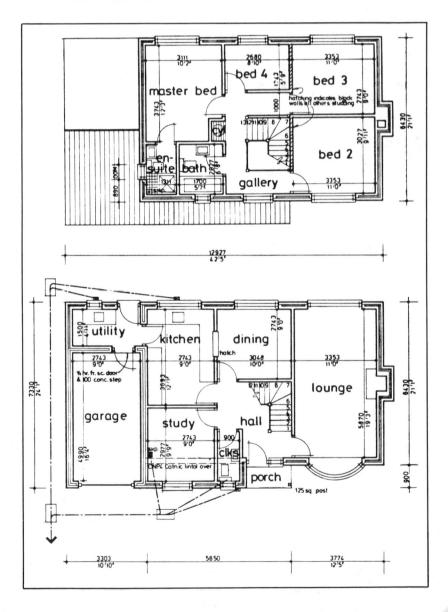

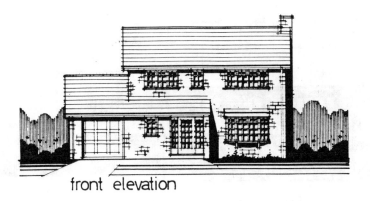

front elevation

rear elevation

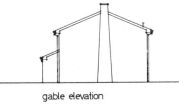

gable elevation

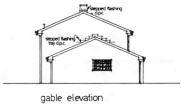

gable elevation

The windows used in this house are usually called Georgian windows, although they would have been a novelty to architects in the Georgian era. They are properly called 'full bar windows'. At any rate, although their recent popularity has passed its peak, they retain their appeal for many people, although they do need a lot of painting!

This house was designed to be built on a raft foundation, and the detail shews what is involved in this.

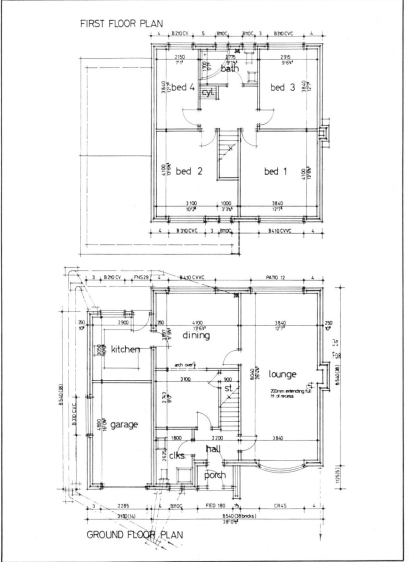

FIRST FLOOR PLAN

bath

bed 4   cyl   bed 3

bed 2   bed 1

GROUND FLOOR PLAN

kitchen   dining   lounge

arch over

garage   st.

clks   hall   porch

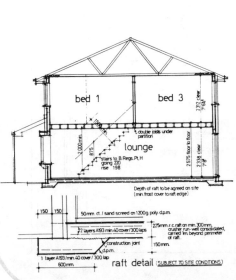

bed 1   bed 3

lounge

double joists under partition

stairs to B.Regs. Pt.H going 220 rise 198

Depth of raft to be agreed on site (min frost cover to raft edge)

50mm ct. / sand screed on 1200g poly d.p.m.

2 layers A193 min 40 cover / 300 laps

construction joint

225mm r.c. raft on min 300mm crusher run well consolidated, carried 1m beyond perimeter of raft

d.p.m.

1 layer A193 / min 40 cover / 300 lap

raft detail (SUBJECT TO SITE CONDITIONS)

blue slate

coursed natural gritstone

timber or timberclad garage doors

front elevation

rear elevation

garage side

side elevation

A straightforward house built in stone under a slate roof. The enclosed front porch will tend to make the hall rather dark, even with glazed doors. This can be helped by providing a window in the side wall of the porch, and perhaps double doors between the porch and the hall itself.

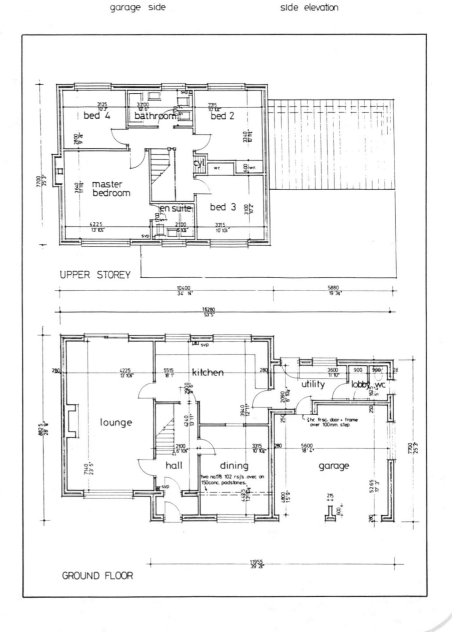

UPPER STOREY

bed 4

bathroom

bed 2

master bedroom

cyl

w.r.

w.r.

en suite

bed 3

GROUND FLOOR

lounge

kitchen

utility

lobby

WC

hall

dining

garage

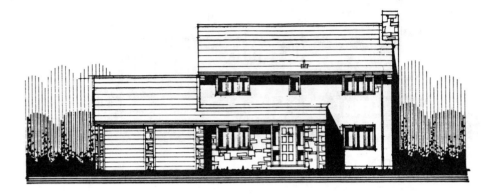

REAR ELEVATION

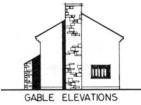

GABLE ELEVATIONS

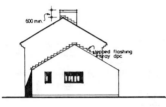

A good example of a medium sized house in a very popular style. This design concept is very cost effective, and the key to this is in the roof, with both parts using trussed rafters of the same span and pitch. This was the most popular shape for a four bedroom home during the 1970s but since then more complex shapes have become more usual.

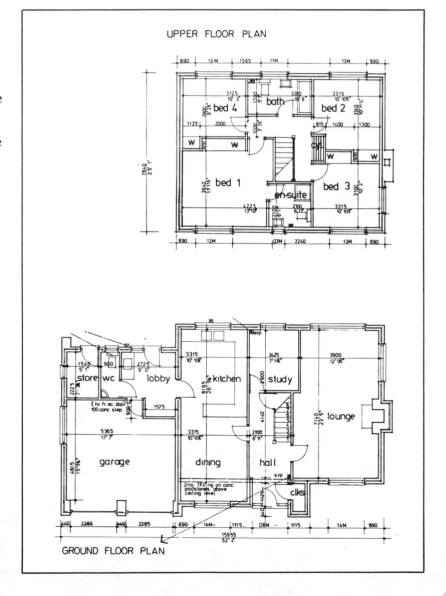

UPPER FLOOR PLAN

GROUND FLOOR PLAN

139

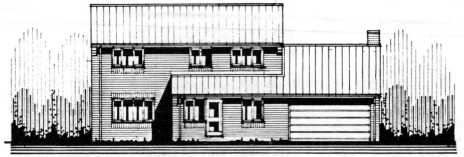

FRONT ELEVATION

REAR ELEVATION

This design for a four bedroom home was drawn for a client who was happy to restrict room in the garage so as to have as large a kitchen and lobby at the back door as was practicable. A garage that is only fifteen feet deep will take most cars, but only just. An extra two feet will make a lot of difference.

The bathroom is big enough for a large corner bath. These continue to gain in popularity, although no-one has yet discovered how to clean the far side of the bath without stepping in the thing.

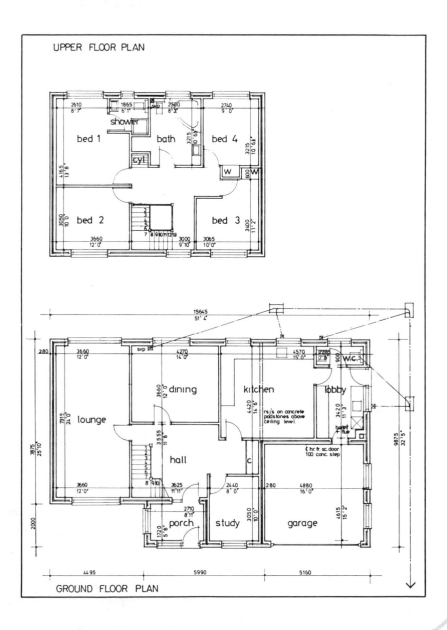

UPPER FLOOR PLAN

GROUND FLOOR PLAN

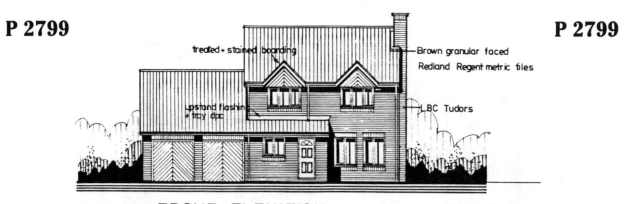

FRONT ELEVATION

A compact and economical four bedroom house with a large double garage and a very large utility room behind it. This is a layout that appeals to those who run a business in the country and whose family cars, and the loads that they carry, are more than usually important.

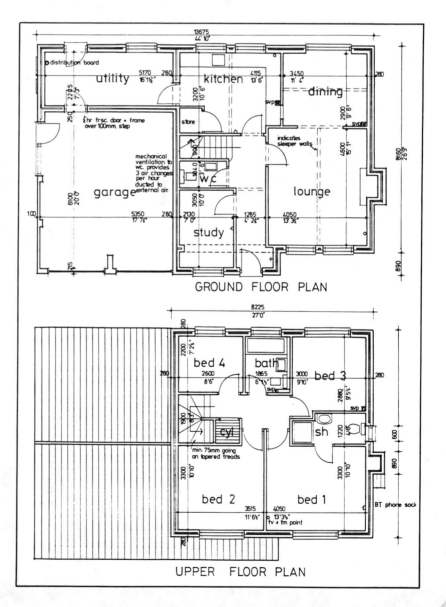

GROUND FLOOR PLAN

UPPER FLOOR PLAN

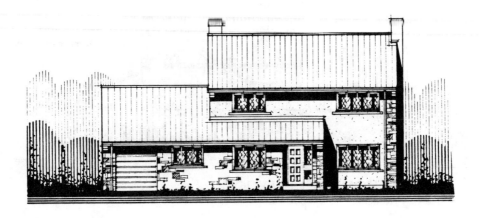

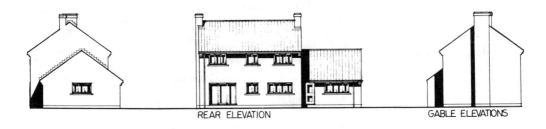

REAR ELEVATION

GABLE ELEVATIONS

This four bedroom house has a lot of ground floor living rooms - lounge, dining room and a family room. The single storey part of the building can be lengthened to turn the single garage into a double garage if you wish.

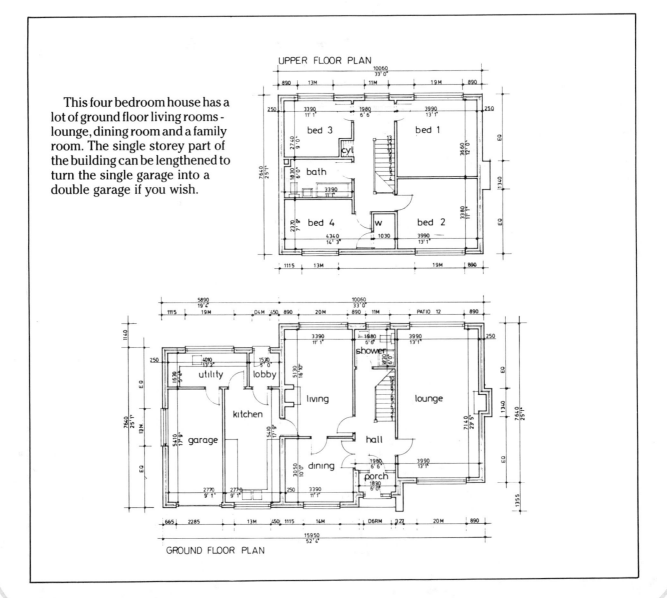

UPPER FLOOR PLAN

GROUND FLOOR PLAN

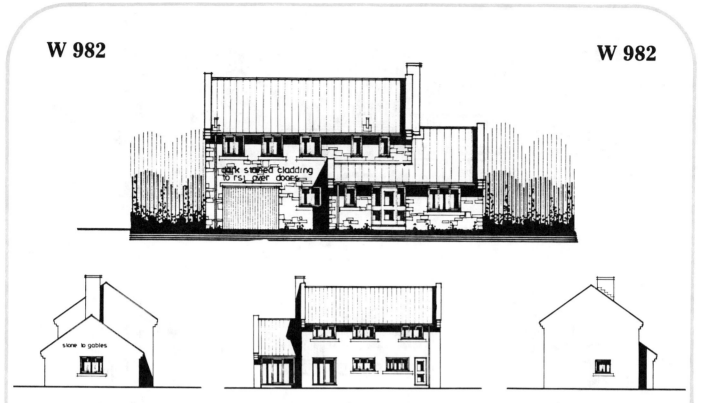

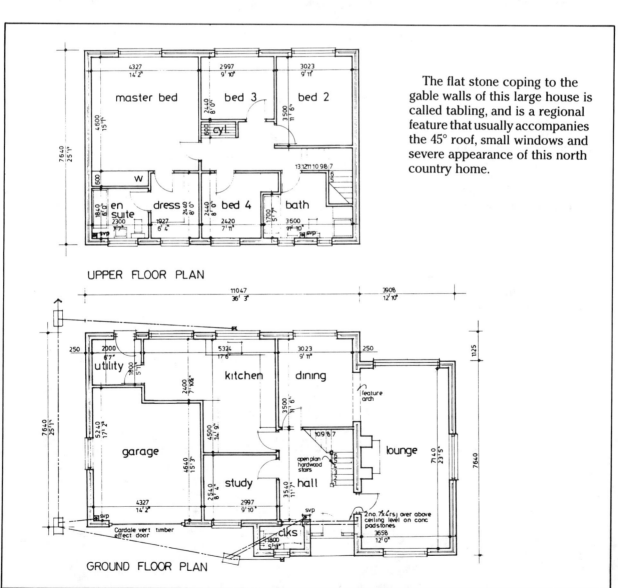

The flat stone coping to the gable walls of this large house is called tabling, and is a regional feature that usually accompanies the 45° roof, small windows and severe appearance of this north country home.

UPPER FLOOR PLAN

GROUND FLOOR PLAN

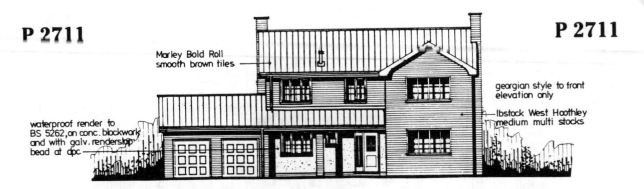

Marley Bold Roll
smooth brown tiles

georgian style to front
elevation only

Ibstock West Hoathley
medium multi stocks

waterproof render to
BS 5262, on conc. blockwork
and with galv. renderstop
bead at dpc

FRONT ELEVATION

stepped flashing
+ tray dpc

150 upstand
flashing + tray
dpc

GABLE ELEVATION   REAR ELEVATION   GABLE ELEVATION

A house with Georgian sash windows to the front, and modern side hung casement windows at the back and sides. An arrangement of this sort needs careful consideration, and in this case it requires accepting that there will be two different types of window in the lounge.

Note that the inside wall of the front porch is to be rendered. This was common fifty years ago, but is unusual now. It is certainly a good way to lighten the appearance of a house that has a canopy over the front door, and emphasises the entrance in a useful way.

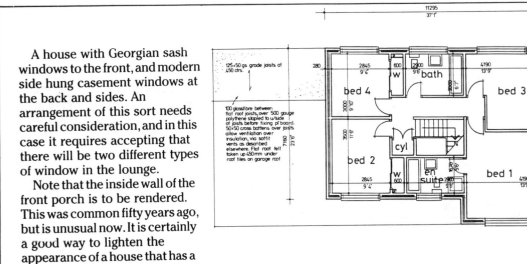

125+50 gs. grade joists at
450 ctrs.

100 glassfibre between
flat roof joists, over 500 gauge
polythene stapled to u/side
of joists before fixing pl board.
50+50 cross battens over joists
allow ventilation over
insulation, via soffit
vents as described
elsewhere. Flat roof felt
taken up 450mm under
roof tiles on garage roof

11295
37'1

280   2845   600   2590   4190   280
       9'4"   9'6"   13'9"

w   bath

bed 4   bed 3

3000
9'10"

cyl

3500
11'8"

bed 2

en
suite

bed 1

2845   w   4190
9'4"   600   13'9"

7160
23'6

16875
55'4½

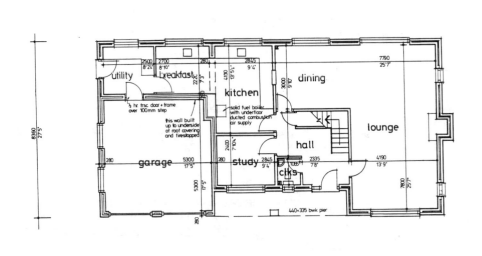

8360
27'5"

2500   2700   280   2845   7790
8'2½"   8'10"   9'4"   25'7"

utility   breakfast   dining

½ hr. frsc door + frame
over 100mm step

this wall built
up to underside
of roof covering
and firestopped

kitchen

solid fuel boiler
with underfloor
ducted combustion
air supply

lounge

hall

garage   5300   study   2845   2335   4190
          17'5"   9'4"   7'8"   13'9"

280   1065   clks
       3'6"

5300
17'5"

440+335 bwk pier

7800
25'7"

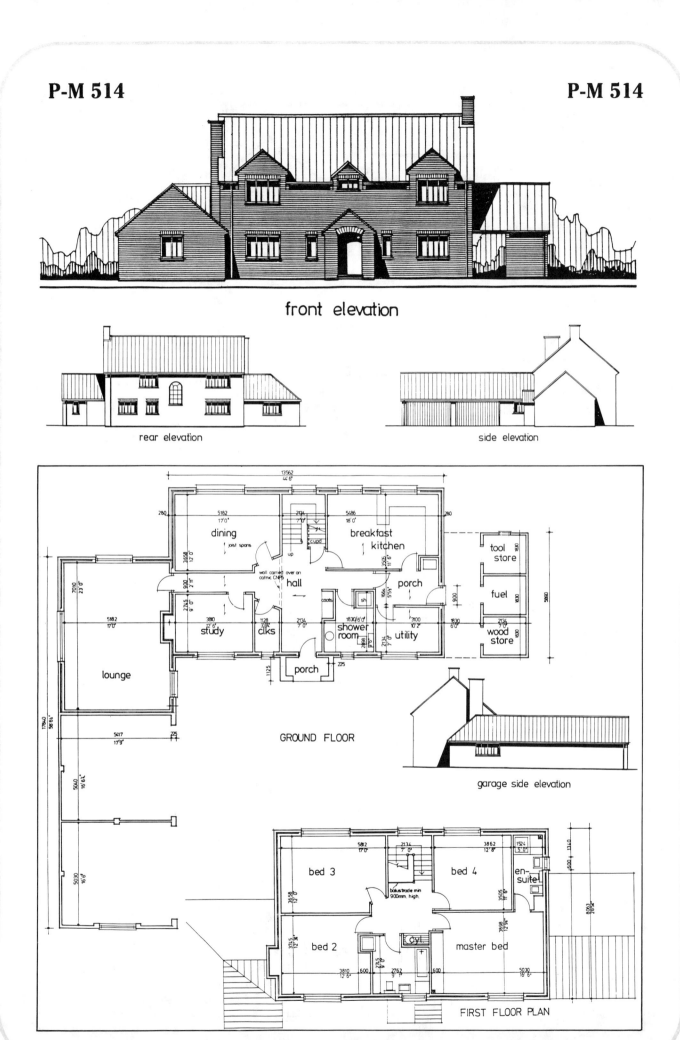

front elevation

rear elevation

side elevation

GROUND FLOOR

garage side elevation

dining

breakfast
kitchen

tool
store

fuel

wood
store

hall

porch

study

clks

shower
room

utility

lounge

porch

FIRST FLOOR PLAN

bed 3

bed 4

en-
suite

bed 2

cyl

master bed

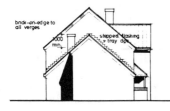

REAR ELEVATION

SIDE ELEVATION

Many architects clients ask for an inglenook fireplace these days, and these need a very large room to set them off. Linking the lounge and dining room with glazed double doors as in this design is one way of arranging this.

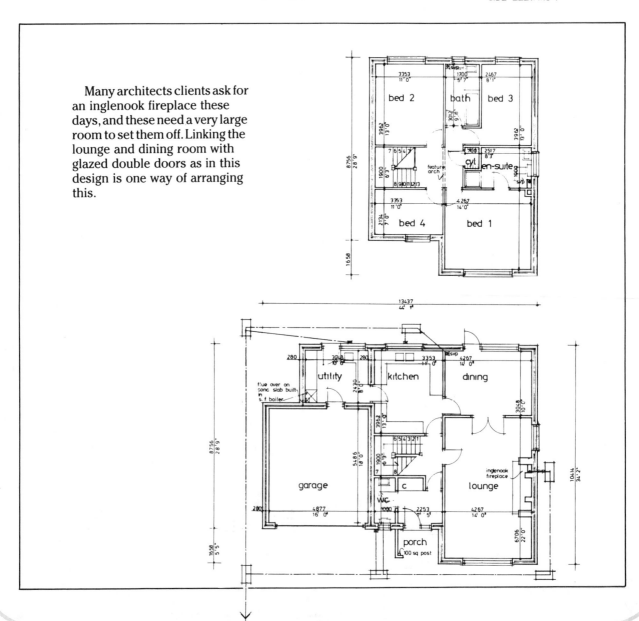

REAR ELEVATION

Two interesting features to this four bedroom house - a balcony reached from the first floor landing, and a wine "cellar". The balcony requires as much careful thought in selecting the balustrading as will be given to choosing the contents of the wine cellar.

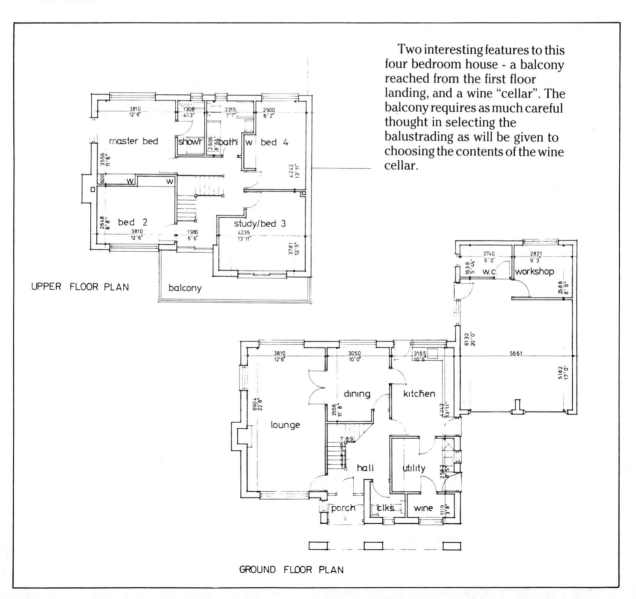

UPPER FLOOR PLAN

GROUND FLOOR PLAN

ENTRANCE ELEVATION

SIDE ELEVATION

REAR ELEVATION

SIDE ELEVATION

This farmhouse was built in a clearing in an oak wood in Lincolnshire, surrounded by sixty foot trees. In this setting the steep pitch to the roof and the porch over the back door looked exactly right, particularly as it was built in a local brick with plenty of brickwork detailing — corbells, dentil courses and so on.

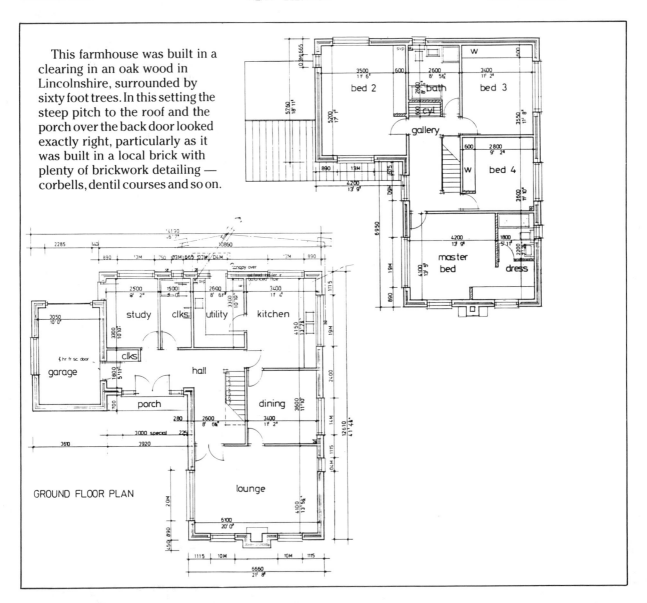

GROUND FLOOR PLAN

rear elevation

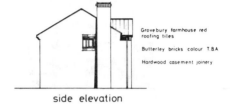

side elevation

Grovebury farmhouse red
roofing tiles

Butterley bricks colour T.B.A

Hardwood casement joinery

stepped lead flashing
+ tray d.p.c

The complex looking roof that gives this family home a lot of its character is really quite simple to build, and should not add a lot to the all important 'costs per sq.ft.'. Inside there is an arch between the lounge and the dining area. This can also be built as a solid wall, with either an ordinary door or feature double doors, and this latter option is now very popular in a house that is laid out in this way.

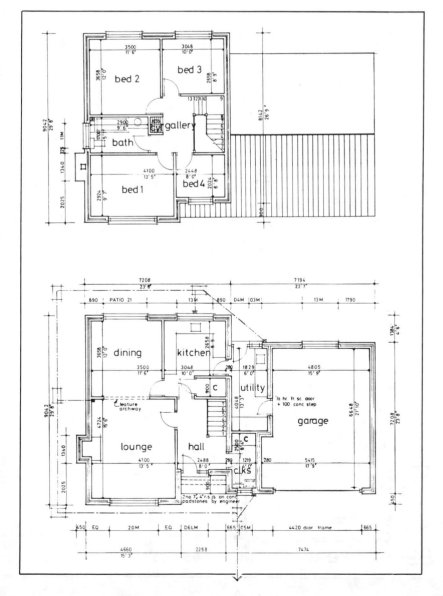

front elevation

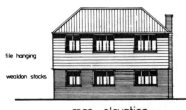

tile hanging

wealdon stocks

rear elevation

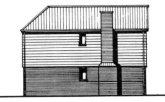

side elevation

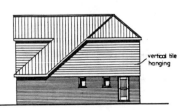

vertical tile hanging

side elevation

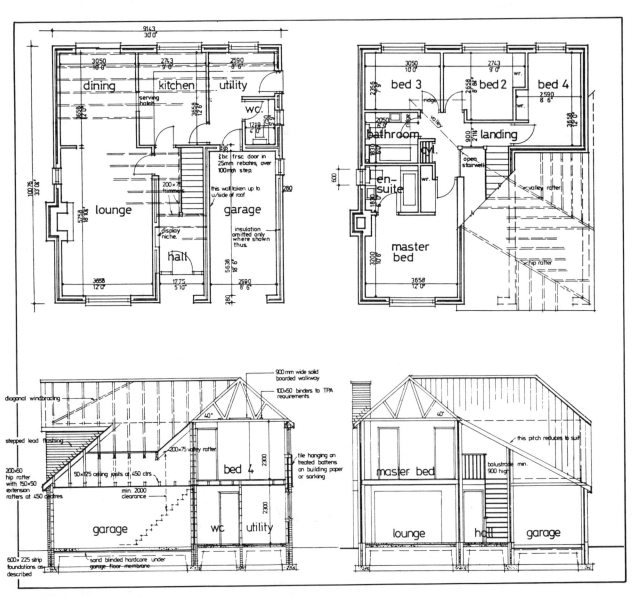

front elevation

facing bwk and tiles to be
agreed with planning authority.

rear elevation

side elevation

A four bedroom home with
bigger than average rooms. The
dining room projects out from the
rear elevation, giving room
dimensions of 13'6" x 10'6" which
will take a very large dining table.

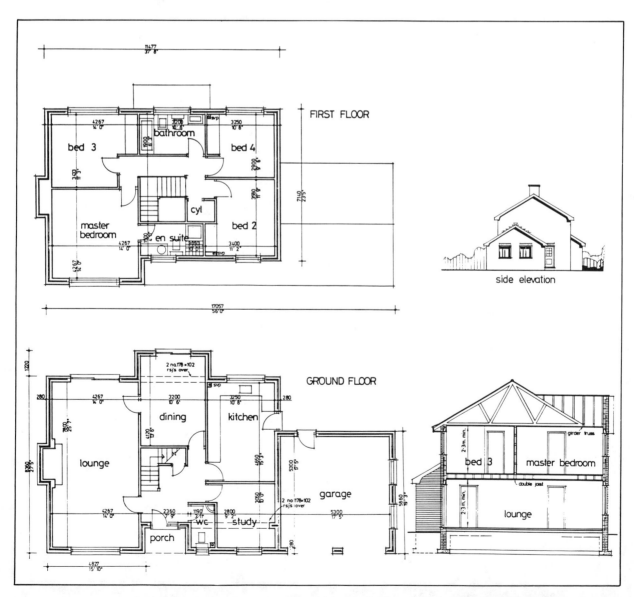

FIRST FLOOR

bed 3

bathroom

bed 4

master
bedroom

cyl

en suite

bed 2

GROUND FLOOR

dining

kitchen

lounge

garage

wc

study

porch

side elevation

girder truss

bed 3

master bedroom

double joist

lounge

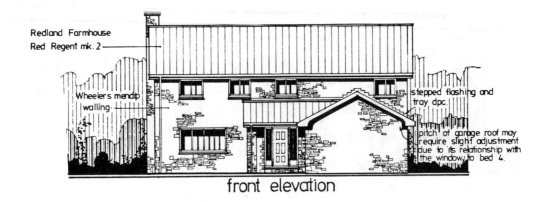

Redland Farmhouse
Red Regent mk. 2

Wheelers mendip walling.

stepped flashing and tray dpc.

pitch of garage roof may require slight adjustment due to its relationship with the window to bed 4.

front elevation

Hardwood joinery, all windows d/g

side elevation

rear elevation

side elevation

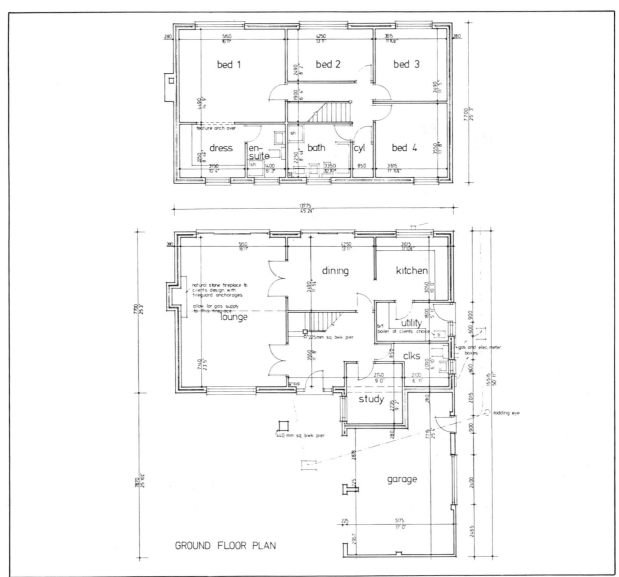

bed 1

bed 2

bed 3

dress

en-suite

bath

cyl

bed 4

feature arch over

sh

sh

dining

kitchen

lounge

natural stone fireplace to client's design with fireguard anchorages.

allow for gas supply to this fireplace

utility

225mm sq bwk pier

boiler of clients choice

gas and elec meter boxes

clks

440 mm sq bwk pier

study

rodding eye

garage

GROUND FLOOR PLAN

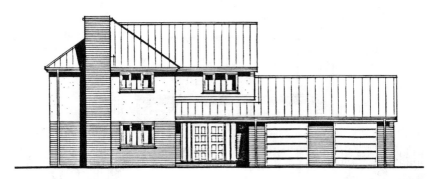

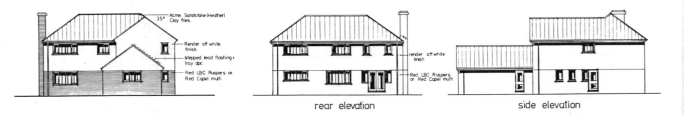

rear elevation   side elevation

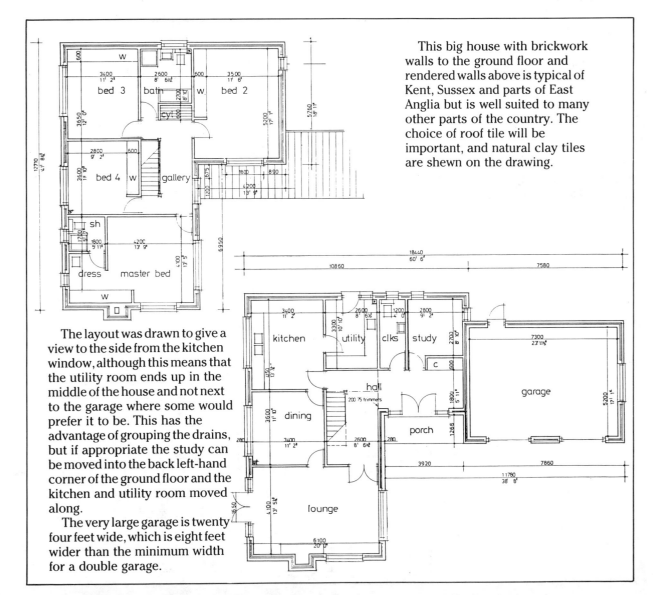

This big house with brickwork walls to the ground floor and rendered walls above is typical of Kent, Sussex and parts of East Anglia but is well suited to many other parts of the country. The choice of roof tile will be important, and natural clay tiles are shewn on the drawing.

The layout was drawn to give a view to the side from the kitchen window, although this means that the utility room ends up in the middle of the house and not next to the garage where some would prefer it to be. This has the advantage of grouping the drains, but if appropriate the study can be moved into the back left-hand corner of the ground floor and the kitchen and utility room moved along.

The very large garage is twenty four feet wide, which is eight feet wider than the minimum width for a double garage.

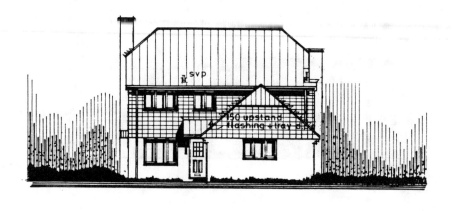

side elevation

stepped lead flashing

second hand plain clay tiles (clients own supply)

white painted brickwork with tile hanging only to front first floor elevation

softwood casement joinery dark stained

600 mm min

rear elevation

side elevation

new embankment

line of exg grd

A house for Kent or Sussex, with tile hanging to the upper storey and a half hip roof. Note that the client for whom this home was designed has opted to have the private bathroom of the master bedroom as large and well equipped as possible, with the minimum size of family bathroom. This is a growing trend.

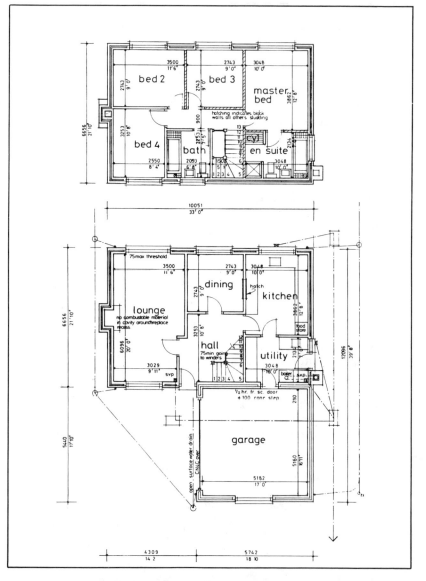

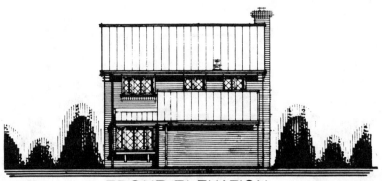

FRONT ELEVATION

stepped lead
flashing &
tray dpc

Marley Modern Dark Brown
roofing tiles

L.B.C. Georgian
red-multi brickwork

Softwood casement joinery
stained with diamond leaded
lights to Front Elevation only

SIDE ELEVATION

s.v.p.fitted durable cage
& weathering slate

REAR ELEVATION

SIDE ELEVATION

The hall and cloakroom which link the garage and the house are the key features of this design. The cantilevered canopy which extends from the dining room window through to the garage gives a courtyard effect, which suits the porthole windows, heavy brick detailing and leaded lights.

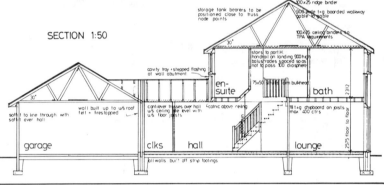

SECTION 1:50

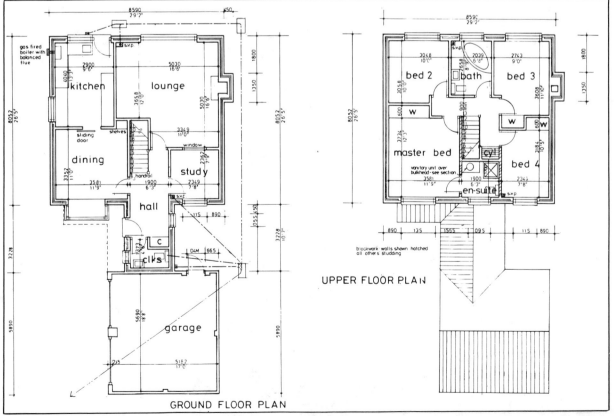

GROUND FLOOR PLAN

UPPER FLOOR PLAN

blockwork walls shown hatched
all others studding

FRONT ELEVATION

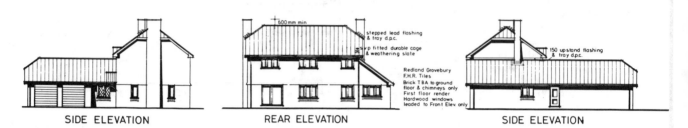

SIDE ELEVATION REAR ELEVATION SIDE ELEVATION

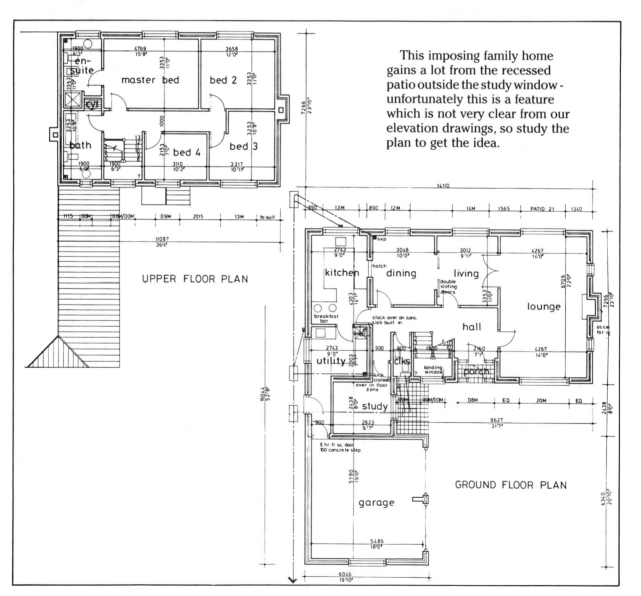

UPPER FLOOR PLAN

This imposing family home gains a lot from the recessed patio outside the study window - unfortunately this is a feature which is not very clear from our elevation drawings, so study the plan to get the idea.

GROUND FLOOR PLAN

front elevation (south)

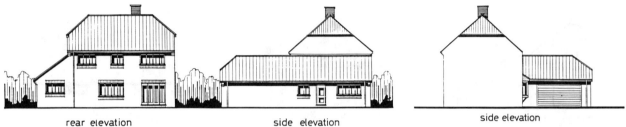

rear elevation   side elevation   side elevation

This house has an open
fireplace set in the wall between
the lounge and the dining room,
so that the fire is enjoyed from
both sides. This is a very striking
feature, but the advice of the Solid
Fuel Advisory Council on suitable
fires and fire canopies is essential.
Bells of Northampton have a fire
that is particularly appropriate.

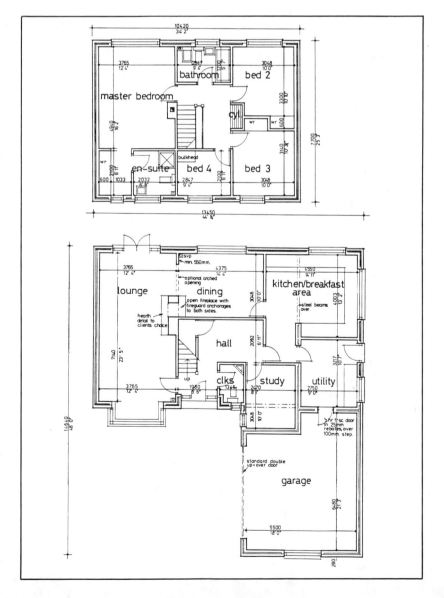

garage side elevation

rear elevation

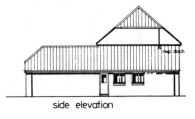

side elevation

This large house with a half-hip roof has a country feel, and would make a splendid farmhouse in the South or West of England. If it is built in that role, then most farmers would want a door leading from the study or farm office to the utility room and back door, and of course this is easily arranged.

Notice that the en-suite bathroom is just as large and well fitted as the main bathroom: this is a new trend, and sometimes the en-suite facilities are larger and more luxurious than the others - which is logical if you consider who is paying for the new home.

The porch roof is supported with gallows brackets, and it is important that these are made from really heavy section timber and should not look skimped. If you have chosen your front door before the gallows brackets are made, a good carpenter should be able to match the style of the door in chamfers or flutings on the brackets.

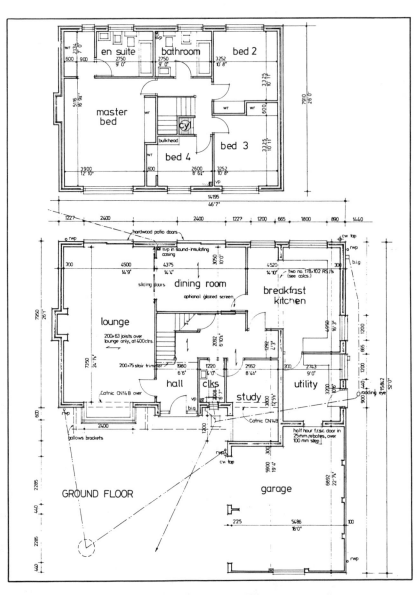

GROUND FLOOR

GABLE ELEVATION

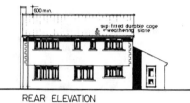

REAR ELEVATION

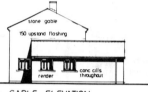

GABLE ELEVATION

Note that the plan of this house has been turned through 90°, and that the garage window is to the front. The office and store between the garage and the house will suit those who work from home, and if required the office door can be moved into the outside wall.

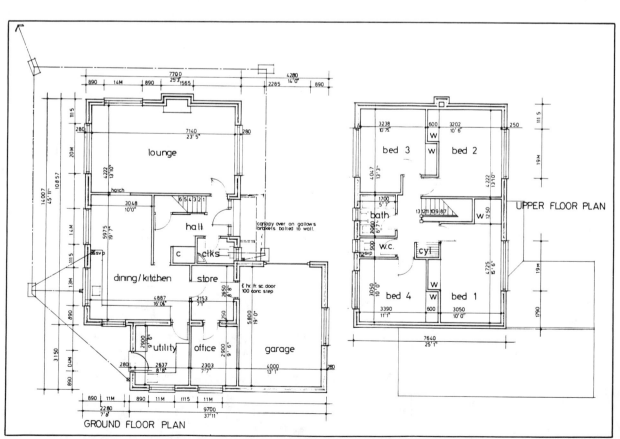

GROUND FLOOR PLAN

UPPER FLOOR PLAN

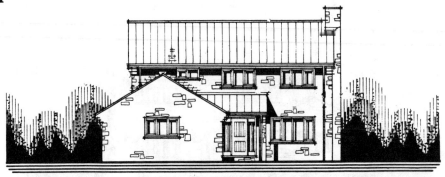

FRONT ELEVATION

SIDE ELEVATION

Marley Modern
roof tiles

boarding

Natural Stone

REAR ELEVATION

SIDE ELEVATION

An interesting house with a lot
of character. The L shaped garage
gives plenty of room for bicycles
and garden tools, and the study is
conveniently by the front door for
someone who has a lot of
business visitors.

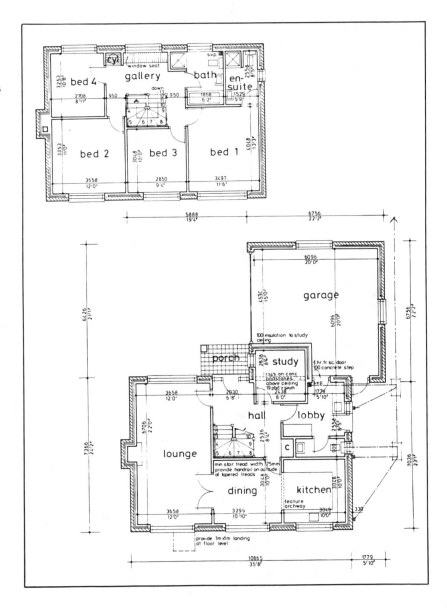

front elevation

side elevation

dark red or red-brown pantiles
upstand flashing + tray

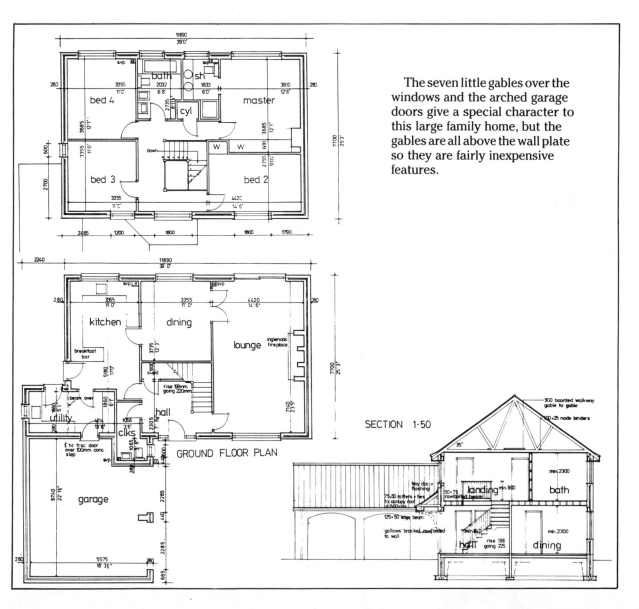

The seven little gables over the windows and the arched garage doors give a special character to this large family home, but the gables are all above the wall plate so they are fairly inexpensive features.

GROUND FLOOR PLAN

SECTION 1·50

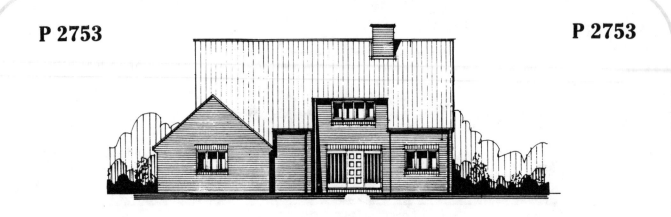

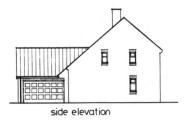

side elevation

rear elevation

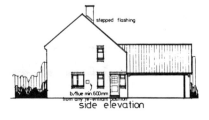

side elevation

An interesting house with a large hall and equally large landing that helps to make it feel even bigger than it actually is. Note the side window to the half landing of the stairs. To be of full height it had to be in the side wall, as there is insufficient clearance for it below the roof at the front. A shallower window in the front wall would have looked out of place in this building which has such a strong vertical emphasis in the joinery.

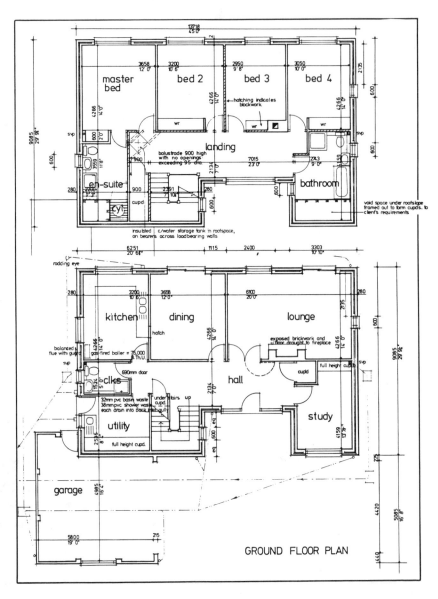

GROUND FLOOR PLAN

front elevation 1·100

side elevation

rear elevation 1·100

side elevation

A compact house designed for a site near Southampton where it had to match the general style of adjacent 1930s properties. The rendered walling to the first floor rises from a sloping brick-on-edge string course in true period fashion, instead of using the galvanised render-stop that is now more usually used.

The dining room is linked with the kitchen through a feature arch, but could easily be built as a separate room with a door into the hall.

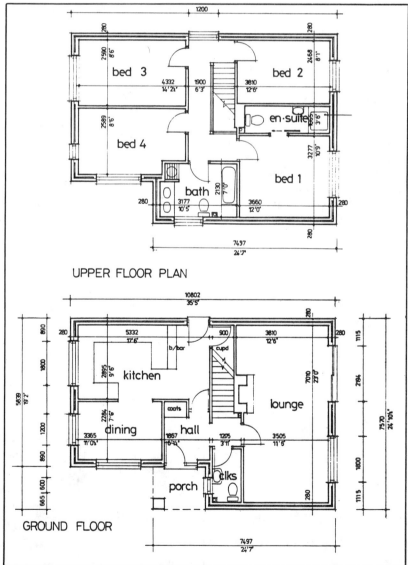

UPPER FLOOR PLAN

GROUND FLOOR

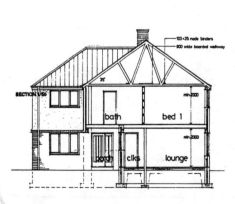

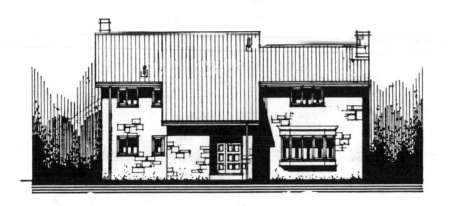

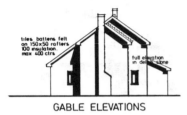

GABLE ELEVATIONS

REAR ELEVATION

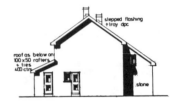

The hall is a key feature of this house, and half of it is two storeys high with a sloping ceiling, as you can see if you study the plans.

The wrought iron balcony to the french windows of the master bedroom suite is an 'optional extra' that can give a lot of character both to the feel of the bedroom itself, and to the rear of the building when seen from the garden.

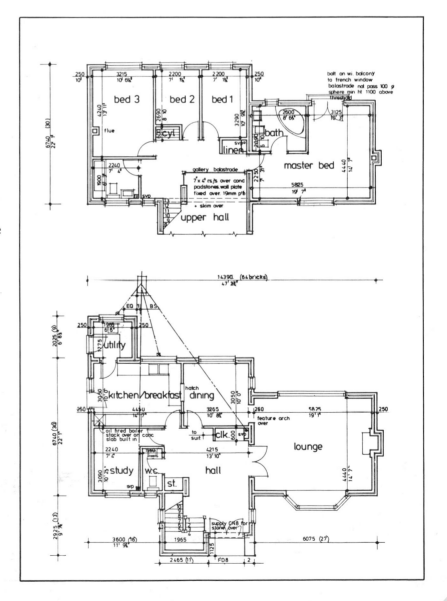

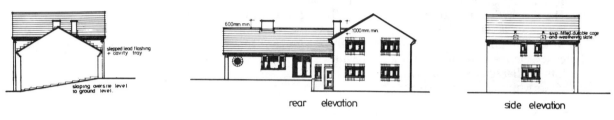

sloping oversite level to ground level.

stepped lead flashing + cavity tray

600mm min.

1000mm min.

rear elevation

s.v.p. fitted durable cage and weathering slate.

side elevation

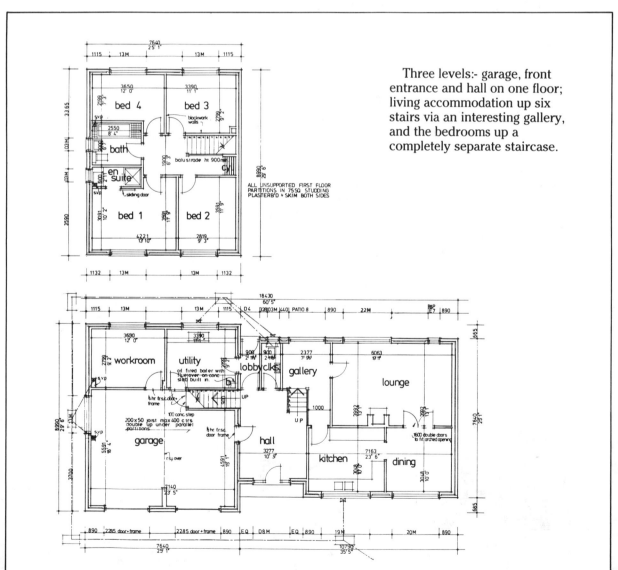

Three levels:- garage, front entrance and hall on one floor; living accommodation up six stairs via an interesting gallery, and the bedrooms up a completely separate staircase.

bed 4

bed 3

blockwork walls

bath

balustrade ht 900mm

en suite

sliding door

cyl

bed 1

bed 2

ALL UNSUPPORTED FIRST FLOOR PARTITIONS IN 75 SQ STUDDING PLASTERB'D + SKIM BOTH SIDES

workroom

utility

oil fired boiler with fluerover on conc. slab built in.

lobby

clks

gallery

½ hr tr.sc.door + frame

lounge

100 conc. step

200 x 50 joist max 400 ctrs double up under parallel partitions

½ hr tr.sc. door frame

UP

UP

garage

r.s.j. over

hall

1600 double doors to fit arched opening

kitchen

dining

front elevation

side elevation

An unusual house this, only seventeen feet wide at any point. The proportion of wall area to floor area is thus rather high, which will not help the building costs. On the other hand, it has lots of character and all round views which always add to value.

Note that it was designed for the garage to face the entrance, so the big window in the lounge faces to the rear, and it can be built on a plot less than forty feet wide.

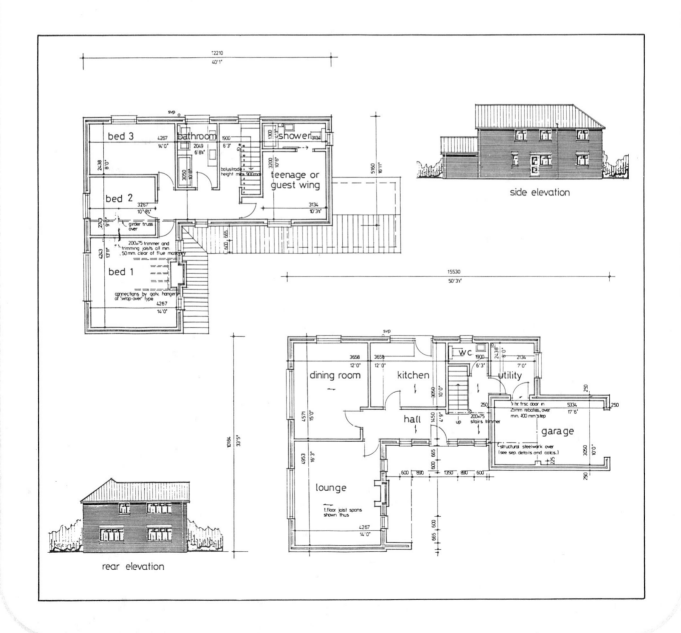

side elevation

rear elevation

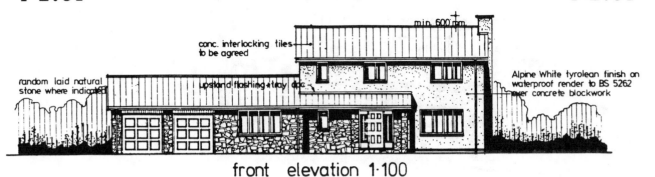

random laid natural
stone where indicated

conc. interlocking tiles
to be agreed

min. 600 mm

upstand flashing + tray dpc

Alpine White tyrolean finish on
waterproof render to BS 5262
over concrete blockwork

front elevation 1·100

garage side

rear elevation

side

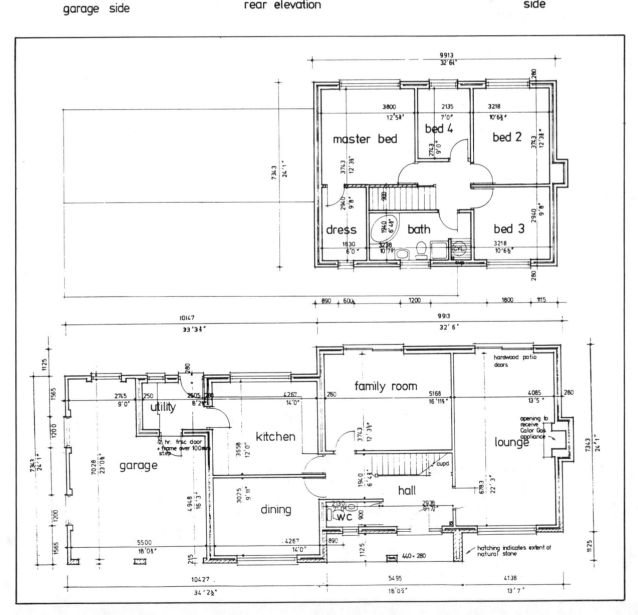

9913
32'6½"

3800
12'5½"

2135
7'0"

3218
10'6½"

master bed

bed 4

bed 2

734.3
24'1"

374.3
12'3¾"

274.3
9'0"

374.3
12'3¾"

900

290.0
9'8"

dress

bath

bed 3

194.0
6'4½"

294.0
9'8"

1830
6'0"

328.8
10'7½"

3218
10'6½"

CYL

280

890   600   1200   1800   1115

10147
33'3½"

9913
32'6"

1125

hardwood patio
doors

family room

1565

280

utility

2745
9'0"

250

260.5
8'2½"

280

4267
14'0"

280

5168
16'11½"

4085
13'5"

280

opening to
receive
Calor Gas
appliance

1200

½ hr. fr.s.c. door
+ frame over 100mm
step

kitchen

374.3
12'3¾"

lounge

734.3
24'1"

734.3
24'1"

7028
23'0½"

garage

365.8
12'0"

194.0
6'4½"

cupd.

678.3
22'3"

hall

4948
16'3½"

302.5
9'11"

dining

293.8
9'7½"

1200

215

213.0

900

WC

1125

1565

5500
18'0½"

215

4267
14'0"

890

440 × 280

hatching indicates extent of
natural stone

1125

10427
34'2½"

5495
18'0½"

4138
13'7"

comestron ceiling to lounge
only

19·7 ▽

1000mm min

19·70

REAR ELEVATION

Grovebury Tudor Brown Tiles

Render & timber tudoring to
first floor Front Elevation only

Redland Ashdown Village mixture
facing brickwork-coloured mortar

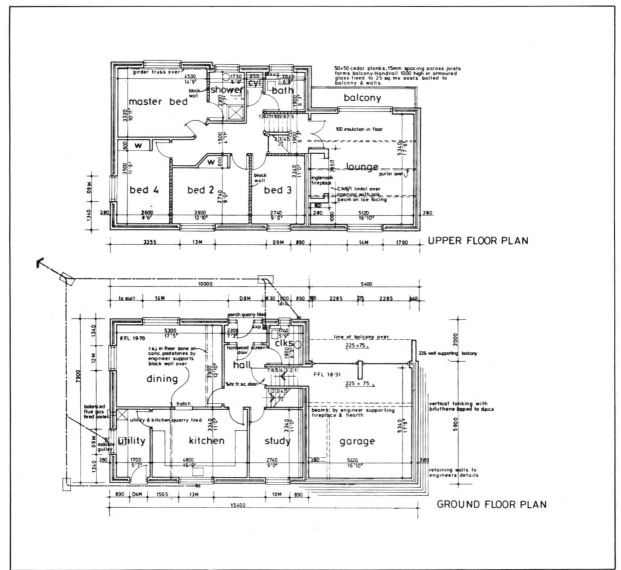

girder truss over
4500
14'9"
1750
5'9"
850
svp
20'6"
master bed
shower
cyl
bath
block
wall
2300
7'7"
balcony
3320
10'11"
1500
4'11"
1900
6'3"
100 insulation in floor
50×50 cedar planks,15mm spacing across joists
forms balcony Handrail 1000 high in armoured
glass fixed to 25 sq. ms posts bolted to
balcony & walls.
w
600
1900
6'3"
5340
17'6"
3500
11'6"
w
600
lounge
purlin over
2550
block
wall
bed 4
bed 2
2740
9'0"
bed 3
3340
11'0"
inglenook
fireplace
CN8/1 lintel over
opening with oak
beam on toe facing
1340
0.9M
2600
8'6"
3900
12'10"
2740
9'0"
280
1000
5120
16'10"
280

3355
1·3M
0·9M
890
1·4M
1790

UPPER FLOOR PLAN

10000
5400
to suit
1·4M
0·8M
830
600
890
365
2285
225
2285
440
porch quarry tiled
1740
5'9"
line of balcony over
225 × 75
1340
12M
FFL. 19·70
5300
17'5"
2200
7'9"
s.v.p.
clks
hardwood screen
door
225 wall supporting balcony
2000
7900
r.s.j. in floor zone on-
conc. padstones by
engineer supports
block wall over
3900
12'10"
hall
FFL 18·31
225 × 75
dining
1/2hr. fr. sc. door
7 6 5 4 3 2 1
1 2 3 4 5
hatch
beams by engineer supporting
fireplace & hearth
vertical tanking with
bituthene lapped to d.p.cs
balanced
flue gas
fired boiler
utility & kitchen quarry tiled
3340
11'0"
3340
11'0"
5340
17'6"
5900
0.9M
roadside
gulley
utility
kitchen
study
garage
1340
1700
5'7"
4800
15'9"
2740
9'0"
280
5120
16'10"
280
retaining walls to
engineers details

890
0·4M
1565
1·3M
1·0M
890
15400

GROUND FLOOR PLAN

conc. interlocking tiles
to be agreed

white spar on w/proof
render to BS 5262,
over conc. blockwork

Tavistock stone

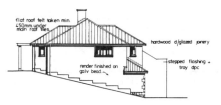

flat roof felt taken min.
450mm under
main roof tiles

hardwood d/glazed joinery

render finished on
galv bead.

stepped flashing +
tray dpc

Another house built into a
steep bank with the garage, front
door and two bedrooms at one
level, and all the living
accommodation and two more
bedrooms on the floor above.

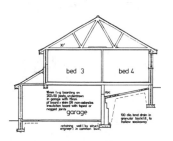

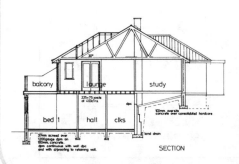

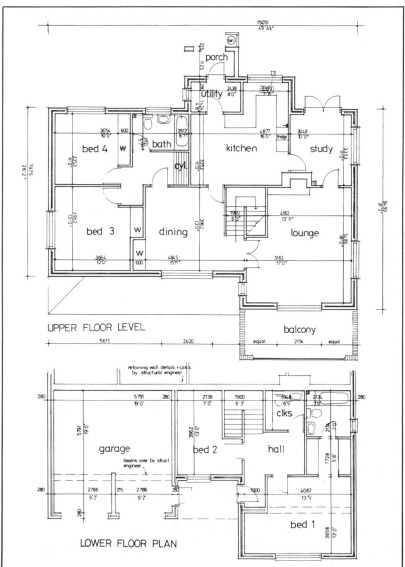

UPPER FLOOR LEVEL

LOWER FLOOR PLAN

SECTION

FRONT ELEVATION

stepped lead flashing
& tray d.p.c.

Marley Mendip Smooth
grey roof tiles

White Dolomite Render
with natural local stone
heads, cills & plinth

SIDE ELEVATION

REAR ELEVATION

SIDE ELEVATION

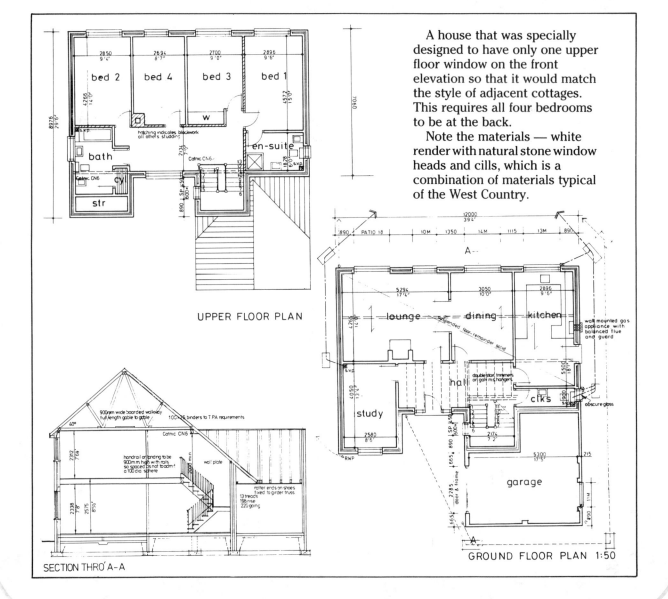

UPPER FLOOR PLAN

A house that was specially
designed to have only one upper
floor window on the front
elevation so that it would match
the style of adjacent cottages.
This requires all four bedrooms
to be at the back.

Note the materials — white
render with natural stone window
heads and cills, which is a
combination of materials typical
of the West Country.

SECTION THRO' A-A

GROUND FLOOR PLAN 1:50

front elevation

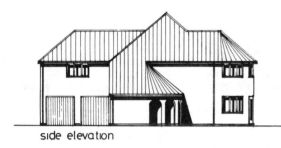

side elevation

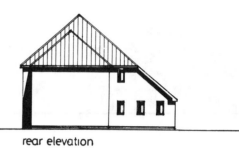

rear elevation

A design study drawn by Design & Materials Ltd for a house in Wales, and which had not progressed beyond this stage at the time that this book went to press. However, it is so unusual and interesting that it was thought worth including.

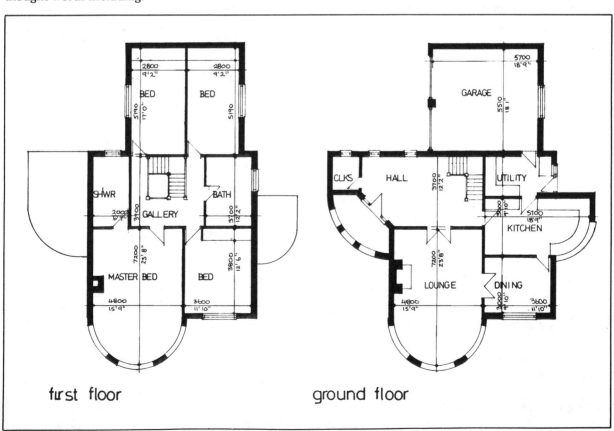

first floor

ground floor

FRONT ELEVATION

REAR ELEVATION

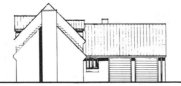

SIDE ELEVATION

SIDE ELEVATION

This farmhouse has a huge kitchen, and an even bigger living room with a dining area that is quite separate from the hall, lounge and study. This traditional separation of the working day end of the house from the rooms used at leisure is still requested by many farmers.

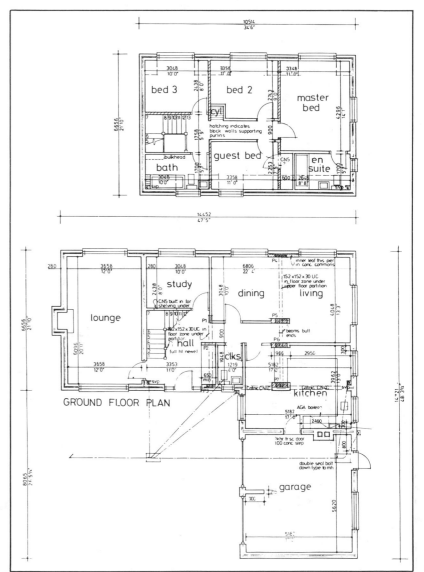

GROUND FLOOR PLAN

front elevation

This home for a steeply sloping site has the garage on the top floor, which is quite unusual. However, as will be seen from these interesting plans, it is a very attractive solution to the problem of a site which falls steeply away from an access road. The lounge has patio windows which open onto a balcony: the effectiveness of this will depend on the choice of balcony railings, and this must be given very careful consideration as they will add (or detract) enormously.

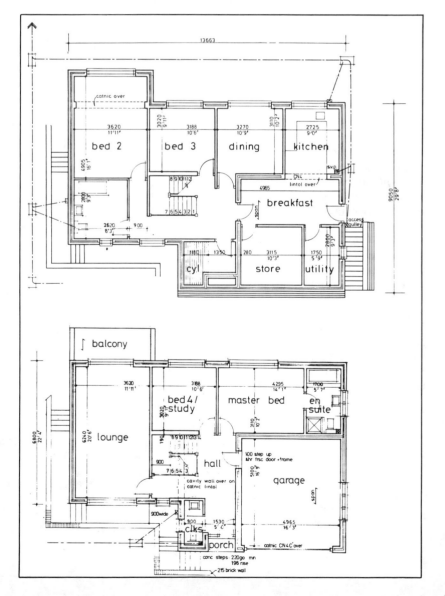

front elevation

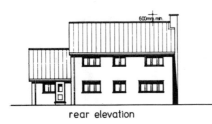

rear elevation

garage side elevation

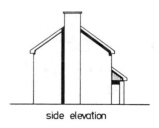

side elevation

A perfectly straightforward four bedroom home of the sort that builders call "estate agents houses" - estate agents love to sell them because everyone wants to buy them.

The first floor box room is an unusual feature in a home like this, and would make a small study or sewing room if desired.

With no windows in one side wall this house can be built on a 50ft plot with the large single garage shewn. If a double garage with a fourteen foot door is required the width of the building is increased by four feet.

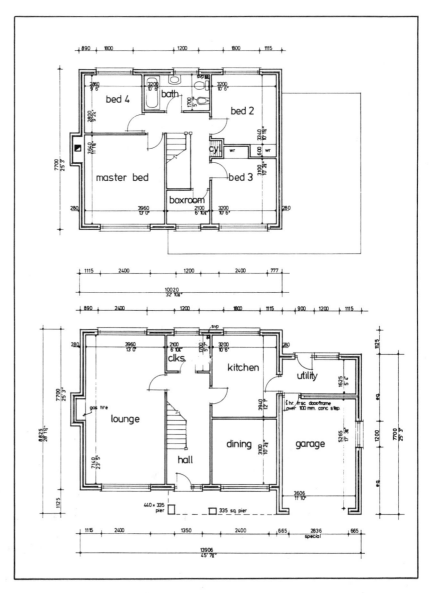

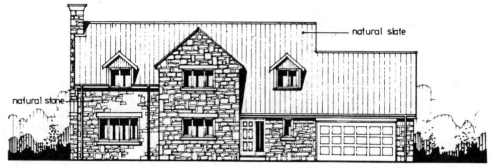

natural slate

natural stone

front elevation

rear

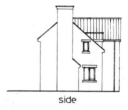

side

garage side

This imposing home is in a style that is best suited to the West or North of the country, and should incorporate the regional stone features appropriate to the county where it is to be built.

Note the playroom over the garage: this can be fitted out as another bedroom with its own bathroom at a later date if required.

en suite

bed 4

bath

bed 3

bed 1

cyl

possible subsequent stud partition

playroom

bed 2

FIRST FLOOR PLAN

lounge

dining

study

utility

kitchen

hall

garage

clks

GROUND FLOOR PLAN

stepped flashing

PLAYROOM

100×50 rafters

purlins

75×225 joists over garage only, (see drg. 2764/4)

GARAGE

UTILITY

SECTION

FRONT ELEVATION

four coarses flemished
bond corbelled out
12mm

150 upstand flashing
+ tray d.p.c

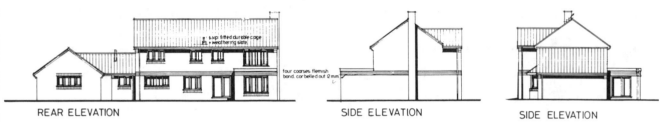

REAR ELEVATION

s.v.p. fitted durable cage
+ weathering slate

SIDE ELEVATION

four coarses flemish
bond. corbelled out 12 mm

SIDE ELEVATION

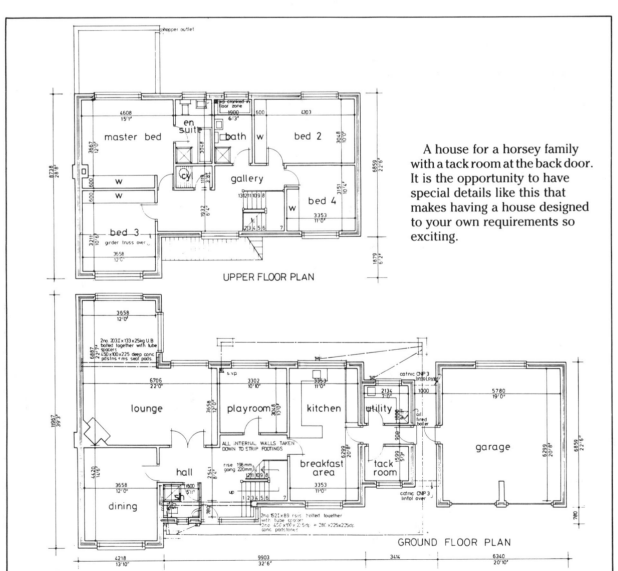

chopper outlet

master bed

en
suite

bath

w

bed 2

4608
15'1"

1900
6'3"

600

4303

3667
12'0"

3048
10'0"

8738
28'8"

600
600

w

w

cy

gallery

bed 4

3151
10'4"

13 12 11 10 9 8

w

3353
11'0"

6859
22'6"

bed 3

girder truss over

3658
12'0"

1932
6'4"

1 2 3 4 5 6

7

3211
10'6"

1879
6'2"

UPPER FLOOR PLAN

A house for a horsey family
with a tack room at the back door.
It is the opportunity to have
special details like this that
makes having a house designed
to your own requirements so
exciting.

3658
12'0"

2no. 203 I x 133 x 25kg U.B
bolted together with tube
spacers
450 x100 x225 deep conc
pad stns + ms. seat pads

catnic CNP 3
lintol over

6887
22'7"

s.v.p.

lounge

playroom

kitchen

utility

garage

6706
22'0"

3302
10'10"

3353
11'0"

2134
7'0"

1000

5780
19'0"

3658
12'0"

3048
10'0"

oil
fired
boiler

11967
39'3"

ALL INTERNAL WALLS TAKEN
DOWN TO STRIP FOOTINGS

6299
20'8"

breakfast
area

tack
room

6299
20'8"

6859
22'6"

4420
14'6"

hall

rise 198 mm
going 220 mm
12 11 10 9 8

1599
5'3"

908

2541
8'4"

3658
12'0"

1800
5'11"

sh

up

1 2 3 4 5 6

7

3353
11'0"

dining

2no. 152 I x 89 risis. bolted together
with tube spacers
2no. 450 x100 x 225 dp. + 2no x225x225 dp.
conc pads stones

catnic CNP 3
lintol over

780

GROUND FLOOR PLAN

4218
13'10"

9903
32'6"

3414

6340
20'10"

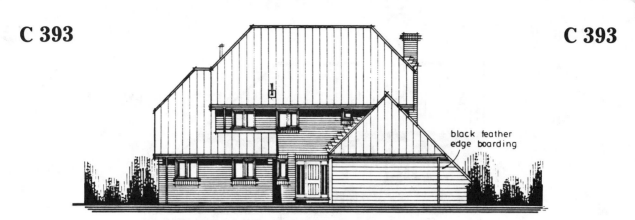

FRONT ELEVATION

SIDE ELEVATION

REAR ELEVATION

Rosemary plain clay
roofing tiles

Ockley Double
Diamond brickwork

Hardwood casement
joinery

black feather
edge boarding

SIDE ELEVATION

black feather
edge boarding

A new farmhouse that takes its character from the use of traditional black feather edge boarding at the gables, with the big car port built in the style of a period cart shed. All very effective, and with a very convenient room layout as well.

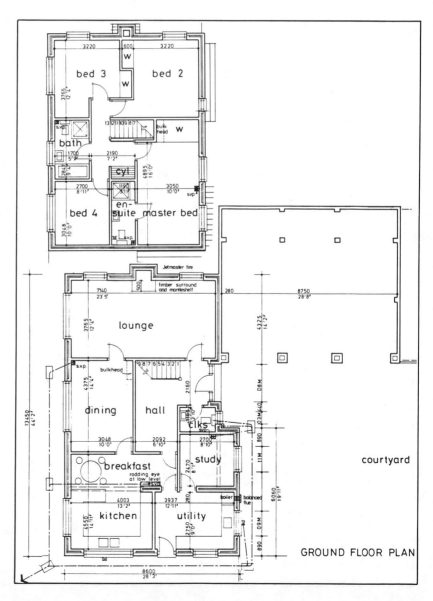

bed 3

bed 2

bath

bed 4

en-suite

master bed

cyl

lounge

Jetmaster fire

timber surround
and mantleshelf

dining

hall

clks

study

breakfast

rodding eye
at low level

kitchen

utility

boiler

balanced
flue

courtyard

GROUND FLOOR PLAN

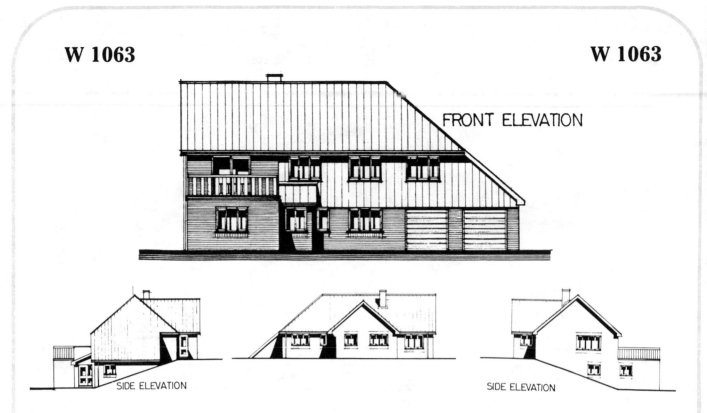

FRONT ELEVATION

SIDE ELEVATION

SIDE ELEVATION

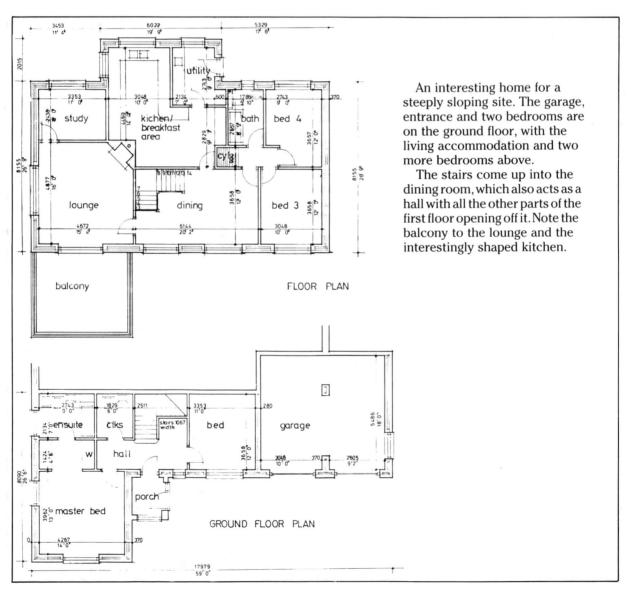

An interesting home for a steeply sloping site. The garage, entrance and two bedrooms are on the ground floor, with the living accommodation and two more bedrooms above.

The stairs come up into the dining room, which also acts as a hall with all the other parts of the first floor opening off it. Note the balcony to the lounge and the interestingly shaped kitchen.

FLOOR PLAN

GROUND FLOOR PLAN

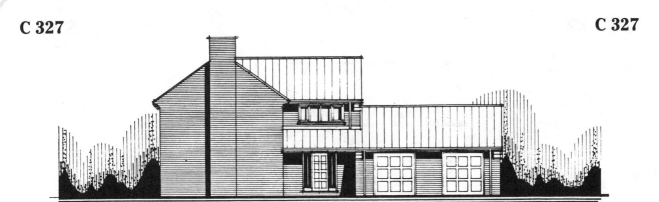

ENTRANCE ELEVATION

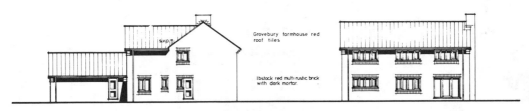

Grovebury farmhouse red
roof tiles

Ibstock red multi rustic brick
with dark mortar.

REAR GARDEN ELEVATIONS

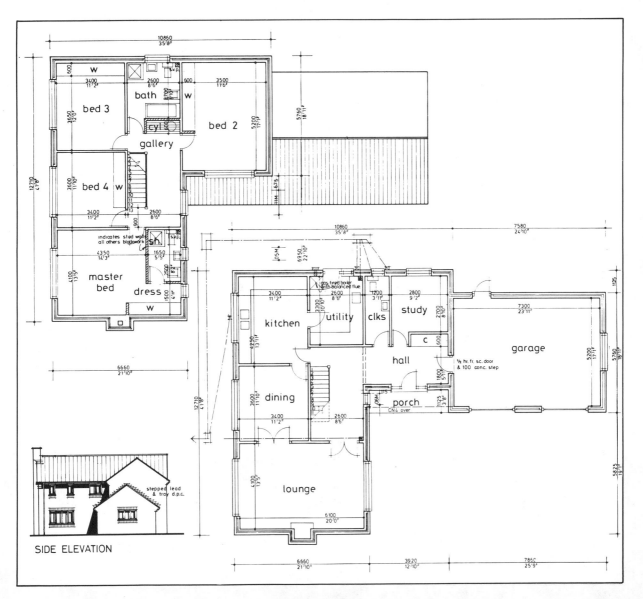

SIDE ELEVATION

front elevation

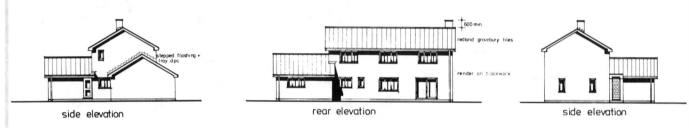

side elevation

stepped flashing + tray dpc

600 min

redland grovebury tiles

render on blockwork

rear elevation

side elevation

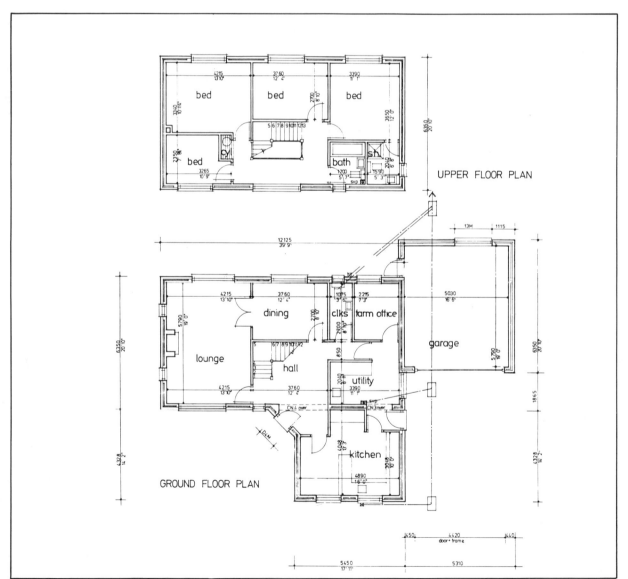

bed

bed

bed

2700
8'10"

3340
10'11"

4215
13'10"

3760
12'4"

3390
11'

3650
12'0"

6350
20'10"

5 6 7 8 9 10 11 12 13

cyl

bath

sh

bed

2730
9'0"

3265
10'9"

1700
5'7"

1590
5'3"

svp

UPPER FLOOR PLAN

12125
39'9"

13M   1115

dining

clks

farm office

5030
16'6"

5790
19'0"

4215
13'10"

3760
12'4"

2700
8'10"

1075
3'6"

2215
7'3"

6350
20'10"

lounge

hall

utility

garage

5790
19'0"

5 6 7 8 9 10 11 12

850

2020

2900
9'6"

1865

4328
14'2"

kitchen

DLM

svp

CN 6 over

CN 3 over

3012
10'0"

3040
10'0"

3390
11'

4890
16'0"

GROUND FLOOR PLAN

4328
14'2"

450   4420   440
door + frame

5450
17'11"

5310

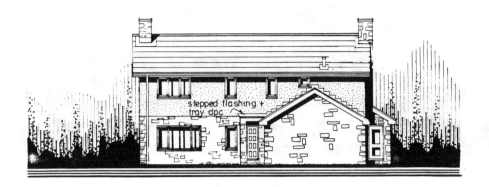

stepped flashing + tray dpc

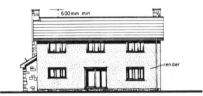

600mm min

render

REAR ELEVATION

Double Roman tile
Somerset Red

150 upstand flashing
& tray dpc

gables & plinth work
Bradstone reconstructed stone

stepped lead flashing
& tray dpc

GABLE ELEVATIONS

This very compact house has the unusual feature of a front entrance set across the angle of an L shaped hall, which helps it to have a very interesting and convenient ground floor layout. In spite of this it is a very straightforward building to construct and has been built many times since D & M first introduced this design in 1979.

It can be built without the garage if required, which enables the study to have a large window looking to the front.

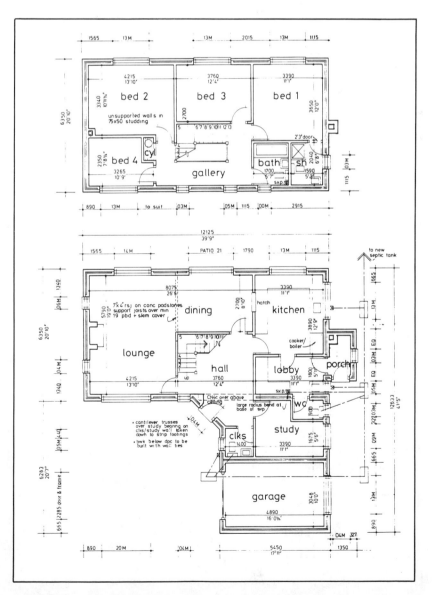

FRONT ELEVATION

REAR ELEVATION   SIDE ELEVATION   SIDE ELEVATION

A clever design for a site where traditional stone features are required, and it combines a traditional external appearance with large rooms inside. The arches to the car port are important and should be built in the traditional style for the area concerned: three centred, five centred, ... you may not know, but the stone mason will. Discuss it with him.

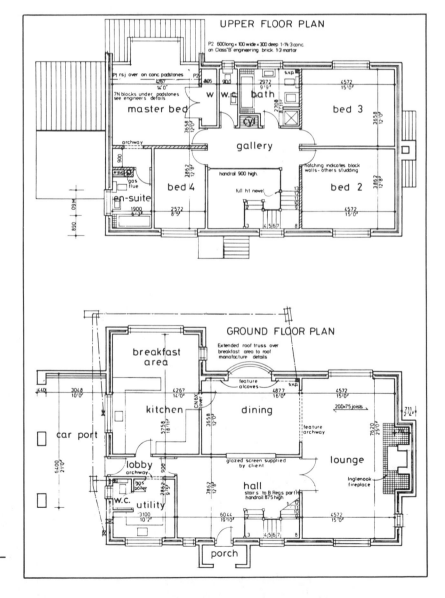

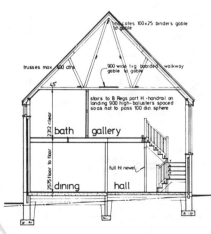

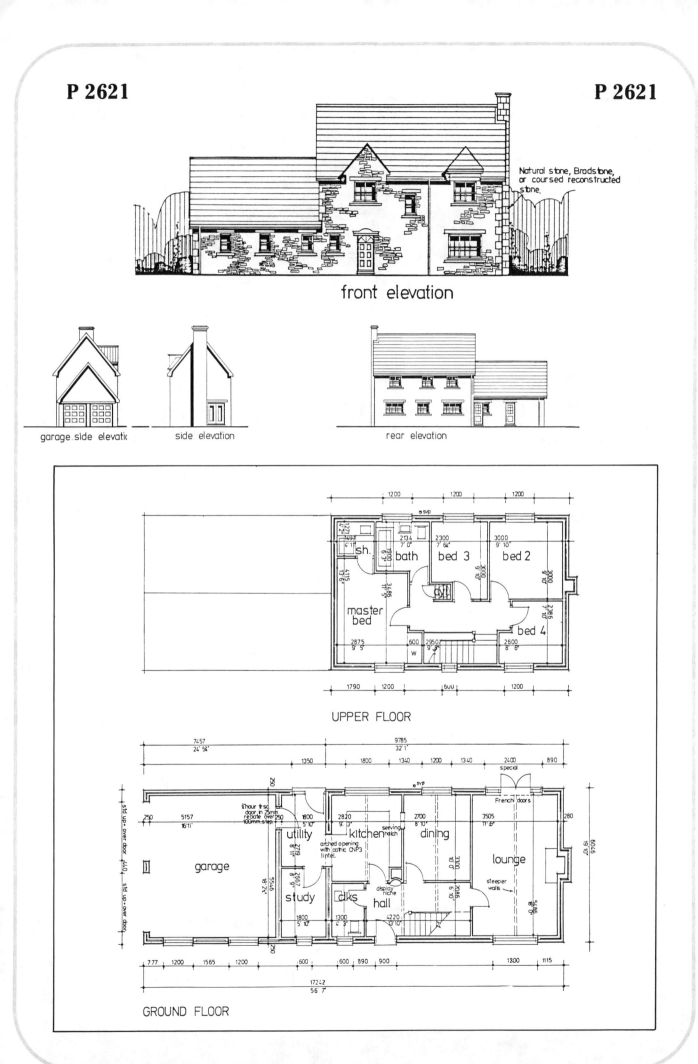

front elevation

garage side elevation

side elevation

rear elevation

Natural stone, Bradstone, or coursed reconstructed stone.

UPPER FLOOR

sh.

bath

bed 3

bed 2

master bed

bed 4

GROUND FLOOR

garage

utility

kitchen

dining

study

clks

hall

lounge

FRONT ELEVATION

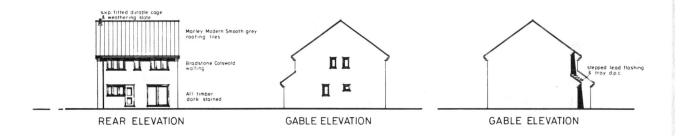

s.v.p. fitted durable cage
& weathering slate

Marley Modern Smooth grey
roofing tiles

Bradstone Cotswold
walling

All timber
dark stained

REAR ELEVATION

GABLE ELEVATION

GABLE ELEVATION

stepped lead flashing
& tray d.p.c.

This is one of the few houses in this book that are deeper than they are wide, and in this design it enables the staircase to be set further back in the building than is usual in a home of this size.

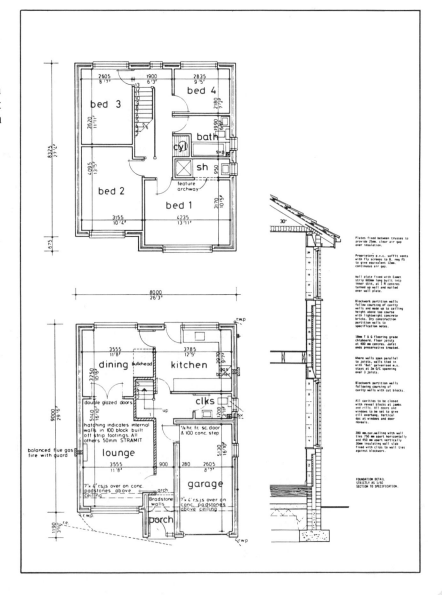

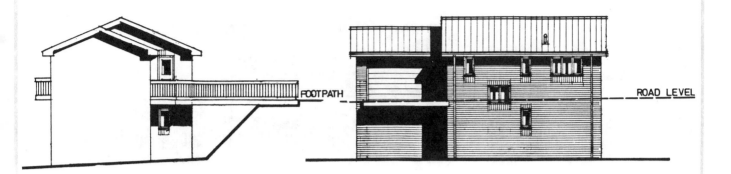

FOOTPATH

ROAD LEVEL

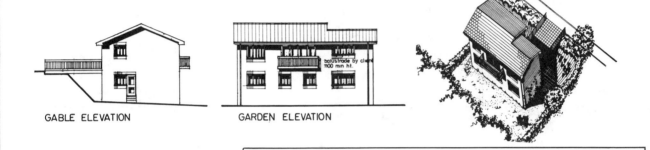

GABLE ELEVATION

GARDEN ELEVATION

What do you do when your building plot is twelve feet below the road? One answer is to build a bridge to a first floor garage as in this clever design by D & M for a site in Sheffield.

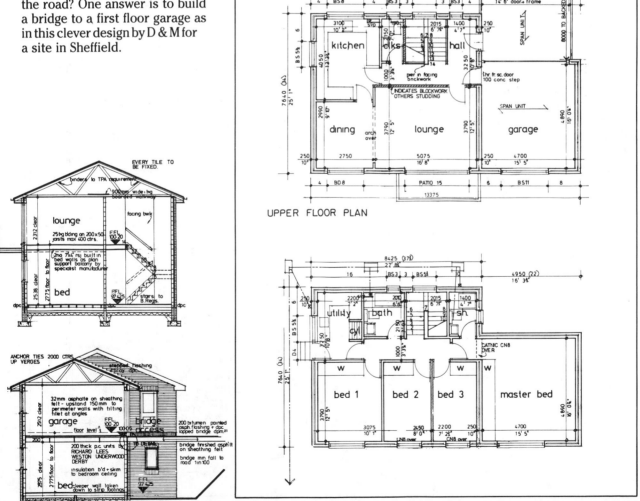

UPPER FLOOR PLAN

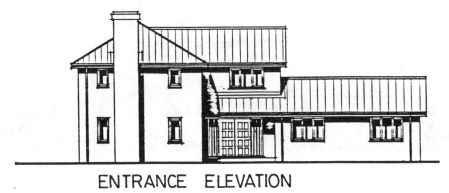

ENTRANCE   ELEVATION

SIDE   ELEVATION

REAR   ELEVATION

SIDE   ELEVATION

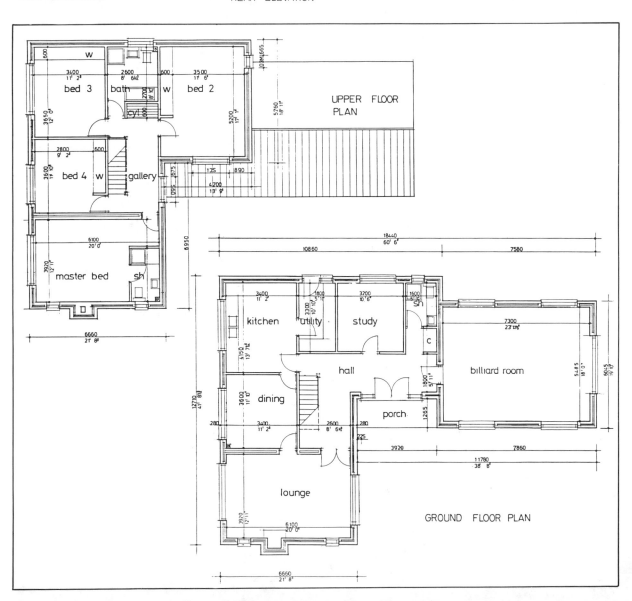

UPPER FLOOR
PLAN

bed 3
bath
cyl
bed 2
w
w

bed 4   w   gallery

master bed   sh

kitchen   utility   study   sh
c
hall   billiard room
dining
porch
lounge

GROUND   FLOOR PLAN

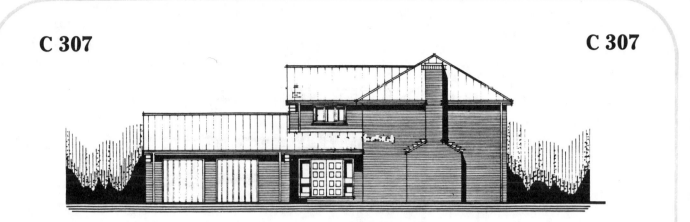

REAR ELEVATION

SIDE ELEVATION

SIDE ELEVATION

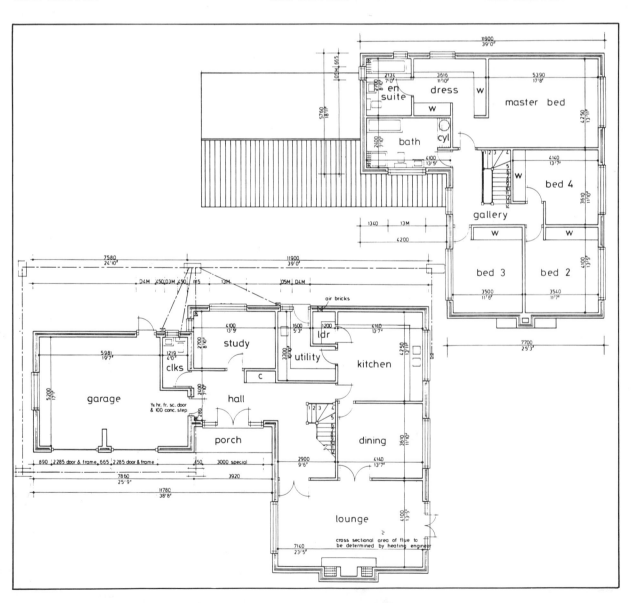

facing bwk. with quoin detail
and flint facing to inset panels.
Brick to be agreed with planning
authority.

vertical tile hanging to
be agreed

front elevation 1·100

rear elevation 1·100

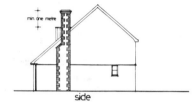

min one metre

side

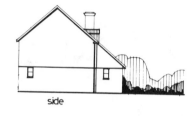

side

The only building in this book to make use of flint as a wall facing material. This is one of the oldest building materials, and certainly the most durable. The way in which it is used varies in different areas, and it is important that it should be incorporated into a building in the traditional local way.

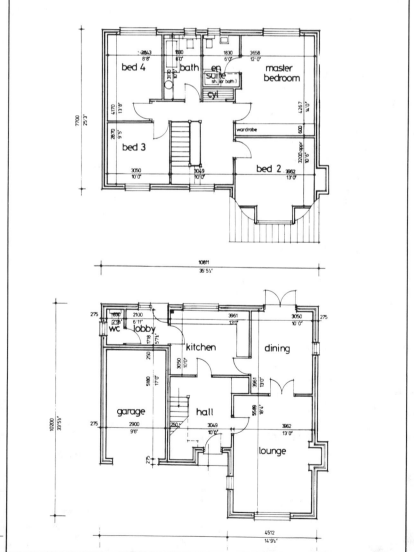

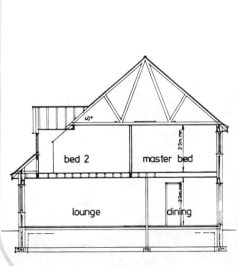

FRONT ELEVATION

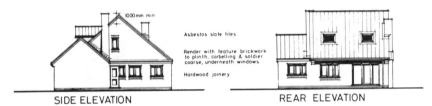

SIDE ELEVATION

Asbestos slate tiles

Render with feature brickwork to plinth, corbelling & soldier coarse, underneath windows

Hardwood joinery

1000 mm min

REAR ELEVATION

SIDE ELEVATION

cheeks & gables to dormers to be dark stained boarding

stepped lead flashing & tray d.p.c.

A dormer bungalow with a number of interesting features. To start with the master bedroom suite is on the ground floor, so that a retired couple need not concern themselves with the upper floor at all except when the family or friends come to stay. This is a feature which many clients ask for when a new home is being designed to their requirements.

Look at the use of glass panelled internal doors, two pairs of them double doors, to give the feel of a much larger property, and to ensure that there is plenty of light in the hall. The landing will also be light and airy thanks to the window at the half landing on the stairs.

Although there are dormers to the front, two sloping velux windows have been used to light the first floor bedrooms at the rear, and this will give substantial cost savings. Whether or not you like these sloping windows in the ceiling is another matter.

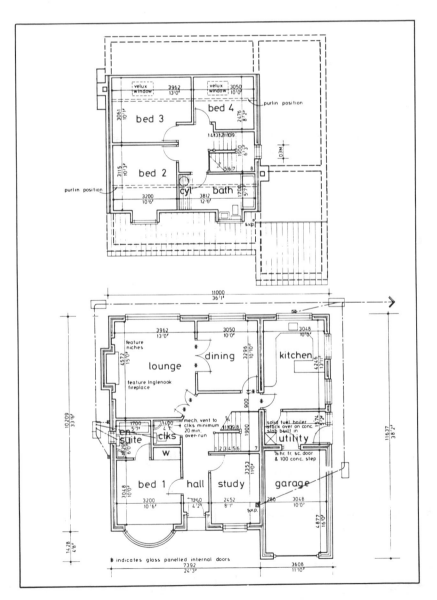

svp fitted durable cage & weathering slate

velux window 3962 13'0"

velux window 3050 10'0"

purlin position

bed 3 3061 10'1"

bed 4 2476 8'2"

1413 3121109

1900 6'3"

purlin position

bed 2 3115 10'3"

5/6/7 8

cyl 3200 10'6"

bath 3812 12'6"

1700 5'7"

1.03m

svp

11000 36'1"

lounge

feature niches 3962 13'0"

dining 3050 10'0"

3396 10'0"

kitchen 3048 10'0"

4572 15'0"

4242 13'11"

feature inglenook fireplace

900

solid fuel boiler stock over on conc. slab built in

1574 5'2"

en suite 1700 5'7" 1400 4'7"

mech. vent to clks minimum 20 min over-run

1300 98

900

1900

utility

10209 33'6"

clks

11637 38'2"

W

123456 7

½ hr. fr. sc. door & 100 conc. step

bed 1 3048 10'0"

hall 7260 4'2"

study 2452 8'1"

3353 11'0"

garage 3048 10'0"

280

4877 16'0"

1428 4'8"

3200 10'6"

svp.

3608 11'10"

* indicates glass panelled internal doors

7392 24'3"

stepped lead flash min pitch 22½°
½ stey d.p.c.

2no 225x150 air bricks
each side of lounge
extension

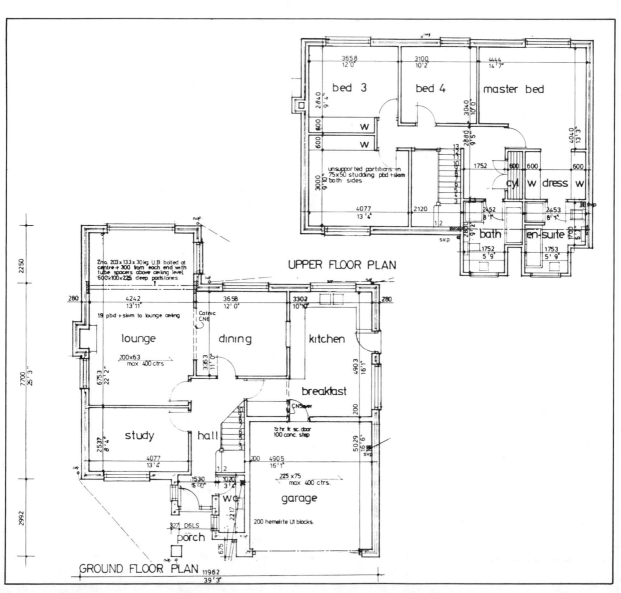

3658
12'0"

3100
10'2"

4444
14'7"

bed 3

bed 4

master bed

2840
9'4"

600

3040
10'0"

4040
13'3"

w

w

2880
9'5"

1752

600

600

600

unsupported partitions in
75x50 studding pbd + skim
both sides

3000
9'10"

cyl

w

dress

w

4077
13'4"

2120

2452
8'1"

2453
8'1"

1 2

bath

en-suite

s.v.p

1752
5'9"

1753
5'9"

UPPER FLOOR PLAN

2250

2no. 203x133x30 kg U.B bolted at
centre + 300 from each end with
tube spacers above ceiling level
600x100x225 deep padstones

280

4242
13'11"

3658
12'0"

3302
10'10"

280

19 pbd + skim to lounge ceiling

Cat nic
CN6

lounge

dining

kitchen

200x63
max 400 ctrs.

6753
22'2"

3653
11'0"

4903
16'1"

breakfast

CN6 over

7700
25'3"

study

hall

½ hr fr sc. door
100 conc. step

5029
16'6"
s.v.p

2537
8'4"

4077
13'4"

200

4905
16'1"

225x75
max 400 ctrs.

1530
5'0"

1020
3'4"

2217

WC

garage

2992

327 D6LS

200 hemelite UI blocks.

675

porch

GROUND FLOOR PLAN

11962
39'3"

front elevation

rear elevation

side elevation

side elevation

Another house with a very large roof slope on the front elevation, so that the choice of roof tiles is most important. Note the irregularly shaped gallery window to the hall: this was the clients choice, and is an interesting feature requiring its own balustrade. An alternative to the window balustrade would have been to have returned the staircase balustrade across to the bedroom door, giving a light well over the front entrance. This would have involved the access to the eaves storage being in the third bedroom over the garage.

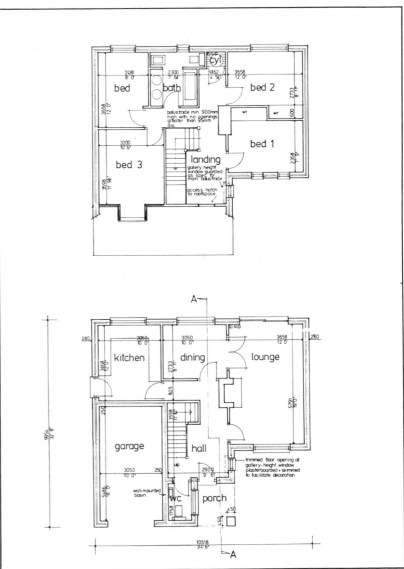

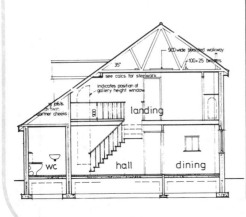

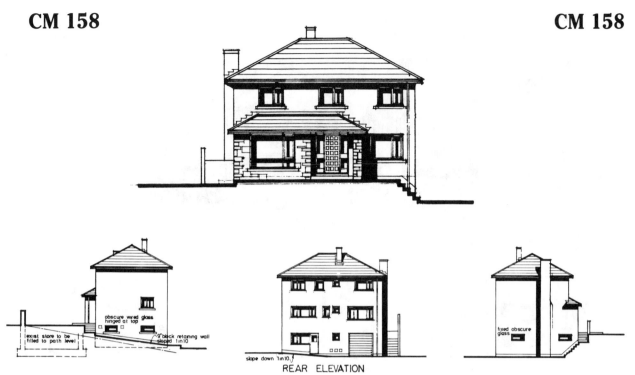

REAR ELEVATION

A house for a sloping site with the garage to the rear, and a great deal of storage in the foundations. The low pitch hip roof has a feel of the 1930s about it, and the window style adds to this, but this house can be built under a modern gable roof with vertical emphasis windows without any difficulty.

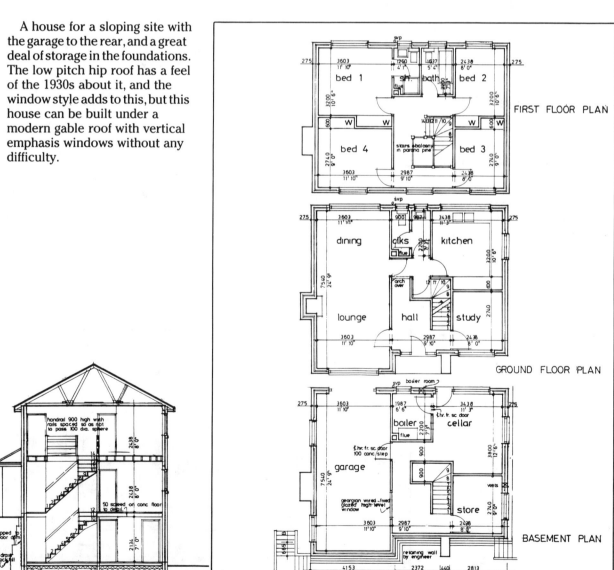

FIRST FLOOR PLAN

GROUND FLOOR PLAN

BASEMENT PLAN

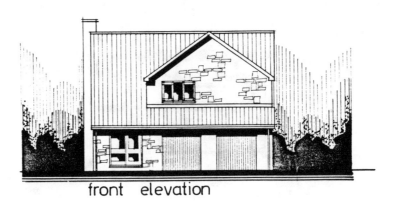

front elevation

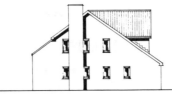

rear elevation

gable elevation

An unusual house for a site with special views, having the living accommodation on the first floor together with the master bedroom suite, and three other bedrooms at ground level. There is a first floor balcony off the lounge, and this is the sort of home that suits a plot of land on the coast, looking out over the sea with access from the back. In this sort of situation the layout is very convenient for those who let out holiday accommodation, as the guests can be on their own on the ground floor.

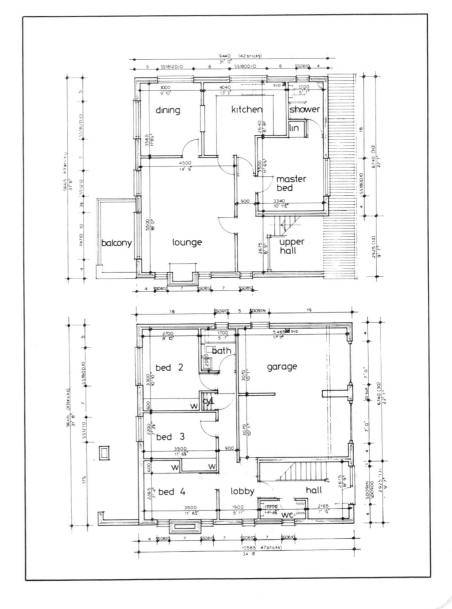

SIDE ELEVATION

REAR ELEVATION

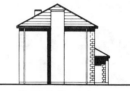

SIDE ELEVATION

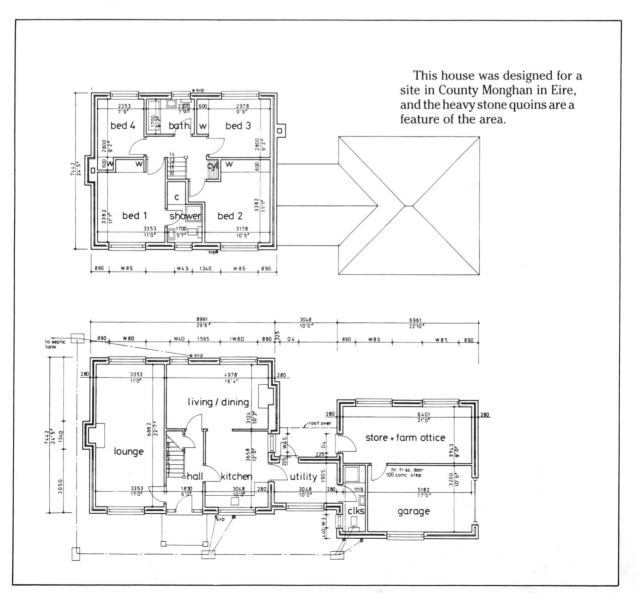

This house was designed for a site in County Monghan in Eire, and the heavy stone quoins are a feature of the area.

front elevation

rear elevation   side elevation   side elevation

The appearance of this interesting home will depend a lot on the roof tiles that are chosen for it. In most parts of the country they will probably be the traditional small 8" x 5" plain tiles, and preferably these should be in mottled colours.

Note that the en-suite bathroom is larger and more lavishly fitted out than the main bathroom — an example of a growing trend.

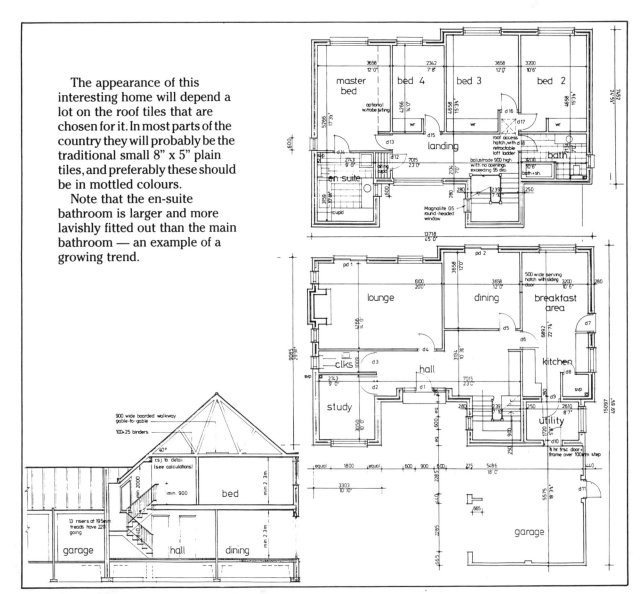

W 1158

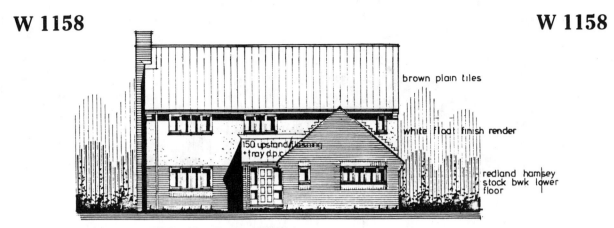

brown plain tiles

white float finish render

150 upstand flashing + tray d.p.c

redland hamsey stock bwk lower floor

FRONT ELEVATION

s.v.p tilted durable cage + weathering slate

rainwater goods to be cast iron

REAR ELEVATION

stepped lead flashing - tray dpc

SIDE ELEVATION

SIDE ELEVATION

A four bedroom home with a particularly large master bedroom, and lots of storage. Most people building to this design will want double doors connecting the lounge to the dining room, instead of having to go through the hall. It is the opportunity to make up your own mind about things like this that makes having a house built to your own design so worthwhile.

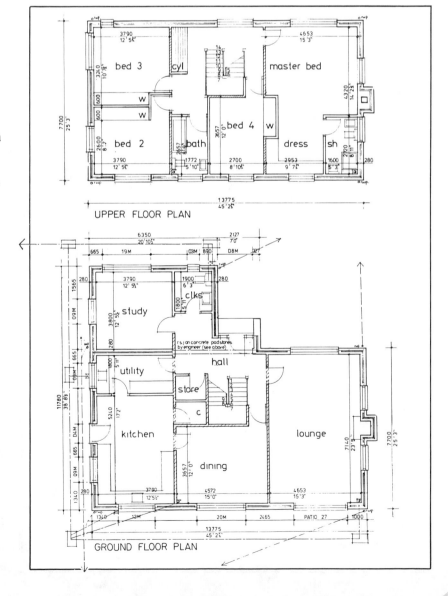

UPPER FLOOR PLAN

GROUND FLOOR PLAN

FRONT ELEVATION

REAR ELEVATION   SIDE ELEVATION   SIDE ELEVATION

Marley Mendip Dark Brown
Granular tiles

Render to upper floor
Bradstone to ground floor

Hardwood casement joinery

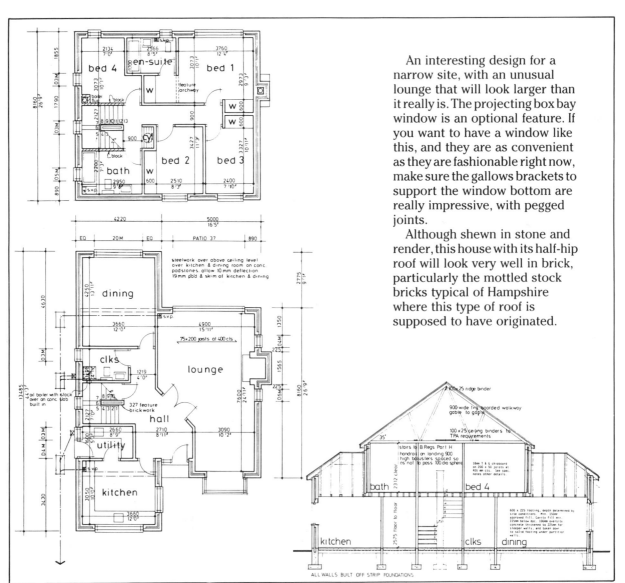

An interesting design for a narrow site, with an unusual lounge that will look larger than it really is. The projecting box bay window is an optional feature. If you want to have a window like this, and they are as convenient as they are fashionable right now, make sure the gallows brackets to support the window bottom are really impressive, with pegged joints.

Although shewn in stone and render, this house with its half-hip roof will look very well in brick, particularly the mottled stock bricks typical of Hampshire where this type of roof is supposed to have originated.

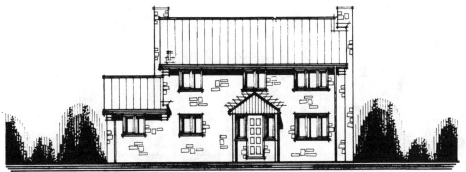

FRONT ELEVATION

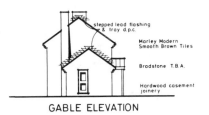

stepped lead flashing
& tray d.p.c.

Marley Modern
Smooth Brown Tiles

Bradstone T.B.A.

Hardwood casement
joinery

GABLE ELEVATION

REAR ELEVATION

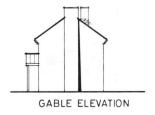

GABLE ELEVATION

A nice conventional four bedroom house of 1310 sq.ft., where the decision was made to have an impressive hall and a stairwell with a gallery above even though this cut down the size of other rooms to some extent. The front porch is shewn here supported on two wooden posts, but the essential is to have the traditional style of front porch in your local area, which may involve dwarf walls, or an open porch gable, or other features.

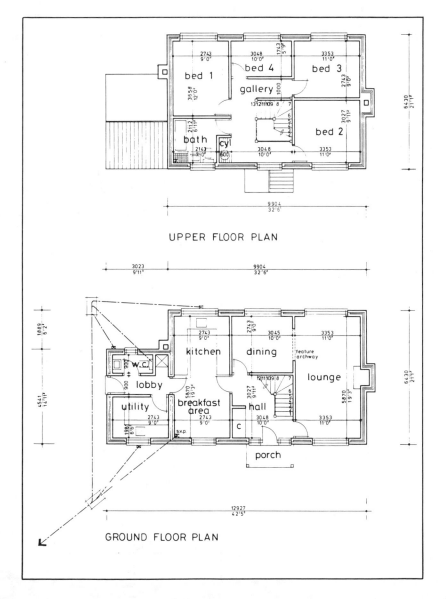

UPPER FLOOR PLAN

GROUND FLOOR PLAN

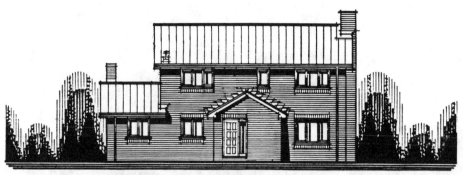

FRONT ELEVATION

SIDE ELEVATION

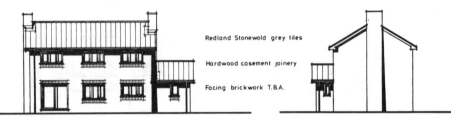

REAR ELEVATION

Redland Stonewold grey tiles

Hardwood casement joinery

Facing brickwork T.B.A.

SIDE ELEVATION

Nearly twenty per cent of the floor area of this four bedroom house is taken up by the large hall and first floor gallery, an area rather larger than the size of the lounge. Is this the right balance? For many people the answer is definitely 'yes', for an impressive hall, with room for furniture, gives a feeling of distinction and gracious living to a new home. Others regard a hall as simply a corridor to connect rooms, and want all the emphasis on the rooms themselves. The choice is yours, and make sure you do make a conscious choice after thinking about it. The two approaches are very different.

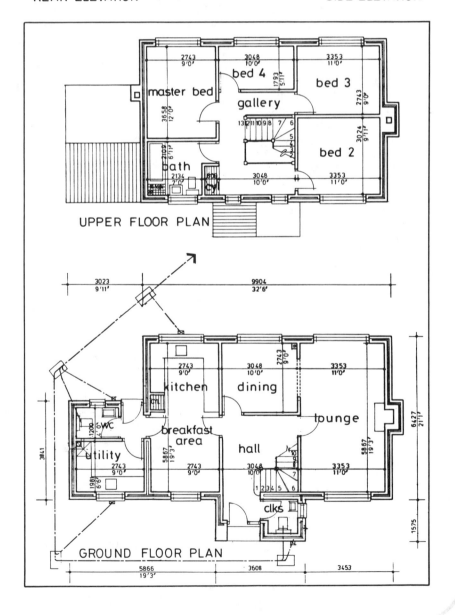

UPPER FLOOR PLAN

GROUND FLOOR PLAN

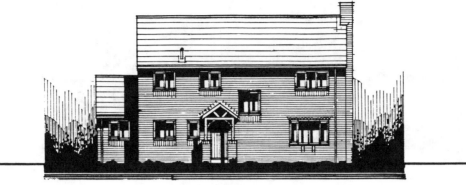

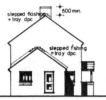

GABLE ELEVATIONS

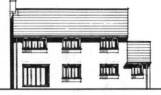

REAR ELEVATION

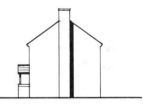

A nice Victorian porch with a matching bow window are the key features on the front of this house, and they must be designed to complement each other. The porch should be built from heavy section timber. This really is important: where timber appears to be holding up an important part of the structure it should be massive, and look as solid as masonry. The difference in cost between a skimpy 4 x 4 post and a solid 8 x 8 one with chamfered corners is negligable in terms of the total cost of the house, and will make a huge difference to the finished building.

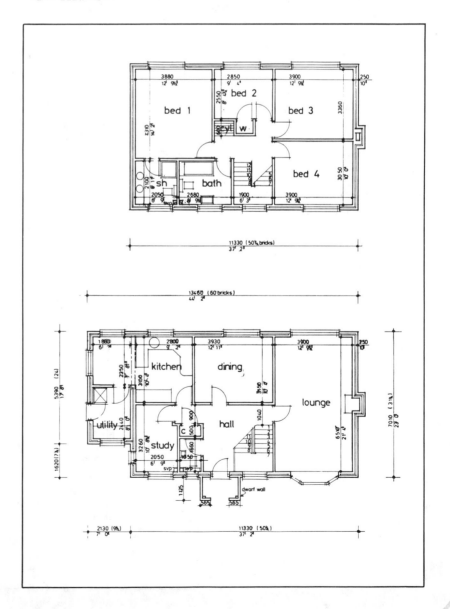

FRONT ELEVATION

REAR ELEVATION   SIDE ELEVATIONS

A lot of careful thought has gone into choosing the materials for this new home: Red Rustic facing bricks from the Elliot brickyard, under Sandtoft Old English pantiles. In the last few years the brick and tile manufacturers have revived many of their old types that they probably thought would never be made again, and it is well worth while looking at them all very carefully. In this house the choice of bricks is to compliment the hardwood joinery as well as the tiles.

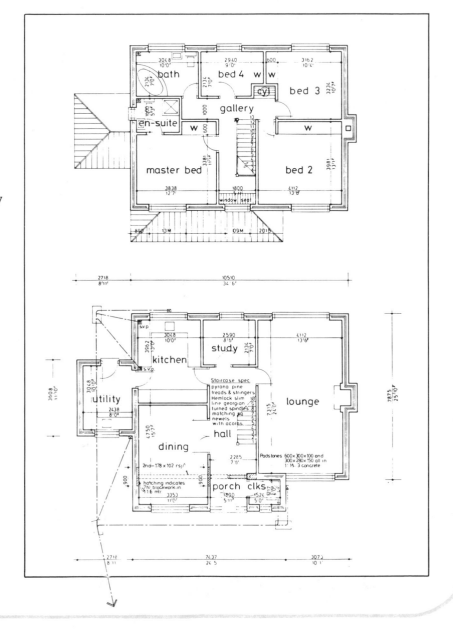

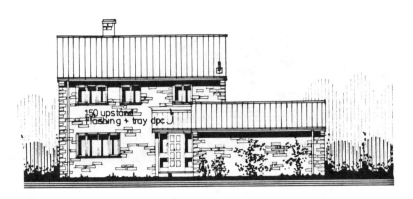

This plan is an interesting example of a design prepared to meet a situation where a garage and a close boarded large gate had to be allowed for in the total scheme of things. The garage door, which is a non-standard width of twelve feet, and the gate were certain to be very prominent features, and so were specified to be diagonally boarded as shewn. They were stained to be a perfect match with the stained windows and doors of the new house, and definitely added to the appearance of the buildings in a very satisfactory way.

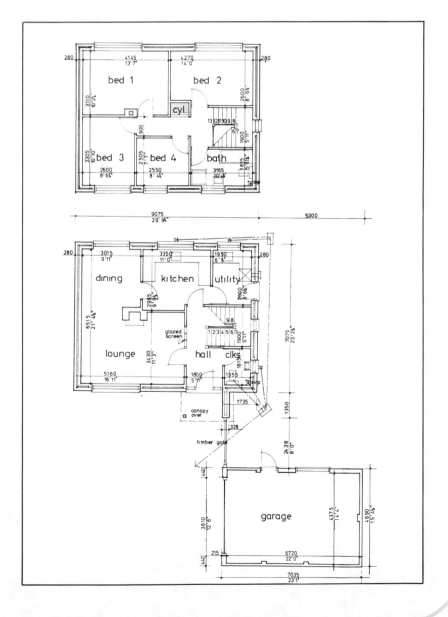

front elevation 1·100

rear elevation

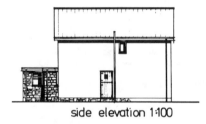

side elevation 1·100

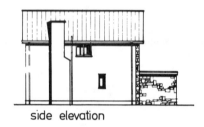

side elevation

Houses with a garage projecting from the front elevation under a flat roof were very popular in the 1960's, and are still appropriate to infill sites where neighbouring properties were built at this time. The style is still fashionable in parts of

Wales, Devon and Cornwall, and looks at its best when built in a mixture of stone and rendered walling as shewn here.

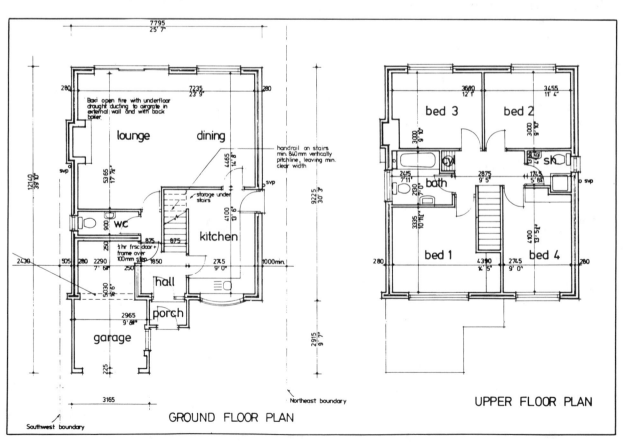

GROUND FLOOR PLAN

UPPER FLOOR PLAN

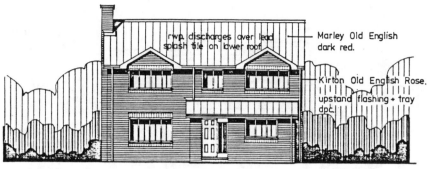

front elevation

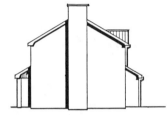

The names of the materials specified for this house demonstrate the designers intentions for the feel of the new home. They are both period types, Butterley Kirton Old English Rose bricks and Marley Old English Tiles. Both brick and tile manufacturers are now making materials that match those used a hundred years ago, with mottled colours and slightly irregular shapes, and they are deservedly popular.

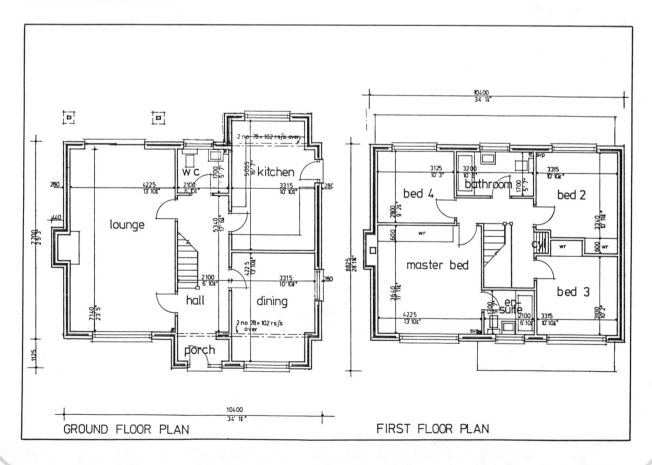

GROUND FLOOR PLAN   FIRST FLOOR PLAN

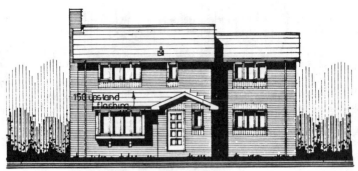

FRONT ELEVATION

REAR ELEVATION

GABLE ELEVATIONS

A home with an unusual kitchen layout, having the back door opening directly into the kitchen, and not into the utility room. It is more usual to have this the other way round, but in this case the client wanted both the back door and the view from the kitchen window to be to the rear.

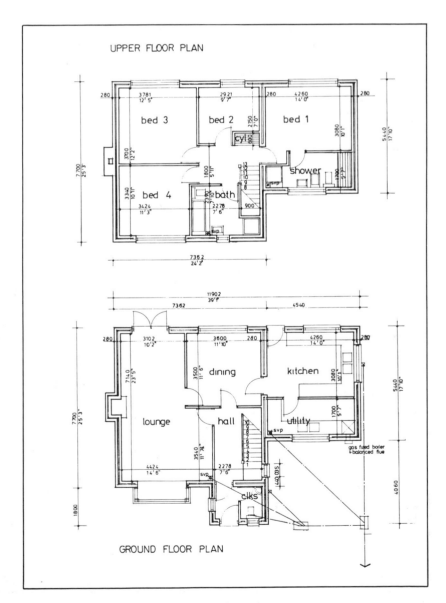

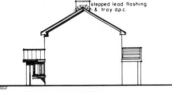

SIDE ELEVATION

REAR ELEVATION

Morley Bold Roll tiles
Mosbrough Red

Brickwork T.B.A
(red/orange mixture)

Hardwood Casement
joinery

SIDE ELEVATION

A staircase that is central in the
first floor landing is unusual,
especially in a house of this size,
but it gives lots of character and
permits a very convenient
bedroom layout. The bay
windows on gallows brackets and
the balcony from the master
bedroom are other attractive
features of this family home.

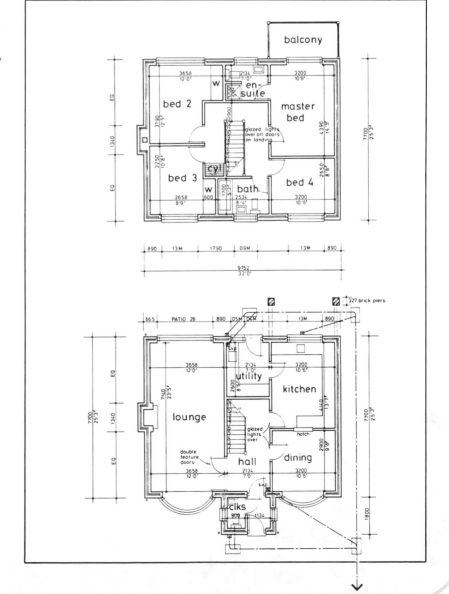

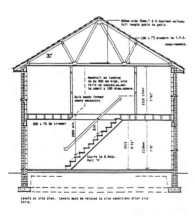

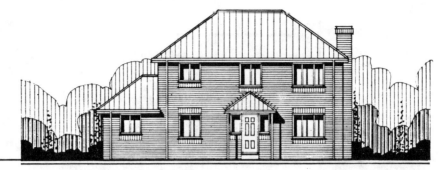

front elevation

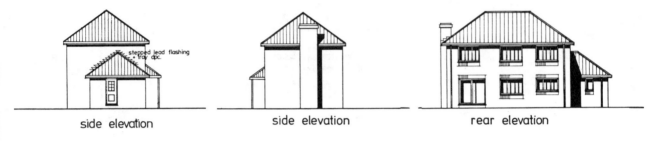

side elevation

side elevation

rear elevation

A very straightforward design for a house with a conventional layout and a hall with a feature staircase.

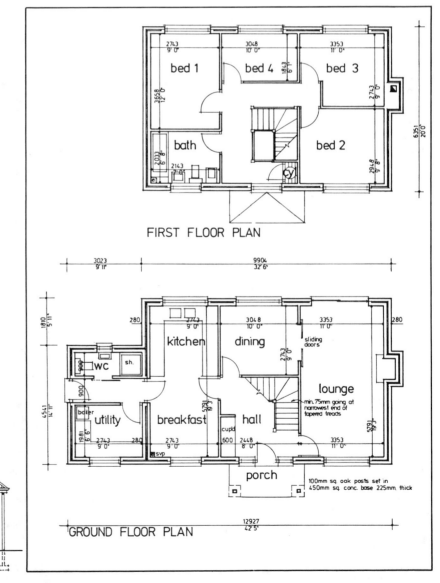

FIRST FLOOR PLAN

bed 1
bed 4
bed 3
bath
bed 2

GROUND FLOOR PLAN

kitchen
dining
sliding doors
WC
sh.
lounge
min. 75mm going at narrowest end of tapered treads
boiler
utility
breakfast
hall
cupd
porch
100mm sq. oak posts set in 450mm sq. conc. base 225mm. thick

stepped lead flashing tray dpc.

bed 4
landing
dining
hall

The Potton Collection

As described at length in earlier pages our domestic architecture has moved from being determined by architectural fashion, or, more often, by what the developers wanted to build, to being determined by what the house buyer wanted. In the last fifteen years there has been a consumer revolution in housing, with the designs of new houses reflecting the ideals and aspirations of the families that were going to live in them. In the forefront of this change has been a Bedfordshire firm called Potton Limited.

Potton's remarkable story started with its Chairman's daughter restoring a cottage in Potton village in 1979, and then finding that it had a value far in excess of a comparable new modern home. This led Pottons' management to realise that people wanted cottage style features from an earlier more leisurely age, and were unable to find them in the austere designs of contemporary new homes. It presented a classic slot in the market, and they had the good fortune to have the resources to meet the challenge. By 1982 a Potton cottage style home was the hit of the Ideal Home Exhibition, and a Potton home now has become a synonym for period style living with modern convenience at the very top of the market.

There are three ranges of Potton homes, of which the original and best known is a Heritage range. Heritage designs are not modern structures with period features, but are based on medieval post and beam construction, with massive structural timbers that are left exposed and give the rooms their own special character. The fifteenth century approach comes from fifteenth century construction techniques and the massive frame permits the walls to be positioned in any required way, with only the stairway and inglenook fireplace as fixed features. How this works in practice for homes built for twenty first century living is described overleaf.

The second range of Potton homes reaches back to the elegance of the traditional Queen Anne house, and is presented as the company's Rectory designs. 18th Century rectories and vicarages, built by wealthy patrons of church livings, epitomised the very best of the restrained elegance of the architecture of the age, and in general have not been altered or 'improved' as widely as other buildings of the period. Potton have based their range of designs in this style on actual surviving buildings of the period, and they are well established as worthy successors of the originals.

Like the 18th Century originals, the Potton rectory homes have load bearing walls, without the post and beams of the Heritage range. Their structures are engineered to the highest standards, and there is no compromise over either materials or design details. These include traditional box sash windows, large entrance halls with staircases that are lit by windows on the half landing, and period fireplaces in classically proportioned rooms. All this conveys the elegance of a bygone era.

Finally, Potton have recently launched a range of budget homes to take their philosophy of home design into a lower price bracket. These Shire homes have well balanced proportions, attention to detail and light and airy rooms with modern layouts that retain a cosy cottage feel. There are inglenook fireplaces, exposed brick features and lots of natural wood to create a warm and friendly atmosphere. Like all the Potton homes they are very energy efficient and designed for low heating bills.

House and bungalow designs from these ranges which are shown on the following pages are the copyright of Potton Limited. They are not available from Plan Sales Services like the other designs in this book, and enquiries for them should be addressed to Potton Limited at The Old Foundry, Willow Road, Potton, Nr. Sandy, Bedfordshire, SG19 2PP.

*Gransden design home with traditional
Essex pargetting in bold relief on
the plaster work.*

Aisle frame construction.

HERITAGE COTTAGES

Brick and Welsh slate

The Heritage designed houses are based on aisle frame construction, traditional in concept and appearance but modified to take advantage of modern timber technology. The huge timber posts and beams of seasoned timber are on a scale not seen in British architecture for hundreds of years until re-introduced by Potton in the early 80's, and they immediately put a stamp of authenticity on these remarkable homes.

The strength of the structure of a Heritage home comes from the massive timbers of the aisles, as seen in the drawing opposite. By using cantilever cross frames to carry all first floor construction, the external flank walls are very lightly loaded, so that rearrangement of walls or doors, or even subsequent alterations and extensions to the whole building are a relatively simple matter.

The main frames and end walls enclose a series of 3.4 metre square spaces, extended on each side by the 'aisles'. The squares are either joined directly, one to another, to make large rooms, or are linked and articulated by the standard stair and fireplace bays.

The development of the designs on the following pages from these basic units is seen in the drawings in the margin.

To be seen at its best a Heritage home has to reflect the traditional building materials of the area in which it is built, and this can involve hand made bricks and peg tiles, plaster and pantiles, or many other possible combinations of materials. All can be accommodated within the Heritage design concept, and can be used in ways which are totally in character while conforming in all respects to modern building regulations and the best of contemporary building practice.

Stone and stone slates

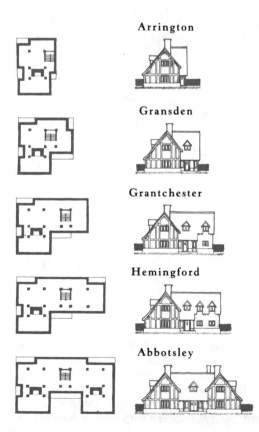

Arrington

Gransden

Grantchester

Hemingford

Abbotsley

Render and peg tiles

Most Heritage homes are built with inglenook fireplaces that give enormous character to the main living accommodation. Only in one respect are they less than authentic; built in under-floor air ducts with deep ashpans ensure that the fire is always bright and easy to keep clean. Appropriate arrangements can be made for wood burning stoves or other modern appliances to suit todays concern with energy conservation.

As is seen from the sketches on the previous page, the inglenook, together with the stairs, is an essential component in the modular build up of these homes, just as they were five hundred years ago.

Gransden home by Potton, with a double garage

Caxton E design

THE
G R A N S D E N . A

The Gransden four bedroomed home has become the best known of all the Potton Heritage designs since it first caused a stir at the Ideal Home Exhibition in 1981. The design illustrated is the original, but a number of variants of the design concept have been developed to meet individual requirements and the characteristics of sites on which they have been built. Another version known as Gransden E appears as the last of the Heritage design homes featured in this book, and has proved equally popular.

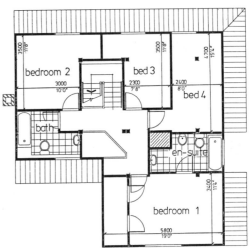

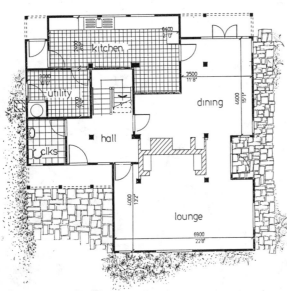

Together with a number of other Heritage design homes, the Gransden can be inspected at the Potton Show House Complex within five minutes drive of the A1 in Bedfordshire, and was in fact the original house to be constructed there.

THE
G R A N T C H E S T E R

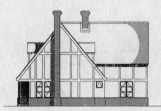

This generously proportioned five bedroomed house has all the usual features of the Heritage range, including the long first floor gallery overlooking the entrance hall, which is generously proportioned and virtually a room in its own right. As is becoming very common with larger homes today, the bathroom which is en suite with the master bedroom is very fully equipped, and is larger than the family bathroom; perhaps this reflects consideration of who paid for the house anyway!

The huge inglenook fireplace in the lounge backs onto another fireplace in the dining room with which it shares a common chimney, and the chimney breast in the dining room has two alcoves which lend themselves to a variety of uses.

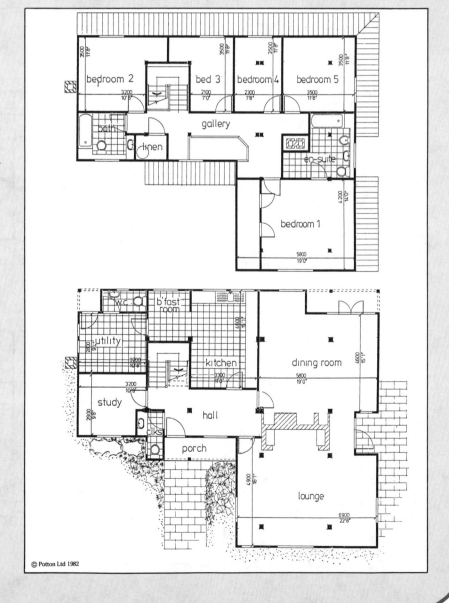

© Potton Ltd 1982

THE

E L T I S L E Y

The Eltisley can be built either with or without the conservatory shown on the drawing here. The square rooms provide generous accommodation in a relatively small house, which looks significantly larger than it really is due to the combination of brickwork and exposed timbers.

The stairs are lit by a window on the landing above, and there is room for a small writing desk or sewing table on the landing which gives a spacious feel to the first floor of this compact home.

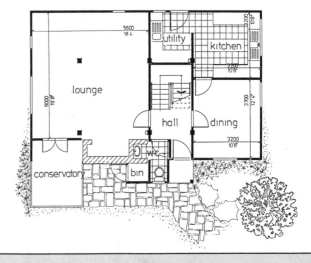

© Potton Ltd 1982

The Potton Collection

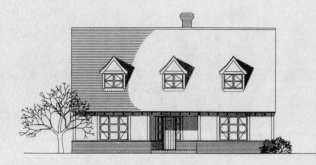

THE

COMBERTON

A rectangular layout is essentially easier and cheaper to build than a more complex structure, and the Comberton design in the Heritage range of houses from Potton is no exception. However, the recessed porches and the three dormers help to avoid a boxy feel, and inside there is remarkably generous accommodation. The large study is a feature which will appeal to many.

This traditional 'rooms in the roof' style requires that the first floor gallery is lit by having glazed lights over the bedroom doors, and the bathroom requires mechanical ventilation unless the site lends itself to velux roof lights in the bathroom and above the stairs.

The kitchen is very generously proportioned for a house of this size, and is well suited to fitting out in the fashionable 'farmhouse kitchen' style.

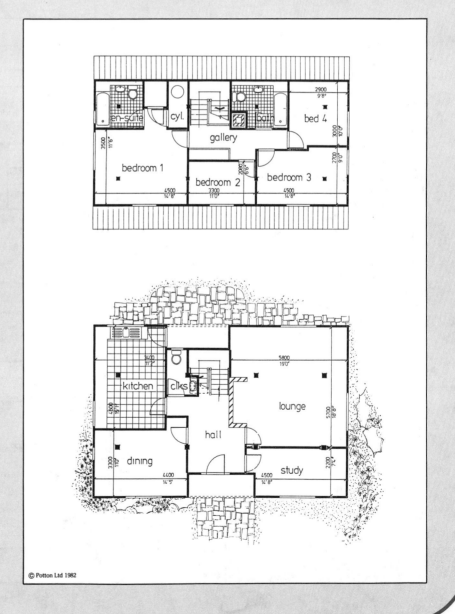

© Potton Ltd 1982

THE

A R R I N G T O N . A

This three bedroomed house has an interesting layout, and can be accommodated on a very narrow plot as none of the key windows look out to the sides. The stairs are well lit, with windows in both the hall and the gallery above, and this gives a spacious impression on entering the front door. The long thin kitchen is essentially a cook's workshop, with little room for anything else, so that the ground floor layout shown is for a family that prefers not to eat in the kitchen. Alternatively, as with all the designs in the Potton collection, the interior walls can be re-arranged.

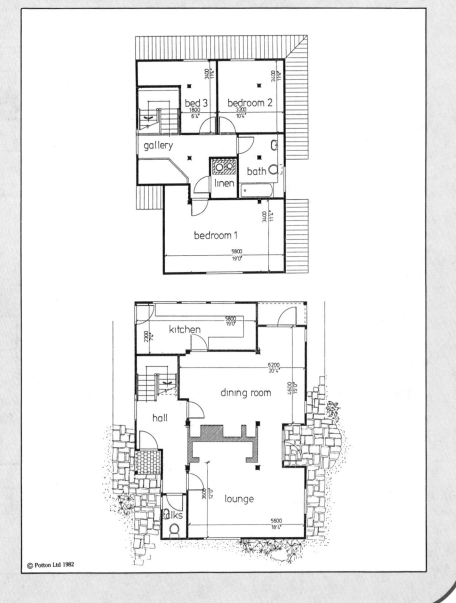

© Potton Ltd 1982

The Potton Collection

THE

ARRINGTON B

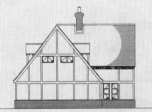

This is a very popular variation on the original Arrington design incorporating an integral garage and additional bedroom accommodation. As shown here some space has been taken up at the back of the garage to provide a utility room, but for those who value outside storage space this can be dispensed with.

The right choice of garage door for a property like this is always most important, and to some extent this will depend on where the house is to be built. The sketch above suggests a timber boarded door, while the elevation drawing shows one in metal; in practice the choice is very wide, and should be made after considering all the options very carefully indeed. As always, it is important that the choice is made after you have seen actual doors of the sort that are of interest, and not from catalogues.

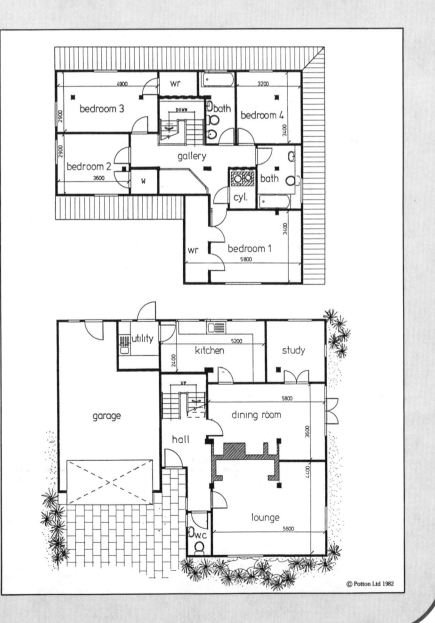

© Potton Ltd 1982

THE
H E M I N G F O R D

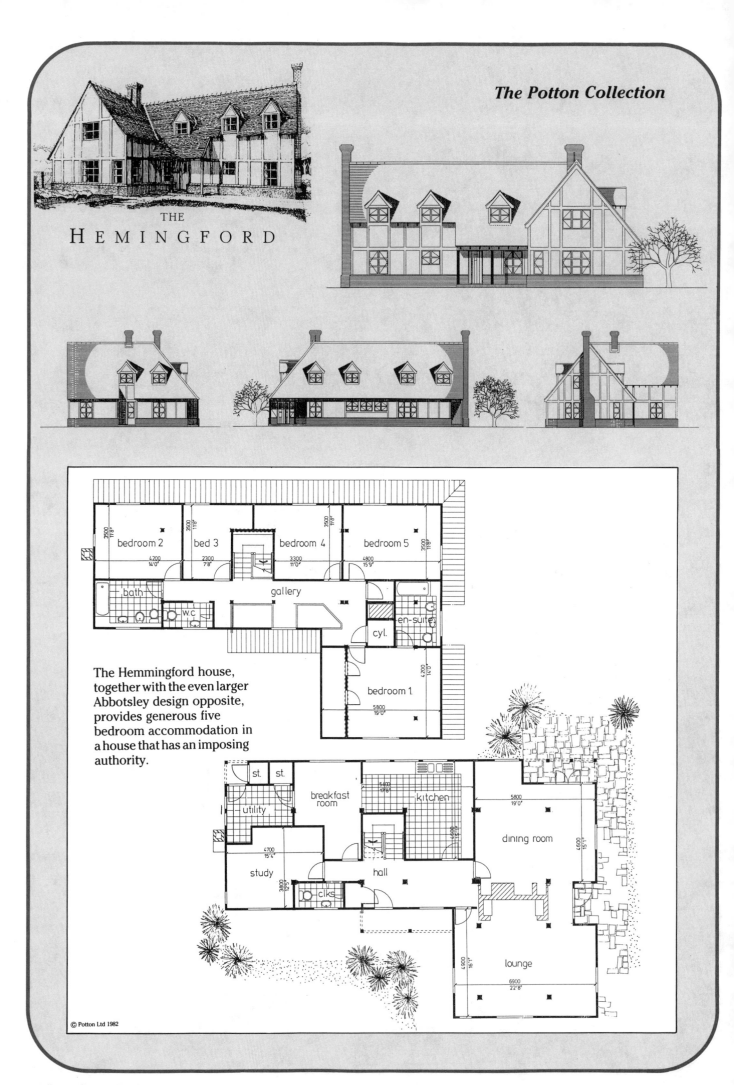

The Hemmingford house, together with the even larger Abbotsley design opposite, provides generous five bedroom accommodation in a house that has an imposing authority.

bedroom 2   bed 3   bedroom 4   bedroom 5

3500 11'8"

4200 14'0"   2300 7'8"   3300 11'0"   4800 15'9"

bath   w.c   gallery   en-suite

cyl.

bedroom 1

4200 14'0"

5800 19'0"

st.   st.

breakfast room   kitchen

5400 17'8"

5800 19'0"

utility

4700 15'4"

4600 15'1"

dining room

study   hall

3800 12'5"

clks

4900 16'1"

lounge

6900 22'8"

© Potton Ltd 1982

The Potton Collection

THE
A B B O T S L E Y

This is the stately home of the Heritage range, with the feeling of the traditional 'E' shaped plan of the Elizabethan manor house. There are no fewer than four fireplaces, serving the lounge, the dining room, the morning room and the study. The boiler has its own seperate chimney, providing the forest of chimney stacks which is so typical of period houses of this size.

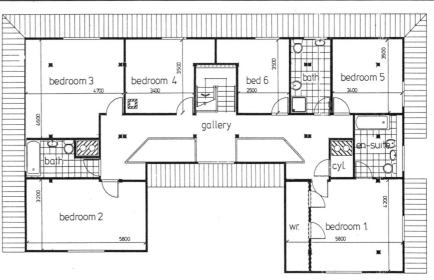

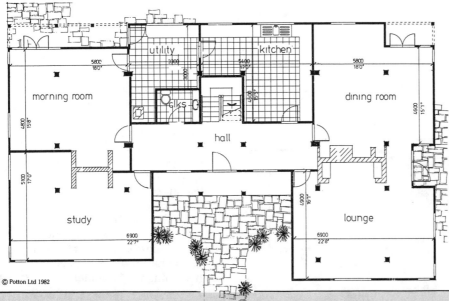

© Potton Ltd 1982

The arrangement illustrated provides six bedrooms, three of which are generous doubles, and three bathrooms. Other arrangements are of the first floor accommodation can be discussed.

As with all the larger Potton Heritage design homes, the hall is lit by a classic gallery, which in this case has two matching ends.

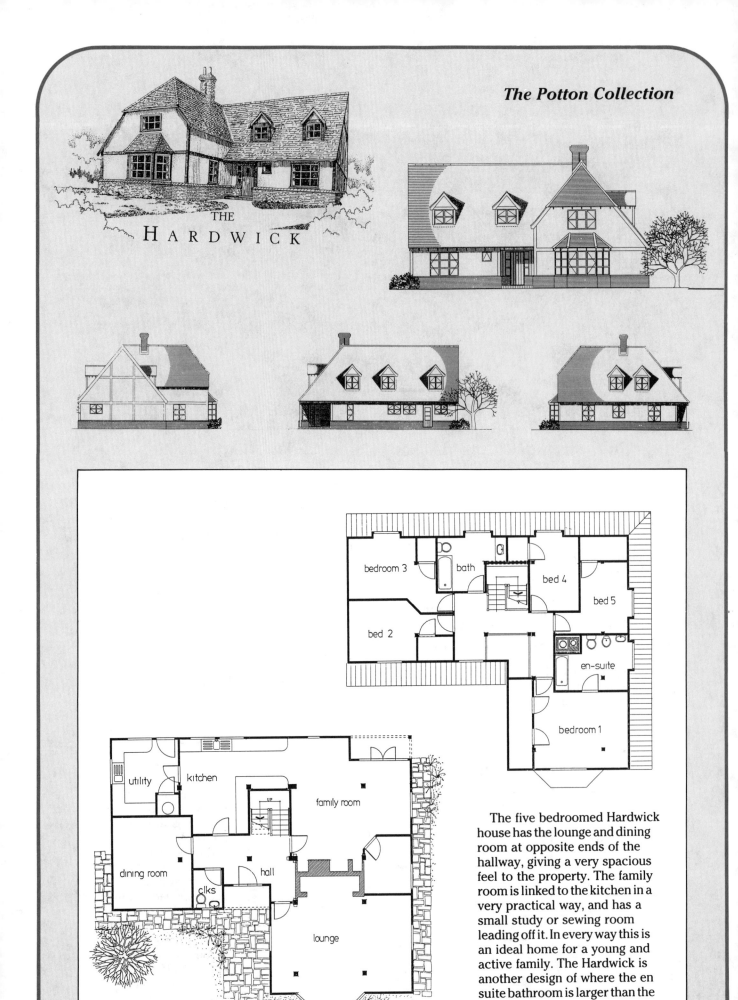

The Potton Collection

THE
H A R D W I C K

bedroom 3   bath   bed 4

bed 5

bed 2

en-suite

bedroom 1

utility   kitchen

family room

dining room   hall

clks

lounge

© Potton Ltd 1982

The five bedroomed Hardwick house has the lounge and dining room at opposite ends of the hallway, giving a very spacious feel to the property. The family room is linked to the kitchen in a very practical way, and has a small study or sewing room leading off it. In every way this is an ideal home for a young and active family. The Hardwick is another design of where the en suite bathroom is larger than the family bathroom, which is becoming very popular.

The Potton Collection

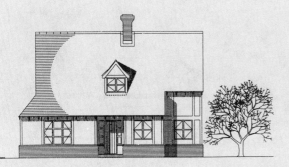

THE
C A X T O N . A

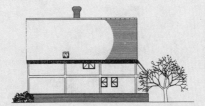

This is another versatile design concept which has a large number of variants. The version shown, which Potton know as Caxton A, has a very interesting ground floor room layout with an angled fireplace in the lounge. Other variants provide for the large inglenook fireplace which is so popular with those who build a Potton home.

The Caxton is 1420 square feet, and is a particularly economical house to build.

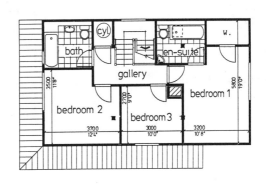

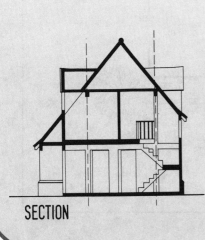

SECTION

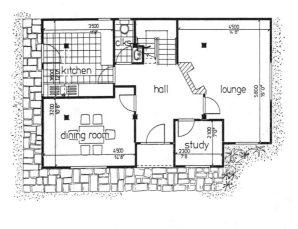

THE
HATLEY

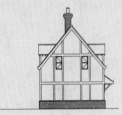

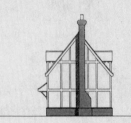

The Hatley design, together with the Gamlingay design shown on the opposite page, are the smallest cottages in the Heritage range. Nevertheless they incorporate many of the features of the larger houses, and have the unmistakable Potton stamp on them.

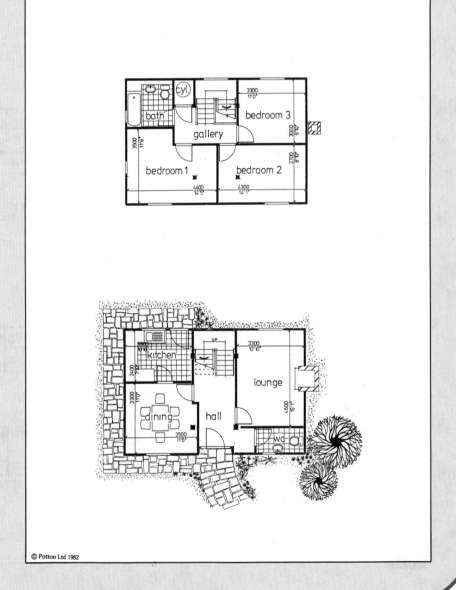

© Potton Ltd 1982

The Potton Collection

THE
GAMLINGAY

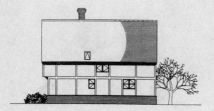

The Gamlingay cottage has an interesting angled hall which permits a small study to be incorporated into the ground floor layout. The hall is well lit by a window on the half landing of the stairs, and the whole property has the feel of a much larger home.

If the Gamlingay is to be built on a narrow site the building regulations will probably require that the windows in the end walls are moved into the front and back elevations. This does not present any problems at all, and the dormer windows that will then be required for bedrooms one and two will add further interest to the appearance of this attractive cottage.

The area of this compact cottage is 1290 square feet.

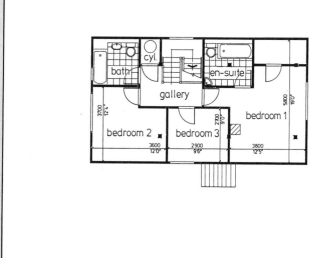

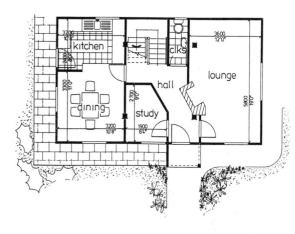

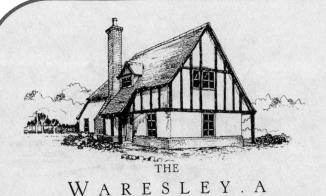

THE
W A R E S L E Y . A

The Waresley is another design with a huge external chimney breast behind the inglenook fireplace. Not only is this an attractive feature in its own right, having the effect of making the house look larger than it really is, and is also absolutely in the character of small 16th C. homes built with timber frames.

The first floor gallery has its own window, with room for a small piece of furniture below, and a Waresley home has all of the feel and atmosphere of the larger houses in the Heritage range.

The Waresley A is 1430 square feet.

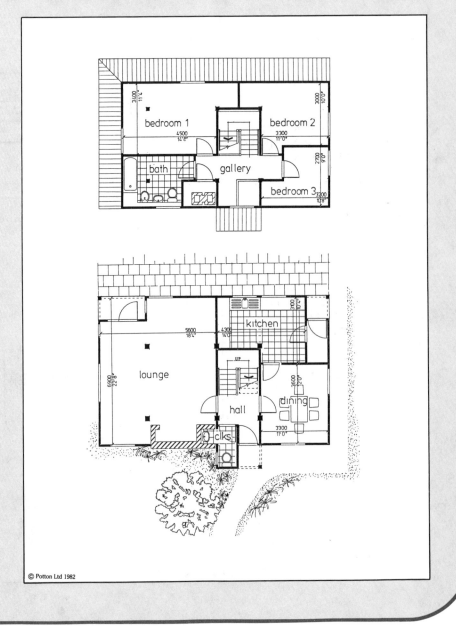

The Potton Collection

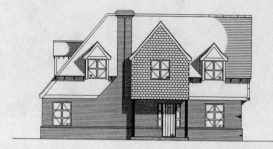

THE
WARESLEY B

At 1750 square feet this popular derivative of the Waresley design concept is much larger than the original version featured on the opposite page, and features a fourth bedroom, or alternatively a sitting room or study, constructed in the large dormer which is jettied out over the entrance door.

A corresponding dormer to the rear elevation permits an en suite bathroom to the master bedroom suite. Note how the chimney from the inglenook fireplace is used to warm the first floor airing cupboard.

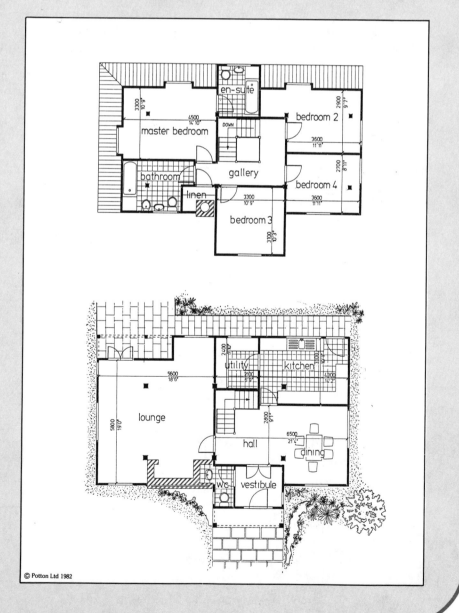

© Potton Ltd 1982

THE
A S H L E Y

Soon after the Heritage range of Potton homes was introduced the company received many requests for a four bedroomed Heritage house that could be fitted onto a ten metre wide plot. The Ashley house is the result of this, and provides a double garage, generous living accommodation including a small first floor study, four bedrooms and two bathrooms. It retains the character of the Potton homes designed for larger plots in rural areas and enables a prestige property to be built in an area where land is at a premium.

In spite of all the constraints of the limited overall width, it has been possible to provide the first floor gallery with its own window which lights the stairway and hall in a way more usually found in a far larger property.

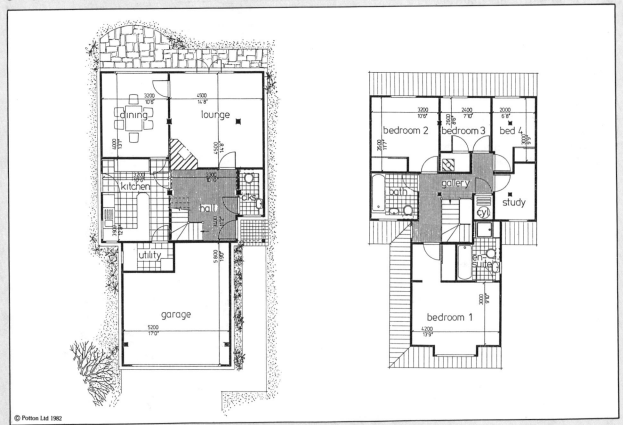

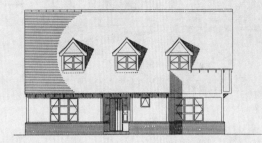

THE

C A X T O N . E .

This variant of the popular Caxton design has three dormers on the front elevation instead of the single dormer to the Caxton A, and a different layout with four bedrooms instead of three. There are still both en suite and family bathrooms.

Note that the plan shows the fireplace and chimney in the rear wall of the lounge, while the artists sketch shows it in the gable end wall, and with the whole cottage built to the opposite hand. All the Potton designs can be built in mirror image in this way, and whether or not to ask for your plans to be drawn to one hand or the other deserves very careful consideration when relating a design to your plot.

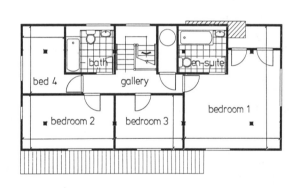

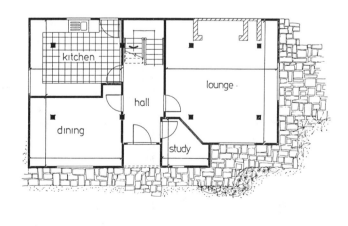

© Potton Ltd 1982

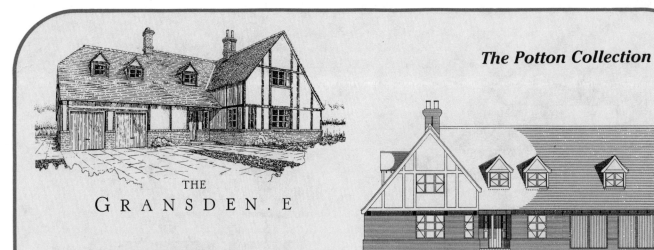

THE
G R A N S D E N . E

The Potton Collection

The Gransden E house is a larger version of the original Gransden design with which we introduced this collection of Potton houses. The increase in the external dimensions permits a study on the opposite side of the hall to the lounge, providing peace and quiet in a family house! This rearrangement permits the front door to be completely recessed in a porch, adding further interest to this design which is so typical of all that has given the Potton Heritage range of homes their reputation.

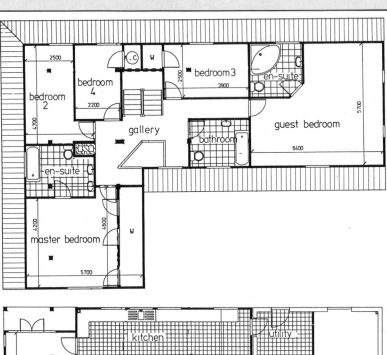

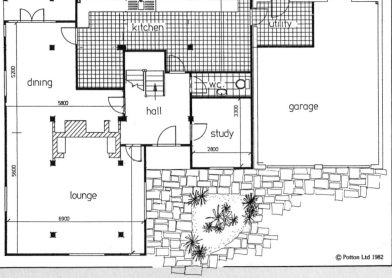

© Potton Ltd 1982

RECTORY HOUSES

*An elegant Queen Anne style home in a tranquil setting to introduce the
Potton Rectory designs*

RECTORY HOUSES

There are five designs in the Potton Rectory range of Queen Anne style houses, and all are immediately recognisable as being absolutely perfect modern interpretations of the spirit of the best of the 18th Century originals. Ranging in size from 1530 square feet to over 3000 square feet, they can suit either a site in a village street or small town, or will stand alone in landscaped grounds. Like the originals, they are designed for connoisseurs, and as with the originals there is no compromise on any of the details.

The drawing room in one of the larger Rectory Homes

Rear view of a Milchester design home.

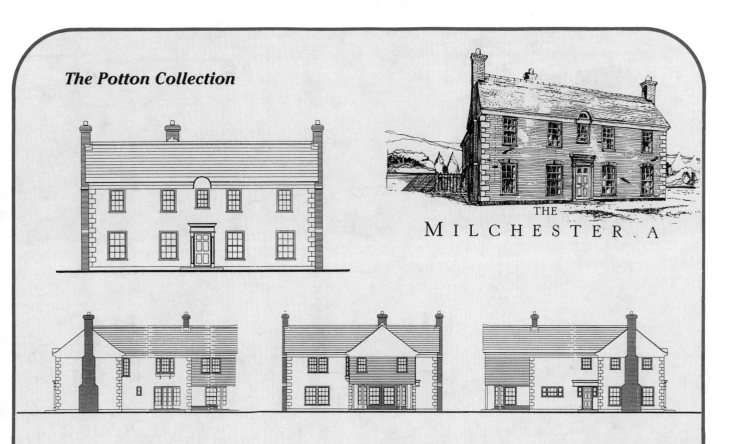

THE
M I L C H E S T E R . A

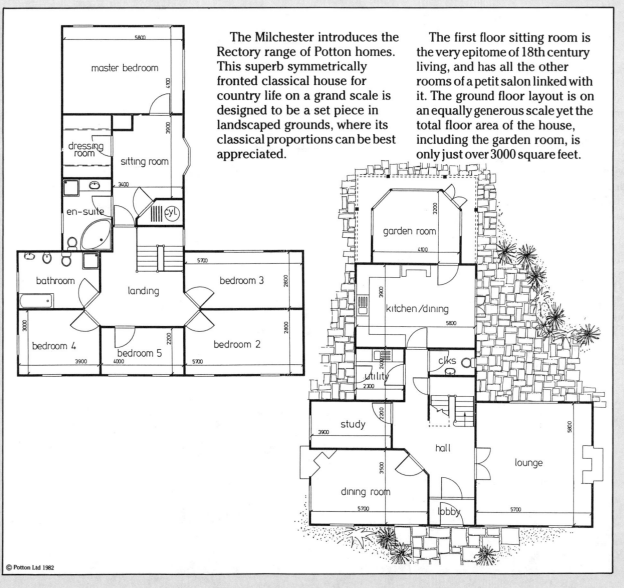

The Milchester introduces the Rectory range of Potton homes. This superb symmetrically fronted classical house for country life on a grand scale is designed to be a set piece in landscaped grounds, where its classical proportions can be best appreciated.

The first floor sitting room is the very epitome of 18th century living, and has all the other rooms of a petit salon linked with it. The ground floor layout is on an equally generous scale yet the total floor area of the house, including the garden room, is only just over 3000 square feet.

THE PAPPLEWICK

At 1530 square feet the Papplewick design is the smallest of the Rectory range of Potton homes, but it is an imposing house which is equally well suited to a site fronting a village street, or to a large garden. The classically proportioned rooms, with double doors into the drawing room, give a classic environment for those who value the elegance of a less hurried way of life.

Incidentally, the original Papplewick Rectory was the fictional scene for D.H. Lawrence's novel 'The Virgin and the Gypsy'. However, building a Papplewick design does not guarantee involvement in elemental relationships, nor make them complusory.

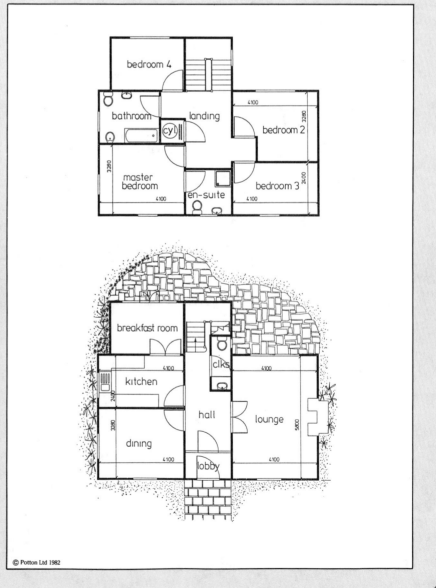

© Potton Ltd 1982

THE
B R A N D H A M

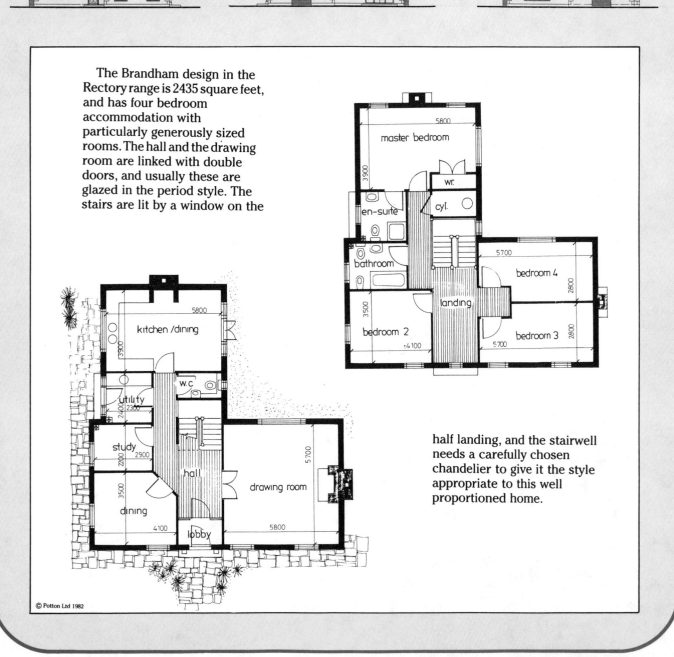

The Brandham design in the Rectory range is 2435 square feet, and has four bedroom accommodation with particularly generously sized rooms. The hall and the drawing room are linked with double doors, and usually these are glazed in the period style. The stairs are lit by a window on the

half landing, and the stairwell needs a carefully chosen chandelier to give it the style appropriate to this well proportioned home.

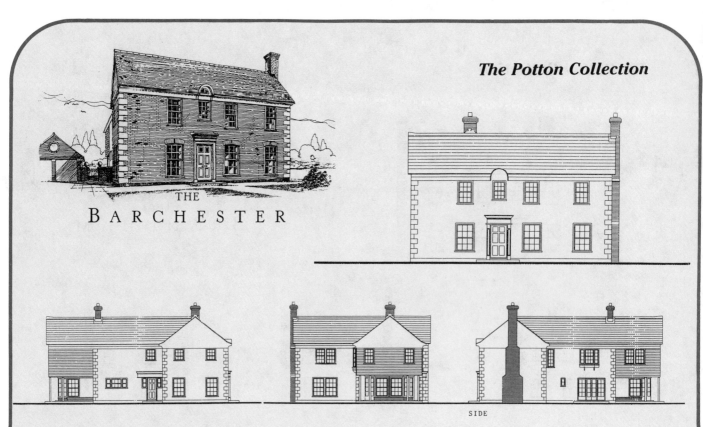

THE
B A R C H E S T E R

SIDE

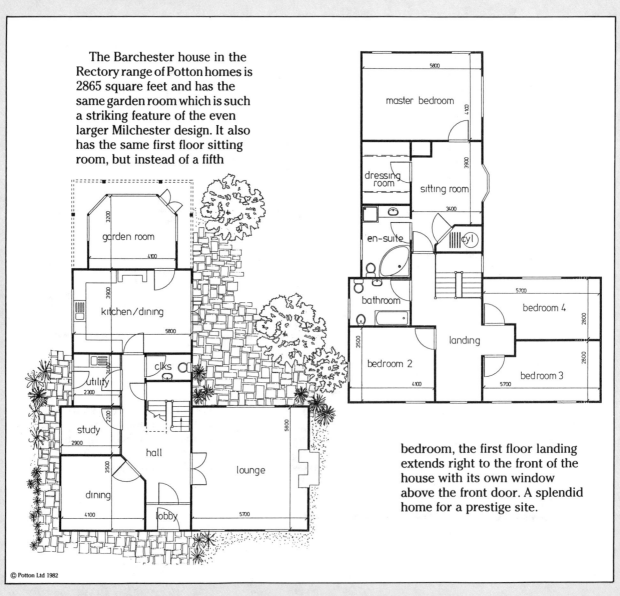

The Barchester house in the Rectory range of Potton homes is 2865 square feet and has the same garden room which is such a striking feature of the even larger Milchester design. It also has the same first floor sitting room, but instead of a fifth

bedroom, the first floor landing extends right to the front of the house with its own window above the front door. A splendid home for a prestige site.

garden room
kitchen/dining
utility
clks
study
hall
dining
lobby
lounge

master bedroom
dressing room
sitting room
en-suite
cyl
bathroom
landing
bedroom 2
bedroom 4
bedroom 3

© Potton Ltd 1982

The Potton Collection

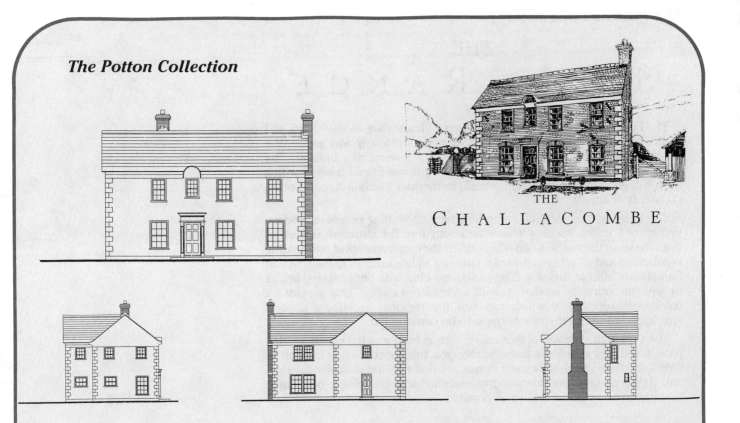

THE
CHALLACOMBE

The Challacombe house of 1900 square feet is a larger version of the Papplewick with a larger drawing room and generous four bedroom accommodation. The first floor study can be used as a fifth bedroom if required. A feature of the design is that the arrangement of the corridors on both floors, and the absence of windows in the rear elevation of the projecting wing, makes it easy to extend this design in the future.

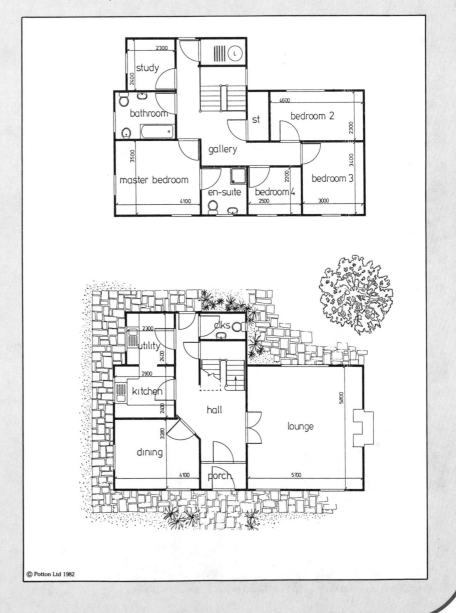

© Potton Ltd 1982

THE
S H I R E   R A N G E

The Potton Heritage and Rectory ranges of homes are at the luxury end of the housing market, and for some years the company was aware of a demand for homes to Potton standards in a lower price bracket. The outcome is the Shire range of bungalows — plus one Shire house — which offer a high standard of design, excellent thermal insulation, and Potton standards of construction.

The Shire homes are built using load bearing walling panels, a modern system of housing building where the strength of the structure is derived from the walls themselves, and which meets the requirements of the building regulations and all other standards. Virtually all homes built in the USA and Canada are built in this way. The panels are clad with either facing bricks or with masonry for rendering, with a ventilated cavity. This provides a traditional appearance which can suit the regional architectural style approprite to where the new home is to be constructed.

The very high standard of thermal insulation built into the plinth, walling panels and roof of a Shire home enable you to expect heating bills up to 35% lower than you would expect from a new home with standard insulation, and this is a major consideration to many families planning a new home that has to be as cost effective as possible.

Shire bungalow

Interior of a Shire bungalow

The Potton Collection

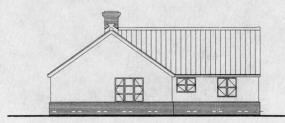

THE
WILBRAHAM

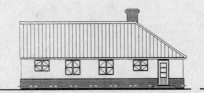
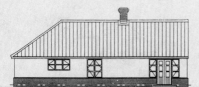
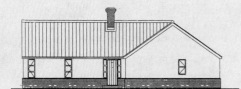

This three bedroom bungalow with generous living accommodation is typical of the Shire range of Potton timber frame homes with panel wall construction. They vary in size from 935 to 1785 square feet, and are remarkably cost effective to construct. The styling can be varied within limits, and can be adapted to suit regional design requirements in all parts of the country.

All the Shire bungalows have high levels of insulation built into the walling panels, and are very energy efficient.

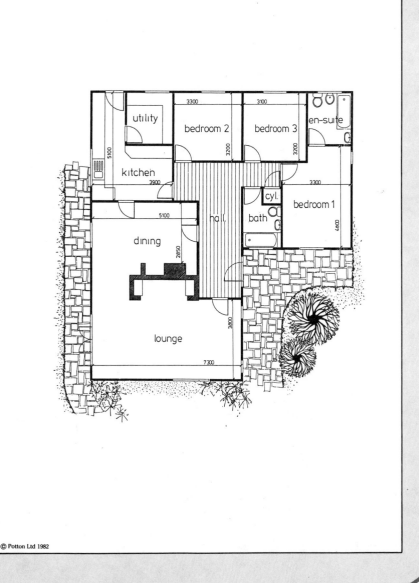

THE
H A R L T O N . A

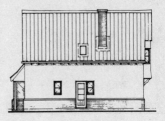

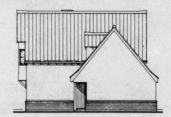

The Harlton is the only two storey house in the Shire range of homes, and is available with either a single or a double garage. The double garage version has five bedrooms.

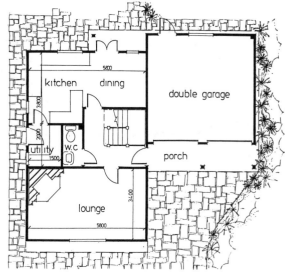

© Potton Ltd 1982

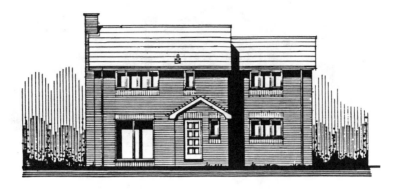

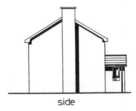

side

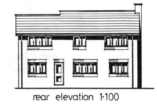

rear elevation 1·100

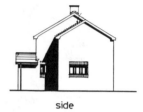

side

Putting the master bedroom suite on the other side of a cavity wall from the rest of the bedrooms like this ensures privacy, and provides good sound insulation from the lounge if the parents of a noisy family like to go to bed before their offspring do!

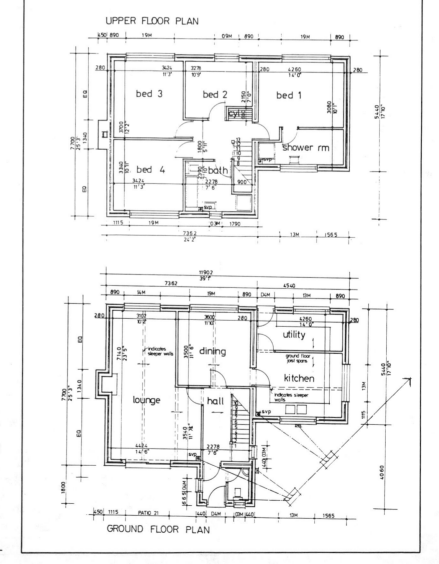

UPPER FLOOR PLAN

bed 3

bed 2

bed 1

cyl

shower rm

bed 4

bath

GROUND FLOOR PLAN

lounge

dining

hall

utility

kitchen

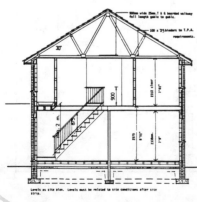

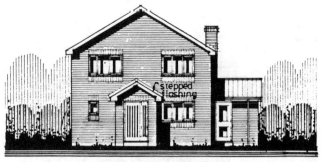

FRONT ELEVATION

REAR ELEVATION

SIDE ELEVATIONS

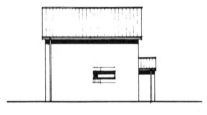

A compact four bedroom home for a site with all round views: the kitchen windows look out to the front and one side, and the living room looks out to the back and the other side. The fourth bedroom is small in order to provide room to install a shower in the bathroom at a later date: most people building this house will want to forget the shower and move the relevant wall to increase the bedroom width to 8ft. This will not present any problems.

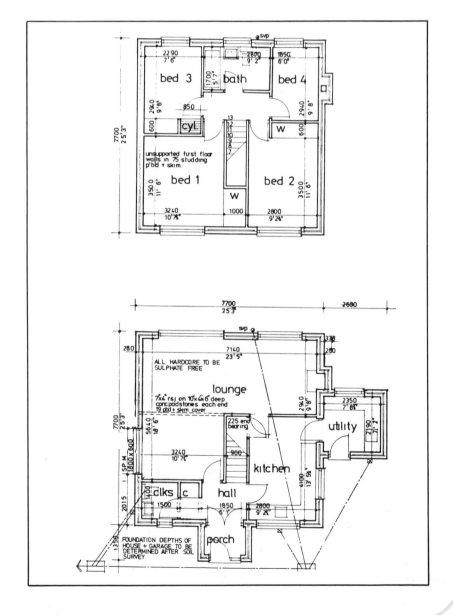

FRONT ELEVATION

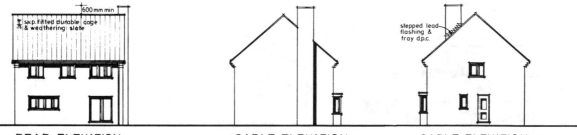

REAR ELEVATION　　　　GABLE ELEVATION　　　　GABLE ELEVATION

A simple, straightforward home that is economical to build and has traditionally arranged accommodation. People often say they want to get away from an 'ordinary' layout like this, perhaps forgetting that it is popular just because it is so convenient, and makes such good use of space.

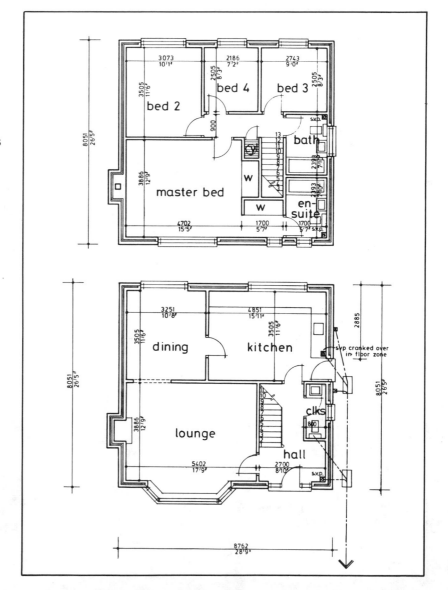

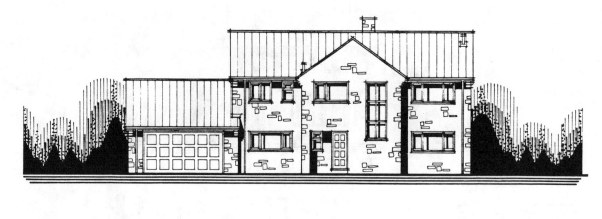

REAR ELEVATION

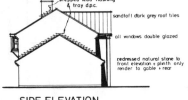

stepped lead flashing
& tray d.p.c.

sandtoft dark grey roof tiles

all windows double glazed

redressed natural stone to
front elevation + plinth only
render to gable + rear

SIDE ELEVATION

SIDE ELEVATION

This large house was built on a hill top in West Yorkshire in 1985, and looks magnificent. Note the first floor living room with its window seat to take advantage of a splendid view.

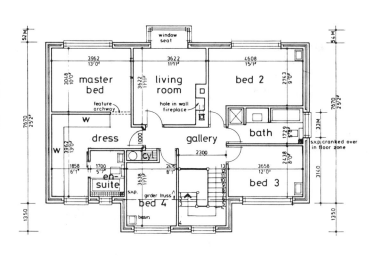

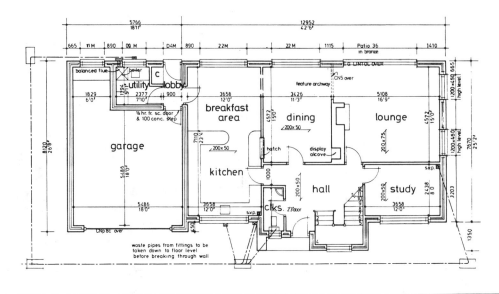

FRONT ELEVATION

An unusual and complex house with a first floor balcony to the rear elevation. The three bedrooms and two bathrooms are very large, and if required the first floor layout could be altered to allow for four bedroom, two bathroom accommodation.

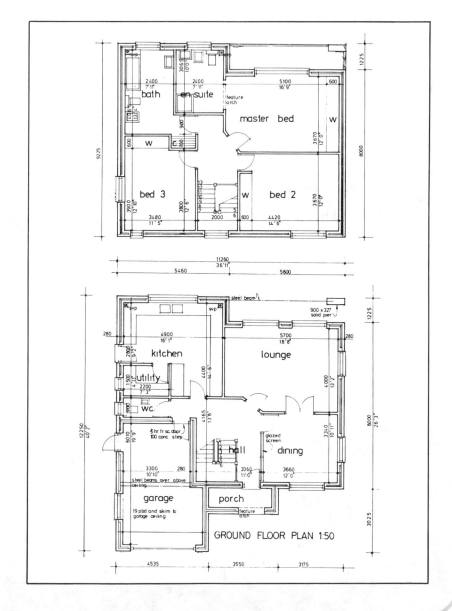

GROUND FLOOR PLAN 1:50

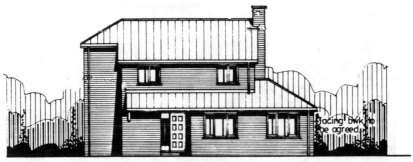

front elevation

side elevation   rear elevation   side elevation

The section below shews how part of the roof of this house is cut back to give this distinctive style.

The lounge with its two deep window bays has a lot of character, and there is an option to have glazed double doors between the lounge and the dining room which would give a very spacious feel to a modestly sized home.

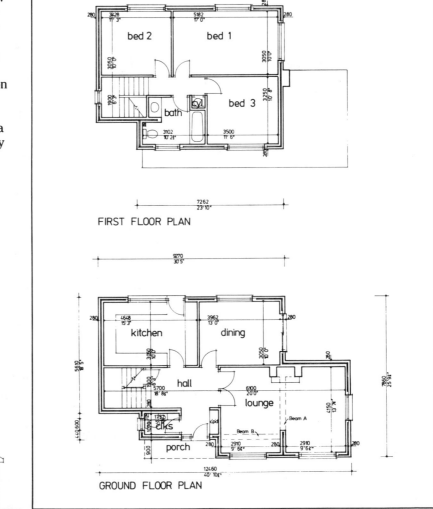

FIRST FLOOR PLAN

GROUND FLOOR PLAN

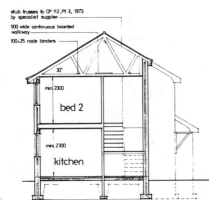

front elevation

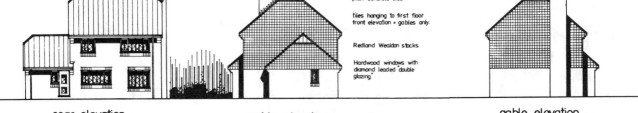

rear elevation

gable elevation

gable elevation

plain concrete tiles.

tiles hanging to first floor
front elevation + gables only.

Redland Wealdon stocks.

Hardwood windows with
diamond leaded double
glazing.

Lots of character in this house,
with Wealdon stock bricks —
multi-coloured and irregular in
shape —, tile hanging to the first
floor walls, and hardwood joinery
and diamond leaded lights.

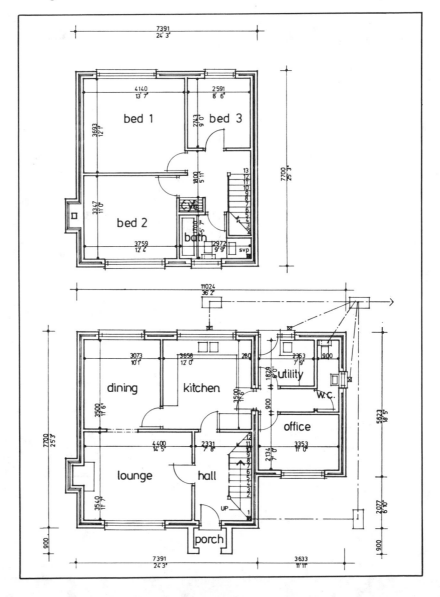

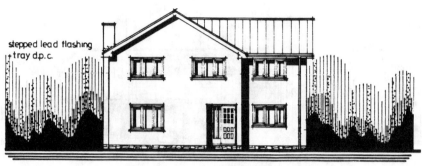

stepped lead flashing
+ tray d.p.c.

FRONT ELEVATION

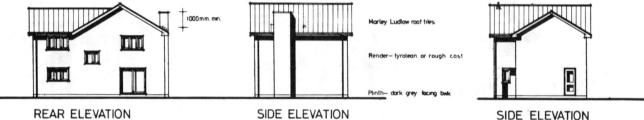

1000 mm. min.

Marley Ludlow roof tiles

Render— tyrolean or rough cast

Plinth— dark grey facing bwk

REAR ELEVATION   SIDE ELEVATION   SIDE ELEVATION

This is a house to have a rough cast rendered finish, unrelieved with any contrasting material other than the brickwork plinth. This can look rather severe, but if the house is large enough, as this is, and it is in the right setting, it should look quite imposing. The choice of tiles is very important in this situation.

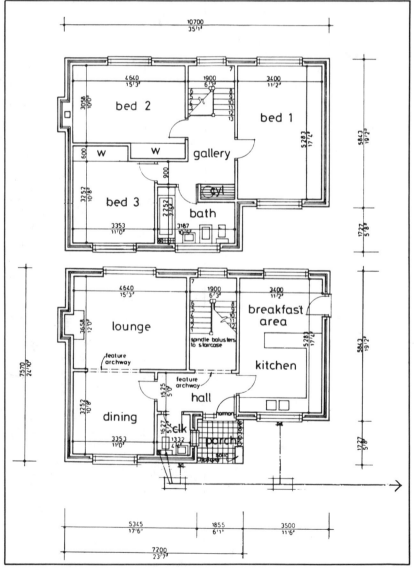

FRONT ELEVATION

REAR ELEVATION

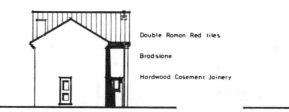

Double Roman Red tiles

Bradstone

Hardwood Casement Joinery

SIDE ELEVATION

SIDE ELEVATION

A three bedroom house with large rooms and a compact layout that keeps down the overall size. It is shewn for construction in stone, and the choice of stone for a house like this is just as important as the choice of the design. The range is from split face artificial stone which costs less than brick, to cast artificial stone often indistinguishable from the real thing and costing 50% more than bricks, to reclaimed stone from demolitions which is difficult to use, to new stone from a quarry which will cost a great deal. All these options are illustrated and discussed at length in the companion book to this called Home Plans for the '80s.

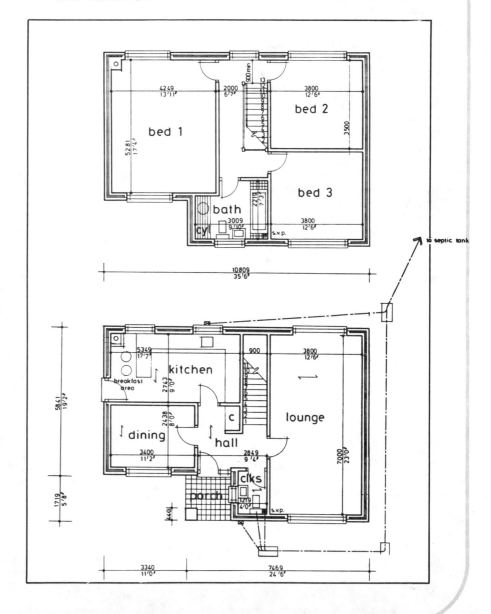

Front elevation

Rear elevation

Side elevation

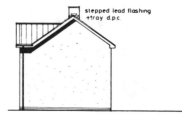

Side elevation

This neat, conventional house is economical to build and is very compactly laid out. It is illustrated here with a rough cast rendered finish on a brick plinth, with a brick chimney and brick soldier courses above and below the windows. Contrasting render and brickwork like this is always very effective, but it is important that the junction of the two materials should be crisp and clean cut. One of the best ways of doing this is to use proprietory render stop laths at the horizontal joints, and it is important to discuss this with whoever is doing the rendering.

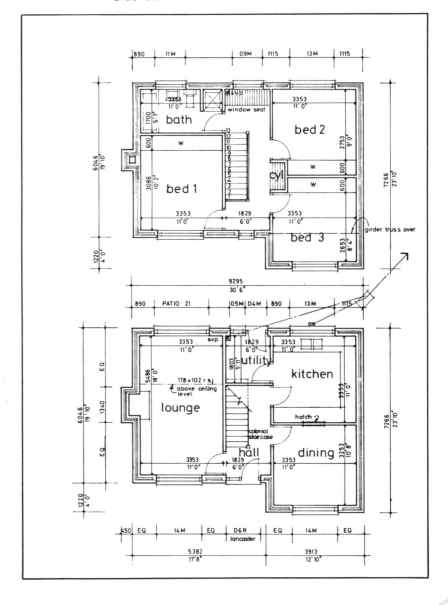

FRONT ELEVATION

SIDE ELEVATION   REAR ELEVATION   SIDE ELEVATION

Marley bold roll roof tiles
in old english dark red.

stepped lead flashing
& tray d.p.c.

30°

Butterley Mixture
Brickwork

s.v.p fitted durable cage
& weathering slate

lead flashing +
tray dpc

A house for a narrow site with
an interesting arrangement of the
rooms. The inglenook fireplace
was designed to suit the client of
D & M Ltd who built this house,
and of course it can be replaced
with a fireplace that will be flush
with the wall, giving a lot more
room in the lounge.

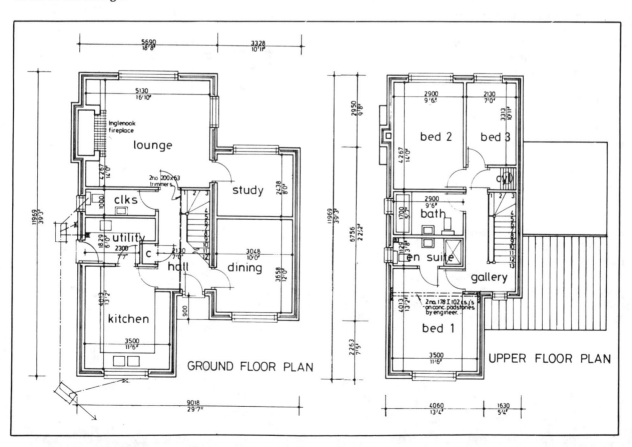

GROUND FLOOR PLAN

UPPER FLOOR PLAN

FRONT ELEVATION

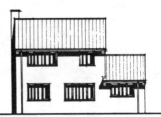

REAR ELEVATION

GABLE ELEVATIONS

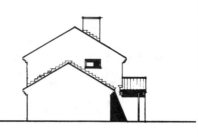

The key to the design concept for this house is to be found in the note at the head of the stairs: — "build in lintol for opening to future extension". Besides this, the ceiling joists to the kitchen and utility room are big enough to act as floor joists, so that two more bedrooms can be built above the single storey part of the house when required. An extension like this is easily arranged at the design stage, and the extra cost of providing for it all is very little. For instance, using 8" x 2" timber for the ceiling instead of 5" x 2" costs very little extra, and will save taking the whole ceiling down when the new rooms are to be built above. This forethought can also extend to the planning consent, which can show that the home is to be built in two stages if this can be negotiated at the planning office, avoiding having to make another application when the extension is required.

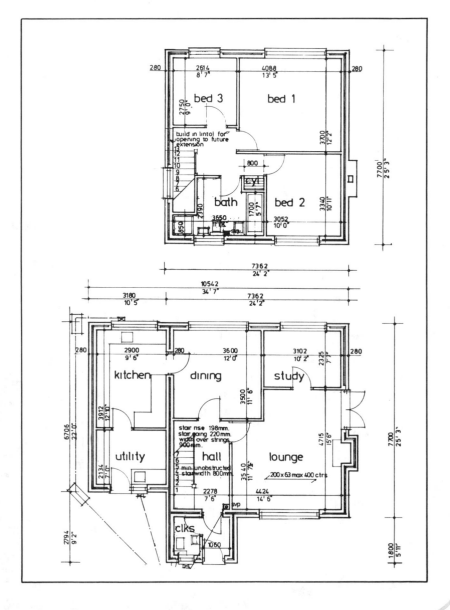

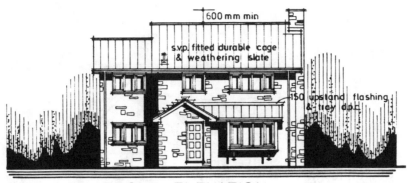

FRONT ELEVATION

s.v.p. fitted durable cage & weathering slate

600 mm min

150 upstand flashing & tray d.p.c.

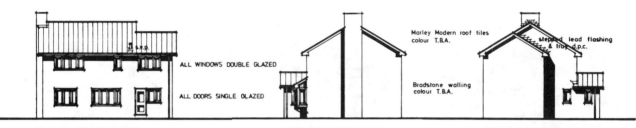

REAR ELEVATION

ALL WINDOWS DOUBLE GLAZED

ALL DOORS SINGLE GLAZED

SIDE ELEVATION

Marley Modern roof tiles colour T.B.A.

Bradstone walling colour T.B.A.

stepped lead flashing & tray d.p.c.

SIDE ELEVATION

A really big dining kitchen is the key feature of this three bedroom home, together with a large L shaped lounge. The note of the materials reads "colour TBA". This is architects' shorthand for "to be agreed", and suggests that there was an argument about this with the planners, and that consent was granted subject to this matter being resolved before the walls were built up!

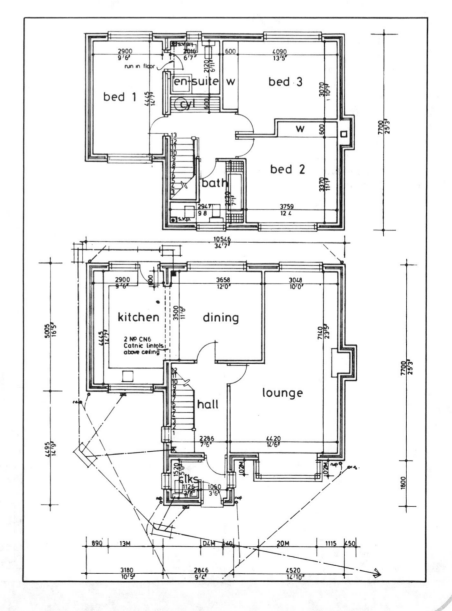

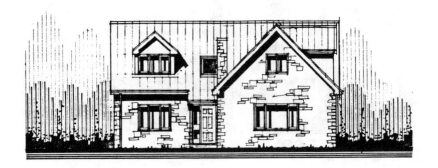

REAR ELEVATION

SIDE ELEVATIONS

This dormer bungalow has a great deal more accommodation than its compact appearance may suggest. The layout shewn in the plan has a large lobby at the back door with a shower and WC to suit a farmer. This is easily rearranged to give a bathroom leading off the ground floor bedroom, making it very suitable for an elderly person.

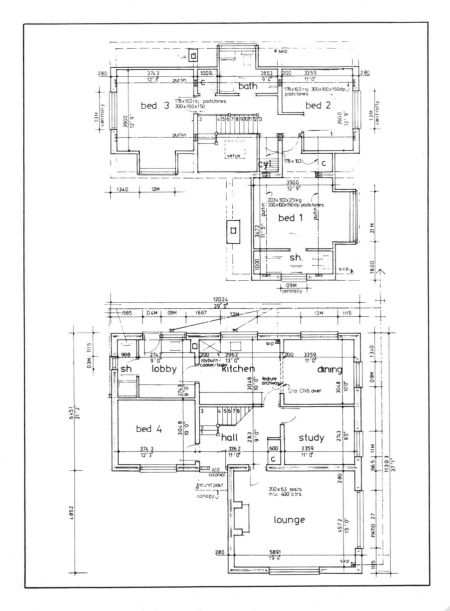

W 819

FRONT ELEVATION

W 819

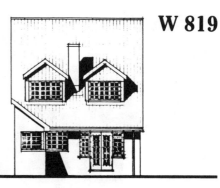

REAR ELEVATION

GABLE ELEVATION

This house was built in South Yorkshire on a very narrow plot. There was a lot of argument with the planners about it, but both sides of the building were masked by other structures, and consent was eventually obtained. Four bedrooms on a site only 28ft wide!

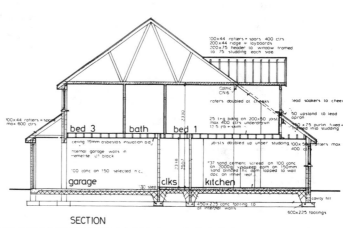

SECTION

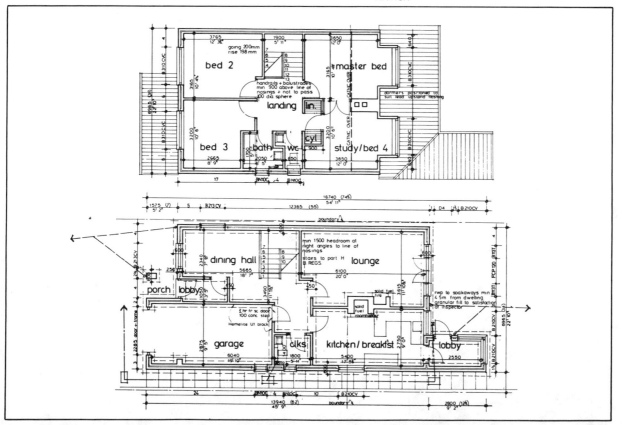

FRONT ELEVATION

Marley Heritage

Redland Wealdon 4000 brickwork

Hardwood casement joinery

GABLE ELEVATION

600mm min

s.v.p. fitted durable cage & weathering slate

REAR ELEVATION

stepped lead flashing & tray d.p.c.

GABLE ELEVATION

A dormer bungalow with half hips to the three dormers as well as to the two levels of the main roof. The arrangement of the purlins means that there will be 'exposed beams' in the bedrooms, but this is a feature that is usually welcomed by those building a new home in this style.

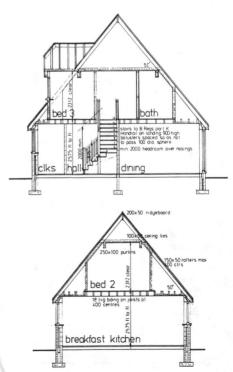

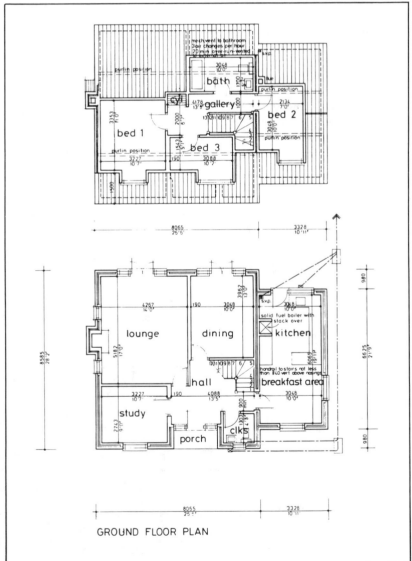

GROUND FLOOR PLAN

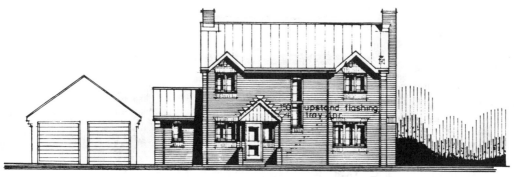

front elevation

rear elevation   gable elevation   gable elevation

100 x 50 rafters + ties
max. 400 ctrs. on
200 x 50 bearers bolted
to top of posts-
ext ply underdrawn

Marley modern dark grey tiles

Butterley old english rose brickwork

Hardwood casement joinery

Arched heads

This "village street" house is only twenty feet deep, which the planners sometimes require in conservation areas. However, it would look just as well on an isolated site, and the 'front to rear' dimensions can be increased to give larger rooms if required.

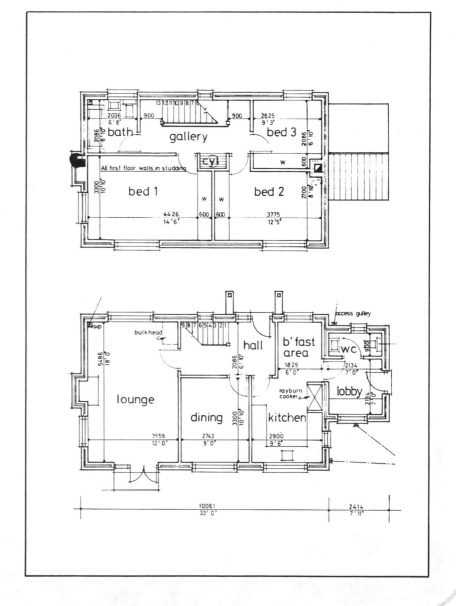

FRONT ELEVATION

600 min.

REAR ELEVATION

35° pitch

Astbestos type slates.

Hardwood casement joinery

Rough cast render

Dark facing brick plinth
grey or similar colour

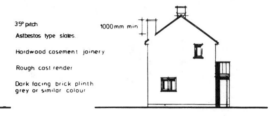

1000 mm min

SIDE ELEVATION

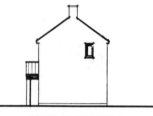

SIDE ELEVATION

This neat little house is only eighteen feet deep, and is the sort of cottage which a planning authority may require for an infill site in a village street where the new building must match the scale of neighbouring properties. The lobby/WC extension to the side which is shewn on the plan is optional, and has not been illustrated in the elevations.

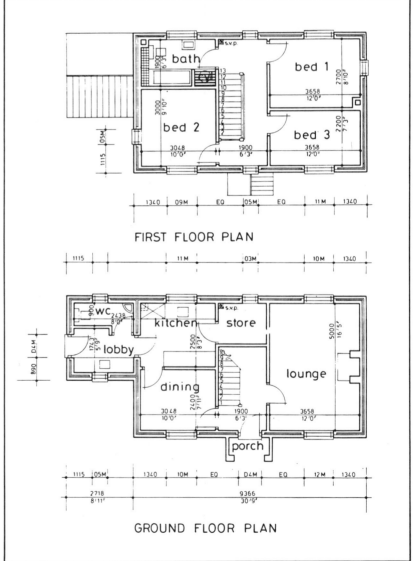

FIRST FLOOR PLAN

GROUND FLOOR PLAN

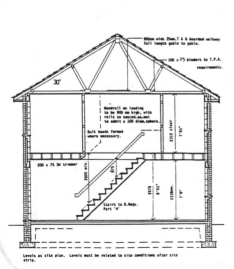

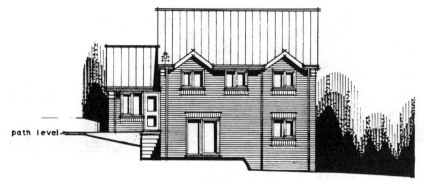

ENTRANCE ELEVATION

path level

SIDE ELEVATION

stepped lead flashing
& tray d.p.c.

ROAD ELEVATION

path level

REAR ELEVATION

Another house with the living accommodation on the first floor and the bedrooms below. In this instance there is a dining hall at a level half way between the two main floors of the home. This suits the sloping site very well, but it does mean that five steps have to be negotiated between the kitchen and the dining table.

Lots of cupboard space in this interesting house.

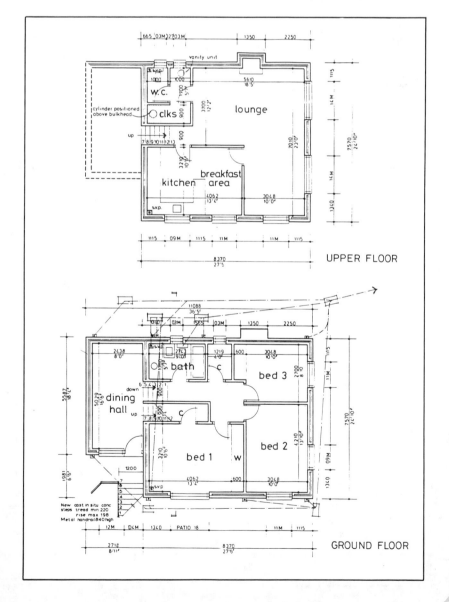

UPPER FLOOR

GROUND FLOOR

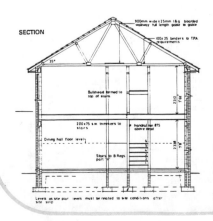

SECTION

front elevation

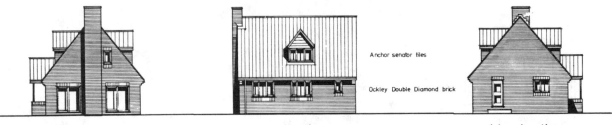

side elevation   rear elevation   side elevation

Anchor senator tiles

Ockley Double Diamond brick

Another 'country cottage' design, this time with three bedroom, two bathroom accommodation. The hall/lounge/dining room are all open-plan, but this can easily be divided into separate rooms, and a small study can be fitted in if required.

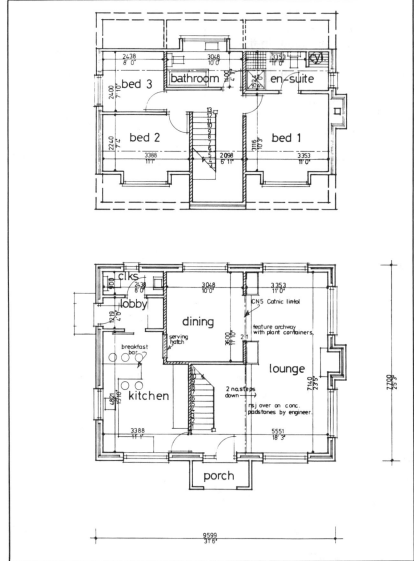

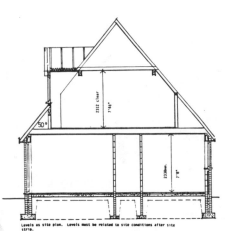

Levels as site plan. Levels must be related to site conditions after site strip.

228

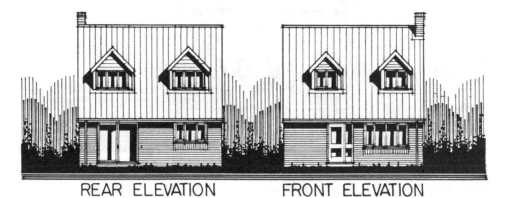

REAR ELEVATION   FRONT ELEVATION

GABLE ELEVATIONS

This attractive home is only 26ft. wide and will suit a narrow plot. It is shewn here without a kitchen door, but one can easily be provided in the side wall if required.

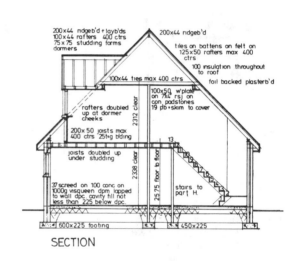

SECTION

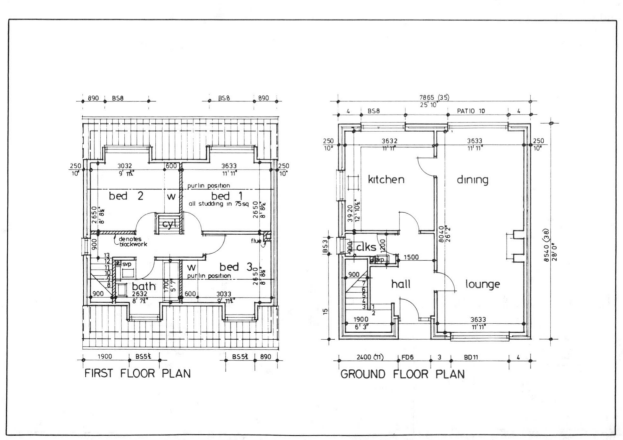

FIRST FLOOR PLAN   GROUND FLOOR PLAN

front elevation

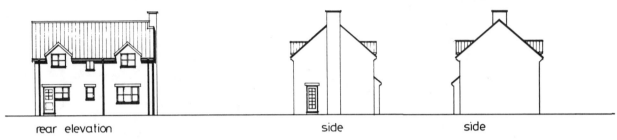

rear elevation

side

side

This compact house of just under 1200 sq.ft. is in a style well suited to the West Midlands and parts of the North, but the simple and convenient layout can be used as the basis of a home in any regional style.

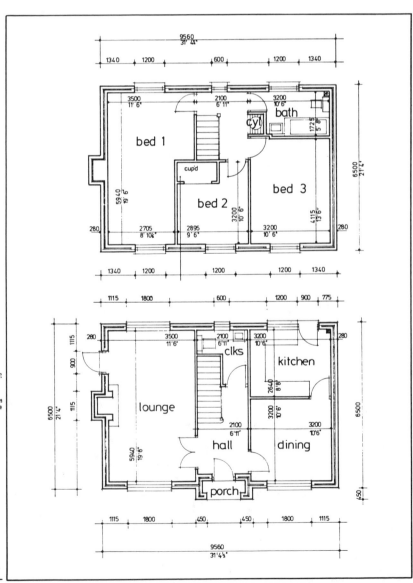

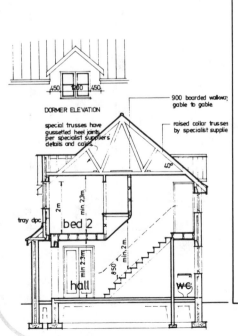

DORMER ELEVATION

900 boarded walkway gable to gable

raised collar trusses by specialist supplie

special trusses have gussetted heel joints per specialist suppliers details and cales.

FRONT ELEVATION

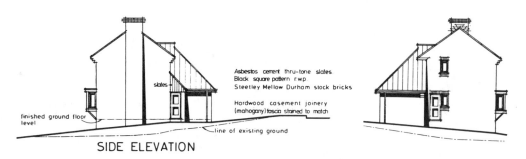

Asbestos cement thru-tone slates
Black square pattern r.w.p.
Steetley Mellow Durham stock bricks

Hardwood casement joinery
(mahogany) fascia stained to match

slates

finished ground floor level

line of existing ground

SIDE ELEVATION

A relatively small home, but with lots of interest and character that will make it feel larger than it really is.

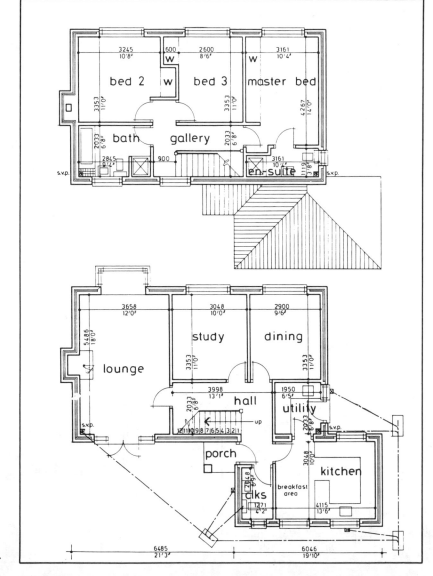

REAR ELEVATION

side

front elevation

Staffordshire Blue tiles

Ann Twyford Ltd Wallstone coursed pitched face

windows from Magnet + Southerns georgian range

side

rear elevation

A large three bedroom home that could be built with four bedrooms if required. The large area of landing outside the door to the master bedroom is quite large enough for a desk and chair, and can be used as a study for childrens homework or anything else.

The materials specification is for artificial stone walls under Staffordshire blue tiles, all chosen to suit the surroundings.

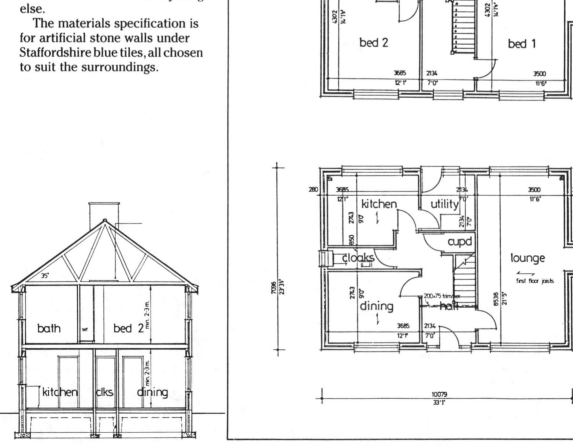

FRONT ELEVATION

150 upstand flashing & tray d.p.c.

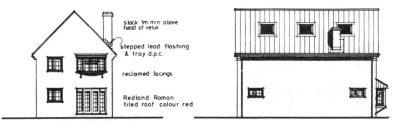

slack 1m min above head of velux

stepped lead flashing & tray d.p.c.

reclaimed facings

Redland Roman tiled roof colour red

REAR ELEVATION

SIDE ELEVATIONS

An interesting house built in London, where it replaced an older property which was demolished to make room for this one. The plot was very narrow indeed, and the house fills it with no room to spare, so provision has been made to be able to fit out two more bedrooms in the roof at a future date. To do this the drawings show a traditional rafter roof, 8" x 2" ceiling joists to become floor joists for the top floor, and a first floor store which is big enough for a circular staircase.

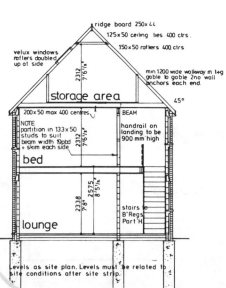

ridge board 250x44

125x50 ceiling ties 400 ctrs.

150x50 rafters 400 ctrs

velux windows rafters doubled up at side

min 1200 wide walkway in t+g gable to gable 2no wall anchors each end.

2312 7'6¼"

storage area

45°

200 x 50 max 400 centres

BEAM

2312 7'6¼"

NOTE partition in 133x50 studs to suit beam width 19pbd + skim each side

handrail on landing to be 900 mm high

bed

2338 7'8"

2575 8'5¼"

stairs to B'Regs Part 'H'

lounge

Levels as site plan. Levels must be related to site conditions after site strip.

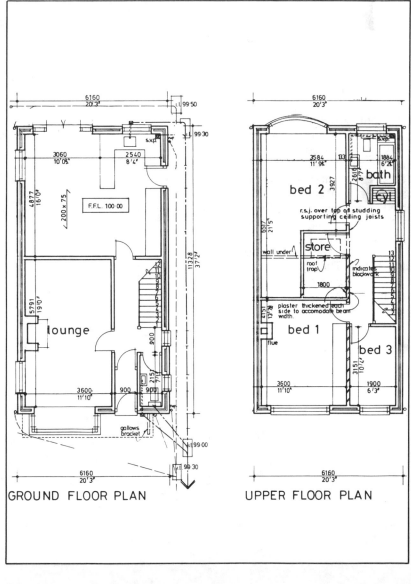

GROUND FLOOR PLAN

UPPER FLOOR PLAN

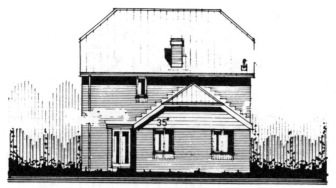

FRONT ELEVATION

A house built at a fish farm, so that it was described on the drawing as a 'Fish Farmhouse', which somehow sounds very wrong. However, the house itself is very right, with some most unusual features.

To start with, the need for a rarely used front door is met by angled french windows at the junction of the lounge and dining room, and the two busy back doors lead into the kitchen and utility rooms. The hall is a room in its own right, with no external door and plenty of room for it to be used as a study.

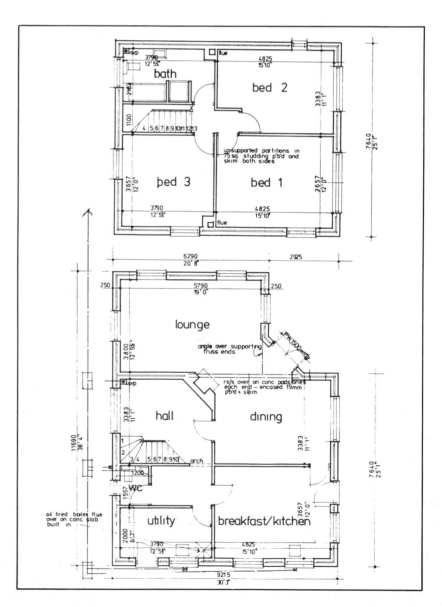

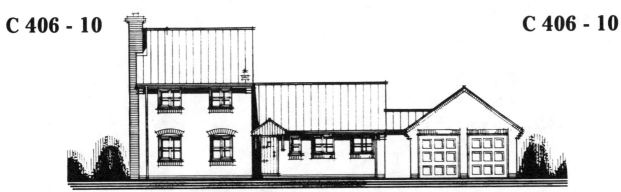

FRONT ELEVATION

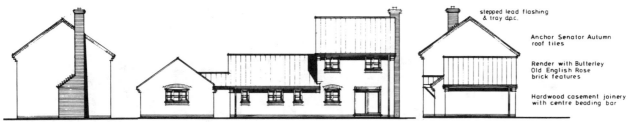

GABLE ELEVATION   REAR ELEVATION

stepped lead flashing
& tray d.p.c.

Anchor Senator Autumn
roof tiles

Render with Butterley
Old English Rose
brick features

Hardwood casement joinery
with centre beading bar

GABLE ELEVATION

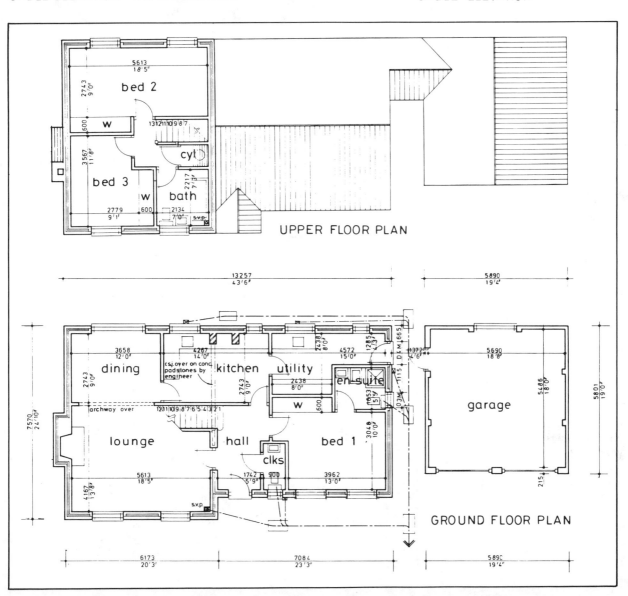

UPPER FLOOR PLAN

GROUND FLOOR PLAN

rear elevation   side elevation

This compact house has a rural feel about is, and is shewn here to be built with a rendered finish. This will look best with hardwood joinery, and particular care should be taken with the gallows bracket supporting the porch roof by the front door: this should be made from really heavy section hardwood with pegged joints.

The house will suit sites where the views are to the right and rear, and another window can be fitted in the side wall of the dining room if required, and would match the side window in the master bedroom above.

Note the deep half landing to the stairs with its own window. This is big enough for an occasional table or other piece of furniture, and with some rearrangement of the stairs can be made wider still to accommodate a writing desk if this is the sort of place you would choose to write your letters, or your next novel!

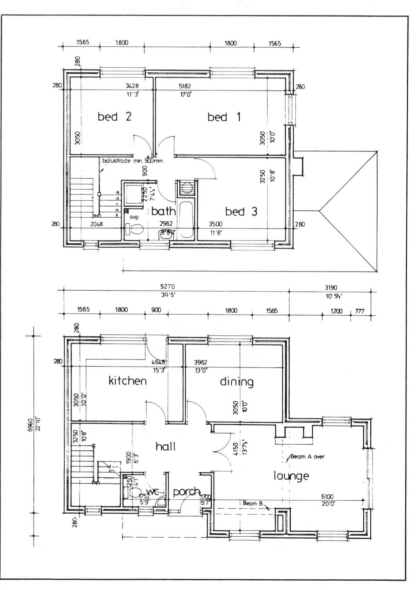

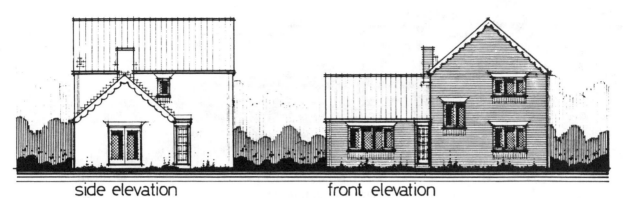

side elevation   front elevation

side elevation   rear elevation

A few years ago it would have been unthinkable to build a new home with scalloped barge boards and leaded lights to windows: these days these Victorian features are considered very appropriate in the right setting, particularly when the new building must blend in with older properties.

The 'corner' front door and angled entrance to the lounge are features which add a lot of character to a property like this.

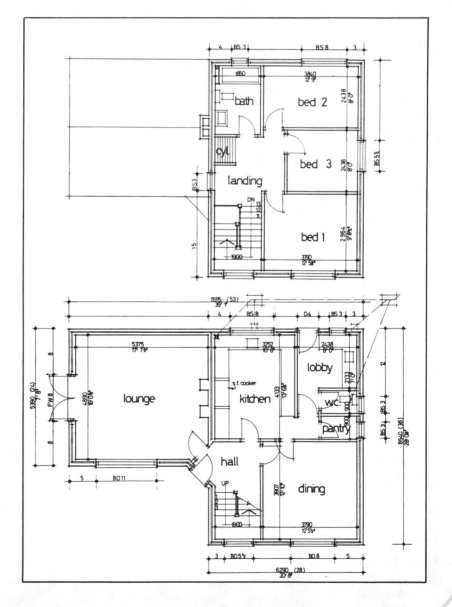

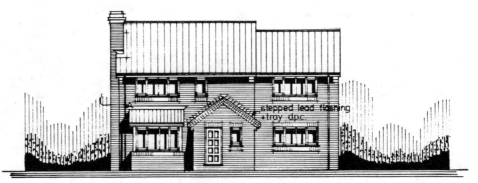

front elevation

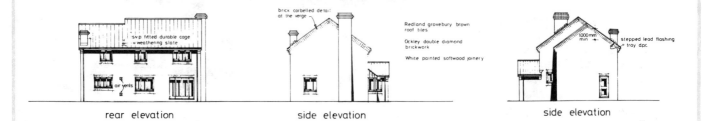

rear elevation   side elevation   side elevation

brick corbelled detail
at the verge

Redland grovebury brown
roof tiles

Ockley double diamond
brickwork

White painted softwood joinery

svp fitted durable cage
+ weathering slate

air vents

stepped lead flashing
+ tray dpc

1000mm
min

A good house for a plot of land in an area where the planners will want a complex roof line, and where you will wish to meet this requirement at the minimum cost. This home was built in Ockley Double Diamond bricks, with a lot of brick detailing and plenty of character in the chimneys. Elaborate brickwork like this goes well with an involved shape.

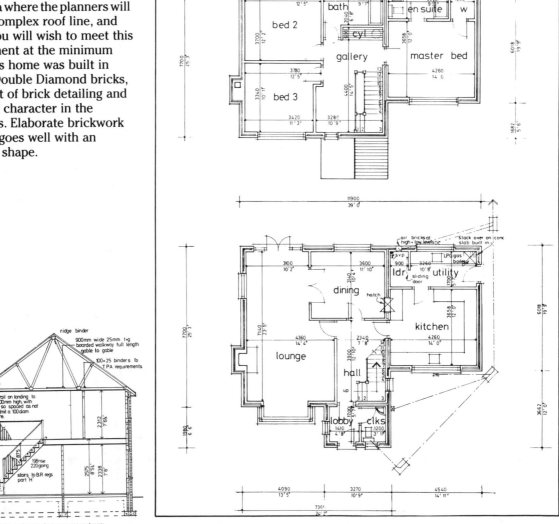

front elevation   rear elevation

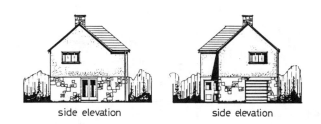

side elevation   side elevation

A house for a site where the
views are to the front and rear,
with the entrance at the side.

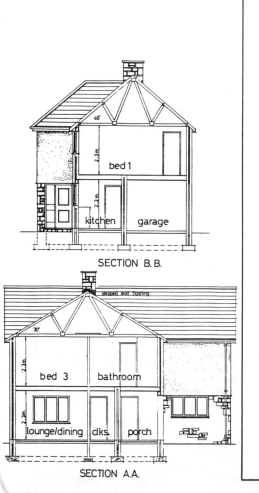

SECTION B. B.

SECTION A.A.

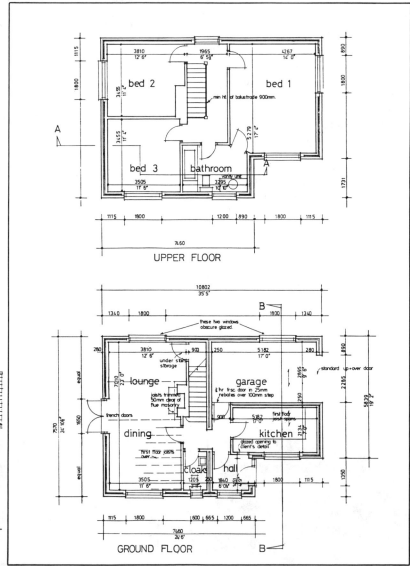

UPPER FLOOR

GROUND FLOOR

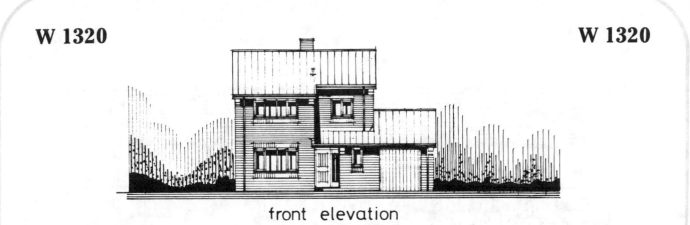

front elevation

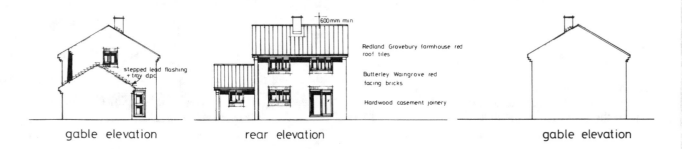

gable elevation

rear elevation

Redland Grovebury farmhouse red roof tiles

Butterley Waingrove red facing bricks

Hardwood casement joinery

gable elevation

stepped lead flashing + tray dpc

600mm min

A three bedroom house with part of the first floor wall at the front set back to add interest to the appearance. Another unusual feature in a home of this size is a fireplace on an internal wall, and the stack going up through the centre of the house: houses that are under square roofs like this usually have the chimney on an outside wall.

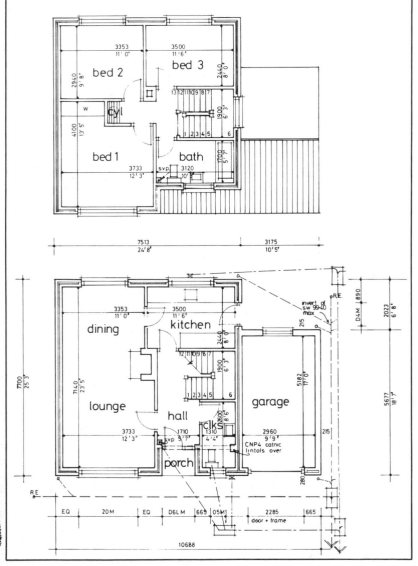

FRONT ELEVATION

REAR ELEVATION

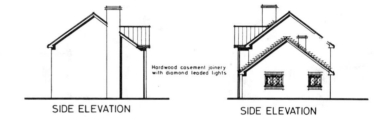

SIDE ELEVATION

Hardwood casement joinery
with diamond leaded lights

SIDE ELEVATION

This compact three bedroom house has a staircase that makes a 180° turn by using winder treads. This saves a lot of space when compared with stairs with a half landing, which in this case would add additional two feet to the width of the hall, and thus to the whole building.

It is drawn for construction in brick with a feature stone wall to the front of the cloakroom and garage. Stone and brick do not complement each other as well as stone and render unless great care is taken in selecting the bricks. In this case the leaded light windows will be the key feature to the look of the property, and the area of stone is quite small. Nevertheless, the choice of both stone and brick were most important.

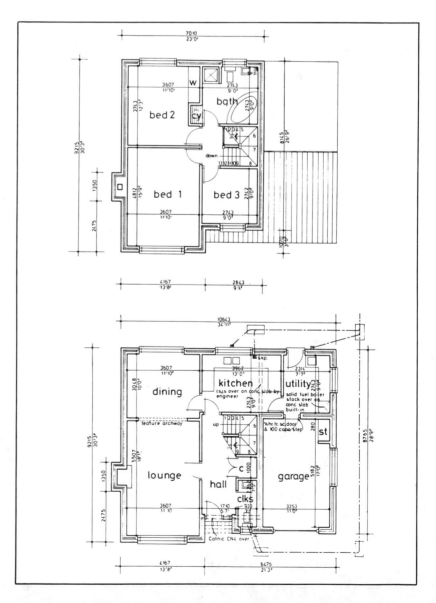

front elevation 1·10

side

side elevation

rear

A straightforward conventional three bedroom house to fit on a narrow plot. Designs like this are so popular because they are convenient, cost-effective to build, and always a good re-sale proposition. If you have a plot for which the conventional design would be something like this,

beware seeking a design that is 'different' without giving it all very careful consideration.

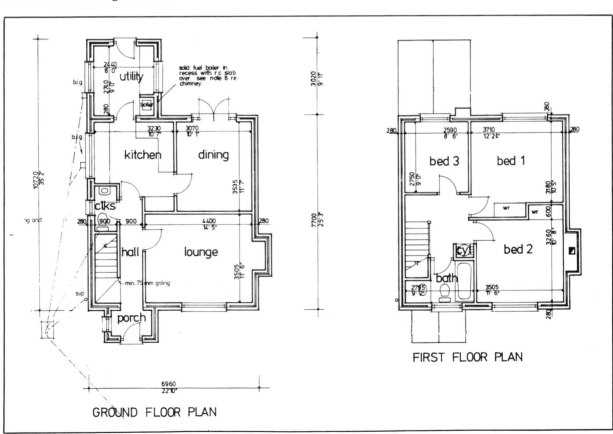

GROUND FLOOR PLAN

FIRST FLOOR PLAN

FRONT ELEVATION

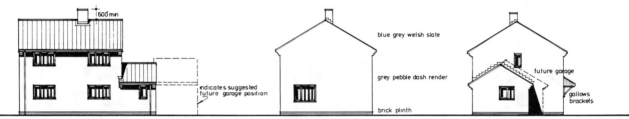

REAR ELEVATION   GABLE ELEVATIONS

This is a design for a farm
cottage, where there had to be a
big utility room, a farm kitchen,
and provision for a garage to be
built at a later date. It was built
with the utility room door on the
front elevation because this
suited the site, but it would be
more usual to move it to the side
of the building, which will
improve the appearance
considerably.

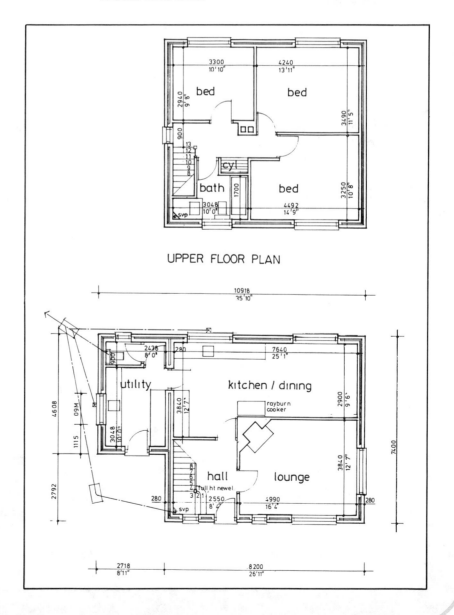

UPPER FLOOR PLAN

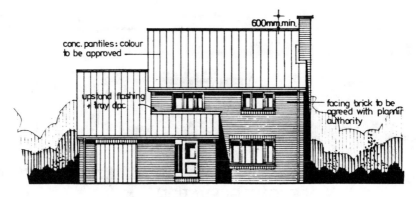

600mm. min.

conc. pantiles : colour
to be approved

upstand flashing
+ tray dpc

facing brick to be
agreed with plannir
authority

front elevation

stepped lead flashing + tray dpc

side elevation

side elevation

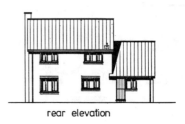

rear elevation

A three bedroom house with
virtually the same floor area as
the four bedroom design number
P2799. It is useful to compare the
two if you are undecided whether
you want three or four bedrooms,
and to see exactly how the two
layouts affect the position of the
stairs and the bathroom.

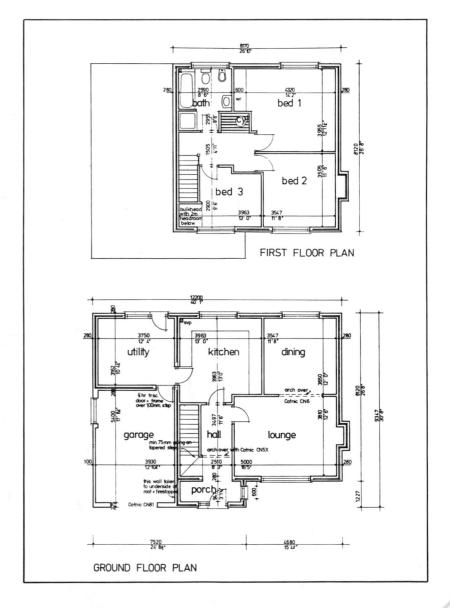

FIRST FLOOR PLAN

GROUND FLOOR PLAN

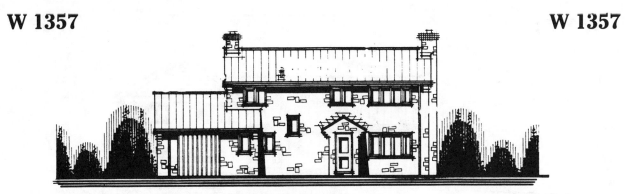

FRONT ELEVATION

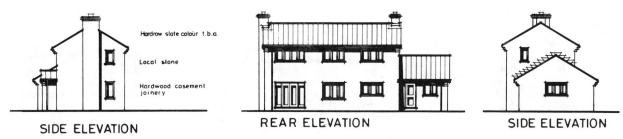

Hardrow slate colour t.b.a.

Local stone

Hardwood casement joinery

SIDE ELEVATION   REAR ELEVATION   SIDE ELEVATION

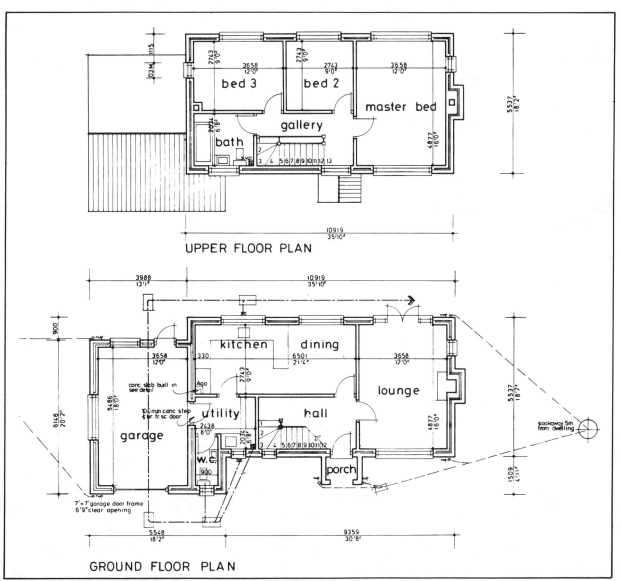

bed 3

bed 2

master bed

gallery

bath

UPPER FLOOR PLAN

kitchen   dining

lounge

conc. slab built in
see detail

Aga

100mm conc step
s.br. fr. sc door

utility

hall

garage

w.c.

porch

soakaway 5m
from dwelling

7' × 7' garage door frame
6'9" clear opening

GROUND FLOOR PLAN

W 1311

FRONT ELEVATION

new embankment

existing garden level

REAR ELEVATION

SIDE ELEVATION

SIDE ELEVATION

existing garden level

existing garden level

existing garden level

A split level home is a very popular way of building on a site which slopes from one side to the other, and this interesting house with the rooms split between three different levels is one of the most effective ways of arranging a split level layout. Within the general arrangement the different rooms can be changed around to suit family needs, and because there are only six steps between any two levels it has much of the feel of a bungalow, which is popular with the elderly.

The study and utility room shewn in this layout can be rearranged to make another bedroom suite, and this is a convenient way of providing a granny flat.

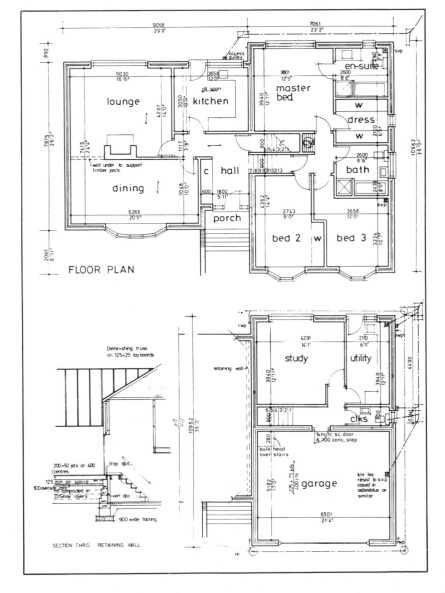

FLOOR PLAN

SECTION THRO' RETAINING WALL

FRONT ELEVATION 1:100

REAR ELEVATION   SIDE ELEVATION   SIDE ELEVATION

concrete interlocking tiles
colour & type to be agreed

stepped flashing
& tray d.p.c. at
roof abutments

150 upstand flashing
& tray d.p.c.

facing brickwork to be agreed
with planning authority

upstand flashing
& tray d.p.c.

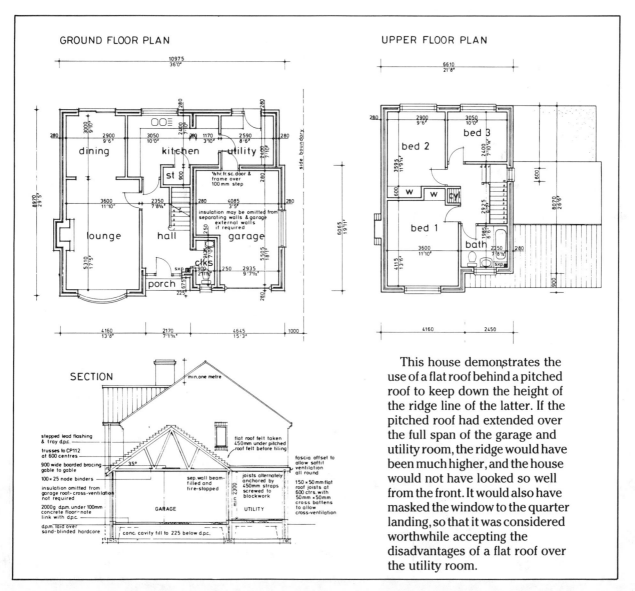

GROUND FLOOR PLAN

UPPER FLOOR PLAN

SECTION

stepped lead flashing
& tray d.p.c.

trusses to CP112
at 600 centres

900 wide boarded bracing
gable to gable

100 × 25 node binders

insulation omitted from
garage roof:-cross-ventilation
not required

2000g d.p.m. under 100mm
concrete floor:- note
link with d.p.c.

d.p.m. laid over
sand-blinded hardcore

min.one metre

flat roof felt taken
450mm under pitched
roof felt before tiling

fascia offset to
allow soffit
ventilation
all round

sep.wall beam-
filled and
fire-stopped

joists alternately
anchored by
450mm straps
screwed to
blockwork

150 × 50 mm flat
roof joists at
600 ctrs. with
50mm × 50mm
cross battens
to allow
cross-ventilation

GARAGE   UTILITY

conc. cavity fill to 225 below d.p.c.

This house demonstrates the use of a flat roof behind a pitched roof to keep down the height of the ridge line of the latter. If the pitched roof had extended over the full span of the garage and utility room, the ridge would have been much higher, and the house would not have looked so well from the front. It would also have masked the window to the quarter landing, so that it was considered worthwhile accepting the disadvantages of a flat roof over the utility room.

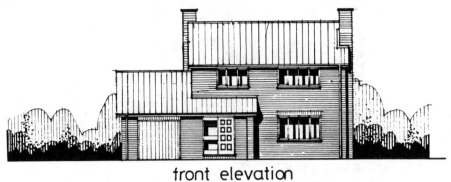

front elevation

garage side

rear elevation

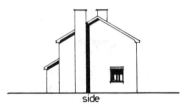

side

A conventional three bedroom home of the sort that is built in thousands up and down the country. Popular because it is cost-effective to build, convenient to live in, and always a good re-sale proposition. This particular version has a larger garage than usual, with plenty of room for bicycles, a chest freezer and garden tools.

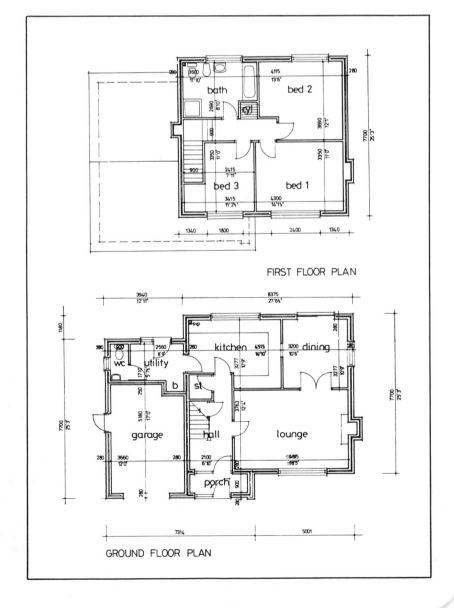

FIRST FLOOR PLAN

GROUND FLOOR PLAN

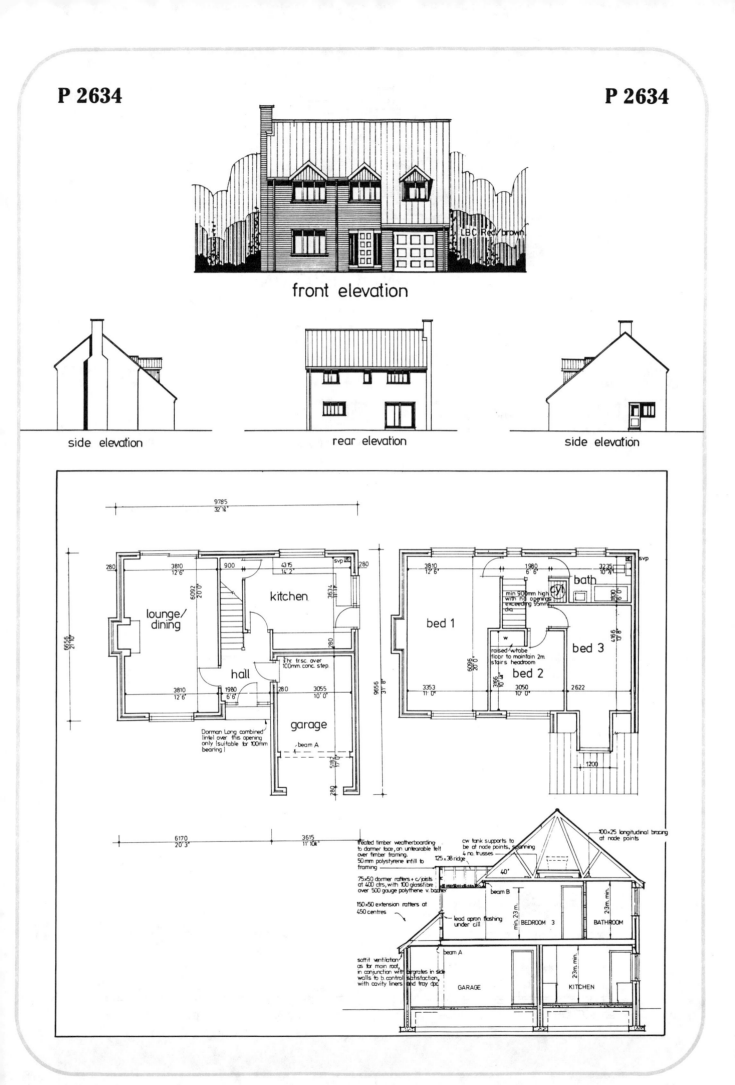

front elevation

side elevation

rear elevation

side elevation

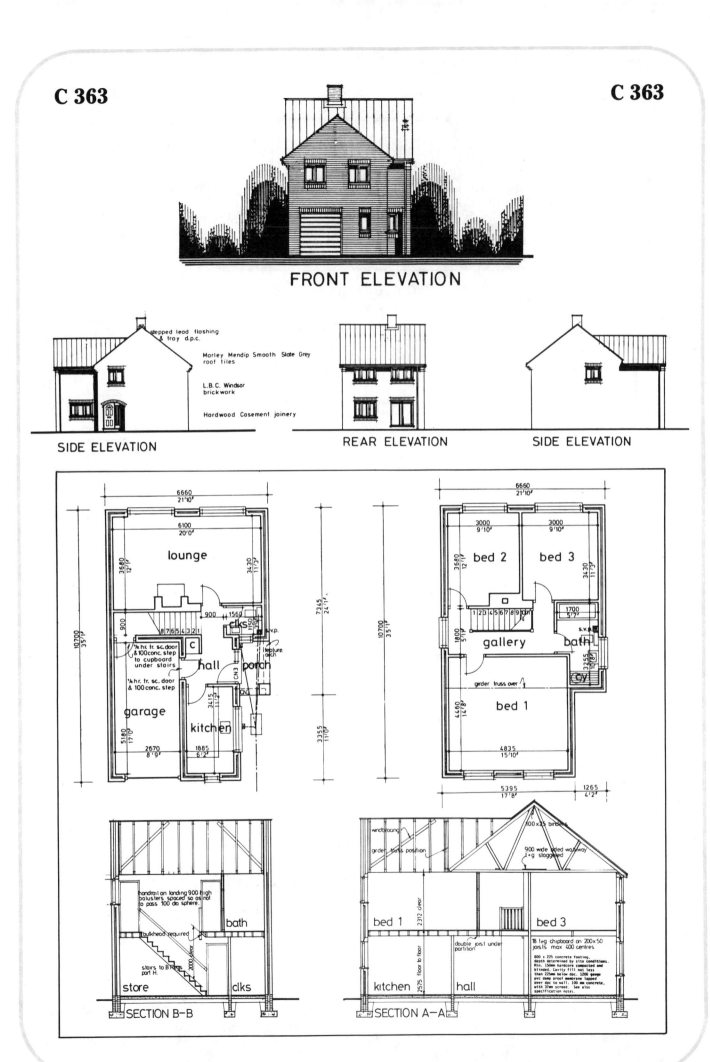

FRONT ELEVATION

SIDE ELEVATION

stepped lead flashing & tray d.p.c.

Marley Mendip Smooth Slate Grey roof tiles

L.B.C. Windsor brickwork

Hardwood Casement joinery

REAR ELEVATION

SIDE ELEVATION

6660
21'10"

6100
20'0"

3680
12'1"

lounge

3430
11'3"

10700
35'1"

900

900

1560

clks

8765 4 3 2 1

½ hr. fr. sc. door & 100 conc. step to cupboard under stairs

C

hall

½ hr. fr. sc. door & 100 conc. step

garage

5180
17'0"

3415
11'2"

kitchen

2670
8'9"

1885
6'2"

s.v.p.

feature porch

CN3

CN1

7345
24'1"

3355
11'0"

10700
35'1"

6660
21'10"

3000
9'10"

3000
9'10"

3680
12'1"

bed 2

bed 3

3430
11'3"

1 2 3 4 5 6 7 8 9 10 11

1700
5'7"

1800
5'11"

gallery

s.v.p.

bath

3255
10'6"

cyl

girder truss over

bed 1

4460
14'8"

4835
15'10"

5395
17'8"

1265
4'2"

handrail on landing 900 high balusters spaced so as not to pass 100 dia sphere.

bath

bulkhead required

stairs to B regs part H.

2000 clear

store

clks

SECTION B-B

windbracing

girder truss position

100 x 25 binders

900 wide sided walkway t+g staggered

bed 1

2312 clear

bed 3

double joist under partition

2575 floor to floor

18 t+g chipboard on 200 x 50 joists max 400 centres

600 x 225 concrete footing, depth determined by site conditions. Min. 150mm hardcore compacted and blinded. Cavity fill not less than 225mm below dpc. 1200 gauge pvc damp proof membrane lapped over dpc to wall. 100 mm concrete with 37mm screed. See also specification notes.

kitchen

hall

SECTION A-A

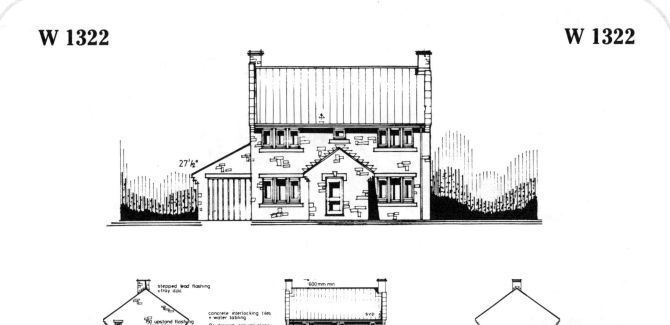

27'½°

stepped lead flashing
+ tray d.p.c.

concrete interlocking tiles
+ water tabling
Re dressed natural stone

150 upstand flashing
+ tray d.p.c.

Hardwood casement joinery
with artificial stone mullians
cills + headers

600 mm min

svp

side elevation   rear elevation   side elevation

A plan drawn for a cottage on a small infill plot in a picture book Yorkshire village, working to the clients very specific requirements. It not only provides exactly the arrangement of rooms to suit their living pattern, but also from outside has all the feel and character of the adjacent cottages.

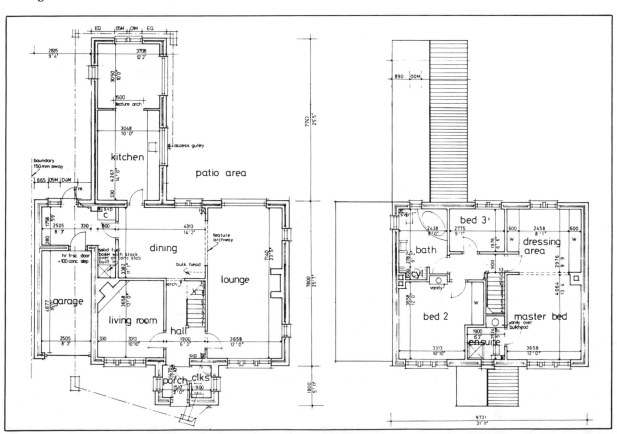

front elevation

rear elevation 1·100

dark grey plain clay tiles

Warren Carr Masoncrete
reconstructed stone, with
stone lintels + cills

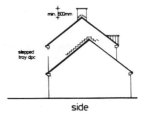

side

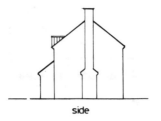

side

An effective design that looks a great deal more complex than it really is. The three gables over the first floor windows in the front elevation are purely decorative, and a cost-effective trussed rafter roof is used. Note the diagonally boarded wooden up-and-over garage doors.

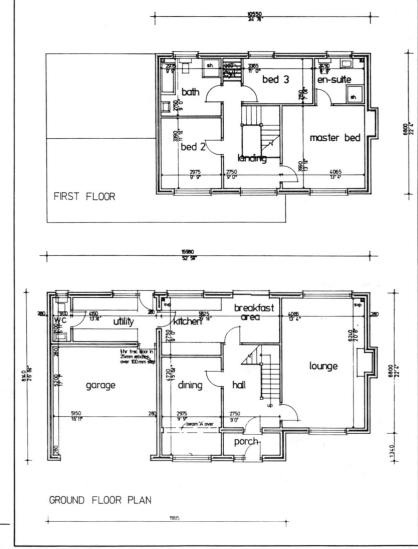

FIRST FLOOR

GROUND FLOOR PLAN

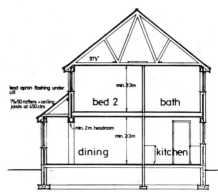

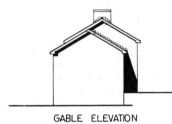

GABLE ELEVATION

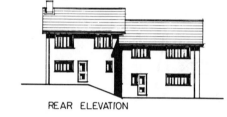

REAR ELEVATION

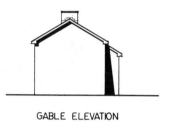

GABLE ELEVATION

This is a house designed to be built in two stages. The left hand part is built first, providing conventional three bedroom accommodation. The right hand half, intended to be constructed later, has an integral garage and, unusually, a huge lounge at the very top of the house.

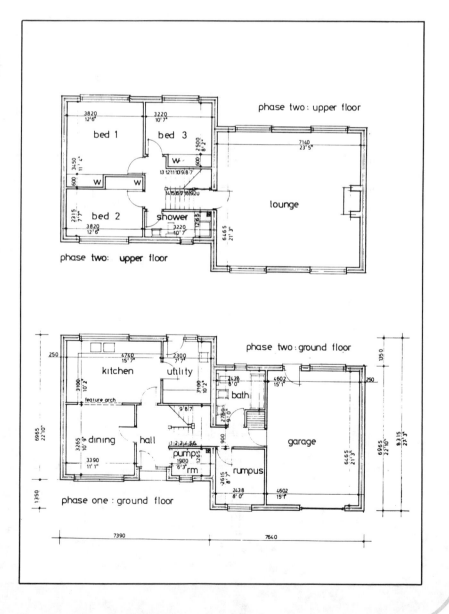

W 1256

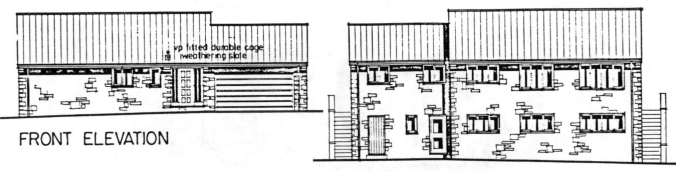

FRONT ELEVATION

REAR ELEVATION

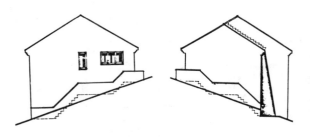

An upside-down house for a steeply sloping site with the living rooms above and the bedrooms and bathroom below. Unusually for this sort of home there is a door giving direct access to the garden at the lower level, adjacent to a utility room and a garden store.

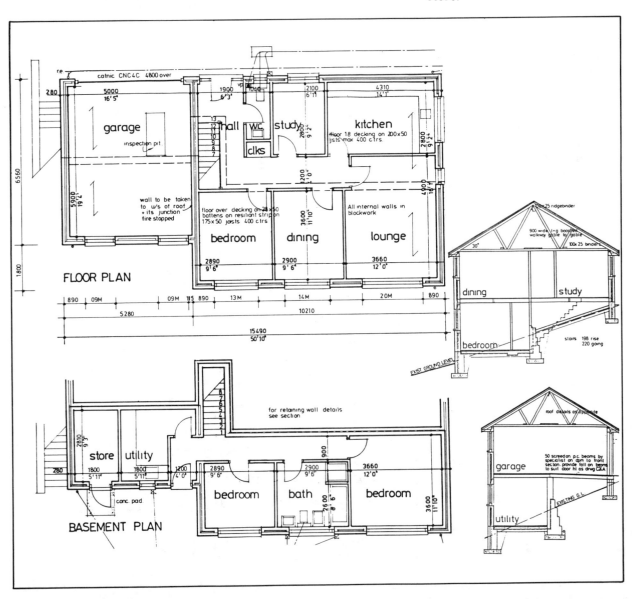

FLOOR PLAN

BASEMENT PLAN

P 2610

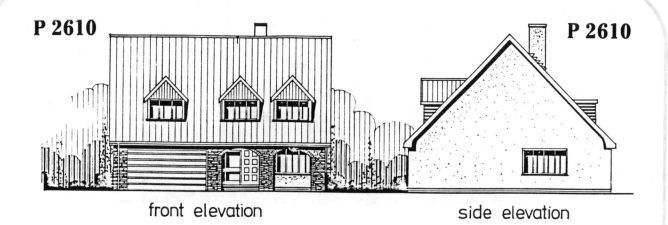

front elevation
side elevation

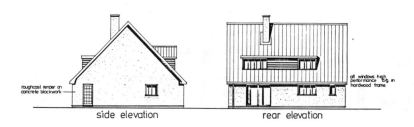

side elevation
rear elevation

This dormer bungalow was designed for a site in Scotland, with gable dormer windows in the roof at the front, and a cheaper flat roofed dormer at the rear. There is a lounge with a dining alcove on the ground floor, and a drawing room of the same size above it, so that it would be quite easy to arrange for this building to be used for two separate flats.

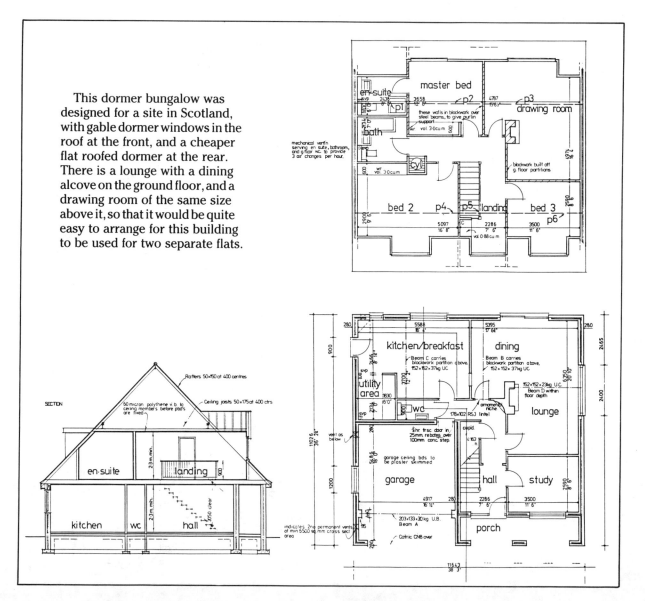

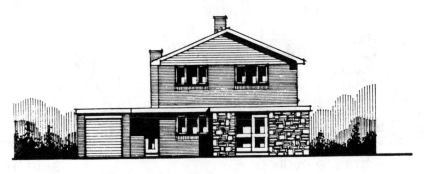

FRONT ELEVATION

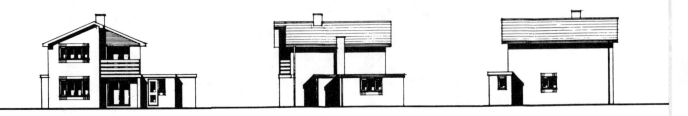

An interesting house for a site in South Wales where flat roofs to single storey parts of a structure are still quite common. The first floor balcony is an attractive feature, although it restricts the size of the adjoining bedroom. If it is not required then this bedroom can be thirteen feet long.

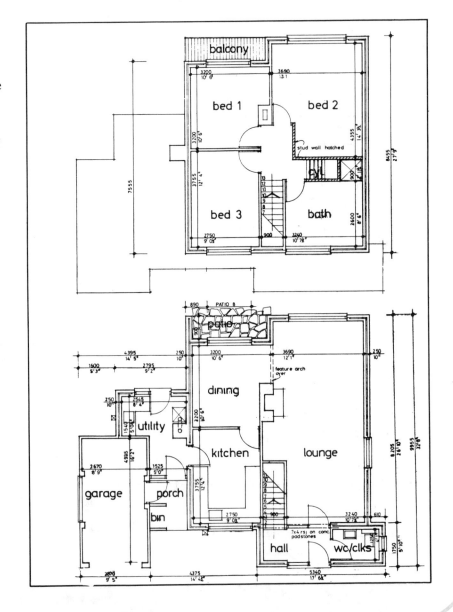

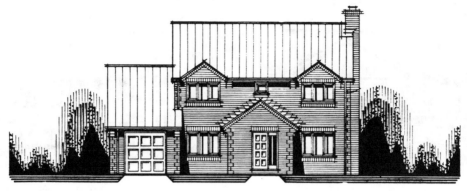

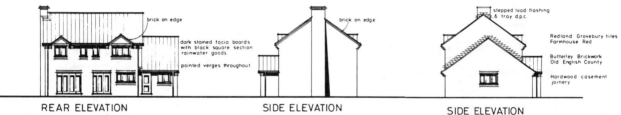

brick on edge

dark stained facia boards
with black square section
rainwater goods

pointed verges throughout

brick on edge

stepped lead flashing
& tray d.p.c.

Redland Grovebury tiles
Farmhouse Red

Butterley Brickwork
Old English County

Hardwood casement
joinery

REAR ELEVATION   SIDE ELEVATION   SIDE ELEVATION

Another house with a
pronounced period feel to it,
needing plenty of features in the
brickwork - corbelled eaves,
dentil courses and brick cills. The
french windows in the rear
elevation are more in keeping
with the style than patio windows,
although many people building
this home would opt for the
convenience of sliding patio
windows.

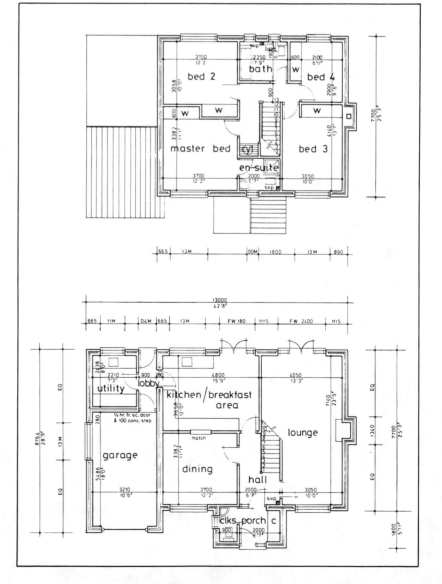

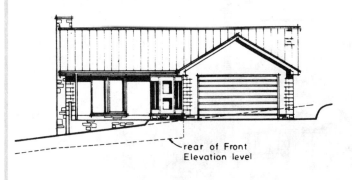

FRONT ELEVATION

rear of Front Elevation level

REAR ELEVATION

Marley Modern grey roof tiles

render with Bradstone quoins

existing garden level

drain

SIDE ELEVATION

banking

SIDE ELEVATION

This "upside-down" house for a sloping site has the garage, entrance and living accommodation on the upper floor with three bedrooms and two bathrooms below. If everything else suits, then this arrangement has many advantages, particularly if there are good views to be enjoyed from the lounge window. The disadvantage is that the front door is the only way out into the back garden, although in this case there is a balcony outside the patio windows in the lounge.

This sort of home is usually fairly expensive to build, but can be expected to have a high re-sale value. The plans are for it to be built on a massive stone plinth, with the superstructure in rendered blockwork with stone features. This sort of design always looks well in stone and render, but if built in brick it can be made to look just as attractive by building planting boxes against the exposed plinth brickwork.

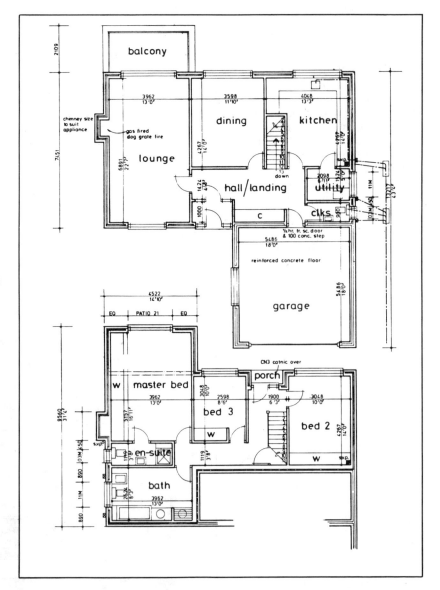

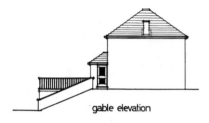

gable elevation

rear elevation

This way of putting a garage below a house on a sloping site is very popular in seaside towns, perhaps because it is there that one hopes for good enough weather to sit out on the terrace formed by the garage roof.

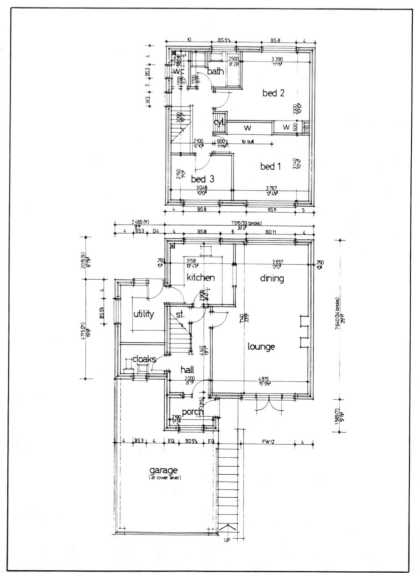

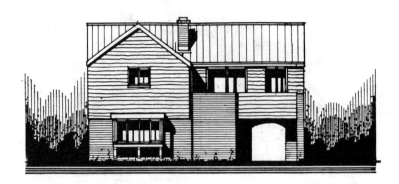

REAR ELEVATION

GABLE ELEVATIONS

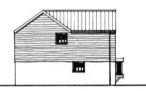

An interesting house: it takes a little time to puzzle out how it works. There are only two bedrooms, a large first floor lounge, and both the main bedroom and the lounge open onto a balcony.

On the ground floor an open car port under the lounge and balcony is an unusual feature. The combination of brick and timber boarding is in a pronounced regional style, and the bay window on gallows brackets adds further character.

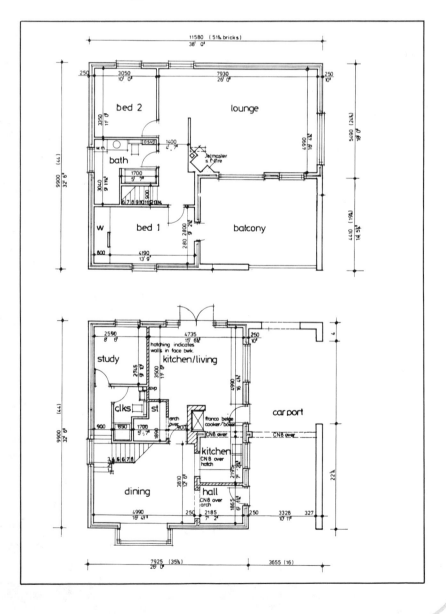

SOUTH

EAST ELEVATION

An unusual house with a most interesting layout and a huge lounge. Many people would want feature double doors from the hall into a lounge like this, but one of the delights of choosing the design of your own home is making your own decision in things like this. Only three bedrooms, but they are all double rooms.

WEST ELEVATION

NORTH

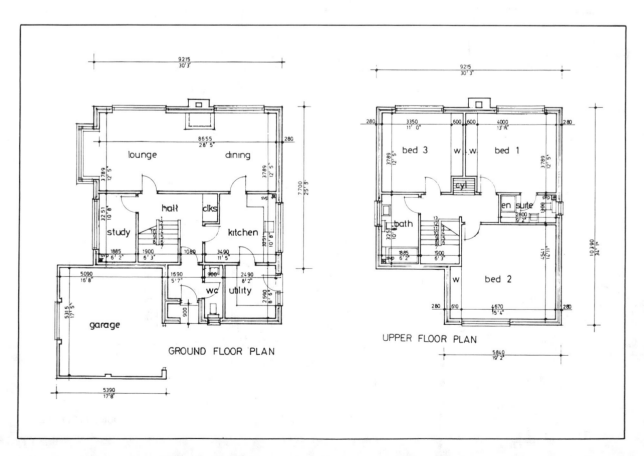

GROUND FLOOR PLAN

UPPER FLOOR PLAN

REAR ELEVATION   SIDE ELEVATION   SIDE ELEVATION

This house and garage are on four different levels, but as there is no internal communication between the garage and the living accommodation the layout is quite simple.

There is a balcony to the lounge, and the drawings shew a fully glazed screen between the two. This needs very careful consideration as it will dominate the lounge. The screen, and the balcony railings, must suit the decor envisaged for the room. If in doubt, revert to ordinary french windows!

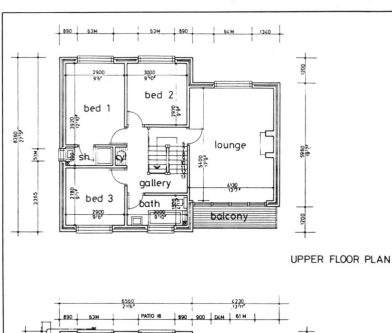

UPPER FLOOR PLAN

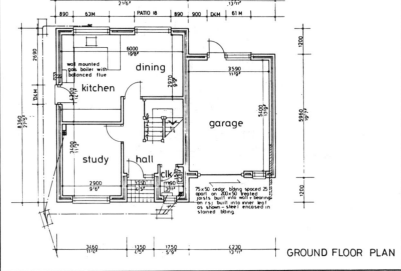

GROUND FLOOR PLAN

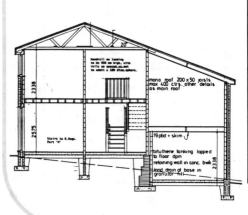

600mm min

FRONT ELEVATION

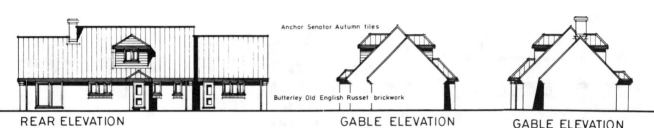

REAR ELEVATION

Anchor Senator Autumn tiles

Butterley Old English Russet brickwork

GABLE ELEVATION

GABLE ELEVATION

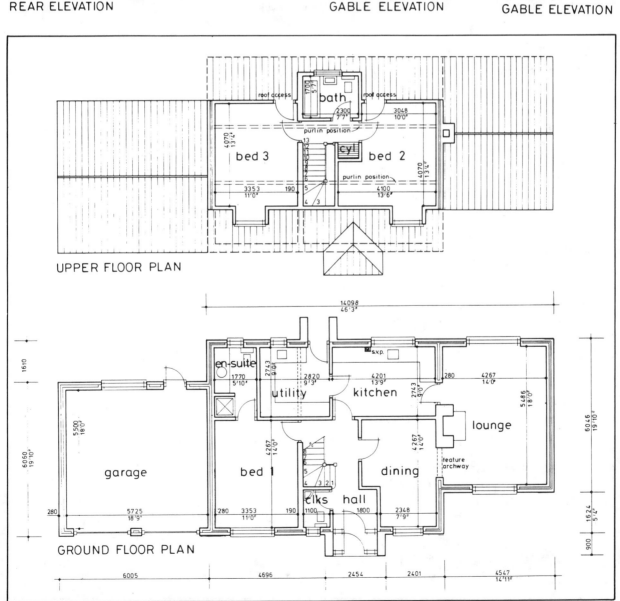

UPPER FLOOR PLAN

bath
roof access
roof access
2300 7'7"
3048 10'0"
purlin position
4070 13'4"
bed 3
cyl
bed 2
4070 13'4"
purlin position
3353 11'0"
190
4100 13'6"

GROUND FLOOR PLAN

14098 46'3"
1610
en-suite
1770 5'10"
2743 9'0"
2820 9'3"
4201 13'9"
280
4267 14'0"
s.v.p.
utility
kitchen
2743 9'0"
5486 18'0"
6046 19'10"
5500 18'0"
lounge
6060 19'10"
4267 14'0"
4267 14'0"
garage
bed 1
dining
feature archway
clks
hall
1624 5'4"
280
5725 18'9"
280
3353 11'0"
190
1100
1800
2348 7'9"
900
6005
4696
2454
2401
4547 14'11"

263

South elevation

North elevation

durable cage + weathering slate

s.v.p. fitted

Redland 50 brown tiles

L.B.C. Dapple lights

Hardwood external joinery.

East elevation

Velux

West elevation

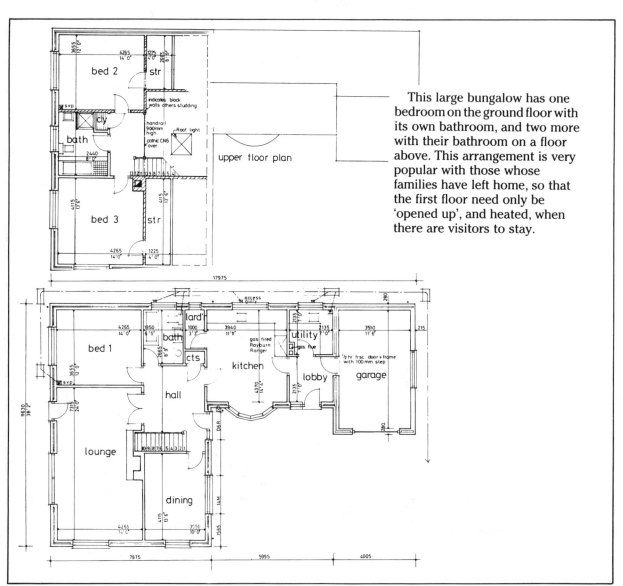

bed 2   str

3655 / 12'0"   4265 / 14'0"   1275 / 4'0"

indicates block walls others studding

svp

cly

bath

2440 / 8'0"

handrail 900mm high

catnic CN6 over

Roof light

upper floor plan

bed 3   str

4115 / 13'6"   4115 / 13'6"

4265 / 14'0"   1225 / 4'0"

This large bungalow has one bedroom on the ground floor with its own bathroom, and two more with their bathroom on a floor above. This arrangement is very popular with those whose families have left home, so that the first floor need only be 'opened up', and heated, when there are visitors to stay.

17975

access gully

lard'r

bath

1950 / 6'5"   1000 / 3'3"   3940 / 11'11"   2135 / 7'0"

utility

3510 / 11'6"   215

bed 1

4265 / 14'0"

cts

kitchen

gas fired Rayburn Ranger

gas flue

lobby

1/2 hr frsc door + frame with 100mm step

garage

3655 / 12'0"

svp

hall

4370 / 14'4"

2135 / 7'0"

280

11630 / 38'2"

7315 / 24'0"

lounge

10 9 8 7 6 5 4 3 2 1

D6R

dining

4115 / 13'6"

4265 / 14'0"   3050 / 10'0"

1565

7975   5995   4005

S 547

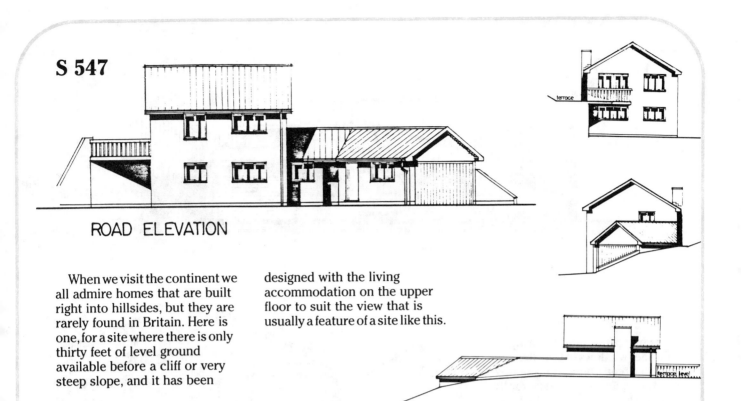

ROAD ELEVATION

When we visit the continent we all admire homes that are built right into hillsides, but they are rarely found in Britain. Here is one, for a site where there is only thirty feet of level ground available before a cliff or very steep slope, and it has been designed with the living accommodation on the upper floor to suit the view that is usually a feature of a site like this.

REAR ELEVATION

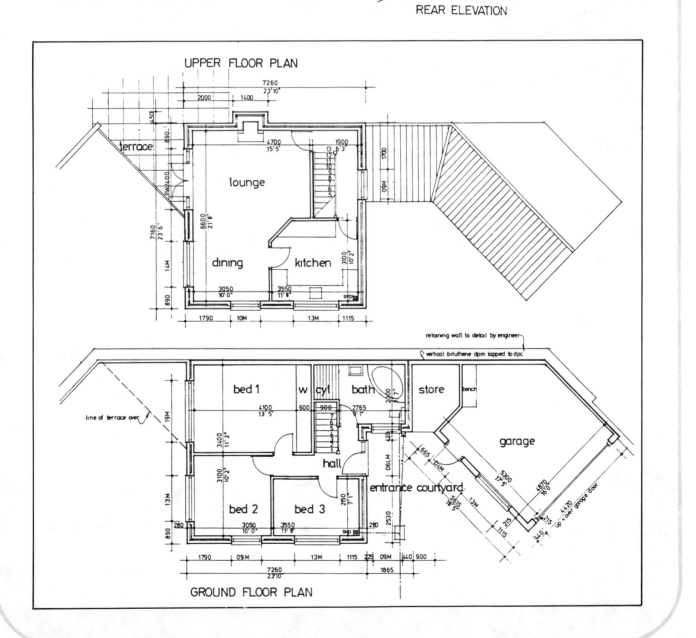

UPPER FLOOR PLAN

terrace

lounge

dining   kitchen

retaining wall to detail by engineer

vertical bituthene dpm lapped to dpc

line of terrace over

bed 1   w   cyl   bath   store   bench

garage

hall

bed 2   bed 3

entrance courtyard

GROUND FLOOR PLAN

265

FRONT ELEVATION

A bungalow with 'eyebrow' dormer windows to both the front and the rear. These were popular in the 1960s, but are now rarely seen. One reason is that a roof with these windows has to be tiled with very expensive 8" x 5" tiles, making this a very costly feature.

Most clients building a home with this layout would want the ground floor bathroom to be en-suite with the main bedroom, especially as there is a separate cloakroom on the ground floor.

GABLE ELEVATIONS

REAR ELEVATION

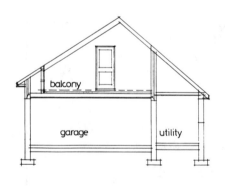

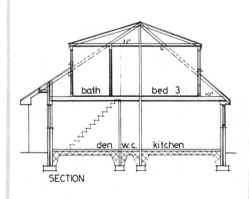

SECTION

W 1189

Roof tiles to be approved.

Reclaimed cheshire bricks

gables to be rendered
with tudor effect timbering.

SIDE ELEVATION   REAR ELEVATION

Only part of the roof space of this large bungalow is used for attic accommodation, but rooms could be put in the rest of the roof if required to give a total of five bedrooms. A decision to make provision for this will have to be made at an early stage, as it requires a purlin roof over the whole structure, while as shewn the main roof can be constructed more economically using trussed rafters.

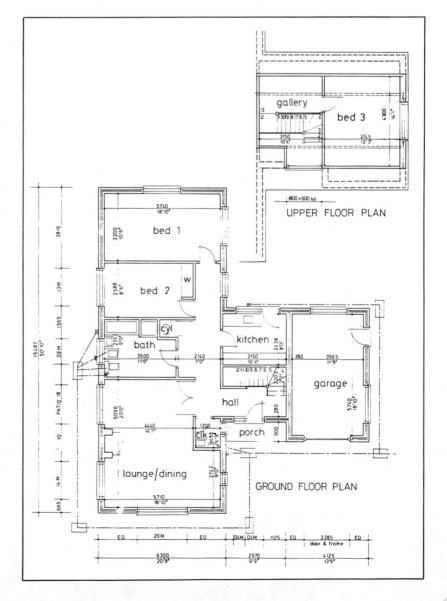

UPPER FLOOR PLAN

GROUND FLOOR PLAN

W 1093

150 upstand
flashing &
tray d.p.c.

FRONT ELEVATION

step fitted durable ridge
& weathering slate

1000mm min

stepped lead flashing
& tray d.p.c.

render

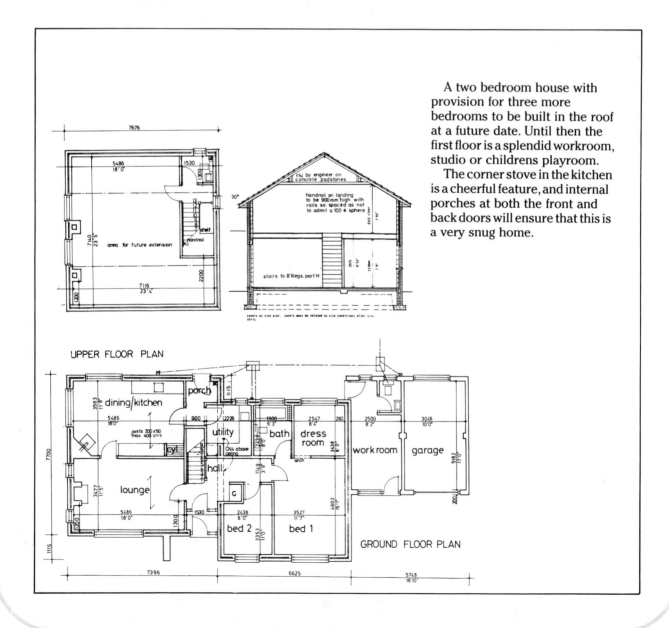

A two bedroom house with provision for three more bedrooms to be built in the roof at a future date. Until then the first floor is a splendid workroom, studio or childrens playroom.

The corner stove in the kitchen is a cheerful feature, and internal porches at both the front and back doors will ensure that this is a very snug home.

UPPER FLOOR PLAN

area for future extension

shelf
handrail

r.s.j. by engineer on concrete padstones

handrail on landing
to be 900mm high with
rails so spaced as not
to admit a 100 ø sphere

30°

stairs to B'Regs. part H

Levels as site plan. Levels must be related to site conditions after site strip.

dining/kitchen

porch

joists 200 x 50
max 400 ctrs

utility

cyl

hall

lounge

bath

dress room

arch

work room

garage

bed 2

bed 1

GROUND FLOOR PLAN

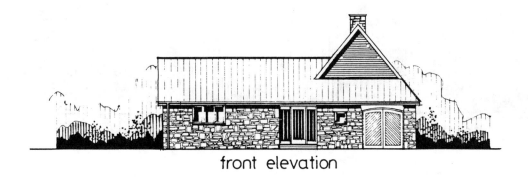

front elevation

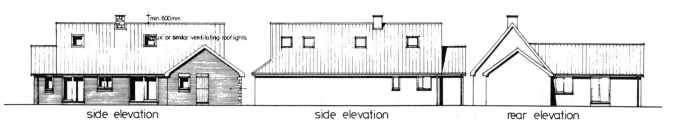

side elevation   side elevation   rear elevation

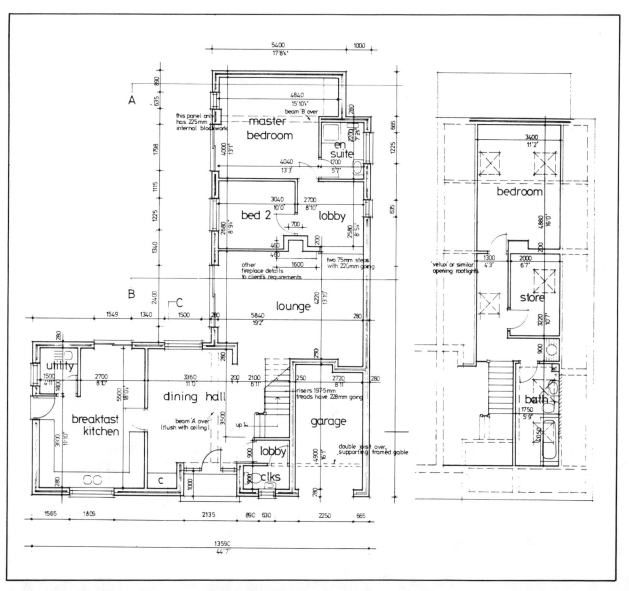

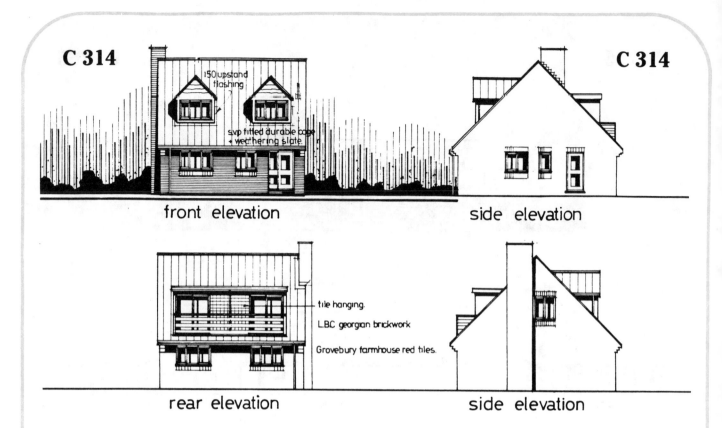

front elevation

side elevation

rear elevation

tile hanging.

LBC georgian brickwork

Grovebury farmhouse red tiles.

side elevation

A very unusual home. From the front it looks like any other dormer cottage, but the bedrooms are on the ground floor together with the utility room. A big lounge/dining room and the kitchen are upstairs, with a balcony set into the roof at the back. Definitely a house for those who have a very special view to the rear.

Remember a house like this will not appeal to everyone, so its resale potential may be limited, and the planners may not be happy about a balcony set in the roof in many areas. Still, a home with special character for a special site, and what fun to live in if you don't mind stairs.

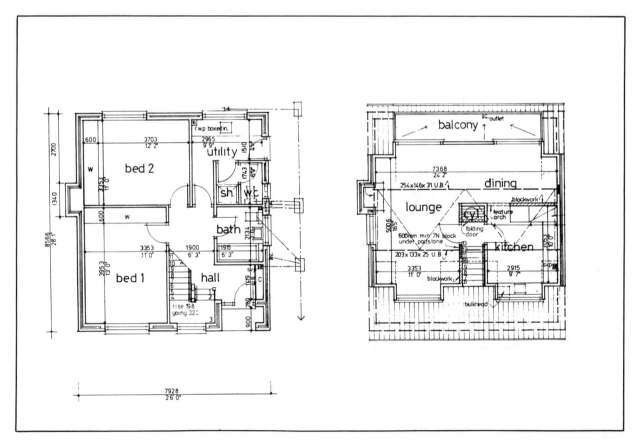

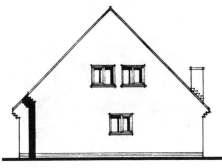

SIDE ELEVATION

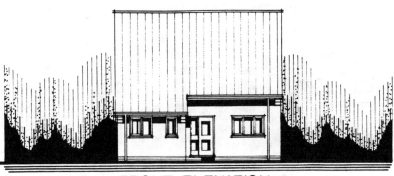

FRONT ELEVATION

SIDE ELEVATION

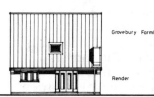

REAR ELEVATION

Grovebury Farmhouse Red

Render

A bungalow with room in the roof for lots more accommodation to be provided at a later date. Architects are often asked for this, and there are a number of designs in this book to meet the requirement. Note the corner fireplace in the lounge. The drawings show the minimum size of chimney to conform to the Building Regulations, but with a steep pitch roof it is likely that a higher chimney will be required if you are building in an exposed situation.

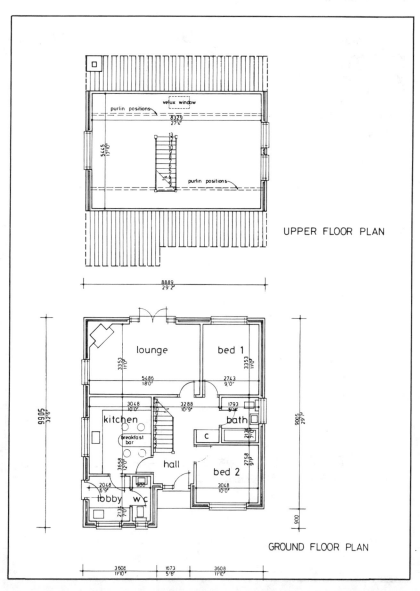

UPPER FLOOR PLAN

GROUND FLOOR PLAN

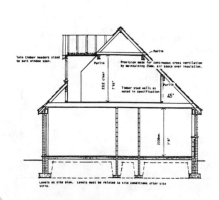

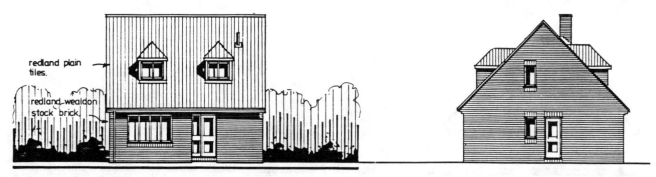

front (north) elevation　　　　　　west side elevation

A dormer country cottage very similar to design W 1251, but with the overall width increased by three bricks — 2'3" — and the lounge moved to the back of the building. The dormers have hip roofs, and were drawn this way because it is the local style where this cottage was built. Gable roofs are more usual.

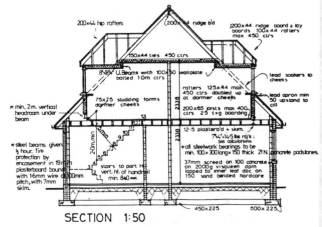

SECTION 1:50

east side elevation　　　　rear elevation

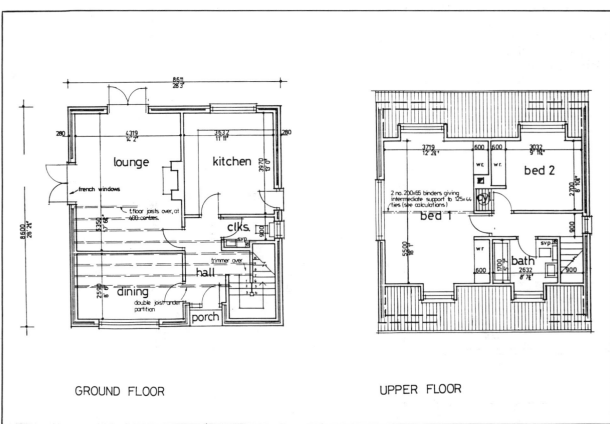

GROUND FLOOR　　　　　　　　　　UPPER FLOOR

FRONT ELEVATION

SIDE ELEVATION

interlocking tiles T.B.A.

Render with brick plinth

Hardwood casement joinery
with curved heads

limestone chippings on 3 layers felt
on 19 boarding s.w. firrings laid to
fall 1:40 min. on 200 x 50 joists max. 400 c/s
galv. holding down straps
every 3rd. joist

REAR ELEVATION

SIDE ELEVATION

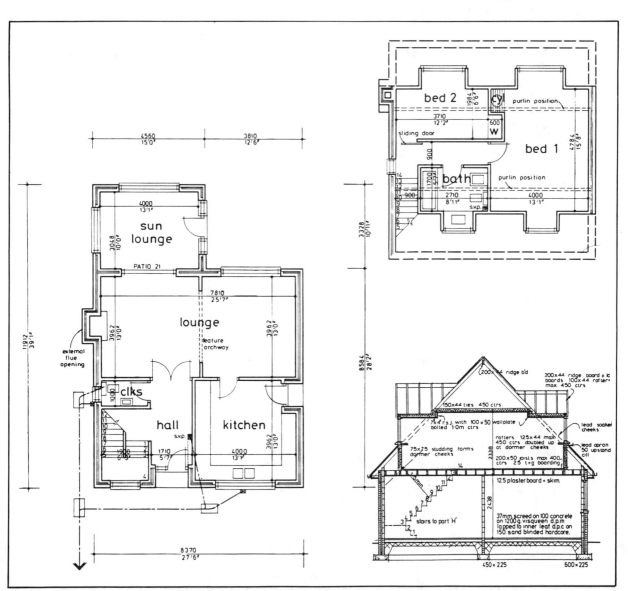

front elevation

rear elevation

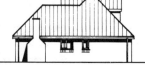

side elevation

side elevation

This dormer bungalow has the master bedroom suite downstairs, with two more bedrooms and the guest bathroom upstairs. This is a very popular arrangement with retired couples who can ignore their first floor except when their family come to stay! The study and lounge can be combined if desired.

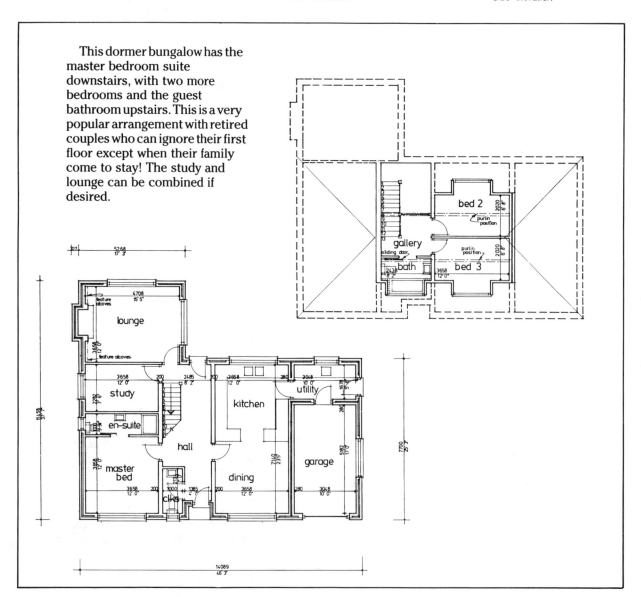

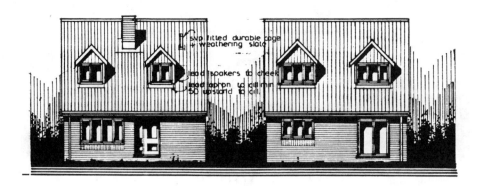

The popular 'dormer cottage' which is now very trendy indeed if you can find a gap in a village street in which to build it. In this version there is a very small utility room at the back door: many would prefer to amalgamate this with the kitchen, giving room for a kitchen table, and to have a small external porch to the back door if it needs weather protection.

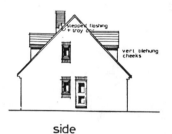

side

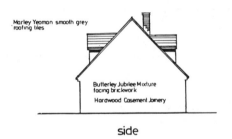

side

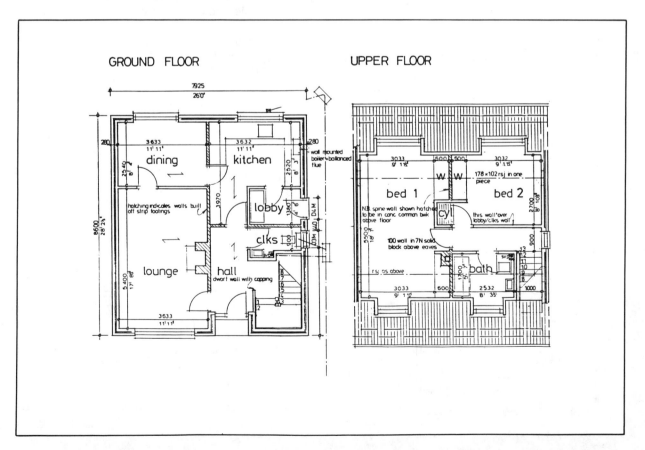

FRONT ELEVATION

SIDE ELEVATION

Marley Mendip tiles
Dark Brown

Redland Chailey brickwork

REAR ELEVATION

s.v.p. fitted durable dope
& weathering slate

SIDE ELEVATION

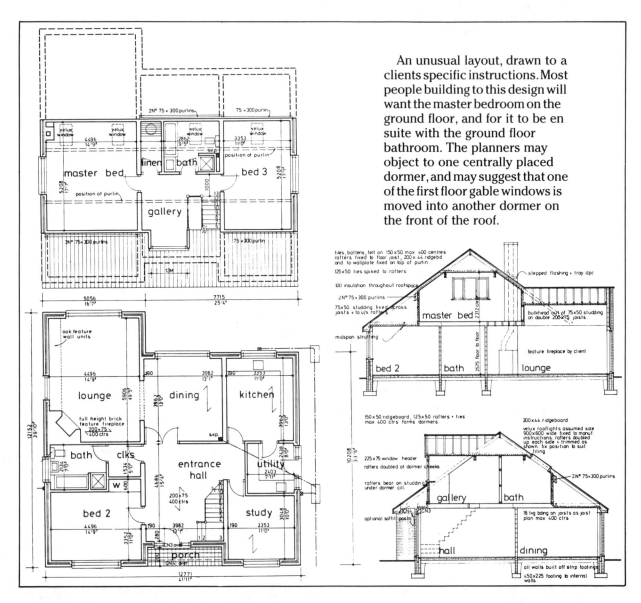

An unusual layout, drawn to a clients specific instructions. Most people building to this design will want the master bedroom on the ground floor, and for it to be en suite with the ground floor bathroom. The planners may object to one centrally placed dormer, and may suggest that one of the first floor gable windows is moved into another dormer on the front of the roof.

front elevation

rear elevation

Balcony balustrade min 1.1m. high to clients specification - spaces not to exceed 100mm.

gable elevation

valley flashing

min 1100 mm.

gable elevation

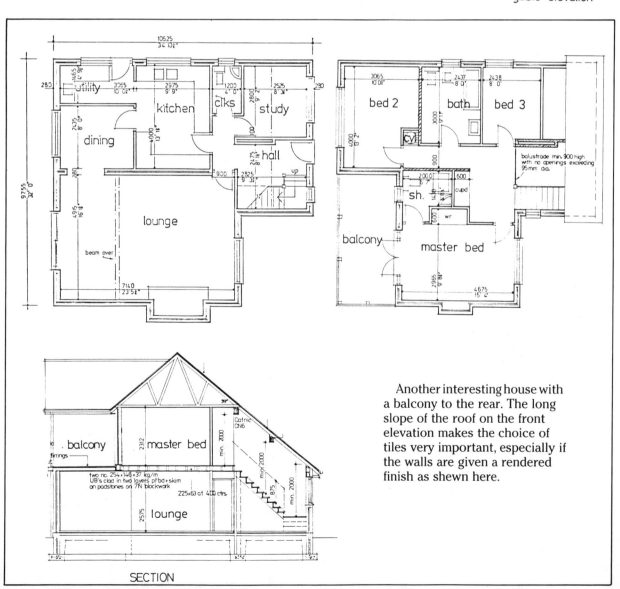

10525
34' 10½"

utility

3065
10' 0½"

2975
9' 9"

1200
4' 0"

2525
8' 3½"

2800
9' 3"

280

280

1465
4' 9½"

kitchen

clks

study

dining

2435
8' 0"

4000
13' 1½"

900

hall

2475
8' 1½"

280

9755
32' 0"

900

2525
8' 3½"

up

4915
16' 1½"

lounge

beam over

7140
23' 5½"

3065
10' 0½"

2437
8' 0"

2438
8' 0"

bed 2

bath

bed 3

4000
13' 2"

3000
9' 9"

cyl

balustrade min. 900 high with no openings exceeding 95mm dia.

2000
6' 7"

600

sh.

1440
4' 9½"

cupd

wr

600

balcony

master bed

2965
9' 8½"

4675
15' 4"

SECTION (lower left section drawing)

balcony

master bed

2312

min 2000

Catnic CN6

firrings

min 2000

two no. 254 x 146 x 37 kg/m UB's clad in two layers pl'bd + skim on padstones on 7N blockwork

225 x 63 at 400 ctrs.

875

min 2000

2575

lounge

SECTION

Another interesting house with a balcony to the rear. The long slope of the roof on the front elevation makes the choice of tiles very important, especially if the walls are given a rendered finish as shewn here.

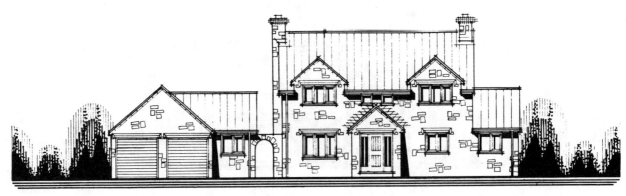

REAR ELEVATION

SIDE ELEVATION

stepped lead flashing
& tray d.p.c.

Redland Grovebury Tiles
Farmhouse Red

Bradstone Trad walling
Weathered Ham

Hardwood Casement joinery

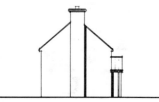

SIDE ELEVATION

This house in the Cotswold style has a layout which is now very popular. It is also very cost effective to build, as the gable features are purely decorative and an ordinary trussed rafter roof can be used with all the consequent cost savings. The trick is to keep the level of the gable window heads below the level of the wall plate. This permits a flat ceiling to the bedroom. Move the windows up in the strictly traditional style and you are necessarily involved in sloping ceilings, purlin roofs - and extra cost!

The off-set kitchen/breakfast area arrangement is interesting, and inevitably the breakfast area will become a family room if small children live in the home. It is just big enough for this, and french windows are shewn in this room. They can be replaced with an ordinary window if they are not appropriate.

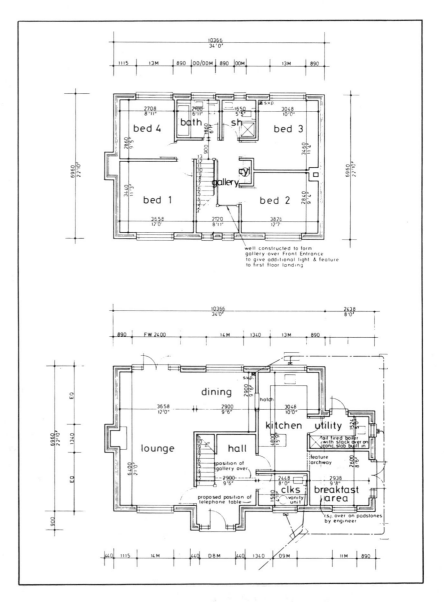

Front elevation

This large bungalow has some very interesting features. No fewer than five of the rooms have more than four walls, and this gives an excitingly different feel to the home as soon as the visitor steps through the porch into the dining hall with its off-set doors into the lounge.

In spite of the complex shape the whole of the roof is supported on the external walls, so that rooms can be rearranged just as you wish. In particular, the utility room area can become a cloakroom with access to the entrance porch if required, and of course the garage doors can be moved to either the front or the rear.

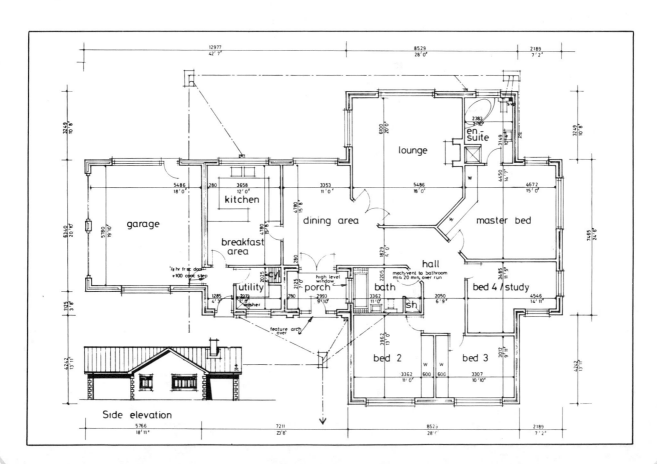

Side elevation

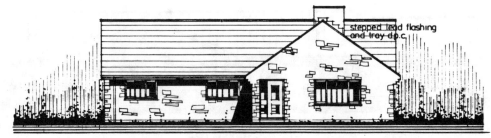

FRONT ELEVATION

SIDE ELEVATIONS   REAR ELEVATION

A bungalow for a family that likes open-plan living, with a kitchen/dining/living area as big as the whole of the rest of the accommodation! An arrangement like this invariably requires a separate utility room or back porch, and here we see both of them. The porch need not be built if it is not required.

The pillar that supports the corner of the roof to the large front porch needs careful consideration in a design like this. It is shewn here as a stone pillar of orthodox size, but could be much more interesting with a little thought.

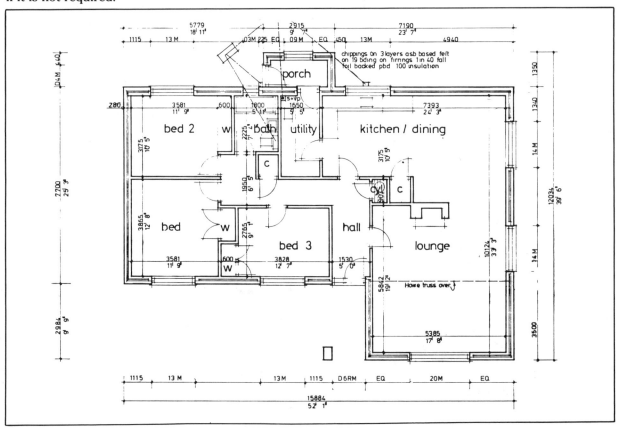

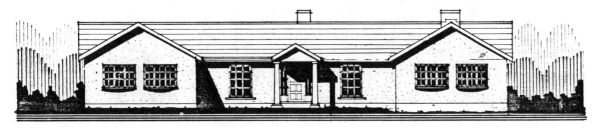

FRONT ELEVATION

The site for this large bungalow was in Southern Ireland, where plots to take a single storey dwelling of this size are still readily available. Note the change of levels in the lounge and the interesting family room.

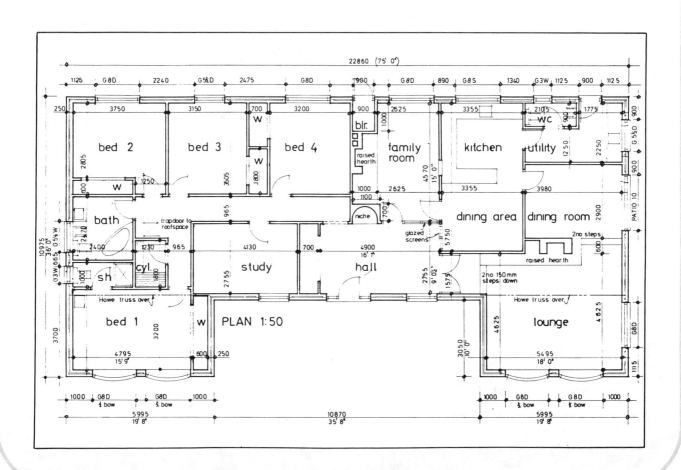

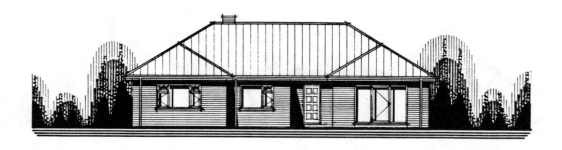

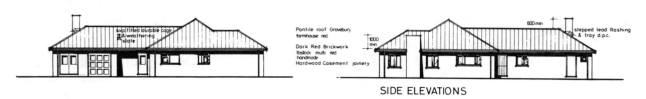

Pantile roof Grovebury
farmhouse red

Dark Red Brickwork
Ibstock multi red
handmade
Hardwood Casement joinery

SIDE ELEVATIONS

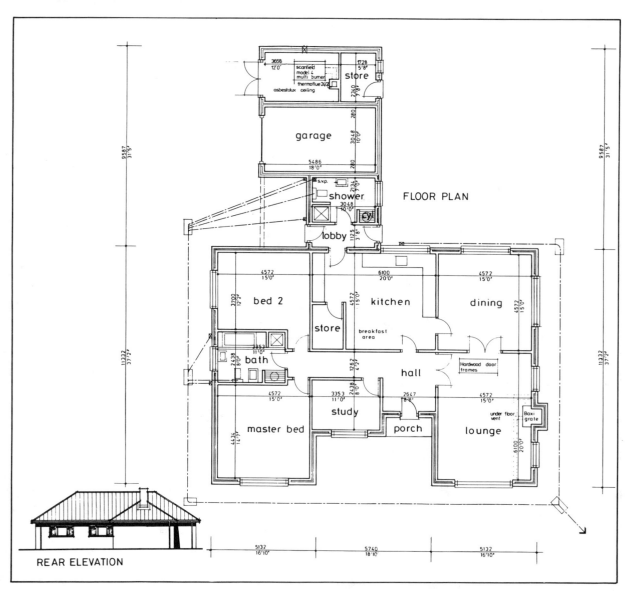

svp fitted durable cage
& weathering slate

1000 min

600 min

stepped lead flashing
& tray d.p.c.

FLOOR PLAN

3658
12'0"

scanfield
model 4
multi burner
thermoflue 24/2
asbestolux ceiling

1728
5'8"

store

2340
7'8"

280

garage

3048
10'0"

5486
18'0"

280

s.v.p.

2134
7'0"

shower

3048
10'0"

1125
3'8"

lobby

4572
15'0"

6100
20'0"

4572
15'0"

3200
12'2"

bed 2

4572
15'0"

kitchen

dining

4572
15'0"

store

breakfast
area

2852
11'0"

2438
8'0"

bath

1262
4'2"

hall

Hardwood door
frames

4572
15'0"

3353
11'0"

2438
8'0"

2647
8'8"

4572
15'0"

study

4436
14'7"

master bed

porch

lounge

under floor
vent

Baxi
grate

6100
20'0"

9587
31'5"

11332
37'2"

9587
31'5"

11332
37'2"

5132
16'10"

5740
18'10"

5132
16'10"

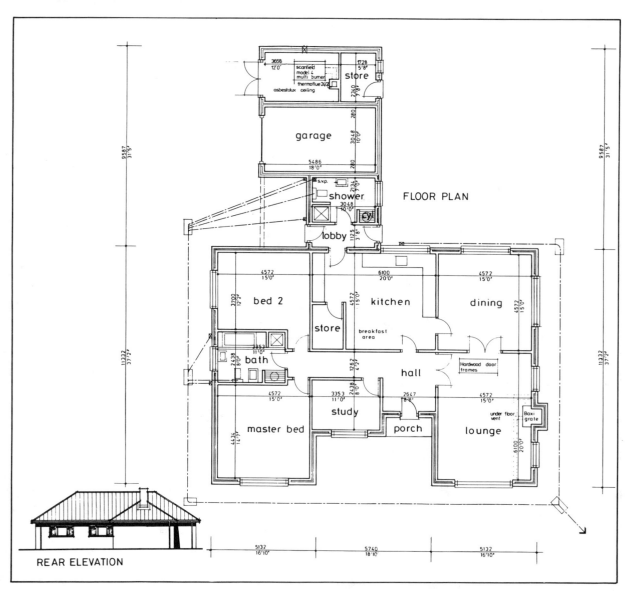

REAR ELEVATION

south west elevation

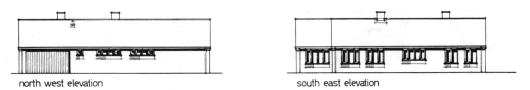

north west elevation

south east elevation

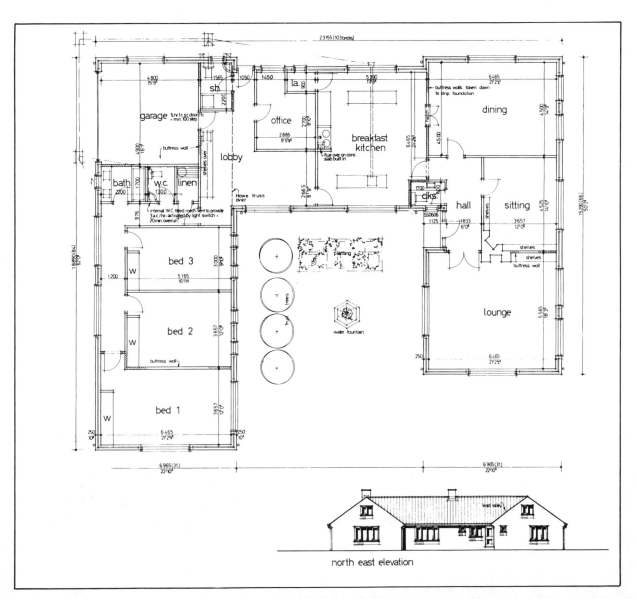

garage

sh.

la.

office

breakfast kitchen

dining

lobby

bath

W.C.

linen

cks

hall

sitting

bed 3

lounge

bed 2

bed 1

planting

trees

water fountain

north east elevation

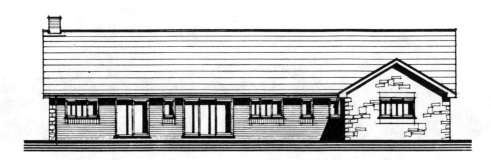

FRONT ELEVATION

REAR ELEVATION

GABLE ELEVATION

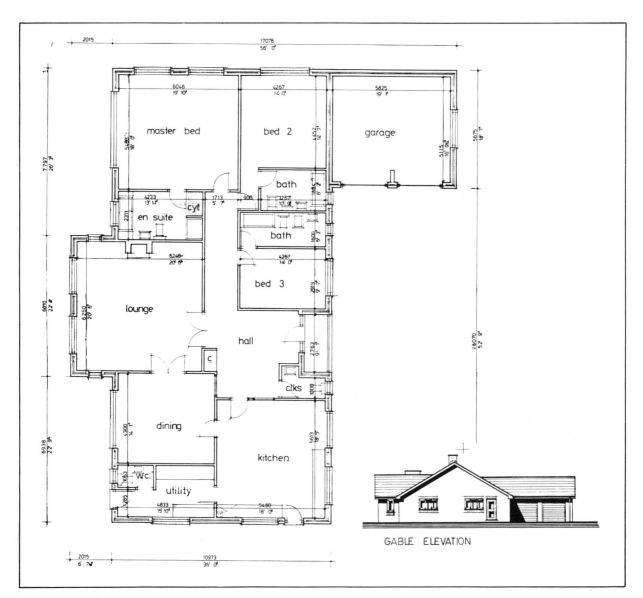

GABLE ELEVATION

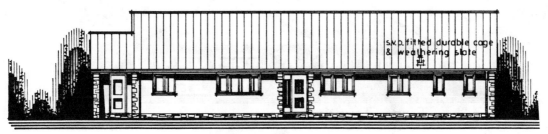

ENTRANCE ELEVATION

REAR ELEVATION

SIDE ELEVATION

SIDE ELEVATION

A bungalow with a wide frontage for a site where the views are all on the opposite side to the front entrance. There is an open plan kitchen/living/dining area that is shewn here entered through a feature archway. It could also be reached by going down two or three steps, giving an interesting change of levels.

The study is tiny, with no more room in it than is required for a desk, a bookcase and a filing cabinet - anything more was considered distracting!

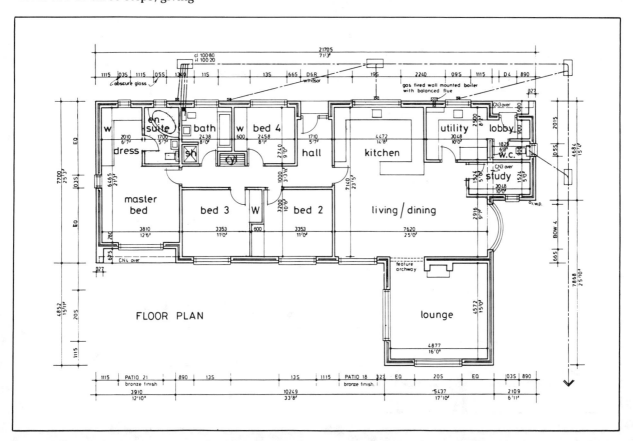

FLOOR PLAN

Front Elevation

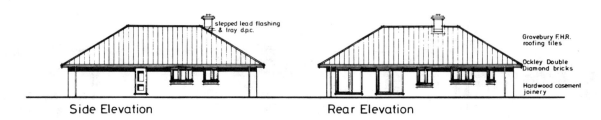

slepped lead flashing
& tray d.p.c.

Grovebury F.H.R.
roofing tiles

Ockley Double
Diamond bricks

Hardwood casement
joinery

Side Elevation

Rear Elevation

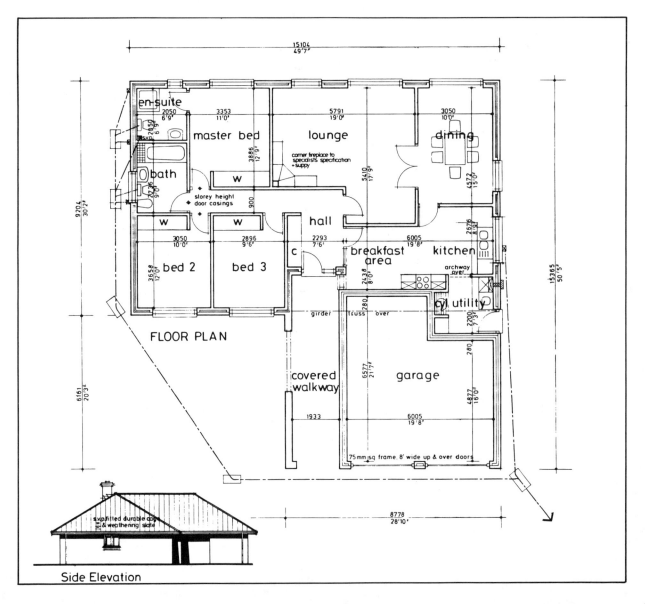

15104
49'7"

en-suite

2050
6'9"

3353
11'0"

5791
19'0"

3050
10'0"

master bed

lounge

dining

2050
6'9"

3886
12'9"

corner fireplace to
specialists specification
+ supply

5410
17'9"

4572
15'0"

bath

w

9204
30'2"

2676
8'9"

storey height
door casings

w

w

hall

2293
7'6"

2896
9'6"

breakfast
area

6005
19'8"

kitchen

2438
8'0"

archway
over

3050
10'0"

c

15365
50'5"

3658
12'0"

bed 2

bed 3

cyl utility

2200
7'3"

280

FLOOR PLAN

280

girder   truss   over

6577
21'7"

covered
walkway

garage

4877
16'0"

6161
20'3"

1933

6005
19'8"

75mm sq frame. 8' wide up & over doors

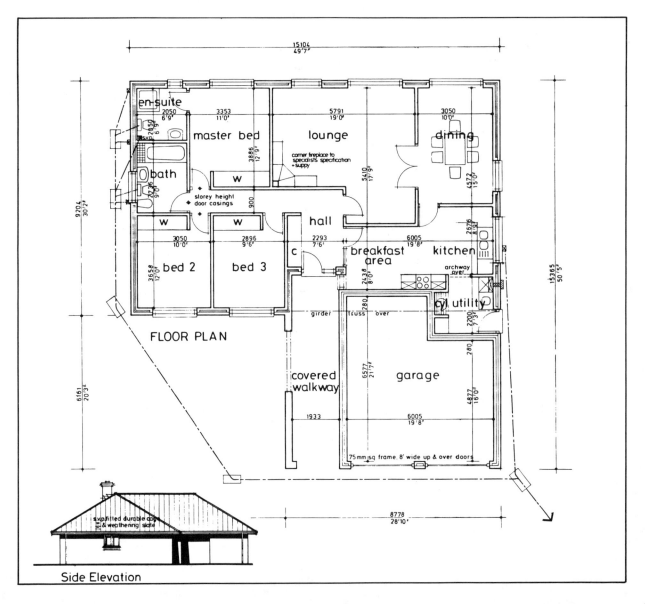

s.v.p.fitted durable dpc
& weathering slate

8778
28'10"

Side Elevation

FRONT ELEVATION

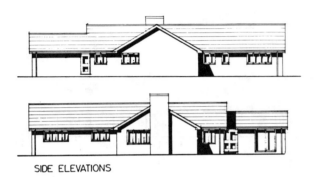

SIDE ELEVATIONS

This bungalow has a three roomed granny flat with its own front door, and has a particularly interesting layout. Although the front door elevation is only 46ft. wide, windows on side walls require that it shall be on a 70ft. plot.

REAR ELEVATION

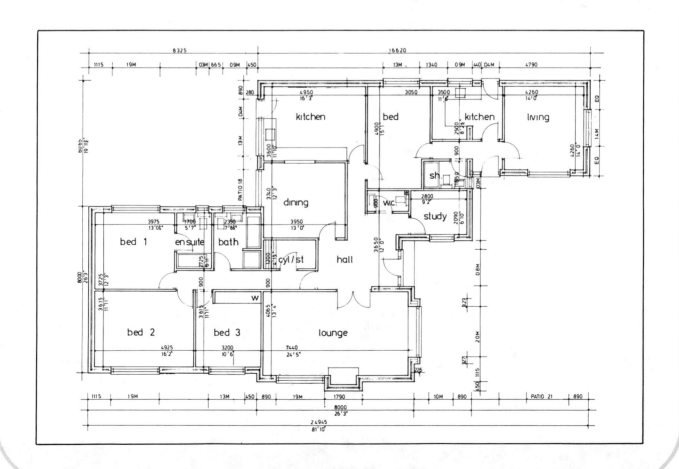

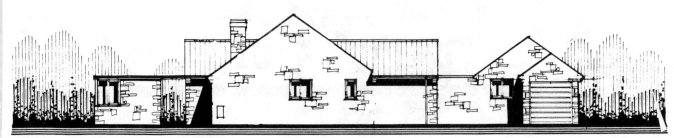

SIDE ELEVATION

FRONT ELEVATION   SIDE ELEVATION   REAR ELEVATION

This plan was drawn to meet the requirements of a very meticulous client in Lincolnshire who always visualised his new home as an integral part of his new garden, planned them both together, and gave a lot of thought to how his garage, workshop and garden store would all be part of the whole development. He built it all himself using sub-contractors, and gave every detail of the construction as much care as went into drawing the plans. The result is a very beautiful home.

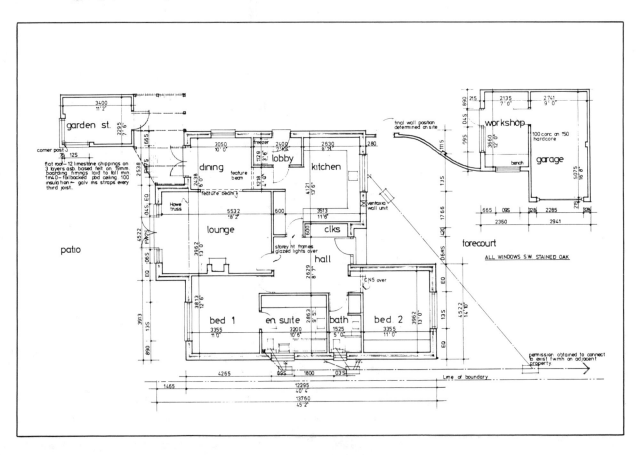

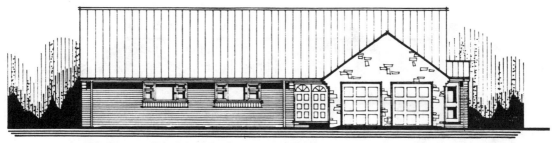

FRONT ELEVATION

SIDE ELEVATIONS

1000 mm min

stepped flashing + tray dpc

900 ht handrail to well provide escape window

trapped gully + drain to well

REAR ELEVATION

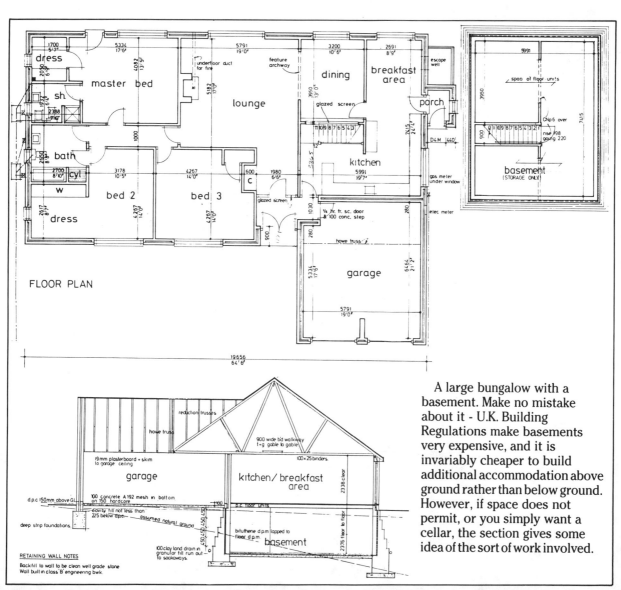

FLOOR PLAN

dress
master bed
sh
bath
cyl
w
dress
bed 2
bed 3
lounge
dining
breakfast area
parch
kitchen
garage
escape well
feature archway
underfloor duct for fire
glazed screen
glazed screen
gas meter under window
elec meter
howe truss
½ hr. fr. sc. door & 100 conc. step
basement (STORAGE ONLY)
span of floor units
skip 6 over
rise 198 going 220

RETAINING WALL NOTES
Backfill to wall to be clean well grade stone
Wall built in class 'B' engineering bwk.

reduction trusses
howe truss
900 wide bld walkway t+g gable to gable
100 × 25 binders
19 mm plasterboard + skim to garage ceiling
garage
kitchen/ breakfast area
2338 clear
d.p.c 150mm above GL
100 concrete A192 mesh in bottom on 150 hardcore
deep strip foundations
cavity fill not less than 225 below dpc
assumed natural ground
bituthene d.p.m lapped to floor d.p.m.
r.c. floor units
basement
2376 floor to floor
100 clay land drain in granular fill run out to soakaways

A large bungalow with a basement. Make no mistake about it - U.K. Building Regulations make basements very expensive, and it is invariably cheaper to build additional accommodation above ground rather than below ground. However, if space does not permit, or you simply want a cellar, the section gives some idea of the sort of work involved.

FRONT ELEVATION

REAR ELEVATION

SIDE ELEVATIONS

This big bungalow has a sunken lounge with steps up through a feature archway to the open plan dining area. This arrangement is very striking, but requires large rooms and careful consideration of the details of the change in levels.

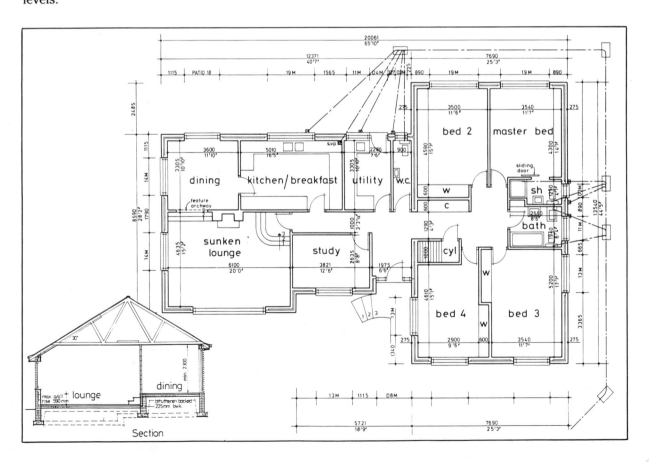

front (northwest) elevation

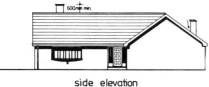

side elevation

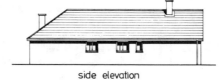

side elevation

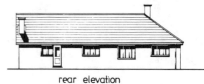

rear elevation

A bungalow with a conventional external appearance but an unusual layout inside. This was designed to enable both the lounge and the master bedroom to enjoy the same view, and the angled entrances to these rooms makes a very unusual and interesting hall.

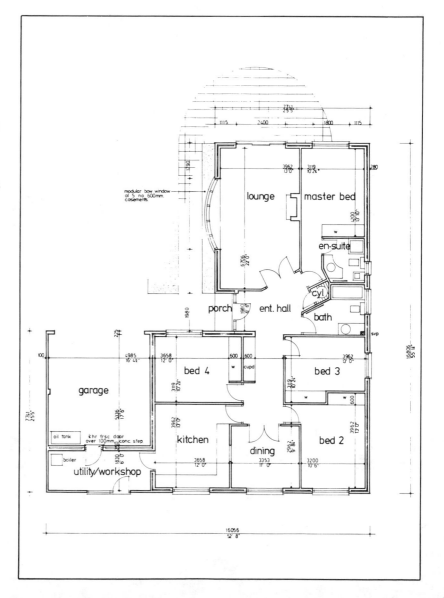

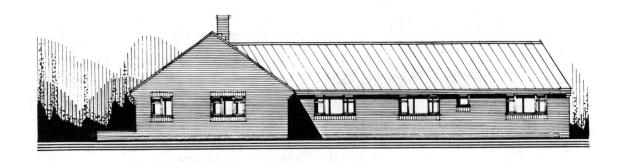

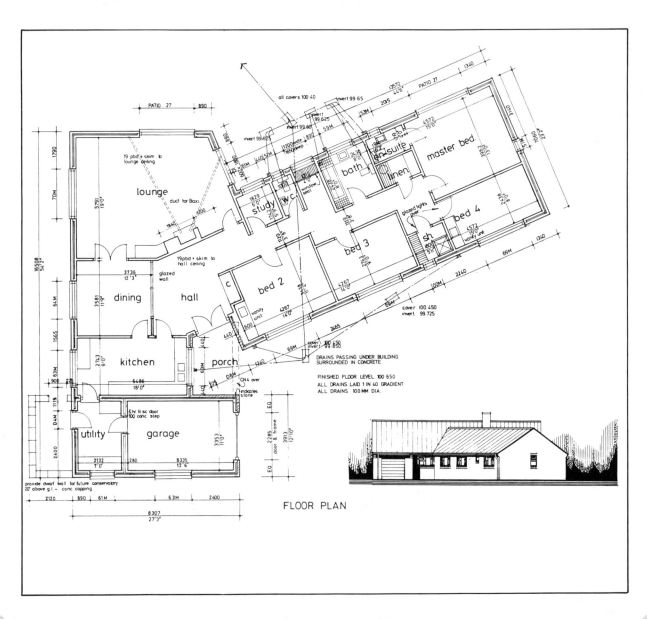

FLOOR PLAN

292

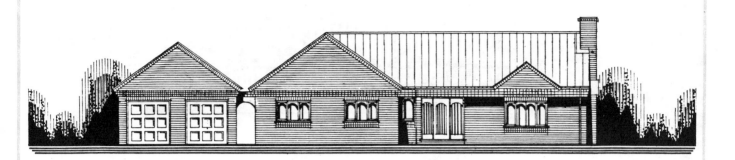

Marley Modern
Dark Grey Smooth tiles
Blockley XVIII Mixture
(wire cut texture) or
Blockley XXI Brindle mixture
(wrekin briar texture)
Raked joints square finish
colour grey to match tiles
Hardwood casement joinery
Blockley shaped bricks to
window cills

This interesting bungalow with arched window heads and a great deal of ornamental brickwork is very much in fashion, particularly in outer London or anywhere along the south coast. The small gable features do not add significantly to the cost as the windows are all below the wall plate of the main roof, but they give lots of character which will add significantly to the value.

The internal layout is a popular arrangement of a standard P.S.S. design concept, and if required the bedroom gable walls can be pushed out by a foot or two to give even larger rooms.

The doorframes to bedrooms three and four should extend up to the ceiling to enable glazed lights over these doors to brighten up the passage between the bedrooms.

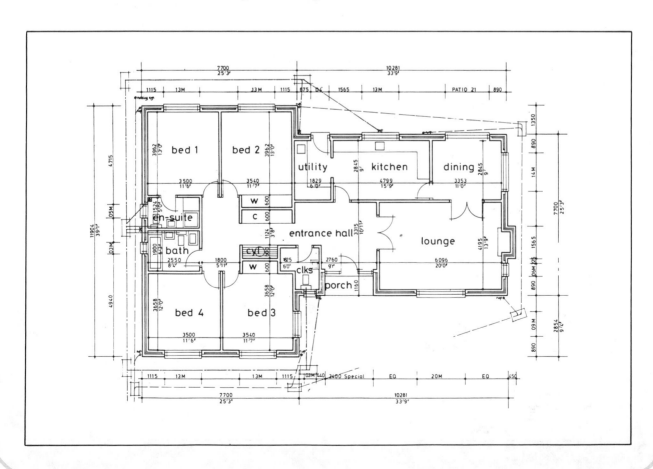

south elevation

This large bungalow has two changes of floor level, with two steps down into the lounge from the hall, and two more down into the two large end bedrooms from the bedroom corridor. The change of levels between the lounge and the dining room is shewn in the section, and this arrangement offers opportunities for really striking decor and furnishing.

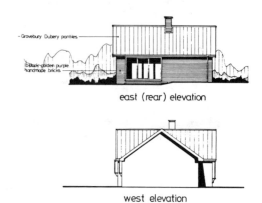

east (rear) elevation

west elevation

north elevation

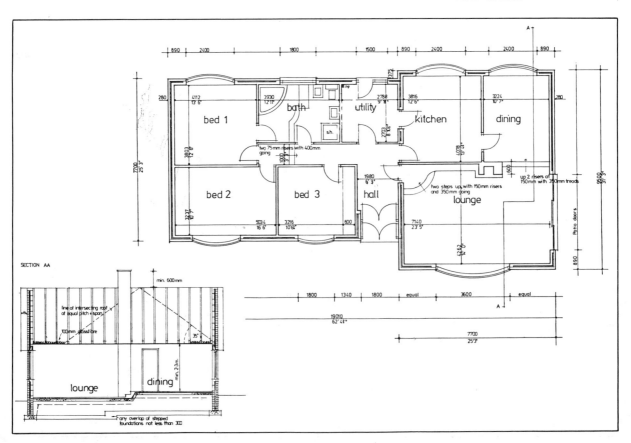

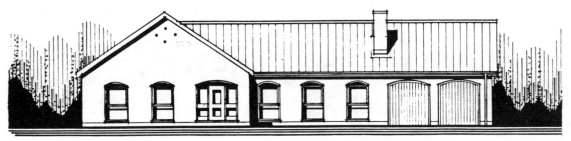

FRONT ELEVATION

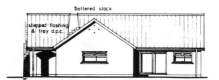

battered stack

stepped flashing
& tray d.p.c.

600 mm min

This big bungalow from Ireland
has a family room linked to the
kitchen which serves as a passage
to the family bedrooms. Unusual,
but a logical arrangement which
saves space.

REAR ELEVATION

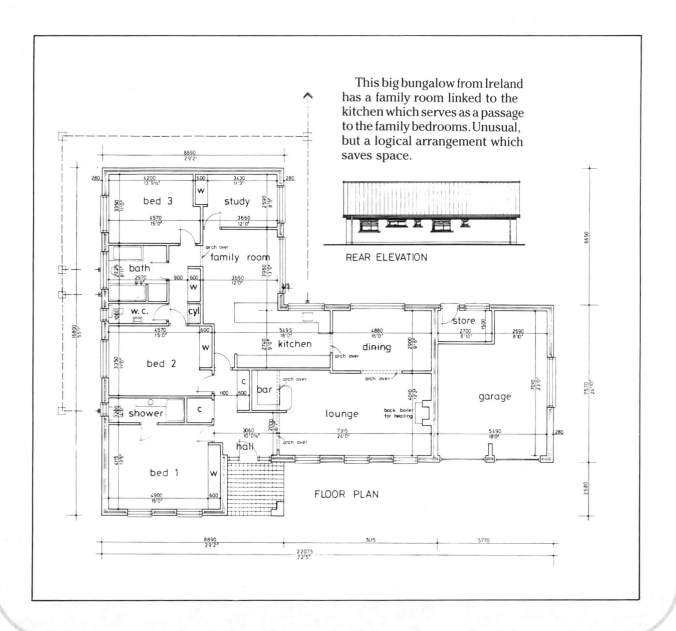

FLOOR PLAN

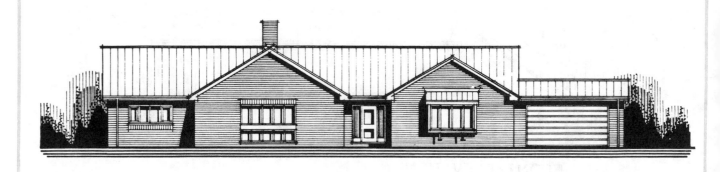

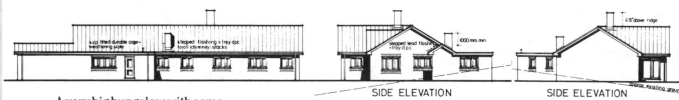

SIDE ELEVATION   SIDE ELEVATION

A very big bungalow with some original features. The big room at the back door is ideal for country living, but most people building a home of this size would want a cloakroom at the front door as well. The windows to the lounge and dining room are unusual: of course, subject to the veto of the planners more conventional windows could be used.

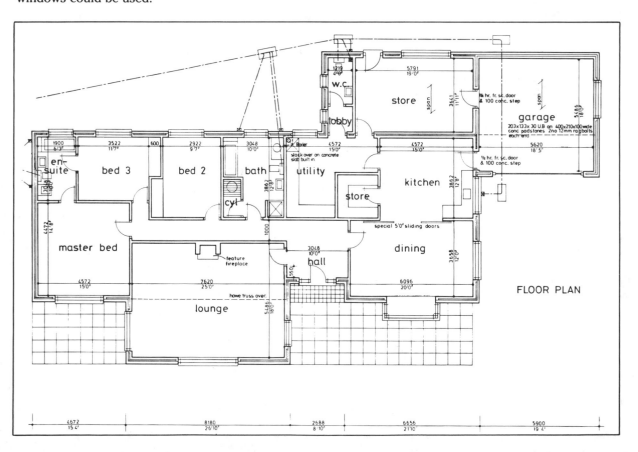

FLOOR PLAN

front elevation 1·100

stepped flashing

hardwood external joinery

side elevation 1·100

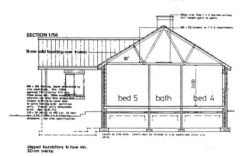

SECTION 1/50

18 mm solid boarding over trusses

30°

2400

bed 5   bath   bed 4

stepped foundations to have min.
300 mm overlay.

Six bedrooms - or seven if you re-designate the study. This very functional bungalow has a lounge with a floor that is two steps down from the level of the rest of the home, with the open plan dining area on the higher level. This arrangement is used in a number of designs in these plan books, and is very effective.

This bungalow was originally designed to be built in light buff colour facing bricks with dark hardwood joinery under a brown tile roof. This is a very good way to ensure a big bungalow looks light and welcoming.

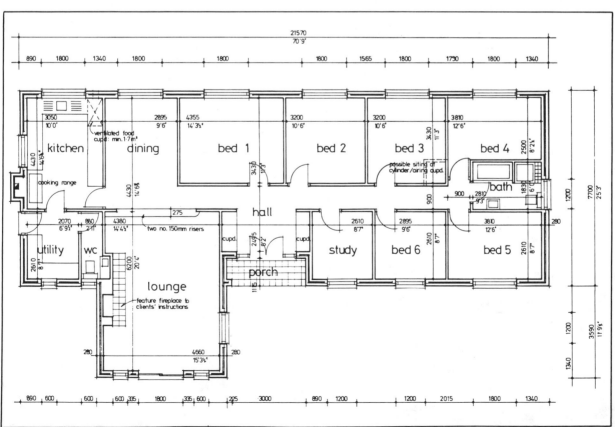

REAR ELEVATION   GABLE ELEVATIONS

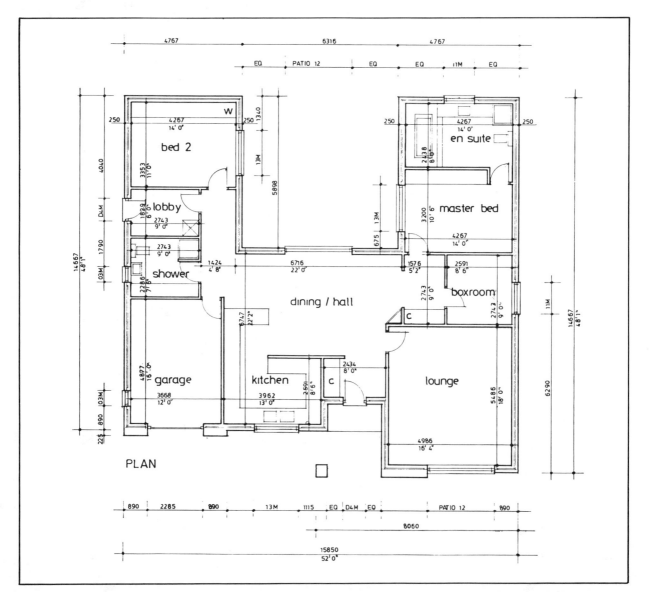

PLAN

front elevation

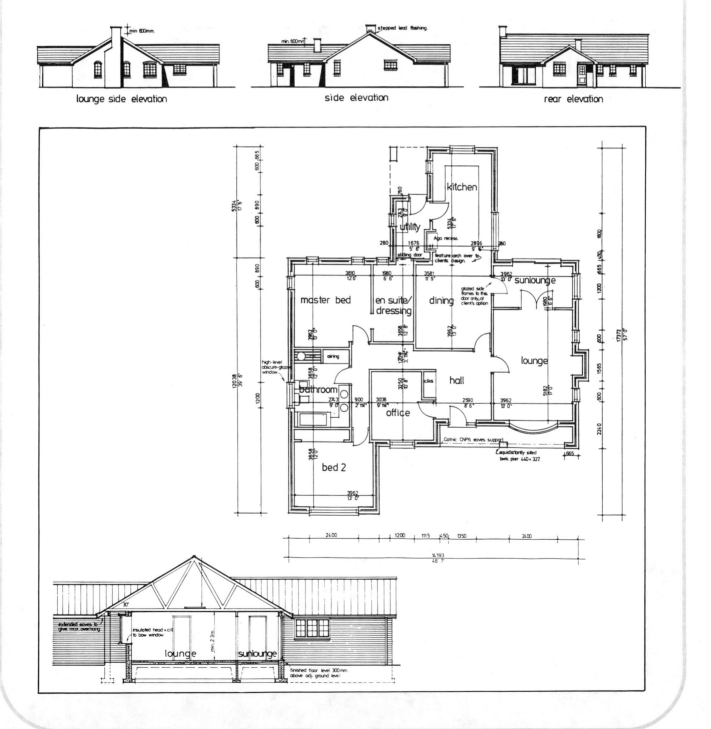

lounge side elevation   side elevation   rear elevation

kitchen

utility

Aga recess

master bed

en suite/dressing

dining

sunlounge

lounge

airing

bathroom

office

hall

clks

bed 2

high-level obscure-glazed window

Catnic CNP6 eaves support

equidistantly sited bwk pier 440 × 327

feature arch over to clients design.

sliding door

glazed side frames to this door only, at client's option

stepped lead flashing.

min 600mm.

min 600mm

extended eaves to give max. overhang

insulated head + cill to bow window

finished floor level 300mm above adj. ground level

lounge   sunlounge

FRONT ELEVATION

REAR ELEVATION   SIDE ELEVATIONS

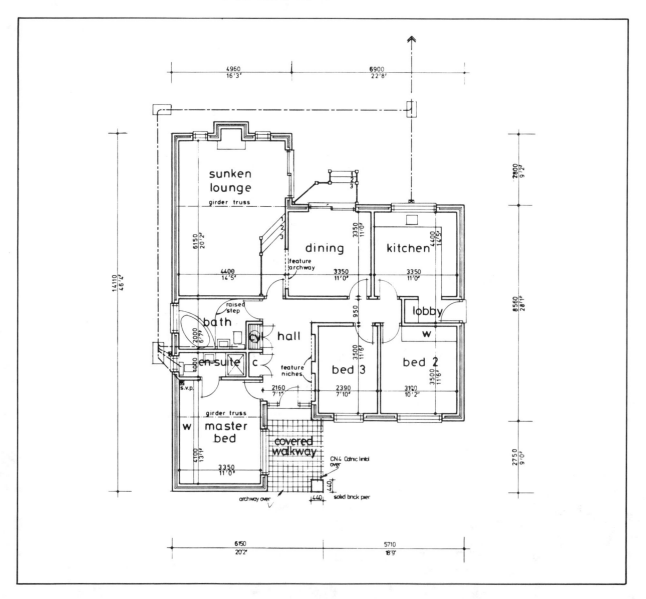

front elevation

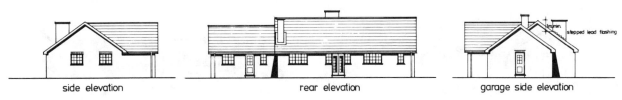

side elevation   rear elevation   garage side elevation

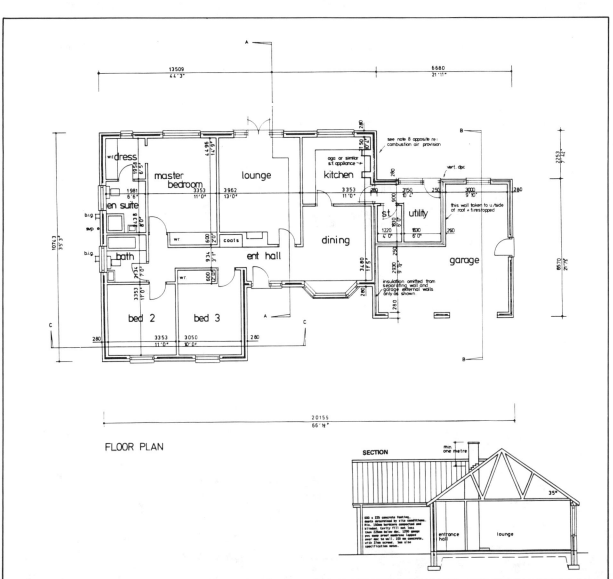

FLOOR PLAN

SECTION

301

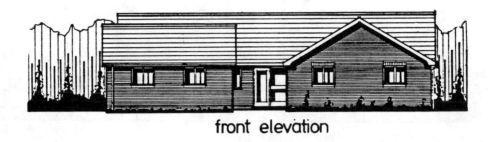

front elevation

side elevation

stepped lead flashing

side elevation

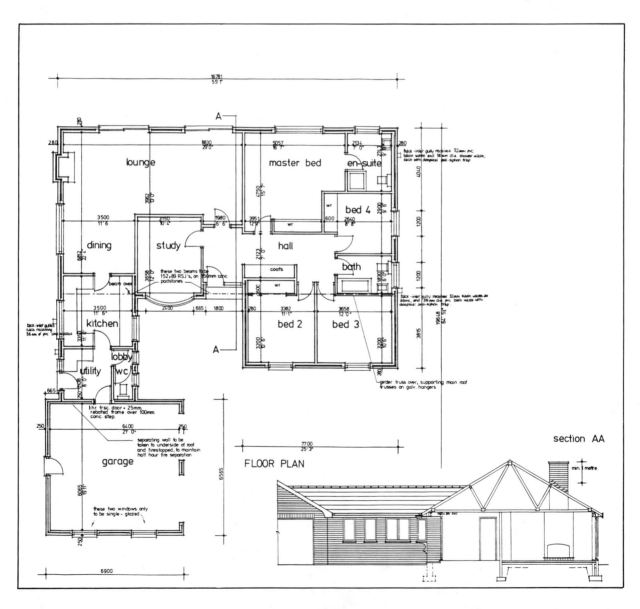

FLOOR PLAN

section AA

302

FRONT ELEVATION

REAR ELEVATION

SIDE ELEVATIONS

Grovebury farmhouse red

Ibstock handmade
regal mixture brickwork

Hardwood casement joinery

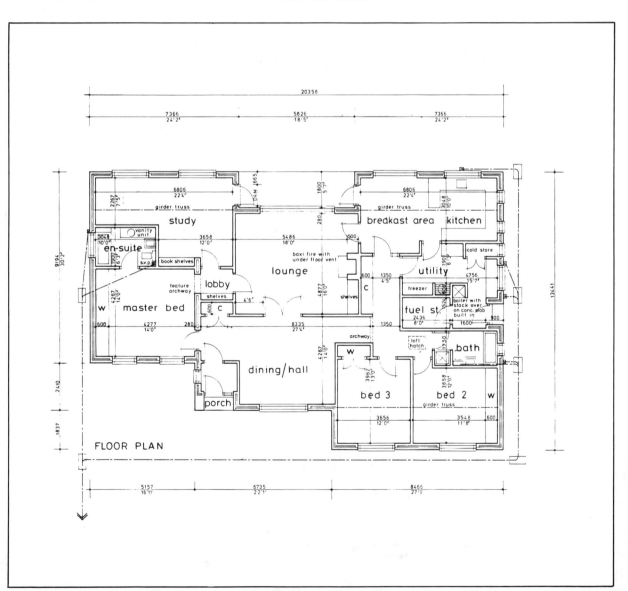

FLOOR PLAN

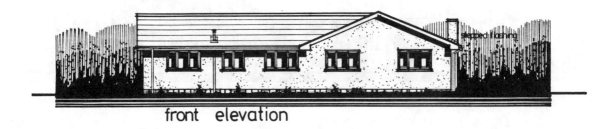

front elevation

side elevations   rear elevation

A guest room with its own small shower room is a very popular feature of new bungalows in tourist areas, where the opportunity for a bed and breakfast business sideline adds to the value of a property even if it is not used in this way. It is obviously particularly convenient if this can be fairly near to the front door, as in this design.

Note the study off the main bedroom: this can be converted into an en-suite bathroom at a future date.

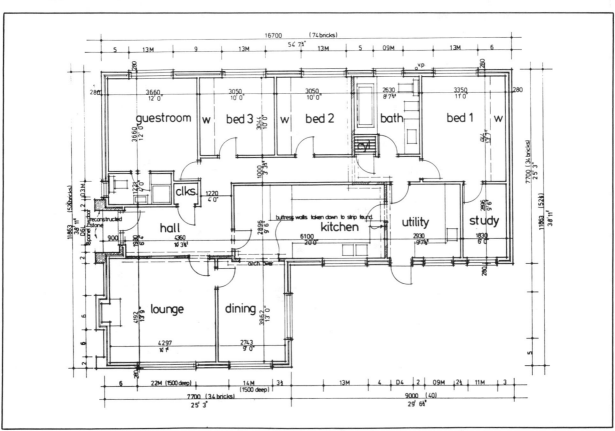

Tudor Homes Supplement

'Tudor home' is an estate agents term, and is not a phrase that would normally be used by an architect. The style often has little in common with the houses of the period that gave it the name, and the term is used simply to describe a house with a simulated exposed timber frame. This suggests that the whole building, or at least the first floor, has a massive structural frame constructed of heavy square timbers.

In fact virtually all of today's tudor houses are built in the same way as all other contemporary homes, with either load bearing masonry walls or modern concealed timber frames. The tudor half-timbering is simply applied as a decorative feature. However, the illusion that the exposed timbers really are the frame of the building is important, and to look right a tudor style house will incorporate other period features.

It will usually have a moderately complex shape, with a steeply pitched roof and relatively small windows. The applied half-timbering will be in a regional style, and may even be adze finished with projecting oak pegs.

Other features may include a jettied first floor with the bedroom walls projecting beyond the ground floor wall, sometimes with heavy joist ends and brackets which seem to support it all. Chimneys may be massive in the style of Elizabethan chimneys, which had room for baking ovens, chambers to smoke hams, or hiding holes for Jesuit priests. These are not todays design requirements but it all contributes to a building style which is very popular, commands high resale values and which gives us houses that are an attractive back-drop to the informal gardens of shrubs and lawn that most people want these days.

Thirty three of the designs on the following pages were drawn to meet the requirements of individuals who had land on which to build, and who wanted a new home to suit their plot, their budget, and their own lifestyle. The other seven are a series of tudor theme designs drawn by Design and Materials Limited to show to clients who want to discuss tudor style homes of under two thousand square feet. All of them can be altered to suit those with different needs.

Tudor Style Homes

In the last few years new homes in the Tudor style have become enormously popular, and there are few parts of the country where they will not be found. A few years ago this would have been unthinkable, and even today the architectural establishment derides the style in no uncertain terms. So how is it that 75% of all new homes advertised in the Sunday Times are in a style which is so disapproved of by contributors to the Architects Journal? It is an interesting story of consumer choice.

For many hundreds of years our domestic architecture was based on structures with walls of stone, brick, or timber. The choice between them depended on the availability and relative cost of these materials in the area concerned. Over much of the country the winner was timber, and so most buildings were constructed from locally cut wooden frames with infill panels in any convenient material, which was usually lath and plaster or brickwork. The framing timbers were sometimes left exposed, and in some parts of the country the timbers and the panels were painted in contrasting colours, often, but not always, black and white.

With the coming of the industrial revolution, cheap transport, and a shortage of cheap heavy timber as forests disappeared, this system of construction was largely abandoned in favour of loadbearing brickwork. The less important and less well constructed homes of the past fell down or were demolished, and the survivors were the best of their type. Most of these were from the 16th and 17th centuries, and came to be known as tudor homes.

In the early and mid nineteenth centuries the surviving tudor homes were not admired. They were too irregular and unplanned for the early Victorians, who were not great admirers of the past anyway. However, in the closing years of the century the romantic movement arrived, fuelled by the novels of Walter Scott, and aroused an interest in a popular version of our gothic heritage. The Victorian Gothic architectural style appeared, bringing with it the towers and spires seen on many of our town halls today. As part of this there was a limited vogue for tudor style homes, as seen in the drawing on the opposite page which is from an 1891 book of home plans.

The Gothic style did not last long, but tudor homes grew in popularity and became the dominent style — in numbers if not in influence — for individually designed detached houses built in the first 30 years of this

Genuine Tudor
— Halls Croft, Stratford on Avon

Victorian Tudor — Design from a book of Home Plans published in 1891

century. To the aesthetes it was a dishonest style: the half timbering was a decorative feature and was not the essential framework of the building. To those who believed that form should follow function the tudor features were unnecessary and bizarre ornaments, and the style was 'pretty' or 'chocolate box'. This ignored the fact that most people liked pretty things, and that chocolate boxes were designed to meet popular taste. Architects believed that it was their responsibility to be arbiters of taste, and that they alone could understand what was appropriate for our built environment. The avant garde houses of this era were built in plain functional styles that were very different from the public taste, but their influence was out of all proportion to the number actually built.

1939 saw the end of house building for a decade, and then the housing shortages of the fifties and sixties, together with the controls inherant in the new planning acts, gave the fashionable architects of the day an opportunity to dictate what was built. Functional architecture became the rule, partly because its stark economy was in keeping with an age of austerity. For the whole of the fifties, sixties and early seventies all new homes right across the country were in the same modern style, with few concessions to regional design features or to building what homebuyers really wanted. At this time the prices of good 1930's houses were higher than the prices of equivalent new homes, and it seems surprising that no one realised that the public actually preferred the pre war designs. Still, remember that this was the era when the experts hypnotised town councils all over the country into believing that council house tenants would prefer to live in tower blocks.

Then, as described in the main text at the front of this book, a combination of factors in the late 1970's reintroduced consumer choice as a factor in housing styles. The so called Georgian Home arrived, followed a few years later by the Tudor Style Home. Perhaps it was simply a swing of the pendulum, perhaps a reaction to all the horrors that planners had sanctioned as acceptable design since the war. Whatever the reason, by the early eighties tudor style homes were again very popular with those who could choose the design of a new home. They are pretty, individual, and our appreciation of them reaches back to an idealised image of a dream home. Choosing a tudor home can be one way of making a dream come true, and that is a good enough ambition for most people.

Tudor Features

Half Timbering

Half timbering is the essential feature of the tudor style, and almost always the timbers are purely decorative and do not contribute to the strength of the building. This means that they can be arranged in any pattern, and this should always be in the local regional style or to match other new tudor style homes in the area. Nothing looks more incongrous than a pattern of half timbering that is unusual or out of place. The distinctive timber frame patterns found in East Anglia should not be used in Devon, or the features of Anne Hathaways cottage transplanted to Kent.

You can discuss the pattern of framing for your new home with your architect or your builder, and you will be able to contribute more to the discussion if you go out and look at all the other half timbering in the area, both on newly built buildings as well as on older ones. Take photos if you like and use them to explain exactly what you want.

Details of the way in which the timbers seem to be fixed are also important. Your architect or designer will make sure that they are actually fixed in a modern way that conforms to the Building Regulations, and this is unlikely to be with traditional pegged joints. If these are part of a local style, insist that pegs are there to be seen, even if they are not essential. The surface finish of the timbers is also important, and there are specialist firms which sell timbers for this purpose with adzed surfaces.

The infill panels between the timbering should also follow local practise, and if you are rendering, a decision about whether you have a plain smooth finish or an uneven rough surface should not be left to the plasterer. In the Eastern counties there has been some return to traditional pargeting or plaster infill. If you are using brickwork then both the choice of bricks and the way in which they are laid will be very important, particularly if you are considering herringbone or basketweave patterns of brickwork.

Proportions

Period tudor cottages were usually long and narrow, with a depth from front to back of about seven metres, which was the length at which the framing beams were most commonly available. In some parts of the country, and particularly in the Cotswolds, the planners may require that new homes in the tudor style have the same proportions. Larger genuine tudor buildings are often a jumble of smaller structures with the same width limitations.

Roofs

Period tudor homes were thatched, or had clay peg tiles or stone slates. These roofing materials required the roof to be at a steep pitch, and half timbering under a shallow pitch roof looks very wrong. Modern tudor style homes are now often built under interlocking pantiles, and this is inevitable given the cost advantages. However, the most attractive way of finishing the roof is to use modern small plain tiles, or, in the right areas, modern stone slates like those made by Bradstone.

Projecting First Floors

These are known as jettied floors, and are a popular feature of tudor homes today if the budget permits. The traditional jettied floor was very complex with a great deal of ornamental carving as shown on the photograph of Halls Croft on an earlier page. The modern equivalent is shown here. This involves a concealed timber frame which is built either on top of masonry ground floor walls, or as part of a structure that is wholly timber framed. In either case the timber frame is completely concealed and the half timbering is still an applied ornamental feature.

Doors and Windows

Traditional tudor doors were very simple, and had an external surface of vertical planks. Windows were small with heavy mullions, as are seen in the photograph of Halls Croft. Modern doors and windows that suit the style are available, and should be fitted with carefully chosen handles and latches. In most circumstances it is preferable to avoid painting joinery and to use modern preservative stains.

Inglenook Fireplaces and their Chimneys

Early half-timbered homes in rural areas had huge fireplaces on outside walls, which were invariably the end walls of a long, narrow building. The chimneys were built well proud of the building to avoid problems at the junction of the thatched roof and the chimney brickwork, and they were very massive. This was both to avoid fire risk and to enable ovens and other chambers to be built into the brickwork. These are hardly reasons to build very large chimneys today but they are a popular feature, often built with an inglenook fireplace where a basket fire is set in a recess at least six feet wide. It is not technically necessary to have a very large chimney stack above an inglenook fireplace, and where space is short on the first floor level a narrow flue can continue as from a modern fireplace. Generally inglenook fireplaces in today's tudor homes are at their most effective in really large rooms, and can look contrived unless the whole room is furnished to suit.

Design Features Index

Designs with five bedrooms or more
SEE PAGES:
8, 9, 15, 24, 26, 27, 28, 29, 31, 32, 33, 38 and 43.

Designs with principal rooms with a front outlook
SEE PAGES:
8, 9, 12, 13, 14, 16, 17, 19, 20, 21, 24, 26, 27, 28, 29, 31, 32, 34, 38, 43, 45 and 46.

Designs with principal rooms with a rear outlook
SEE PAGES:
10, 13, 14, 15, 16, 18, 19, 20, 21, 22, 23, 24, 25, 27, 28, 29, 30, 31, 32, 33, 34, 35, 36, 37, 39, 40, 41, 42, 44, 47.

Designs with granny flats or self contained guest accommodation
SEE PAGES:
25 and 29.

Designs with large offices or studies for those who work at home
SEE PAGES:
9, 10, 11, 12, 13, 14, 15, 22, 23, 25, 26, 27, 31, 35, 40, 41, 42 and 43.

Designs particularly suitable for inglenook fireplace
SEE PAGES:
8, 11, 14, 15, 23, 24, 25, 28, 29, 31, 32, 33, 36, 39, 45 and 46.

Page Index

The Avonmere design from this book's companion volume 'Home Plans' which is described on page 447

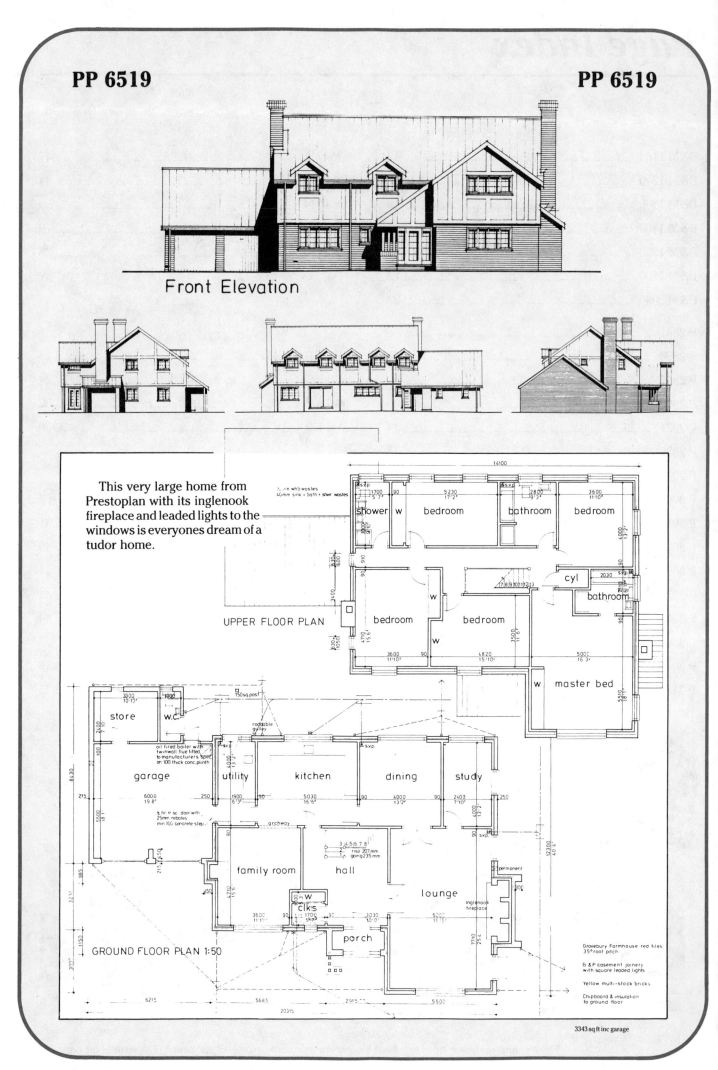

Front Elevation

This very large home from Prestoplan with its inglenook fireplace and leaded lights to the windows is everyones dream of a tudor home.

UPPER FLOOR PLAN

GROUND FLOOR PLAN 1:50

Grovebury Farmhouse red tiles
35° roof pitch

B & P casement joinery
with square leaded lights

Yellow multi-stock bricks

Chipboard & insulation
to ground floor

3343 sq ft inc garage

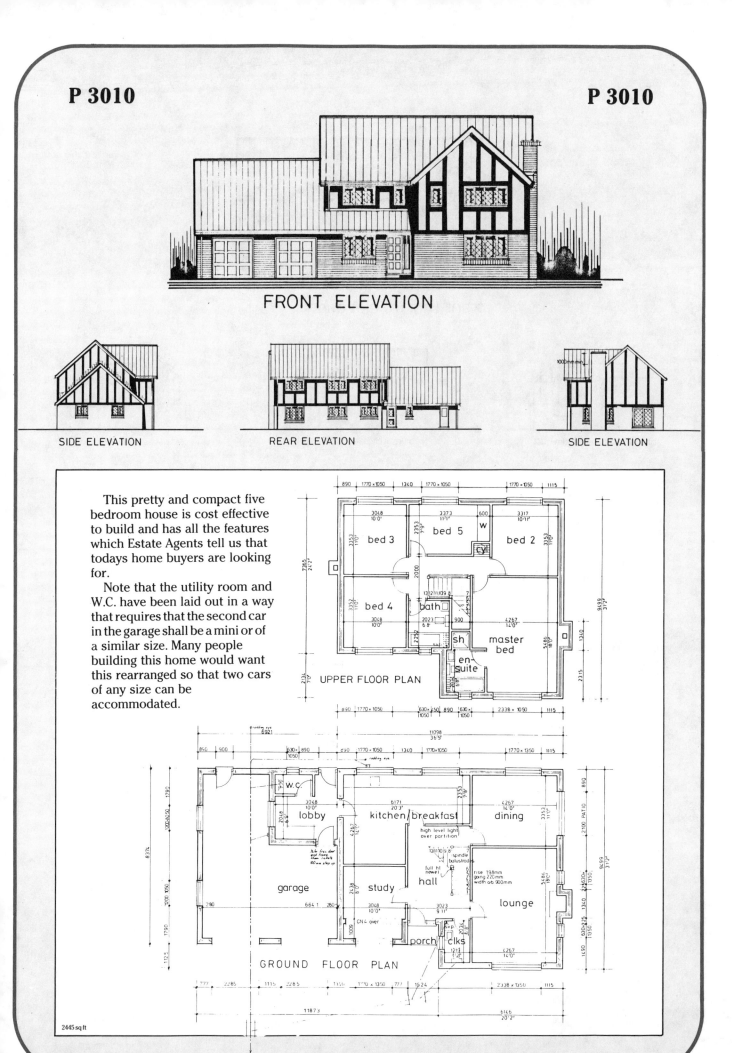

FRONT ELEVATION

SIDE ELEVATION

REAR ELEVATION

SIDE ELEVATION

This pretty and compact five bedroom house is cost effective to build and has all the features which Estate Agents tell us that todays home buyers are looking for.

Note that the utility room and W.C. have been laid out in a way that requires that the second car in the garage shall be a mini or of a similar size. Many people building this home would want this rearranged so that two cars of any size can be accommodated.

UPPER FLOOR PLAN

bed 3
bed 5
bed 2
bed 4
bath
sh
master bed
en-suite
cyl
w

GROUND FLOOR PLAN

W.C.
lobby
kitchen/breakfast
dining
garage
study
hall
lounge
porch
clks

2445 sq ft

front (north) elevation

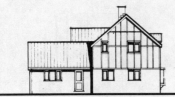

garage side (west) elevation

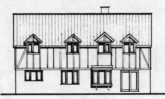

rear (south) elevation

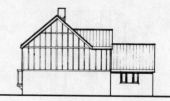

side (east) elevation

The second bedroom and the huge family bathroom in this design can easily be rearranged to provide two single bedrooms with a more modest bathroom, making this a five bedroom home. Downstairs the clients brief was to provide the largest possible study, and this has restricted storage space for outdoor clothes. Having a large farmhouse kitchen without a utility room might make this a problem if this house is built in rural areas. However, there is plenty of room in the twenty foot garage, and the basic plan can accommodate all sorts of alterations to suit individual requirements.

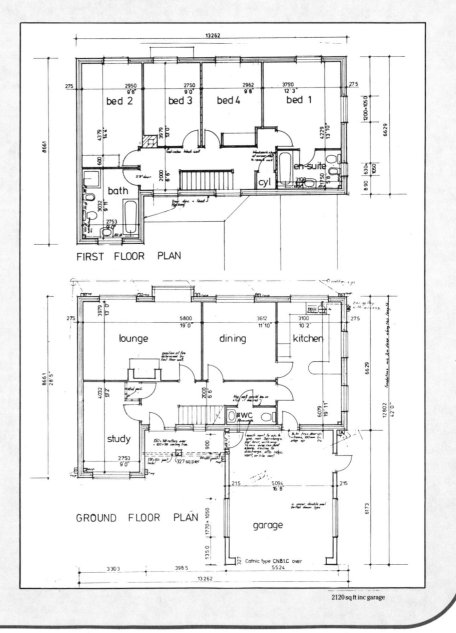

FIRST FLOOR PLAN

GROUND FLOOR PLAN

2120 sq ft inc garage

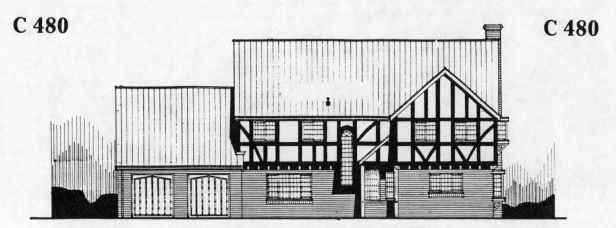

Front Elevation

A very large house for a country life style. It really has everything: the only possible extra would be to have a traditional purlin garage roof to provide extra storage, with access into it from a door in bedroom 4.

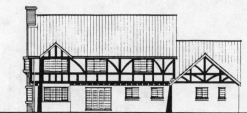

Rear Elevation

Marley Heritage roofing tiles
40° pitch with exposed rafters loose fixed

Timber frame construction to Upper Floor
cantilevered 225mm with tudor effect
light medium brown timber on
magnolia coloured render

Redland Hamsey brickwork to Ground Floor

Hardwood casement joinery with square leaded lights

Ceiling heights
Ground Floor 2500   First Floor 2340

Beam & block floor

w | bed 2 | w | bed 3 | master bed

w | cyl | gallery | dressing room

bed 4 | bath | feature shelf | box room | en-suite

Side Elevation

w.c. | utility | ldr

c | lobby

½ hr. fr. sc. door & 100 conc. step

double garage | kitchen | family room | lounge

dining | parana pine staircase | hall | c

porch | clks | study

porch soffit ext. ply painted

200 mm sq oak beams

GROUND FLOOR PLAN

3457 sq ft

Side Elevation

FRONT ELEVATION

SIDE ELEVATION

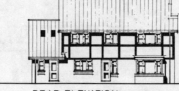

REAR ELEVATION

Hardrow old-stone
standard sizing

Butterley jubilee mixture brickwork
to ground floor

Cement render painted off-white
timber to be stained to match
hardwood joinery

Hardwood casement joinery

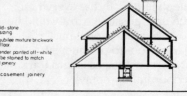

SIDE ELEVATION

Integrating a double garage into the main structure of a house in the way shown in this drawing is unusual, and adds significantly to unit costs. However, it may be unavoidable on a narrow site, and this design from Plan Sales Services is a very attractive way of doing it.

This is another design where the en-suite bathroom is larger than the family bathroom. This is a growing trend, reflecting that those who are actually paying for the building are beginning to realise that they deserve the nicest bathroom in the house.

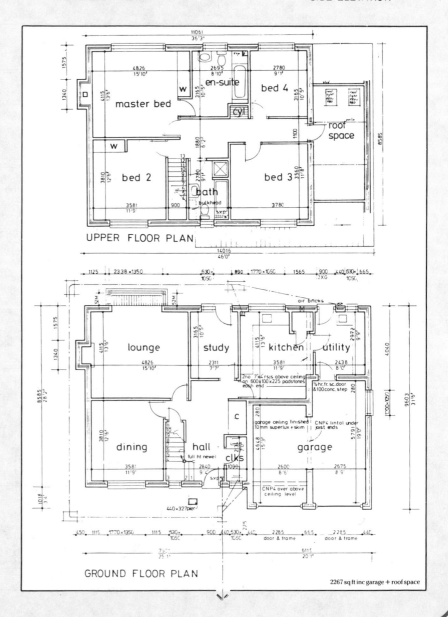

UPPER FLOOR PLAN

GROUND FLOOR PLAN

2267 sq ft inc garage + roof space

W 1376

W 1376

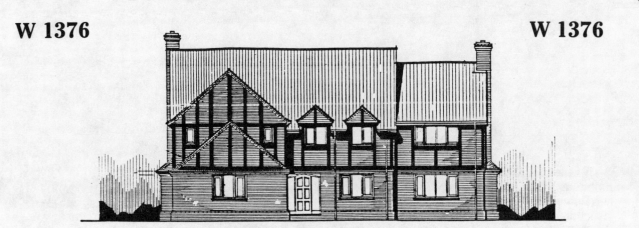

Front Elevation

A large house with a four bedroom, three bathroom layout. The rooms are all very large, and there is considerable scope to rearrange the accommodation to give a five bedroom layout if required.

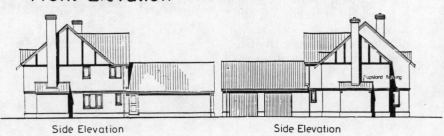

Side Elevation

Side Elevation

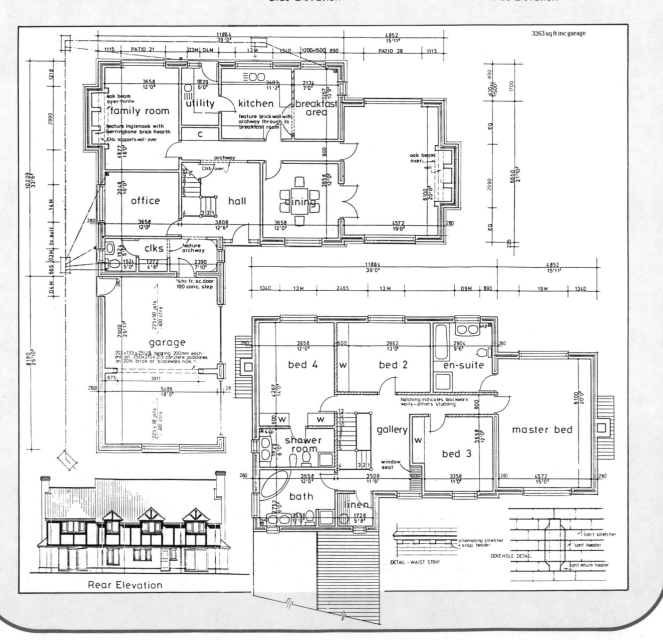

Rear Elevation

This tile hung house has half
timbering to the front gable, and
certainly merits inclusion in a
selection of tudor designs. It is
one of the few house designs in
the book with the staircase right
in the middle of the building, and
this, with the front door hidden in
an internal porch, makes the hall
an important room in its own
right.

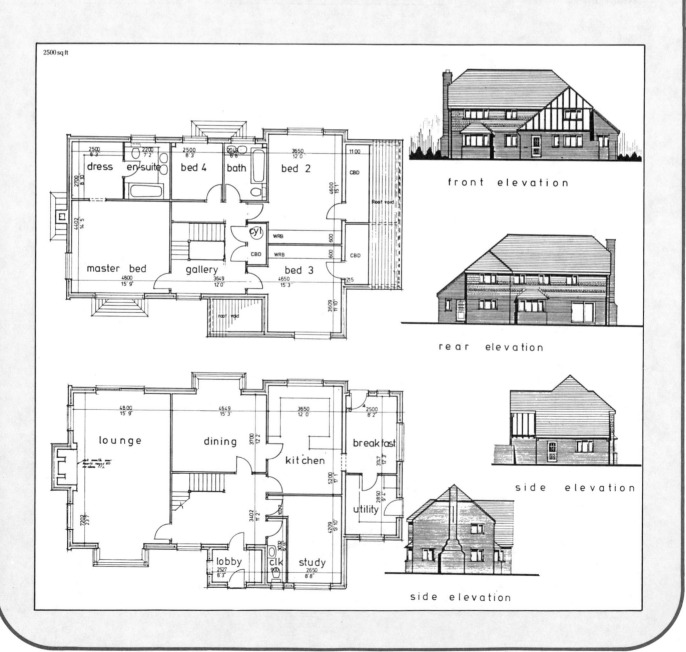

2500 sq ft

front elevation

rear elevation

side elevation

side elevation

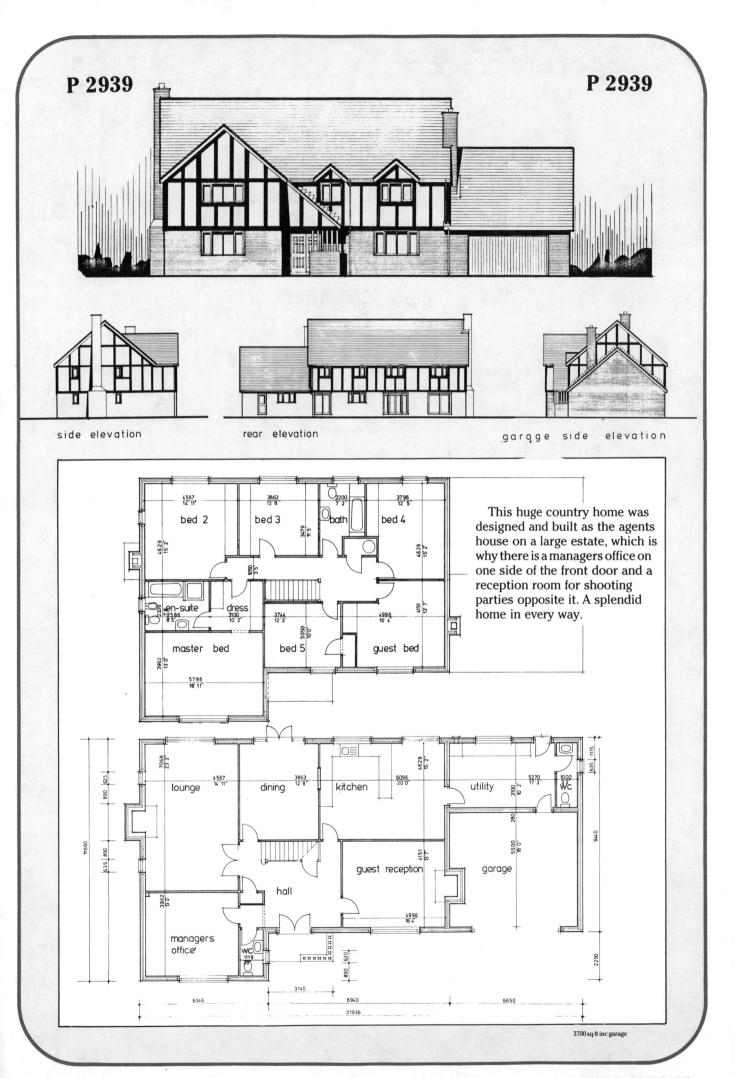

side elevation

rear elevation

garage side elevation

This huge country home was designed and built as the agents house on a large estate, which is why there is a managers office on one side of the front door and a reception room for shooting parties opposite it. A splendid home in every way.

3700 sq ft inc garage

TUDOR HOMES 15

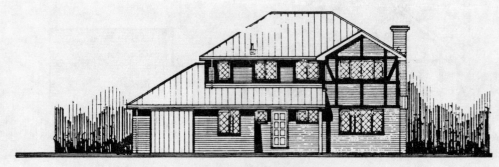

Front Elevation

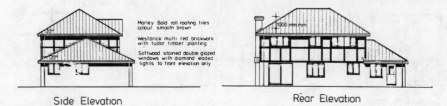

Marley Bold roll roofing tiles
colour smooth brown

Westbrick multi red brickwork
with tudor timber planting

Softwood stained double glazed
windows with diamond leaded
lights to front elevation only.

Side Elevation

Rear Elevation

Side Elevation

This design for a house with half timbering applied to a fairly conventional suburban shape has a very prominent roof, with a large area of tiling. It was built with Marley Bold Roll tiles, which, as the name suggests, have a very distinctive Roman tile appearance. This is appropriate in areas where pantiles are the local roofing material, but in many parts of the country this house will be built under traditional plain tiles. The cost implications of this should be carefully considered.

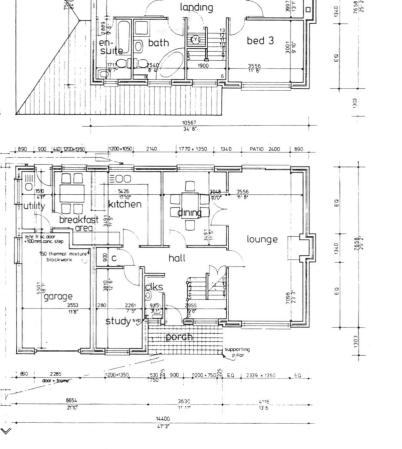

1900 sq ft inc garage

FRONT ELEVATION

SIDE ELEVATION   REAR ELEVATION

This design, and the next six designs on the following pages, were drawn in 1987 by Beverley Pemberton of the D & M design team as design studies for a new range of Tudor designs. They had an instant success, and have been built in many parts of the country, both in their original form and with alterations to suit individual clients.

The sizes vary from 1100 sq ft to 2000 sq ft, and as far as possible they incorporate all the basic features of the "Tudor" design homes of the Edwardian era which established this style which is so popular today.

They can all be built either traditionally or with a timber frame. The basic structures are very cost effective to construct, and features such as projecting plinths, string courses or herringbone brickwork can be included if required and the budget permits.

This design is the smallest in the range, but has all the features expected of a four bedroom detached house, including a utility room, a cloakroom and both family and en-suite bathrooms.

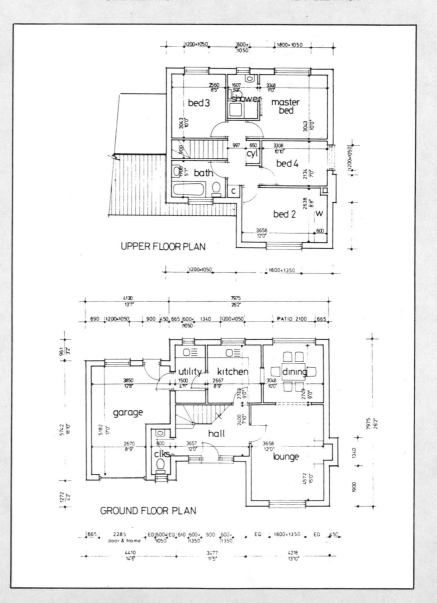

UPPER FLOOR PLAN

GROUND FLOOR PLAN

FRONT ELEVATION

REAR ELEVATION

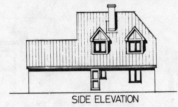

SIDE ELEVATION

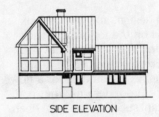

SIDE ELEVATION

This design is 1200 sq ft, and the extra space compared with the first house in this series is used to increase the size of the rooms all round. The lounge and the dining room are at opposite ends of the house, and one way of altering this design is to use the dining room as a study or family room and to combine the kitchen and utility room to make a big dining/kitchen.

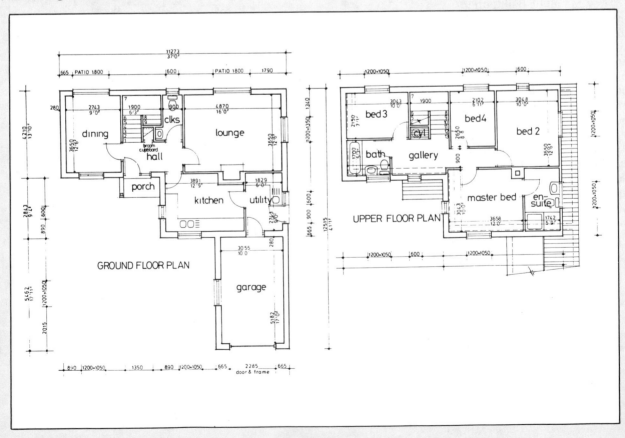

GROUND FLOOR PLAN

UPPER FLOOR PLAN

D & M 1300

D & M 1300

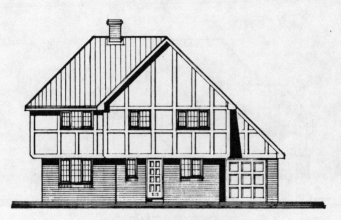

FRONT ELEVATION

The layout of this 1300 sq ft house provides substantially larger rooms, but in the form shown it has lost the cloakroom. Measuring only 22 sq ft from front to back, this design is a very useful one for areas like the Cotswolds where the planners often insist on a modest depth to match existing cottages, but it has all the feel of a larger property.

REAR ELEVATION

SIDE ELEVATION

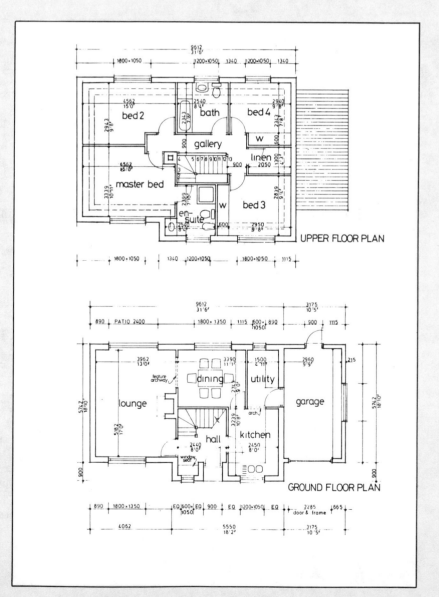

UPPER FLOOR PLAN

GROUND FLOOR PLAN

FRONT ELEVATION

REAR ELEVATION

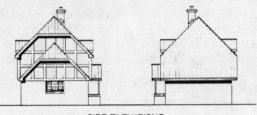

SIDE ELEVATIONS

The depth of this house from front to back has again been kept at under 25 sq ft to conform to the concern of some county design guides that tudor houses should stick to genuine tudor dimensions, at any rate in village street situations.

The layout shown provides for a cloakroom at the back door, which is very popular with those who live in the country. It will be seen that by moving the kitchen to the back of the house this same cloakroom can open into the hall, which is more popular in urban situations.

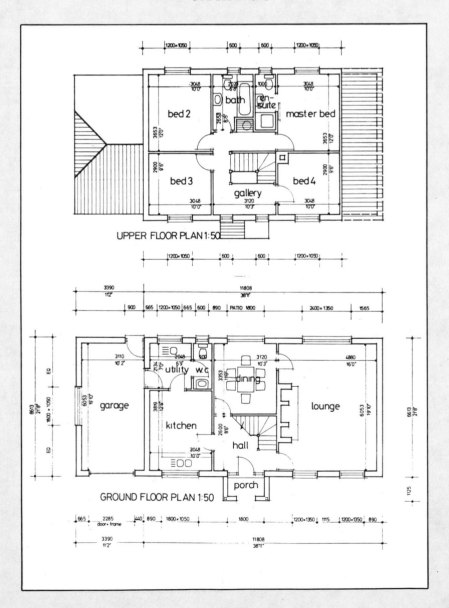

UPPER FLOOR PLAN 1:50

GROUND FLOOR PLAN 1:50

FRONT ELEVATION

REAR ELEVATION

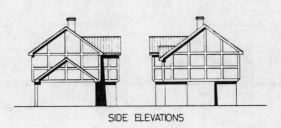

SIDE ELEVATIONS

Like all the seven designs in this series, the D & M 1500 can be built using either traditional construction or a timber frame. With an inglenook fireplace and a large kitchen this series of designs is now moving into the luxury bracket, but the basic structure is simple and cost effective to build.

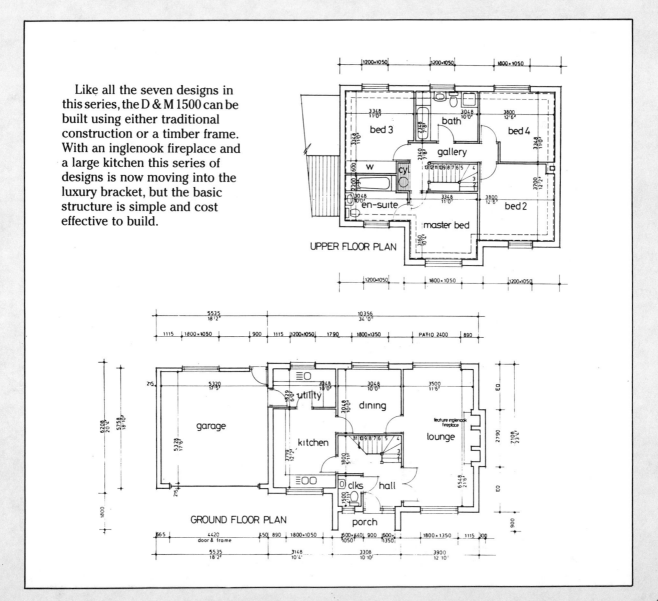

UPPER FLOOR PLAN

GROUND FLOOR PLAN

D & M 1700

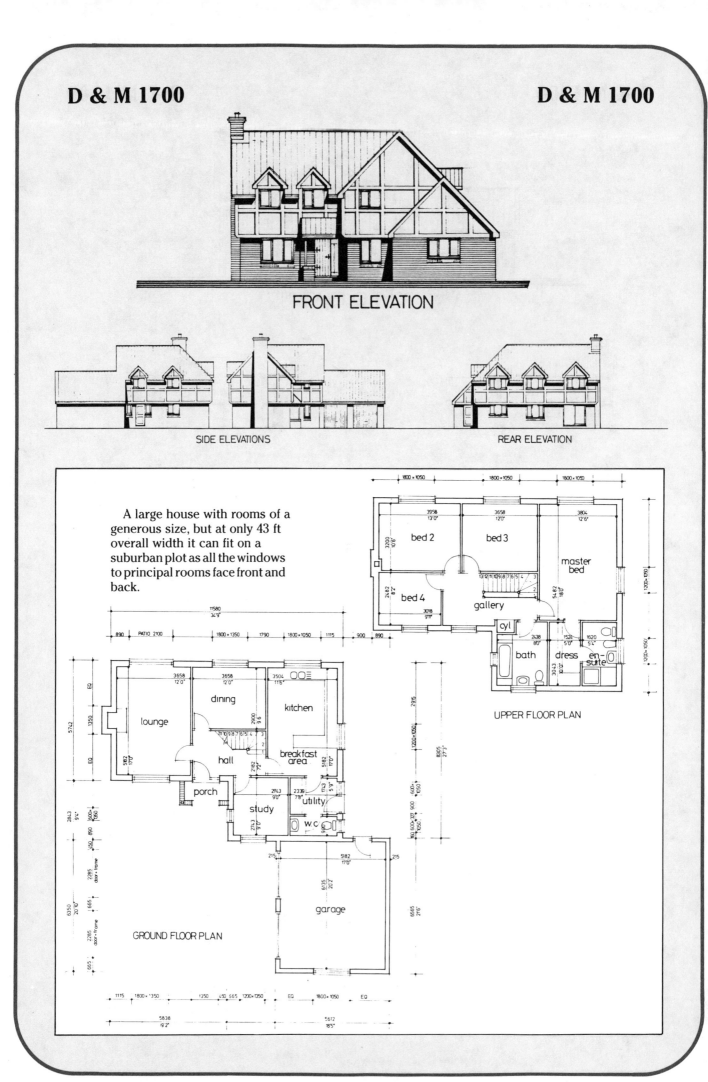

FRONT ELEVATION

SIDE ELEVATIONS

REAR ELEVATION

A large house with rooms of a generous size, but at only 43 ft overall width it can fit on a suburban plot as all the windows to principal rooms face front and back.

UPPER FLOOR PLAN

bed 2

bed 3

master bed

bed 4

gallery

cyl

bath

dress

en-suite

GROUND FLOOR PLAN

lounge

dining

kitchen

hall

breakfast area

porch

study

utility

w c

garage

FRONT ELEVATION

SIDE ELEVATION

REAR ELEVATION

SIDE ELEVATION

A large house for a large plot of land which looks equally well from all directions. The last of the seven 1988 series Tudor designs by Design & Materials Ltd., the basic design concept can be adapted to suit almost any requirement.

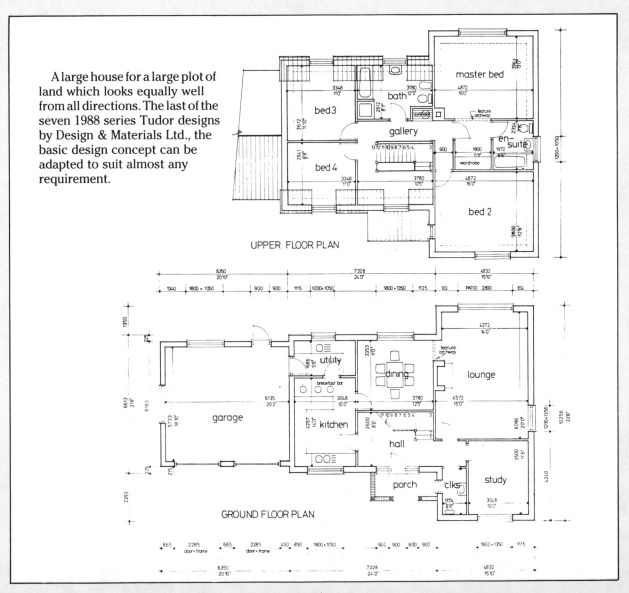

UPPER FLOOR PLAN

GROUND FLOOR PLAN

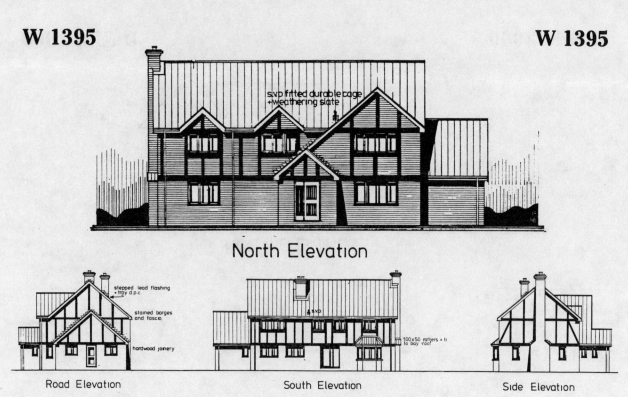

North Elevation

Road Elevation

South Elevation

Side Elevation

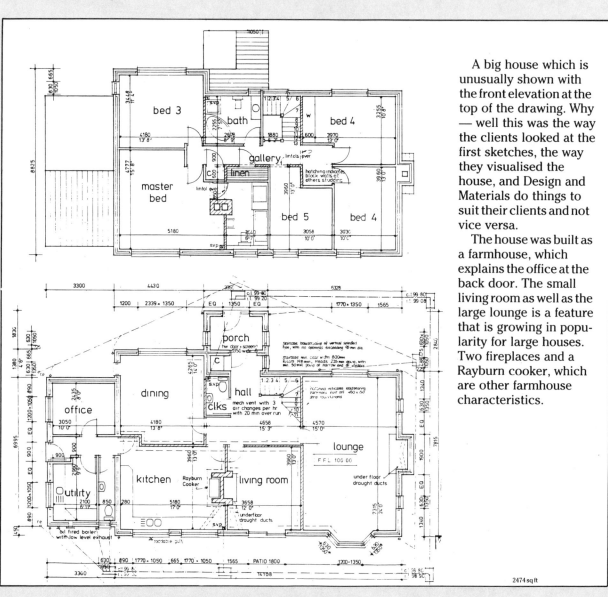

A big house which is unusually shown with the front elevation at the top of the drawing. Why — well this was the way the clients looked at the first sketches, the way they visualised the house, and Design and Materials do things to suit their clients and not vice versa.

The house was built as a farmhouse, which explains the office at the back door. The small living room as well as the large lounge is a feature that is growing in popularity for large houses. Two fireplaces and a Rayburn cooker, which are other farmhouse characteristics.

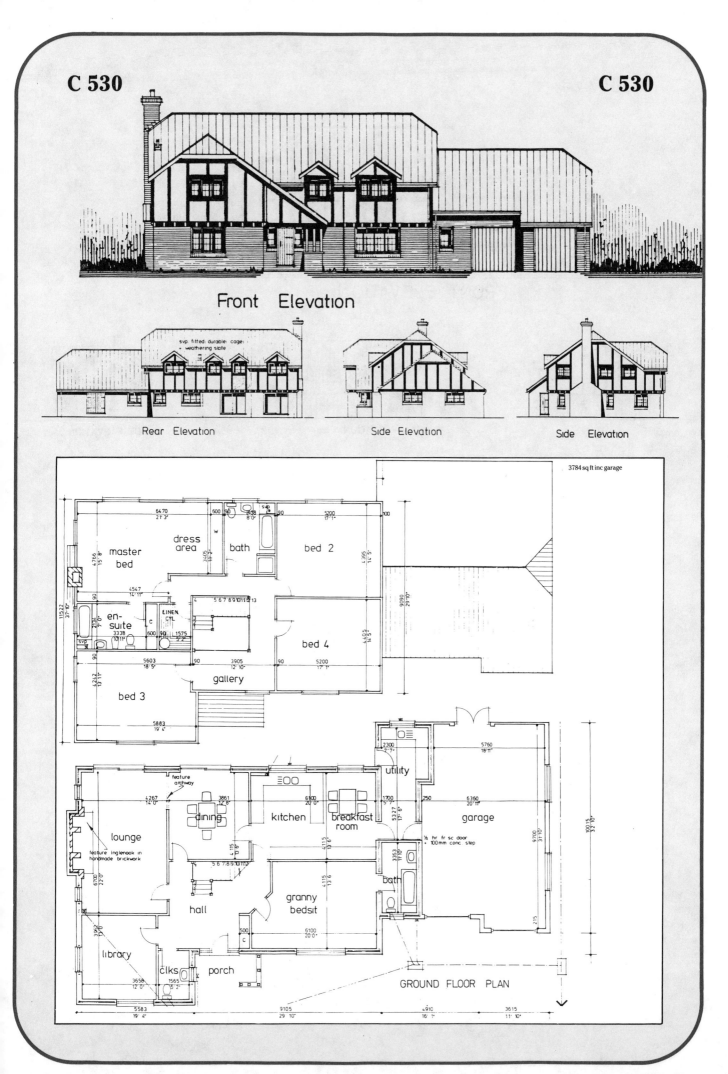

Front Elevation

Rear Elevation

Side Elevation

Side Elevation

3784 sq ft inc garage

master bed

dress area

bath

bed 2

en-suite

LINEN CYL

bed 4

bed 3

gallery

utility

garage

feature archway

dining

kitchen

breakfast room

lounge

feature inglenook in handmade brickwork

hall

granny bedsit

bath

library

clks

porch

GROUND FLOOR PLAN

FRONT ELEVATION

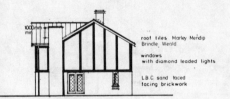

SIDE ELEVATION

roof tiles Marley Mendip
Brindle, Wenld

windows
with diamond leaded lights

LB C sand faced
facing brickwork

REAR ELEVATION

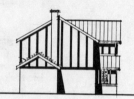

SIDE ELEVATION

Another variation of a five bedroom home that has proved immensley popular over the last two years.

The chimney to the fireplace in the lounge is shewn in a very simple form, and with the minimum height acceptable under the Building Regulations. When the house is under construction the actual way in which the chimney is built can be the subject of a lot of discussion, as most people will want it to be a key feature of a home in this style. Consideration of the chimney shewn in design W1402 would be a good start to the debate. All part of the fun of having a house built to your own requirements.

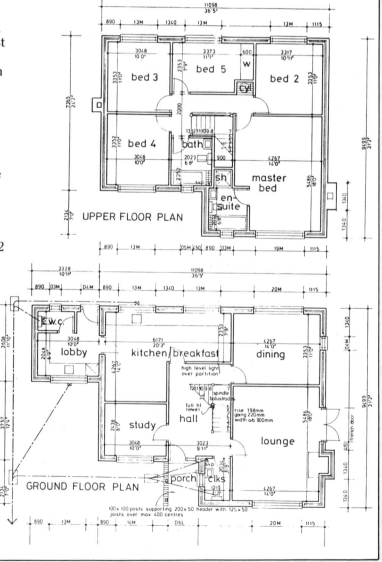

UPPER FLOOR PLAN

GROUND FLOOR PLAN

1890 sq ft

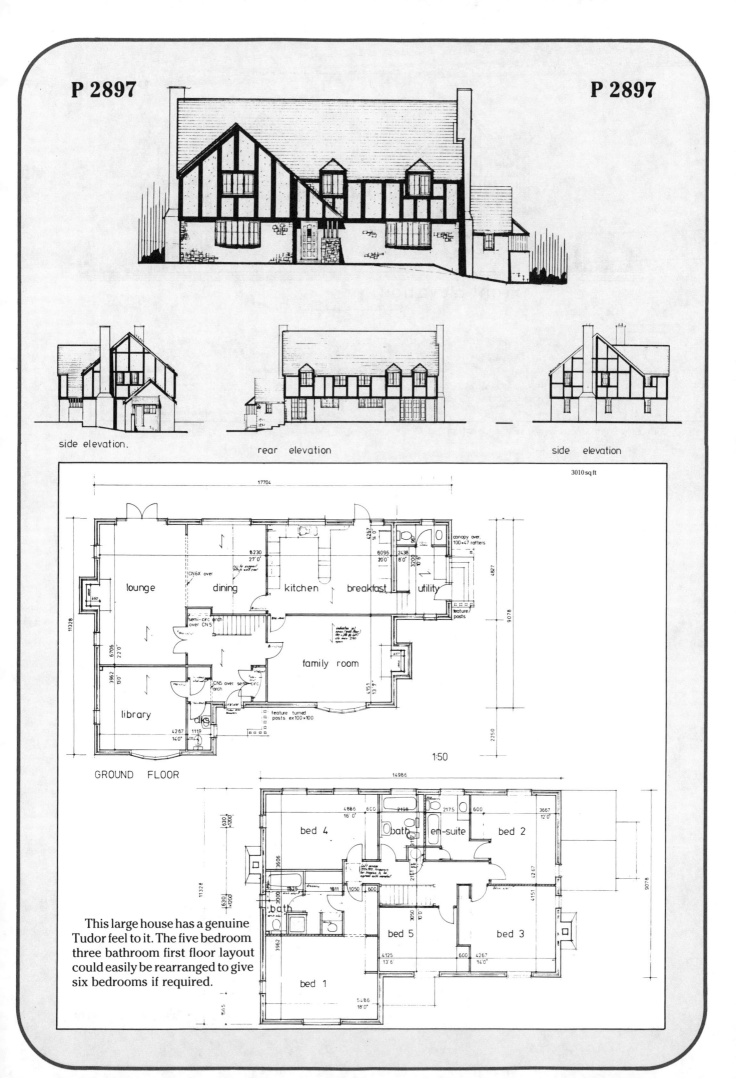

P 2897

P 2897

side elevation.

rear elevation

side elevation

3010 sq ft

lounge

dining

kitchen

breakfast

utility

library

dks

family room

feature turned posts ex 100 × 100

GROUND FLOOR

1:50

bed 4

bath

en-suite

bed 2

bath

bed 5

bed 3

bed 1

This large house has a genuine Tudor feel to it. The five bedroom three bathroom first floor layout could easily be rearranged to give six bedrooms if required.

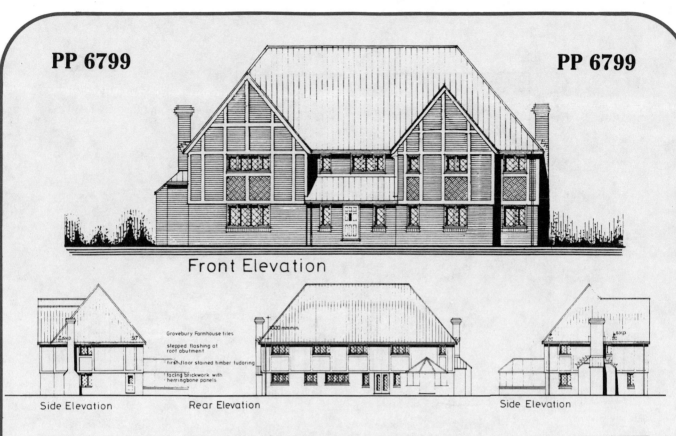

Front Elevation

Side Elevation   Rear Elevation   Side Elevation

Grovebury Farmhouse tiles

stepped flashing at roof abutment

first floor stained timber tudoring

facing brickwork with herringbone panels

Another design for a very large home from Prestoplan. Provision has been made for a conservatory to be built at a later date, and this is shewn on the drawings.

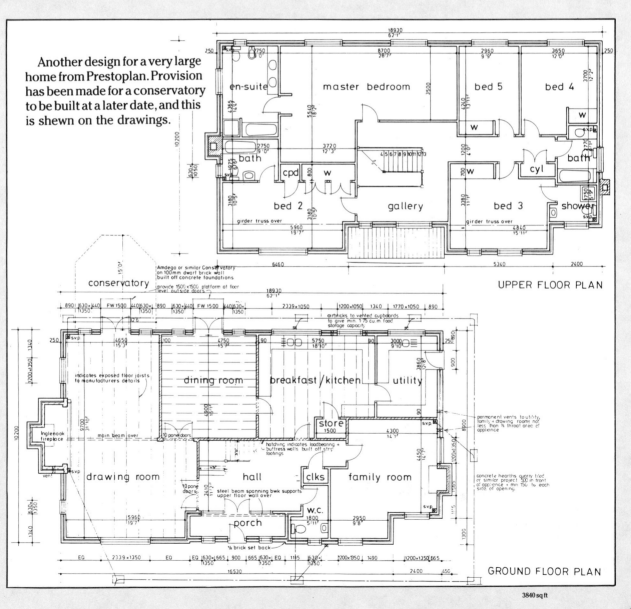

UPPER FLOOR PLAN

en-suite

master bedroom

bed 5

bed 4

bath

cpd

w

gallery

w

cyl

bath

bed 2

bed 3

shower

girder truss over

girder truss over

conservatory

Amdega or similar Conservatory on 100mm dwarf brick wall built off concrete foundations

provide 1500 x1500 platform at floor level outside doors

airbricks to vented cupboards to give min 1 75 cu.m food storage capacity

indicates exposed floor joists to manufacturers details

dining room

breakfast / kitchen

utility

store

Inglenook fireplace

main beam over

10 panel doors

hatching indicates loadbearing + buttress walls built off strip footings

permanent vents to utility, family + drawing rooms not less than ½ throat area of appliance

drawing room

hall

clks

family room

concrete hearths quarry tiled or similar project 500 in front of appliance + min 150 to each side of opening

10 panel doors

steel beam spanning bwk supports upper floor wall over

W.C.

porch

½ brick set back

GROUND FLOOR PLAN

3840 sq ft

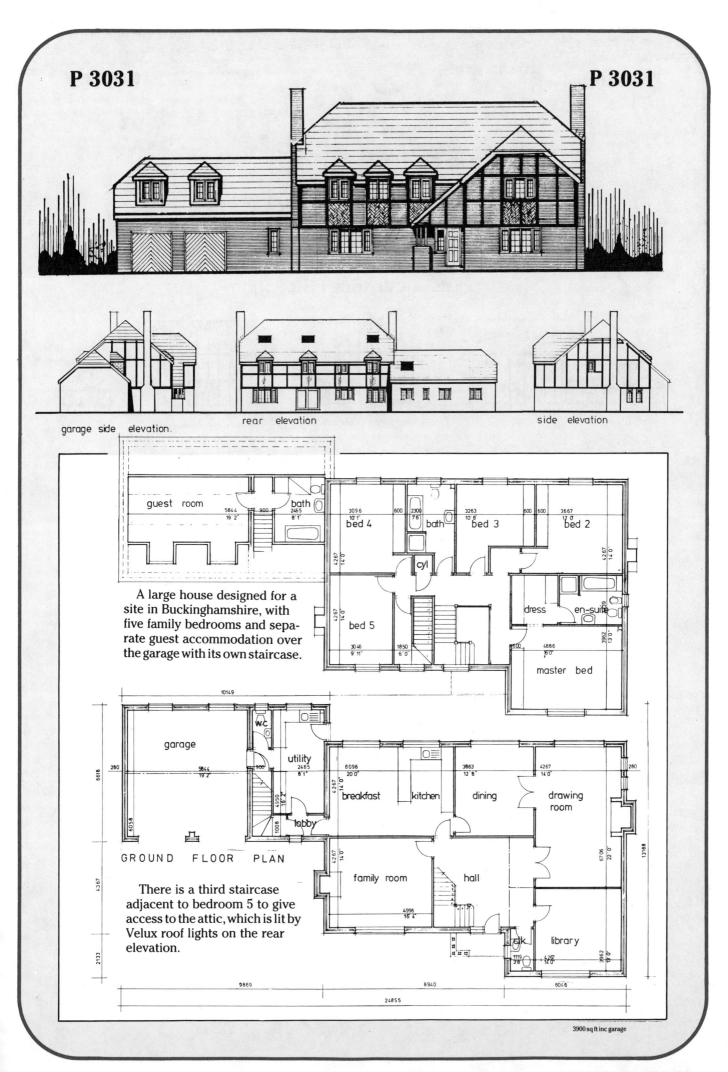

garage side elevation.

rear elevation

side elevation

guest room

bath

bed 4

bath

bed 3

bed 2

cyl

dress

en-suite

bed 5

master bed

A large house designed for a site in Buckinghamshire, with five family bedrooms and separate guest accommodation over the garage with its own staircase.

garage

w·c

utility

breakfast

kitchen

dining

drawing room

lobby

family room

hall

clk

library

GROUND FLOOR PLAN

There is a third staircase adjacent to bedroom 5 to give access to the attic, which is lit by Velux roof lights on the rear elevation.

3900 sq ft inc garage

East (entrance) Elevation

North Elevation

Rear (west) Elevation

South Elevation

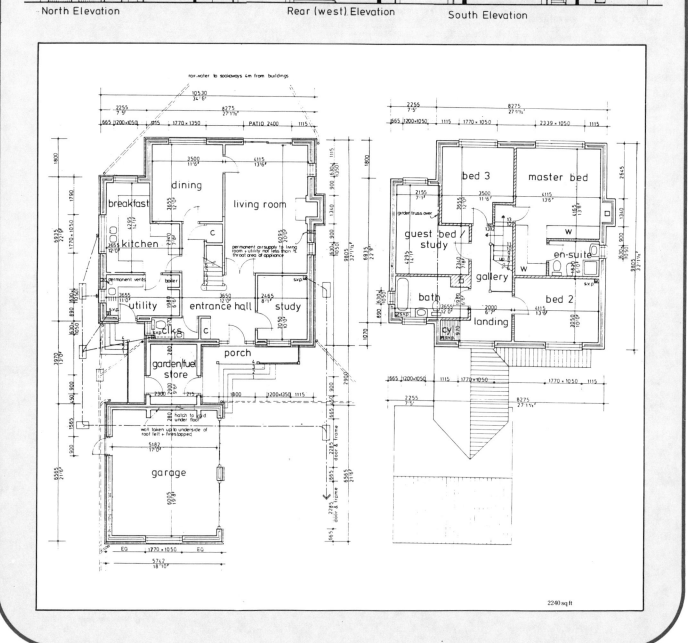

2240 sq ft

A splendid country home designed for a client of Design & Materials Limited with just about every feature for gracious living that one can think of. The inglenook firplace is in a lounge that is large enough to show it to the best advantage, and everything else is on the same generous scale.

45° Pitch, Plain clay tiles

Redland HAMSEY brkwk with tudor plantings

Hardwood joinery with sq leaded lights

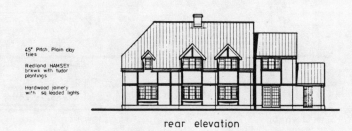

rear elevation

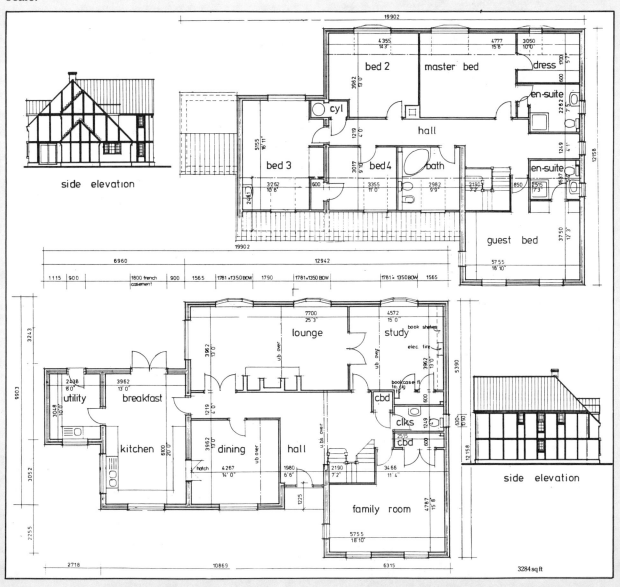

side elevation

side elevation

3284 sq ft

W 1402

W 1402

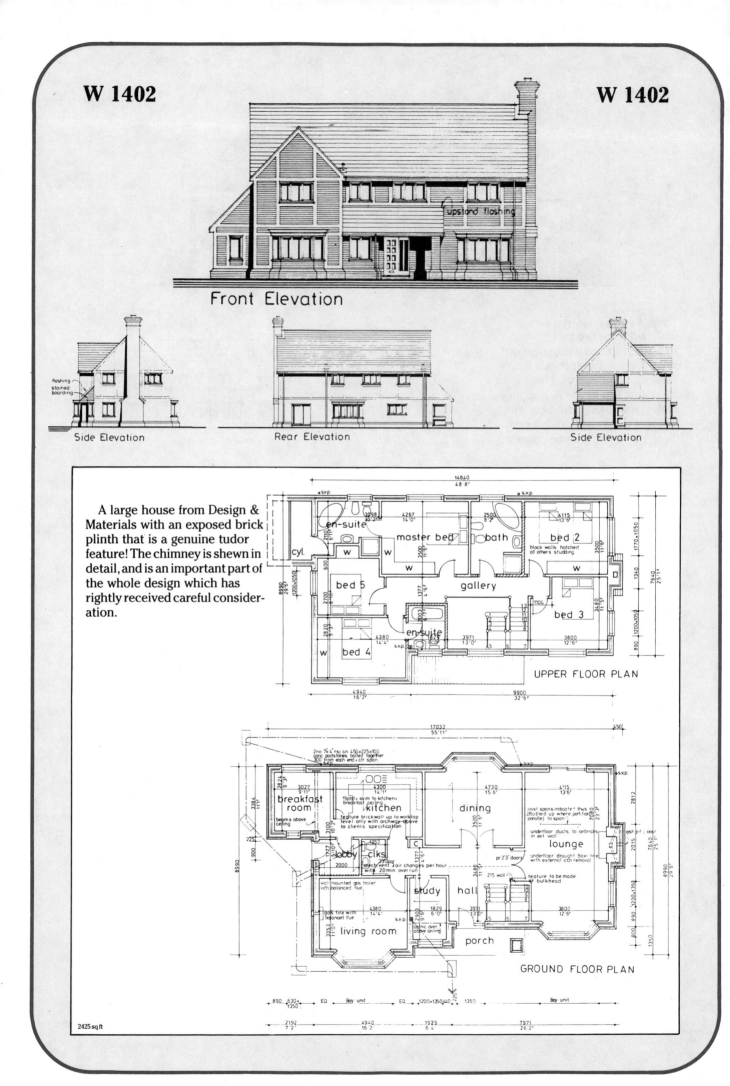

Front Elevation

Side Elevation

Rear Elevation

Side Elevation

A large house from Design & Materials with an exposed brick plinth that is a genuine tudor feature! The chimney is shewn in detail, and is an important part of the whole design which has rightly received careful consideration.

UPPER FLOOR PLAN

GROUND FLOOR PLAN

2425 sq ft

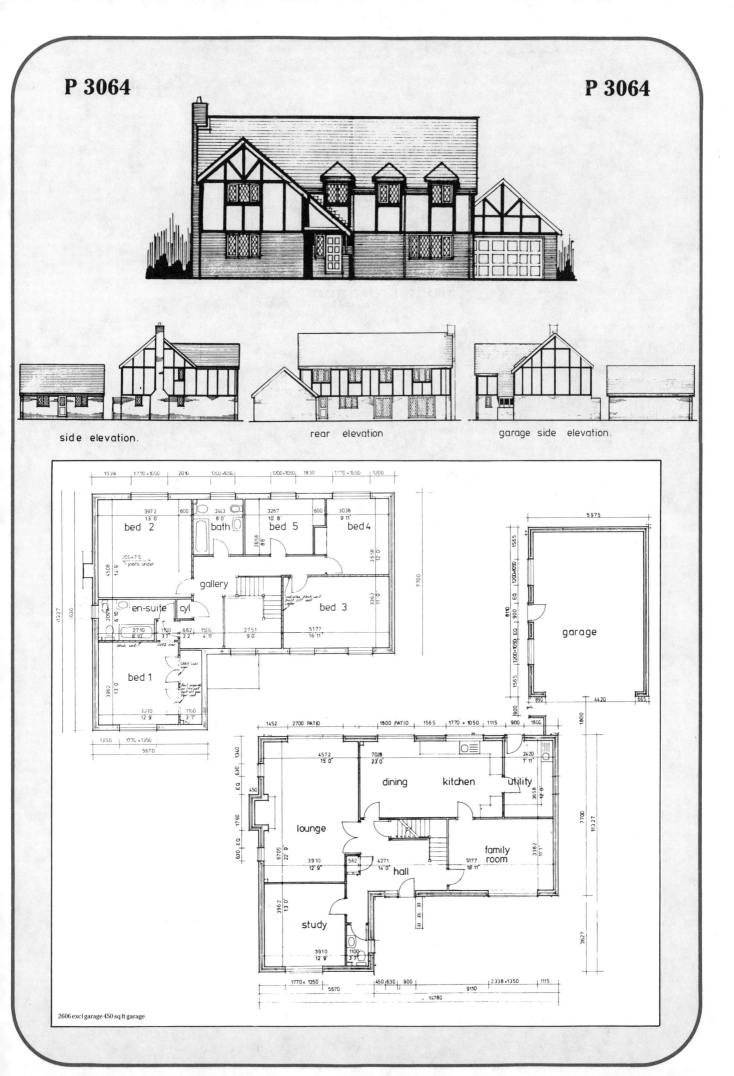

side elevation.

rear elevation.

garage side elevation.

bed 2
bath
bed 5
bed 4

gallery

en-suite
cyl
bed 3

bed 1

garage

dining
kitchen
utility

lounge

family room

hall

study

2606 excl garage 450 sq ft garage

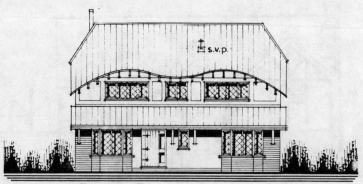

Front Elevation

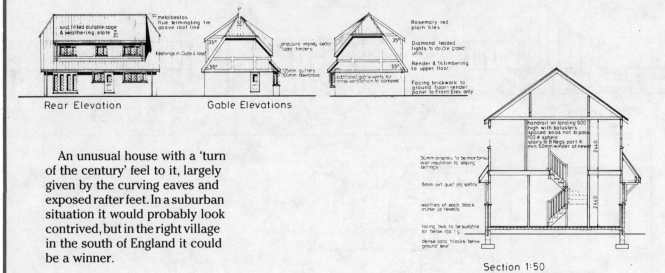

Rear Elevation

Gable Elevations

Section 1:50

An unusual house with a 'turn of the century' feel to it, largely given by the curving eaves and exposed rafter feet. In a suburban situation it would probably look contrived, but in the right village in the south of England it could be a winner.

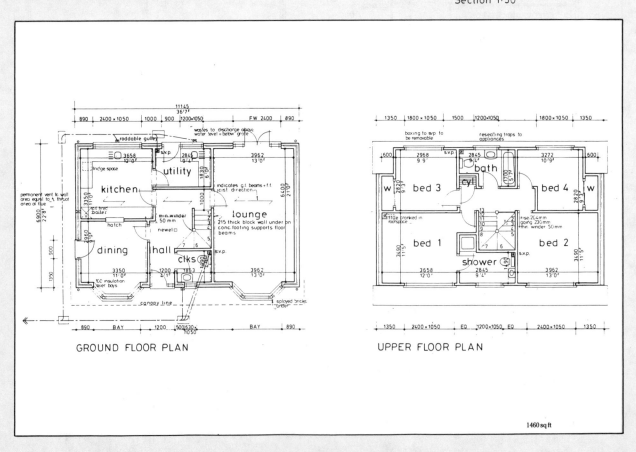

GROUND FLOOR PLAN

UPPER FLOOR PLAN

1460 sq ft

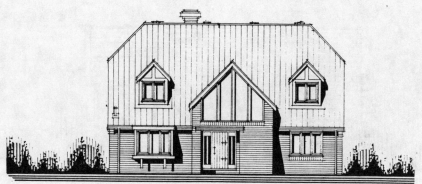

Front Elevation

Side Elevation

Rear Elevation

Redland Regent FHR
roofing tiles with tile hanging
to dormer cheeks
45° pitch

Redland Yellow stock bricks

Dark stained softwood joinery

Side Elevation

An unusual house that got into this Tudor Homes supplement because of its character rather than because it has any specific tudor features. The "half timbering" to the huge front gable is the frame for floor to ceiling glazing, and forms one wall of the gallery. This is a splendid house for an artist, a writer, or anyone else who wants a special and different plan to work.

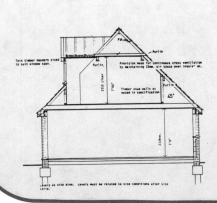

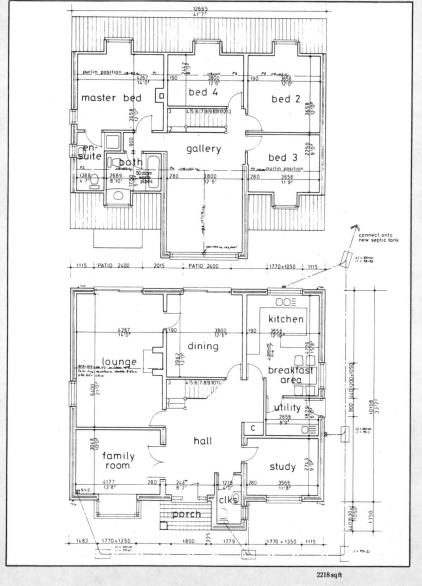

2218 sq ft

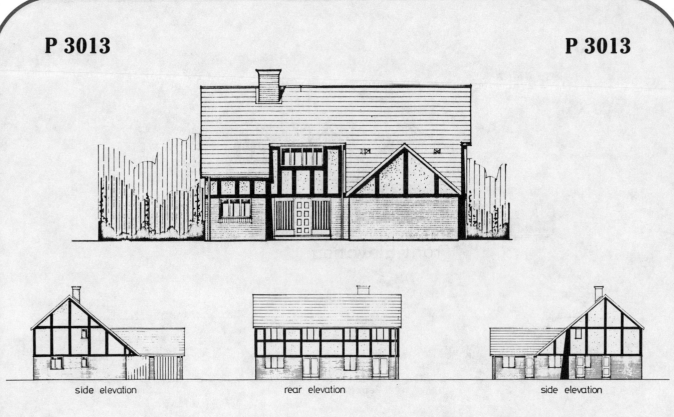

side elevation   rear elevation   side elevation

A design that has a low cottage look to the front, but which is uncompromisingly a house inside. This is a design concept which is very useful in village street situations, where a new house has to fit in with modest buildings on either side, but the cost of the plot dictates that a large home is built on it.

On the first floor the landing has a big window which would suit a large desk or work table, making it in some ways another room.

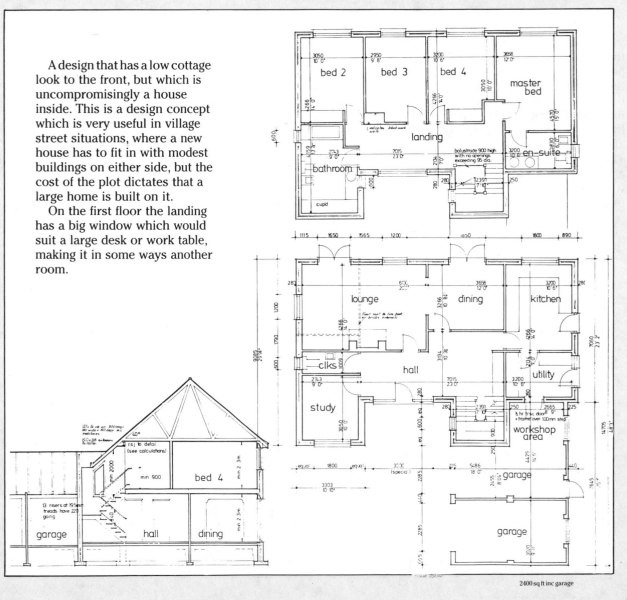

bed 2   bed 3   bed 4   master bed

landing

bathroom   en-suite

cupd

lounge   dining   kitchen

clks

hall   utility

study

workshop area

garage

garage

bed 4

garage   hall   dining

2400 sq ft inc garage

REAR   ELEVATION

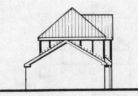

GARAGE SIDE ELEVATION

SIDE   ELEVATION

A nice simple house of 1600 sq.ft. which will be very cost effective to build. If constructed in a part of the country where gable ends are more usual than hip roofs, it can be built with two small gables over the first floor windows, as shewn in design PP6519.

The layout illustrated has only one bathroom, which is unusual these days. However, as the roof construction does not depend on support from any of the first floor partition walls, the bedroom arrangements can be altered to suit the requirements of the family building this new home.

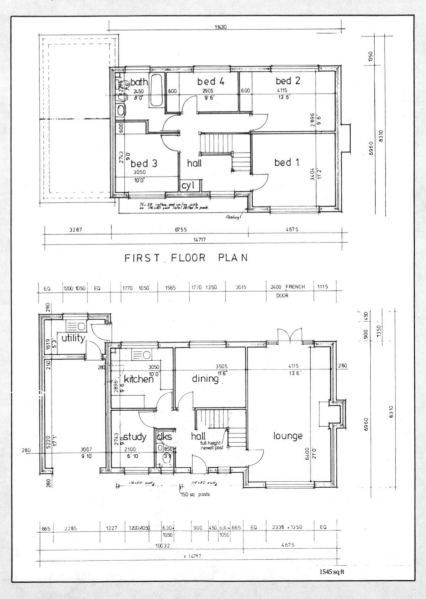

FIRST FLOOR PLAN

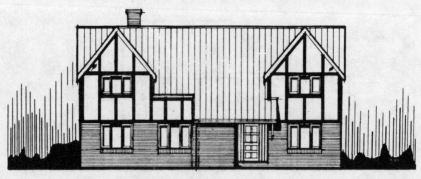

front elevation

rear elevation

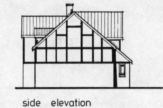

side elevation

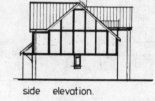

side elevation.

A house with a playroom that is as far away from the study as possible, which many parents will envy. It is unusual for a house of this size to have only one bathroom, but the five bedroom accommodation can easily be rearranged to provide additional facilities.

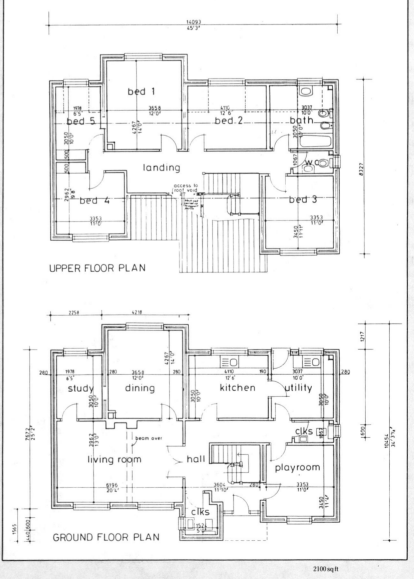

UPPER FLOOR PLAN

bed 1
bed 5
bed 2
bath
landing
w c
access to roof void
bed 4
bed 3

GROUND FLOOR PLAN

study
dining
kitchen
utility
clks
living room
hall
playroom
beam over
clks

2100 sq ft

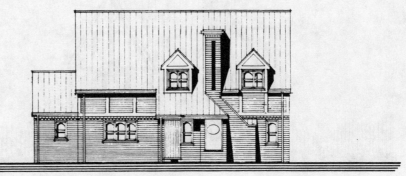

Front Elevation

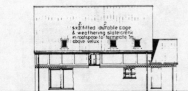

Rear Elevation

Side Elevation

Side Elevation

Another house which has an inglenook fireplace which gives a lot of character to both the whole of the ground floor inside, and to the front elevation outside. Note how the porch has been extended to provide a hidden recess for dustbins or deliveries, with an inset panel of render in a local style. In other situations this panel could be in brickwork to match the style of the chimney behind it.

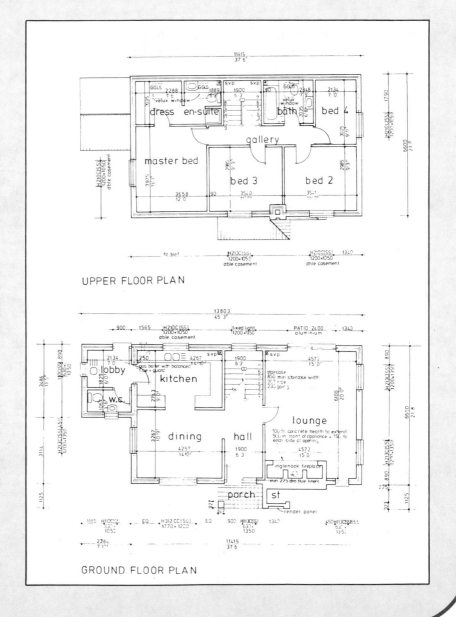

UPPER FLOOR PLAN

GROUND FLOOR PLAN

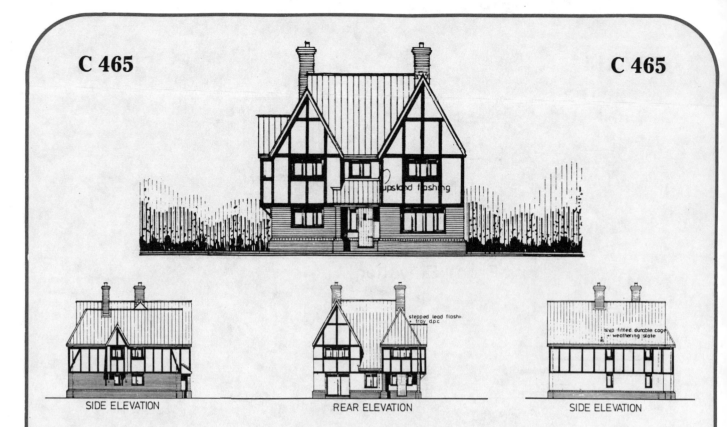

SIDE ELEVATION   REAR ELEVATION   SIDE ELEVATION

The steep pitch of the complex roof, the projecting room on one side, and the balanced chimneys above the main gables give this house a high Victorian look. On the right site, in the right part of the country, it is a splendid tour-de-force, but it is definitely not for suburbia. However, Design & Material who drew these plans for a site for which the design was entirely appropriate will be pleased to draw up a version with a less pronounced Victorian character.

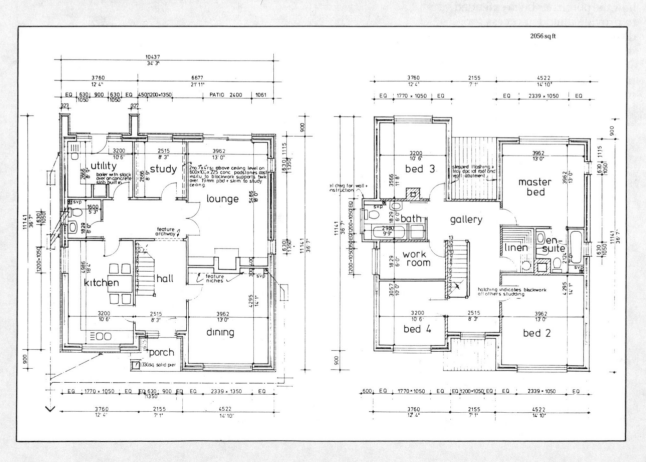

FRONT ELEVATION

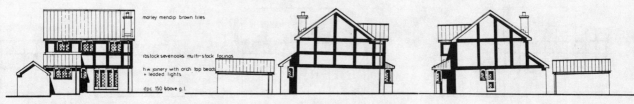

REAR ELEVATION

marley mendip brown tiles

ibstock sevenoaks multi-stock facings

h.w. joinery with arch. top beads + leaded lights

dpc 150 above g.l.

A compact house, with the main building nearly square, but which looks larger and more complex because of the careful arrangement on the site of the garage and back porch. A cost effective house to build.

This is another design with a projecting front porch that is supported by a timber post: as always this support should be really massive.

The lounge is interesting, with the angled door facing the corner fireplace making it an unusual and attractive room, although not an easy one to furnish.

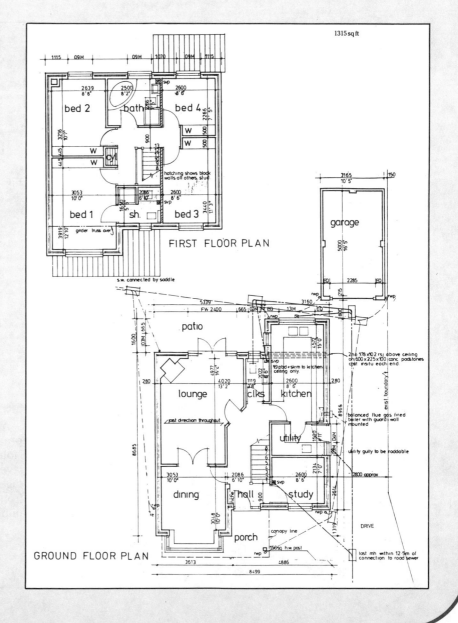

1315 sq ft

FIRST FLOOR PLAN

bed 2

bath

bed 4

bed 1

bed 3

sh.

W

W

W

W

cyl

hatching shows block walls all others stud

girder truss over

GROUND FLOOR PLAN

patio

lounge

clks

kitchen

dining

utility

hall

study

porch

garage

drive

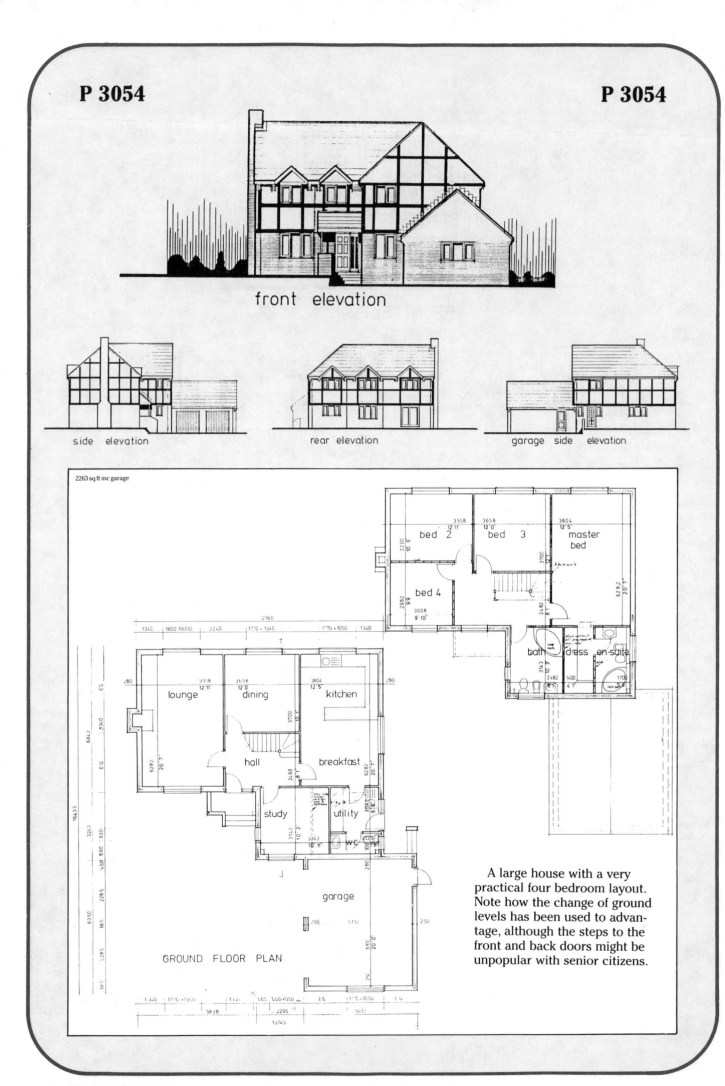

front elevation

side elevation

rear elevation

garage side elevation

2263 sq ft inc garage

GROUND FLOOR PLAN

bed 2

bed 3

master bed

bed 4

bath

dress

en-suite

lounge

dining

kitchen

hall

breakfast

study

utility

wc

garage

A large house with a very practical four bedroom layout. Note how the change of ground levels has been used to advantage, although the steps to the front and back doors might be unpopular with senior citizens.

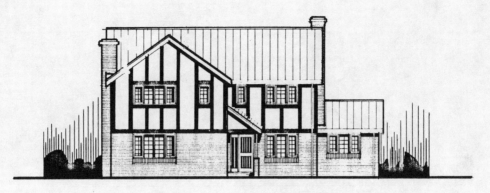

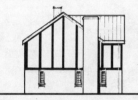

side　elevation

rear　elevation

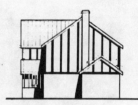

side　elevation

A compact and very attractive house design by Plan Sales Services Ltd for a site in Gwent.

Note the projecting porch to the front door: this will be a key feature and will be much more obvious than would appear from the drawings. The four wooden posts supporting the roof should be really massive, possibly with chamfered corners, and the detailing of the dwarf wall that supports them is most important. Careful attention to this sort of thing is really important, and often the best way of making sure it is right and the right regional style, is to discuss it in detail with the bricklayer and a carpenter — and of course with your architect if you have one.

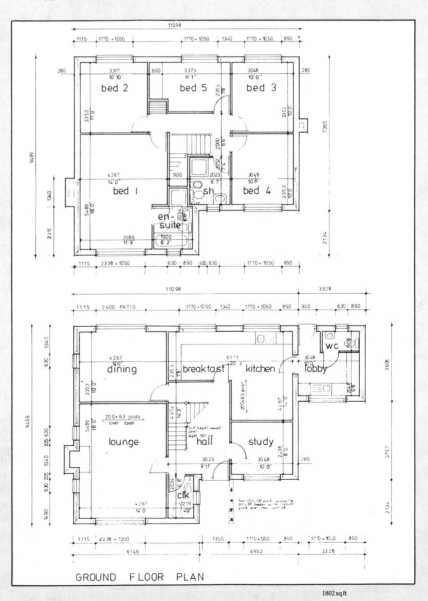

GROUND　FLOOR　PLAN

1802 sq ft

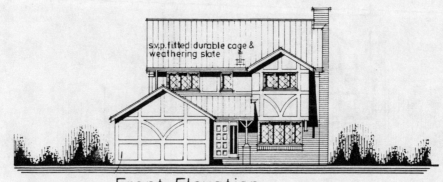

s.v.p. fitted durable cage & weathering slate

Front Elevation

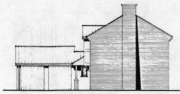

Side Elevation

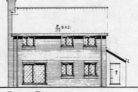

Rear Elevation

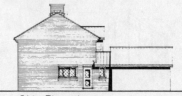

Side Elevation

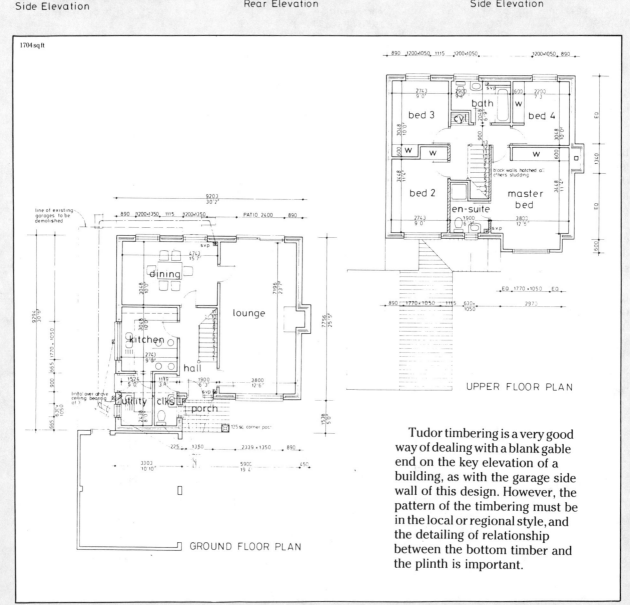

1704 sq ft

GROUND FLOOR PLAN

UPPER FLOOR PLAN

line of existing garages to be demolished

lintal over above ceiling bearing at)

dining

kitchen

lounge

hall

utility   clks

porch

125 sq. corner post

bed 3

bath

w

bed 4

cyl

w   w   w

block walls hatched all others studding

bed 2

en-suite

master bed

Tudor timbering is a very good way of dealing with a blank gable end on the key elevation of a building, as with the garage side wall of this design. However, the pattern of the timbering must be in the local or regional style, and the detailing of relationship between the bottom timber and the plinth is important.

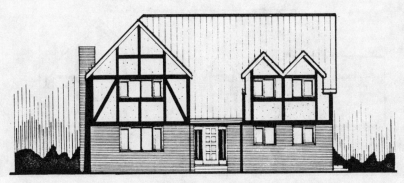

front elevation

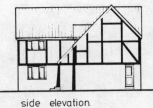

side elevation

rear elevation

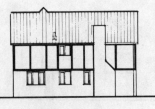

side elevation

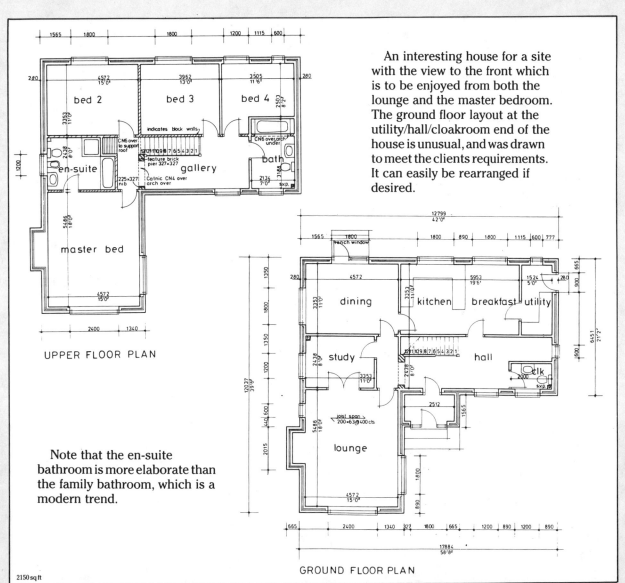

An interesting house for a site with the view to the front which is to be enjoyed from both the lounge and the master bedroom. The ground floor layout at the utility/hall/cloakroom end of the house is unusual, and was drawn to meet the clients requirements. It can easily be rearranged if desired.

Note that the en-suite bathroom is more elaborate than the family bathroom, which is a modern trend.

UPPER FLOOR PLAN

GROUND FLOOR PLAN

2150 sq ft

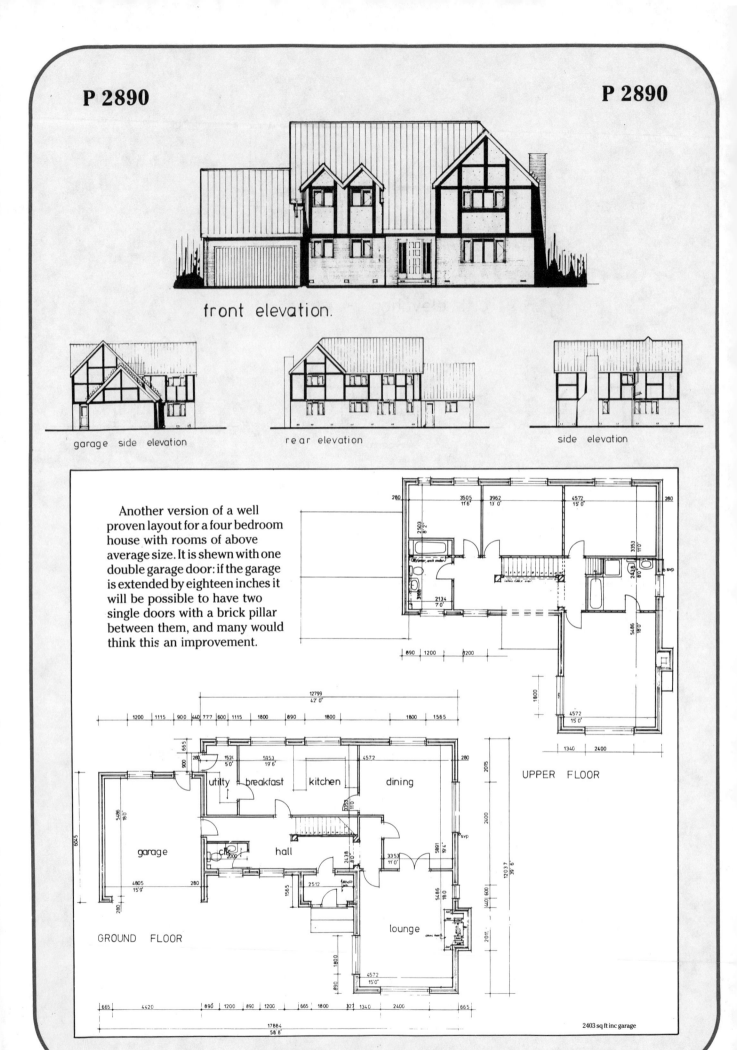

front elevation.

garage side elevation

rear elevation

side elevation

Another version of a well proven layout for a four bedroom house with rooms of above average size. It is shewn with one double garage door: if the garage is extended by eighteen inches it will be possible to have two single doors with a brick pillar between them, and many would think this an improvement.

UPPER FLOOR

utility   breakfast   kitchen   dining

garage   hall

lounge

GROUND FLOOR

2403 sq ft inc garage

Front Elevation

35°pitch Rosemary brown roofing tiles
Render with tudor effect boarding to First Floor
Normanton multicolour brickwork to Ground Floor
Softwood casement joinery with diamond leaded lights to Front Elevation only

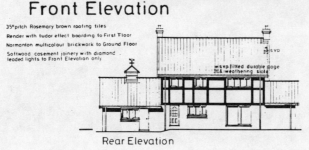

Rear Elevation

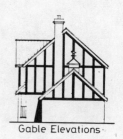

Gable Elevations

UPPER FLOOR PLAN

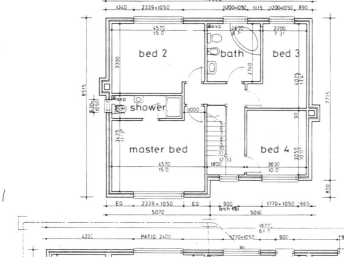

This mock dove cote with its weather vane is a nice touch, and one that can be used with many of the Tudor or regional designs in this book. This house was built with very classy materials: Rosemary tiles, Normanton multi-colour bricks, and diamond leaded lights. The patio windows to the study is an anachronism for a house in this style, and it is a pity that it could not have been on the rear elevation. However, the arrangement shewn suited the site and the client.

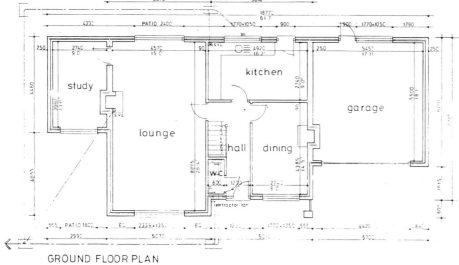

GROUND FLOOR PLAN

1990 sq ft inc garage

west elevation

north elevation   south elevation   east elevation

A bungalow that is designed as two separate blocks linked by a hall is expensive in terms of area of external wall in proportion to floor area, but offers interesting layouts and all round views.

Note the central fireplace as a divider between the lounge and dining room. Fireplaces like this look splendid, but with the low chimney inevitable in a bungalow they sometimes smoke with solid fuel fires. Now that modern coal-effect gas fires are popular this problem can be avoided, and these island hearths are steadily becoming more popular.

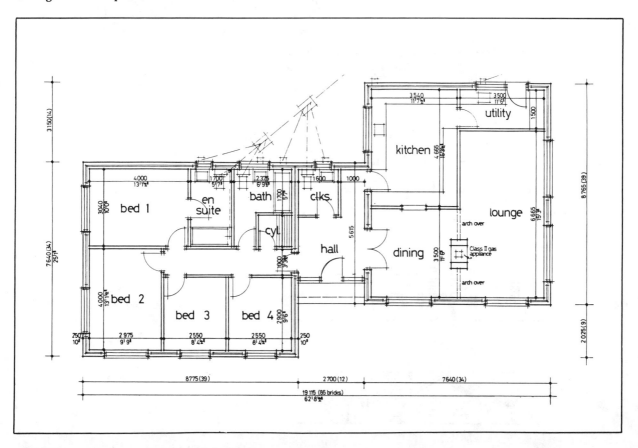

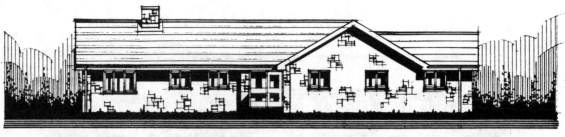

FRONT ELEVATION

This bungalow has four exceptionally large bedrooms, and this is a feature that some people building a new home particularly value. Another feature is the hobbies room behind the garage, linked to the central heating system and with plenty of windows to give good light.

The remainder of the layout is conventional, except that the plan is drawn with an outside WC next to the cloakroom off the hall. If this is not required then the space can be used to double the size of the cloakroom, giving room for a cloaks cupboard, golf bags and all the other things for which a large cloakroom makes such a convenient store.

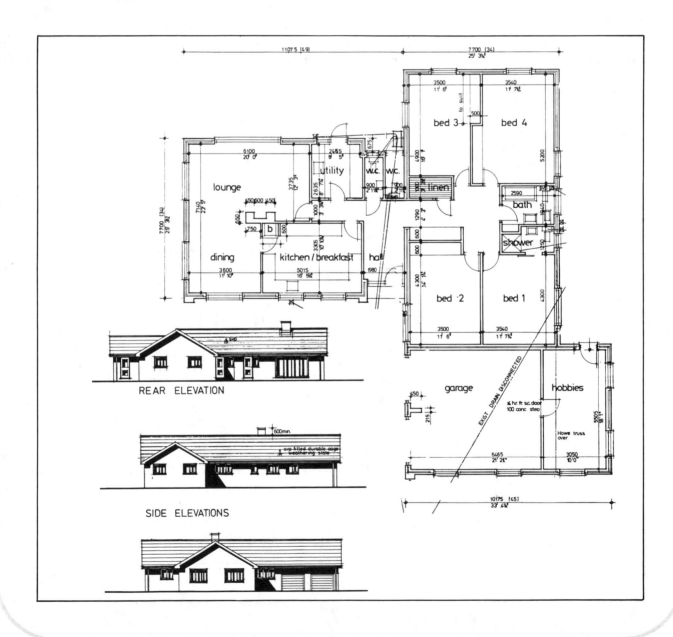

REAR ELEVATION

SIDE ELEVATIONS

FRONT ELEVATION

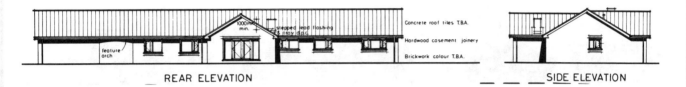

REAR ELEVATION　　　　　　　　　　　　SIDE ELEVATION

SIDE ELEVATION

This very large bungalow has a double garage joined to the bungalow itself with a car port that can provide tandem parking for two further cars on an occasional basis.

The whole building is well over a hundred feet long, and needs a very large site and imaginative landscaping, including large trees, to stop it looking like a railway carriage. This really is important: given the right garden, patios, flower boxes, paths and a carefully designed drive a big bungalow like this can look marvellous. Get the landscaping wrong and it will all be wrong: home and garden need to go together.

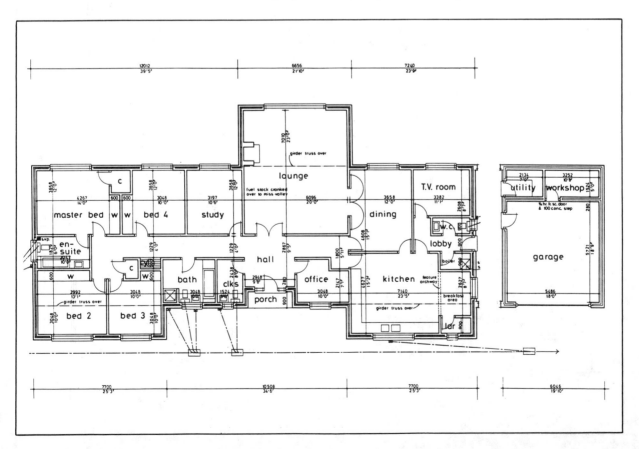

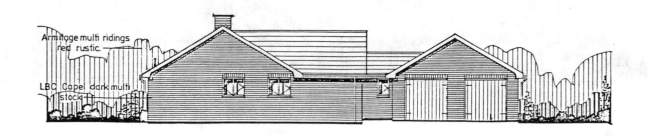

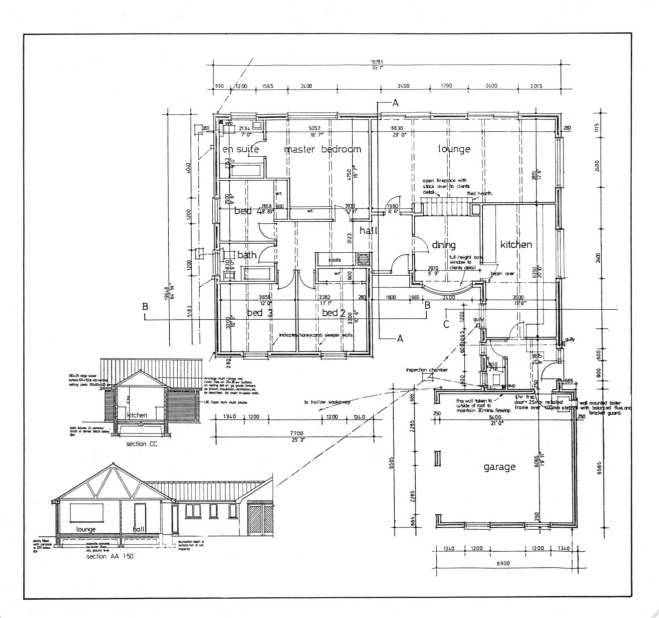

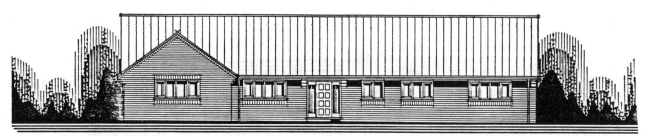

FRONT ELEVATION

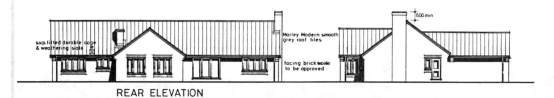

s.x.p. fitted durable cope
& weathering slate

600 min

Marley Modern smooth
grey roof tiles

facing brickwork
to be approved

REAR ELEVATION

This large luxury bungalow has three reception rooms, with separate fireplaces in the lounge and in the sitting room. The master bedroom is comparatively small for a home of this character, but can easily be increased in size by extending the overall length of the bedroom wing.

Although shewn here with three deep windows to the lounge, it is likely that those building this bungalow will want a patio window leading out onto a paved area. It is always important that this sort of patio is not skimped in size: the larger the better, and ideally it should have a dwarf wall or other strong feature associated with it.

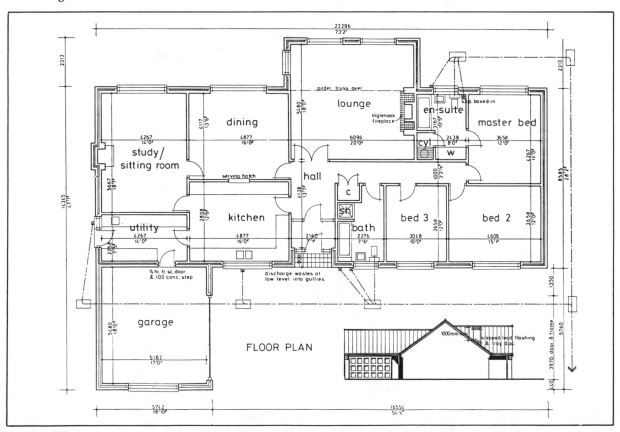

FLOOR PLAN

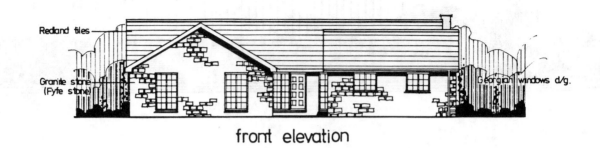

front elevation

Redland tiles

Granite stone
(Fyfe stone)

Georgian windows d/g.

stepped lead
flashing

side elevation

side elevation

rear elevation

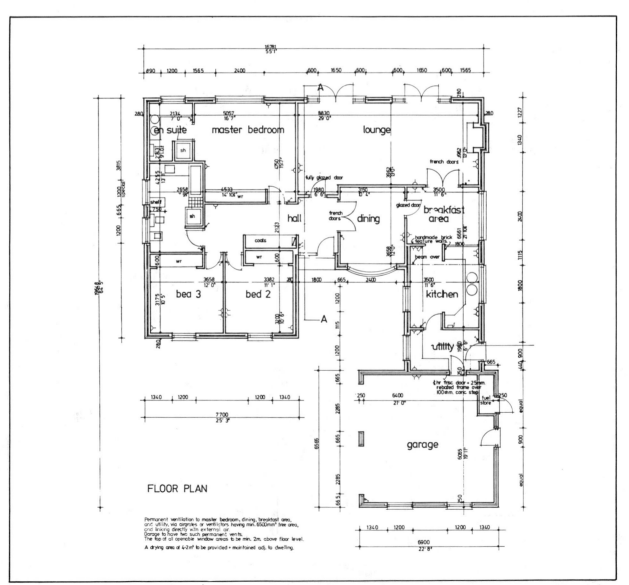

FLOOR PLAN

en suite

master bedroom

lounge

french doors

fully glazed door

glazed door

breakfast
area

hall

french
doors

dining

handmade brick
feature walls.

beam over

coats

wr

bed 3

bed 2

kitchen

utility

garage

fuel
store

1hr frsc. door + 25mm.
rebated frame over
100mm. conc. step.

Permanent ventilation to master bedroom, dining, breakfast area,
and utility, via airgrates or ventilators having min. 6500mm² free area,
and linking directly with external air.
Garage to have two such permanent vents.
The top of all openable window areas to be min. 2m. above floor level.

A drying area of 4·2m² to be provided + maintained adj. to dwelling.

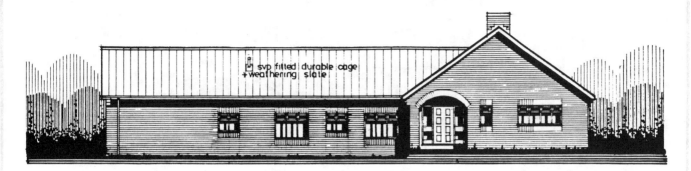

svp fitted durable cage + weathering slate

This bungalow is on two levels and has some interesting features. The large hall and kitchen area have a room height of 8'6", but there are steps down to the lounge and to the bedroom wing which have rooms that are 10'4" high. The lounge is thirty feet long by twenty six feet wide, so that it carries this height with ease and is a most elegant room. The plant trough at the side of the steps up to the dining area gives a special opportunity to the house plant enthusiast.

The master bedroom suite is huge, with a sunken bath as a feature in the bedroom itself, and french windows leading out onto a patio. Of course, if this arrangement does not suit you, a

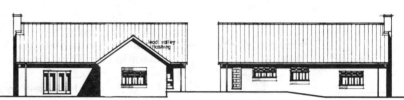

SIDE ELEVATIONS

more conventional bathroom can be arranged and still leave a very big bedroom.

The other two double bedrooms each have a door into the guest bathroom - an arrangement which is unusual but very logical.

A bungalow of this size is normally built on a site with a large garden and it is important

that its design features should be complemented by really imaginative landscaping and the careful choice of the right walling materials. Handmade bricks under a plain tile roof will look particularly effective, especially if squint bricks are used for external window cills and regional brick features are used at the eaves and verge.

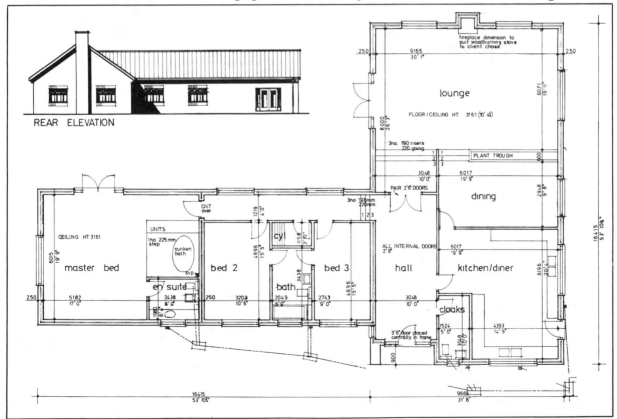

REAR ELEVATION

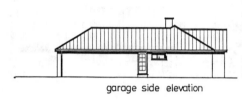

garage side elevation

This large bungalow has a complex roof that is all hips, except for one gable on the rear to emphasise the feature windows to the lounge. The dining room is shewn as an extension of the hall, but can easily become a room in its own right if required.

This is a design that will feel most at home in the Home Counties, built in multi-coloured stock bricks with a plain tile roof.

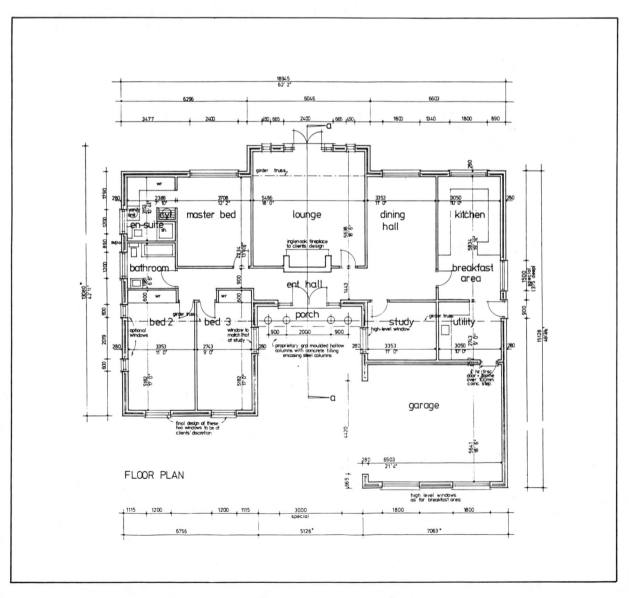

FLOOR PLAN

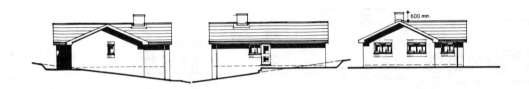

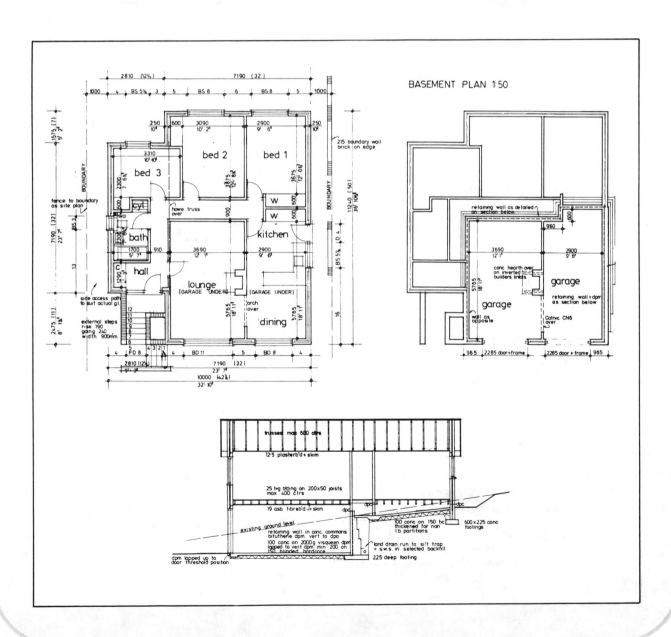

BASEMENT PLAN 1:50

ENTRANCE ELEVATION

REAR ELEVATION

Marley Modern
Smooth grey

Artificial stone to all
elevations

Hardwood casement
joinery

ROAD ELEVATION

s.v.p. fitted durable cage
& weathering slate

6296 20'8"	6808 22'4"	6964 22'10"

to suit | D4M | 22M | 900 | EQ | PATIO 37 | EQ | 450 | 11M | 21M | 1350

cl 98·00
il 197·60

il 97·50

girder truss over   lounge

4900
16'1"

s.v.p.

| 1524 5'0" | 4572 15'0" | 6248 20'6" | 1961 6'5" | 4623 15'2" |

FFL 99·20

FFL 98·21

utility   dining

en-suite   bed 1

3492
11'5"

cyl

3992
13'1"

c

198 rise 220 go

1000

5 4 3 2 1   up

kitchen   hall

3048
10'0"

3048
10'0"

| 5030 16'6" | 1576 5'2" | 1980 6'6" | 3658 12'0" | 2134 7'0" | 4450 14'7" |

358
11'8"

clk   w   bed 2   bath   bed 3

porch

standard Flygt mini
packaged pumping
station for foul
water

cl 99·00
il 97·12

cl 98·00
il 97·23

il 97·00

FLOOR PLAN 1:50

garage

5255
17'3"

standard Flygt
mini packaged
pumping station
surface

stepped lead
flashing &
tray d.p.c.

1000 mm min

| 5182 17'0" |

13M | 05M 327 | 5742

SIDE ELEVATION

exist grdn level

exist grdn level

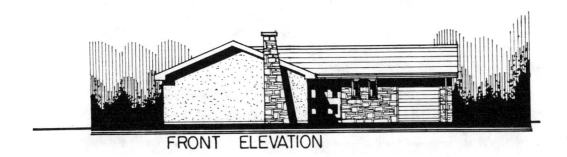

FRONT ELEVATION

SIDE ELEVATIONS　　　　　　　　　REAR ELEVATION

Bungalows with feature chimney breasts built to a batter (or slope) on the front were very popular twenty years ago, and are now enjoying something of a revival. They look at their best in stone with rendered walling elsewhere as shewn here.

This large home has only two bedrooms, and with a workshop next to the garage is an ideal retirement bungalow. It can be built without the integral garage.

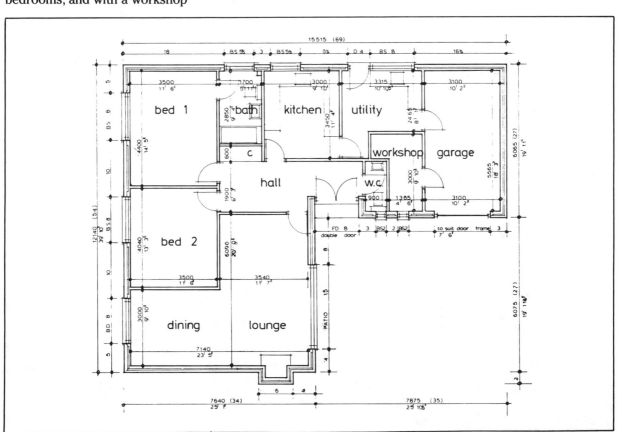

FRONT ELEVATION

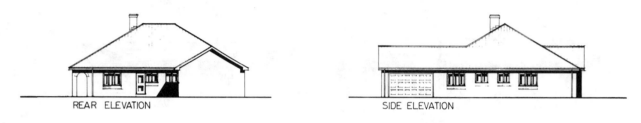

REAR ELEVATION

SIDE ELEVATION

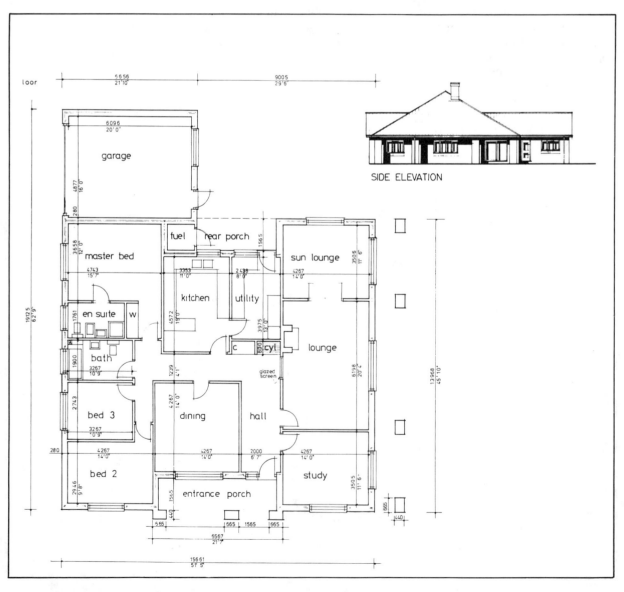

SIDE ELEVATION

floor

5656
21'10"

9005
29'6"

6096
20'0"

garage

4877
16'0"

280

3658
12'0"

master bed

fuel

rear porch

1565

sun lounge

3506
11'6"

4743
15'7"

3353
11'0"

2438
8'0"

4267
14'0"

1761

en suite

w

kitchen

4572
15'0"

utility

3975
13'0"

1900

bath

c

cyl

lounge

6198
20'2"

1912.5
62'9"

3267
10'9"

1239
4'1"

glazed
screen

13968
45'10"

2743

bed 3

4267
14'0"

dining

hall

3267
10'9"

280

4267
14'0"

4267
14'0"

2000
6'7"

4267
14'0"

2946
9'8"

bed 2

1565

entrance porch

study

3505
11'6"

440

665

565

565

1565

665

440

5567
21'7"

15661
51'5"

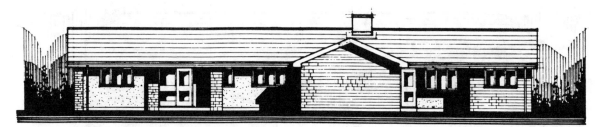

FRONT ELEVATION

REAR ELEVATION

GABLE ELEVATIONS

An interesting bungalow with a granny flat that has an attractive covered patio. The granny flat is quite self contained, and the space available in it can be laid out in a number of different ways.

Note that the boiler is in the garage. This presents an interesting situation, as various authorities recommend against this, but cannot enforce their recommendations under current legislation. The risk is of petrol leaking from a vehicle being ignited by the boiler, which takes its air from the garage. Perhaps this garage is for a diesel car — at any rate, the practise of having a boiler in the garage is widespread.

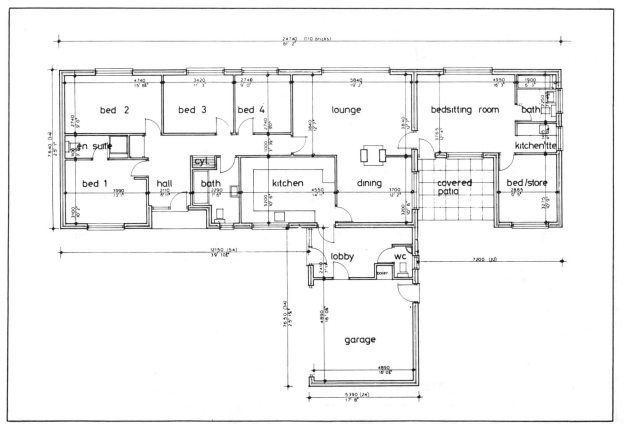

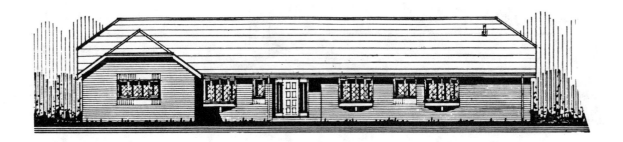

REAR ELEVATION   SIDE ELEVATIONS

This large bungalow with its half hip roof, bay windows and leaded lights has a very gracious feel to it, and needs a beautifully landscaped large garden to set it off. The garage wing can be dispensed with if a detached garage is preferred, but it must be said that the lower garage roof adds complexity and interest to the roof line. If it is not to be built then the relationship of the detached garage to the main building needs very careful consideration.

The inglenook fireplace offers all sorts of scope for imaginative decor, and the lounge floor can be dropped to give more ceiling height, particularly if the lounge is extended. If this is done then the inglenook is probably best changed for a classical fireplace, and this will not present any problem.

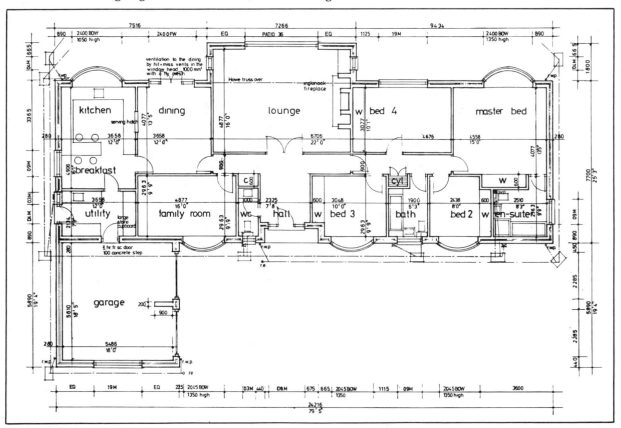

FRONT ELEVATION

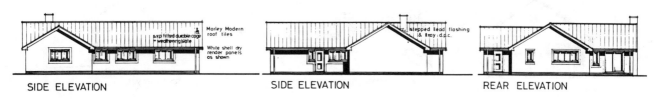

SIDE ELEVATION

Marley Modern
roof tiles

White shell dry
render panels
as shown

s.v.p. fitted ductile cage
+ weathering plate

stepped lead flashing
& tray d.p.c.

SIDE ELEVATION

REAR ELEVATION

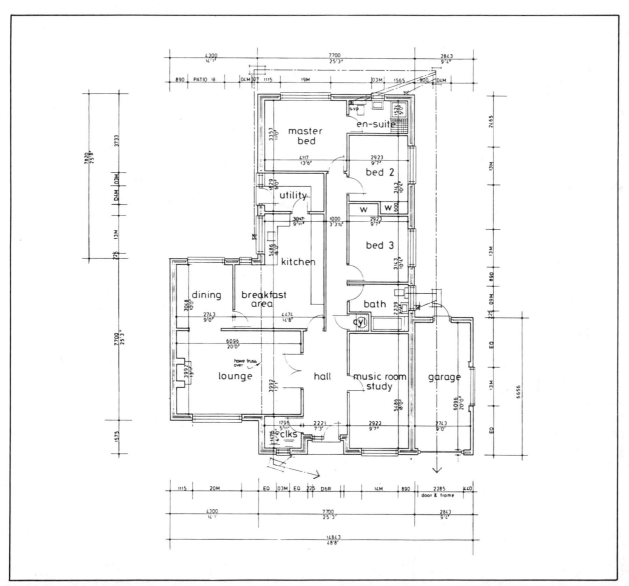

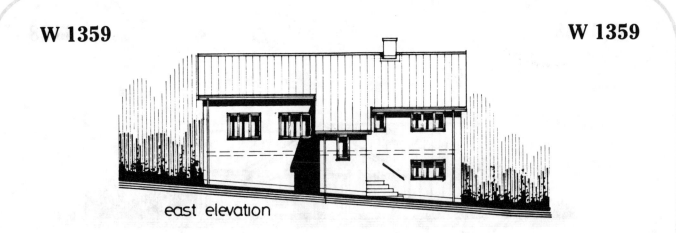

east elevation

north elevation

west elevation

natural slate
roughcast render
hardwood casement joinery

south elevation

It takes a minute or two to work out how this design meets the challenge of a steeply sloping site that falls from the rear left to the front right. The main entrance is at a half way level between the two floors, reached by six steps up from the garage or down seven steps from the hall.

The conservatory is only shewn in concept, and requires careful consideration of the detail design after deciding how it is to be used. If it is to be a sun room, and furnished as such, then quite a different approach is required than that if it is to be a classic conservatory devoted to house plants. Note the sauna — a hot house for humans to match the conservatory for plants?

As with all homes built on steep slopes, the landscaping will be very important, particularly the layout of the steps, paths and patio terrace.

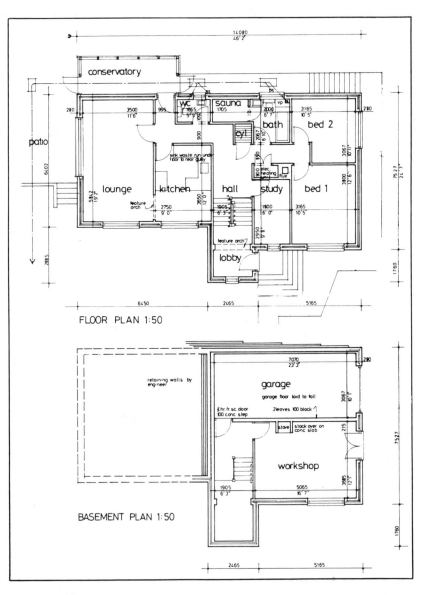

FLOOR PLAN 1:50

BASEMENT PLAN 1:50

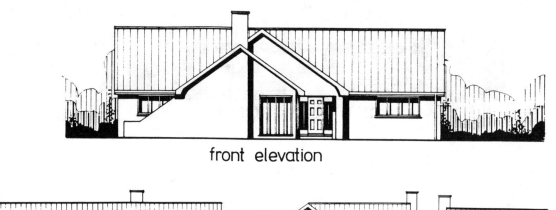

front elevation

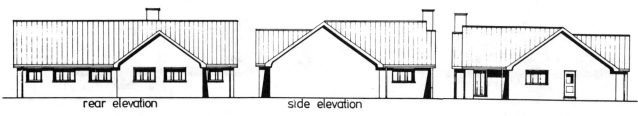

rear elevation   side elevation

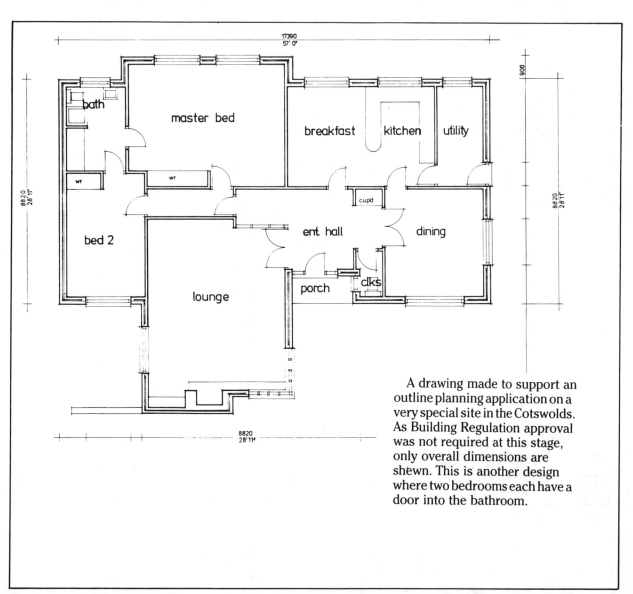

A drawing made to support an outline planning application on a very special site in the Cotswolds. As Building Regulation approval was not required at this stage, only overall dimensions are shewn. This is another design where two bedrooms each have a door into the bathroom.

FRONT ELEVATION

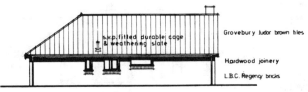

SIDE ELEVATION

ENTRANCE ELEVATION

For many people a back door seems unnecessary, particularly if it means that the milkman has to walk right round the house, and the door itself precludes the ideal kitchen layout. If this is your view then this three bedroom bungalow will appeal to you, and without the garage it can be built on a very narrow site.

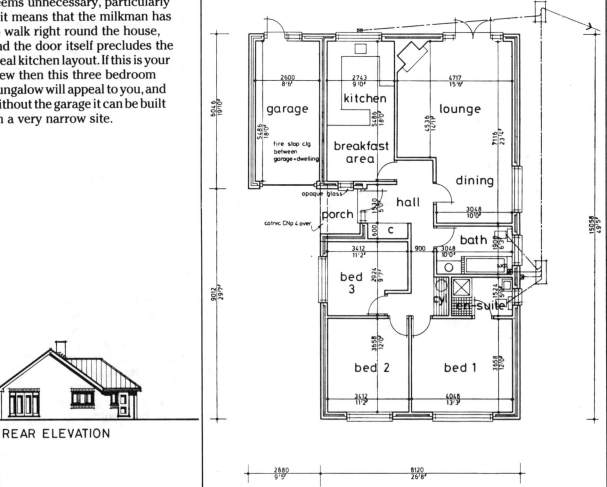

REAR ELEVATION

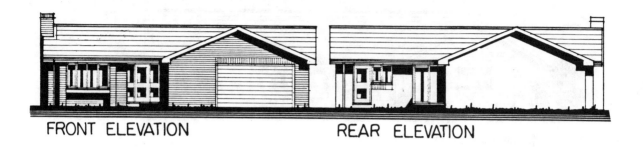

FRONT ELEVATION   REAR ELEVATION

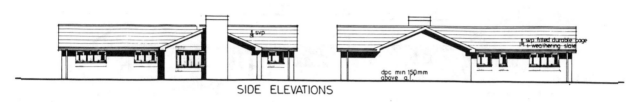

SIDE ELEVATIONS

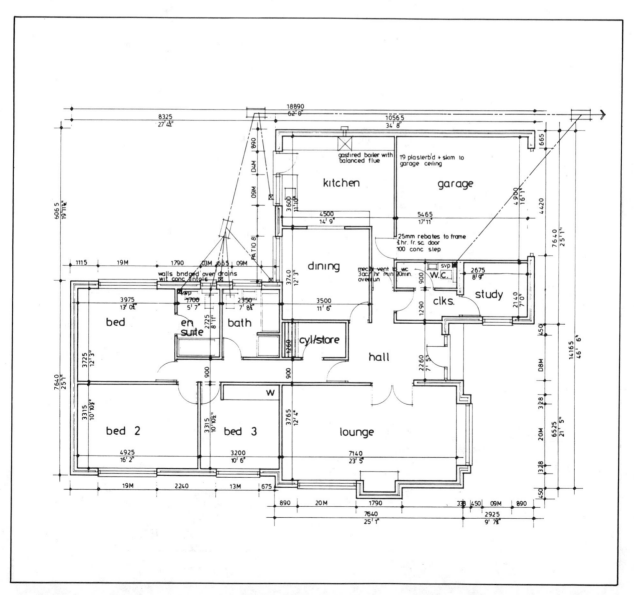

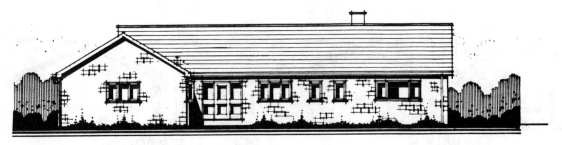

front elevation

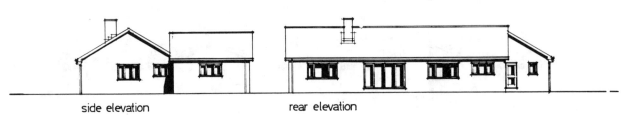

side elevation

rear elevation

A large two bedroom bungalow with lots of living accommodation. Note how the garage roof has a gable rising from the slope of the bungalow roof, which is due to the garage 'overlapping' the end of the main building.

side elevation

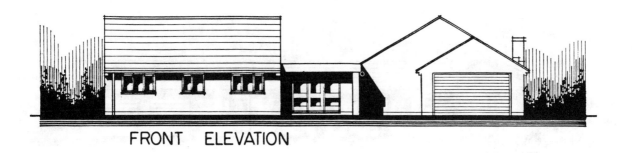

FRONT ELEVATION

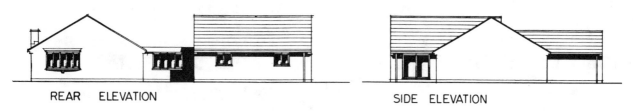

REAR ELEVATION

SIDE ELEVATION

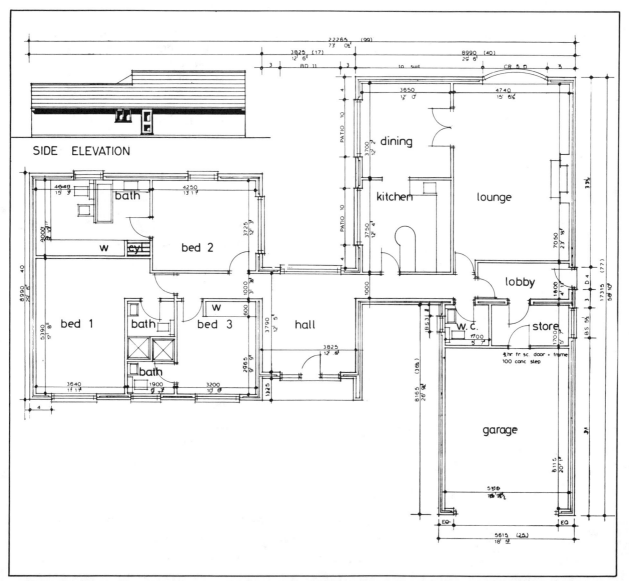

SIDE ELEVATION

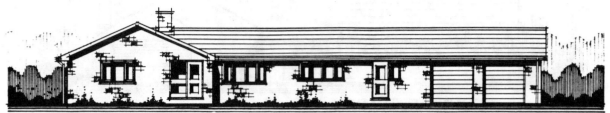

front elevation

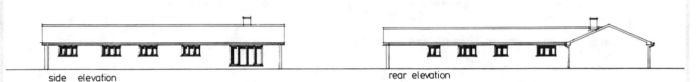

side elevation

rear elevation

This huge bungalow was built in the middle of a field in West Yorkshire, and with plenty of space around it the total effect was most successful. The big 'lobby' or extension of the hall is unusual, but very practicable when the home is for a large busy family.

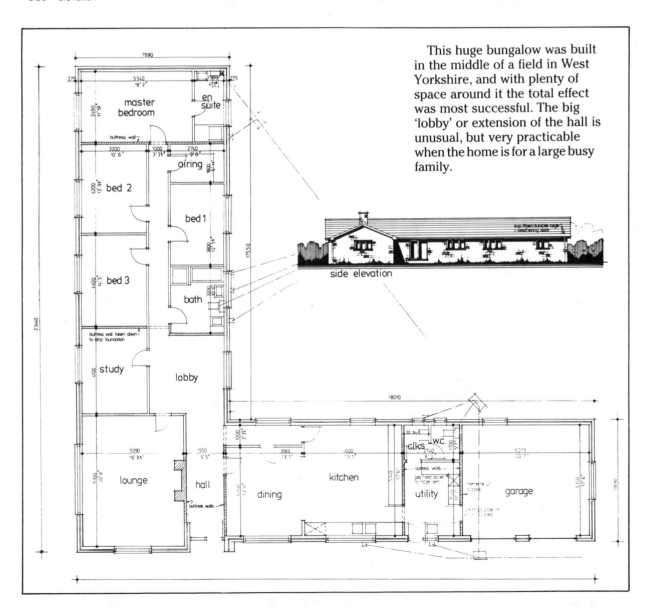

side elevation

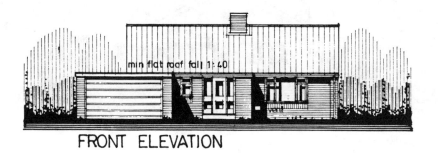

FRONT ELEVATION

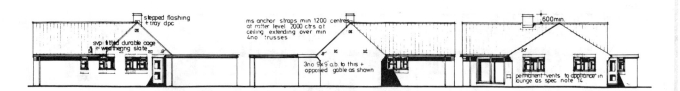

stepped flashing + tray dpc

svp fitted durable cage + weathering slate

ms anchor straps min 1200 centres at rafter level 2000 ctrs at ceiling extending over min 4no trusses

3no 9x9 a.b to this + opposed gable as shown

600 min.

permanent vents to appliance in lounge as spec note 14

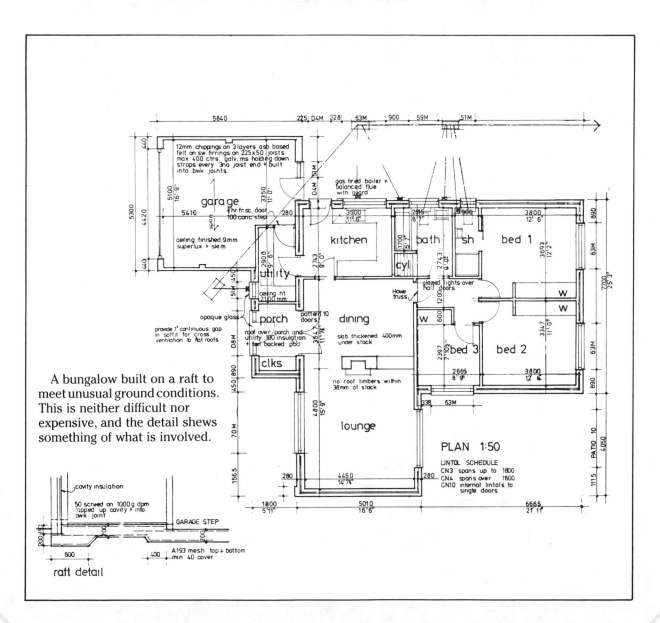

12mm chippings on 3 layers asb based felt on sw firrings on 225x50 joists max 400 ctrs. galv. ms holding down straps every 3no joist end + built into bwk joints.

garage

1 hr. fr. sc. door 100 conc step

ceiling finished 9mm superlux + skim

gas fired boiler + balanced flue with guard

kitchen

bath

sh

bed 1

cyl

utility

ceiling ht 2100 mm

Howe truss

glazed lights over half doors

opaque glass

porch

pattern 10 doors

dining

w

w

provide 1" continuous gap in soffit for cross ventilation to flat roofs

roof over porch and utility 100 insulation + felt backed pbd

slab thickened 400mm under stack

w

bed 3

bed 2

clks

no roof timbers within 38mm of stack

A bungalow built on a raft to meet unusual ground conditions. This is neither difficult nor expensive, and the detail shews something of what is involved.

lounge

PLAN 1:50

LINTOL SCHEDULE
CN3 spans up to 1800
CN4 spans over 1800
CN10 internal lintols to single doors

cavity insulation

50 screed on 1000 g dpm lapped up cavity + into bwk joint

GARAGE STEP

A193 mesh top + bottom min 40 cover

raft detail

FRONT ELEVATION

SIDE ELEVATION   ENTRANCE ELEVATION   REAR ELEVATION

This 'end on' bungalow was built on the East coast, and has a number of interesting features which help it avoid the box look of a rectangular structure. On the road elevation part of the gable wall was pulled back, and provided with a bay window. An ornamental wall was built out to give privacy to the patio outside the french windows, and the two chimneys were unusual. It was built in an orchard of mature trees, and looks very attractive.

Like many housewives who are concerned with a retirement bungalow, the lady concerned with this new home insisted on an old fashioned larder. By having the door to this at an angle she has not lost any usable space in the larder, has gained space in the kitchen, and made a feature of the whole arrangement.

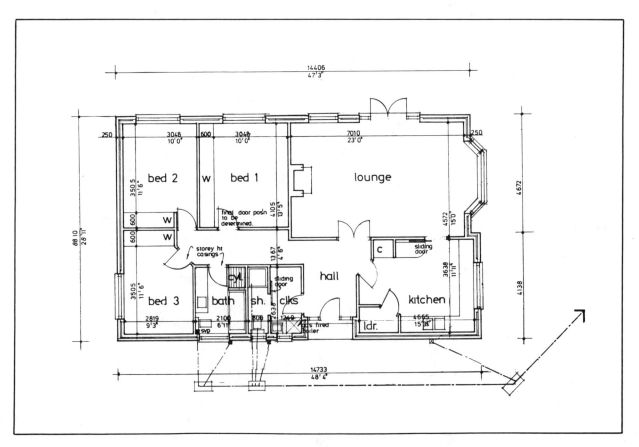

SIDE ELEVATION

GABLE ELEVATION.

SIDE ELEVATION

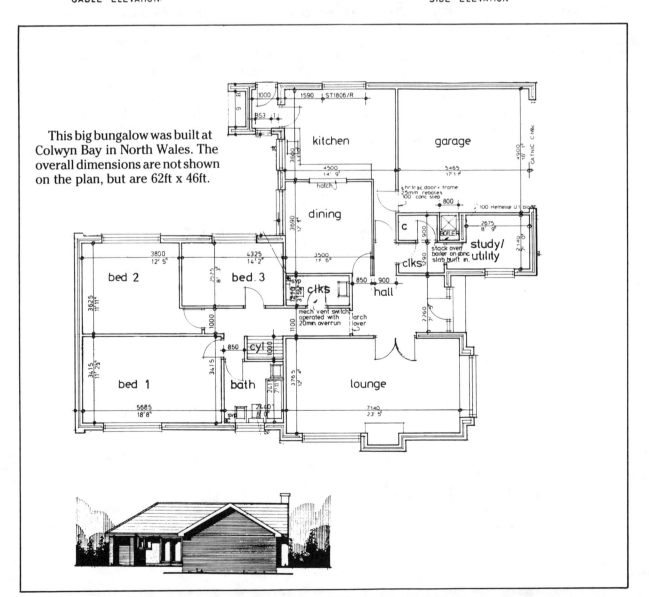

This big bungalow was built at Colwyn Bay in North Wales. The overall dimensions are not shown on the plan, but are 62ft x 46ft.

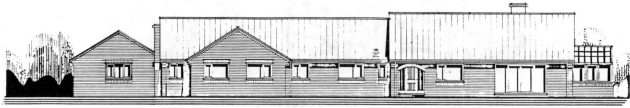

FRONT ELEVATION

This very large bungalow with a granny flat was designed to suit a very special site, and is full of design features that will interest others with a site for a building that is over 100ft long. There are small gables on both the front and the rear elevations, and in most situations it might be a good thing to add to these, with a gable roof over the lounge.

The division between the main part of the bungalow and the granny flat is shewn as a feature archway between bedrooms 3 and 5, and this can be built as a door, or repositioned, to suit the family concerned. As usual, the granny flat has its own entrance.

The conservatory leading from the dining room can be built in many different ways, and one of

the many glass and metal conservatories on the market would be well suited to a role here. Everything depends on how it will be used: as a sun room with houseplants as decor, or as a classic conservatory where the plants have priority and the humans are just visitors! The choice is yours.

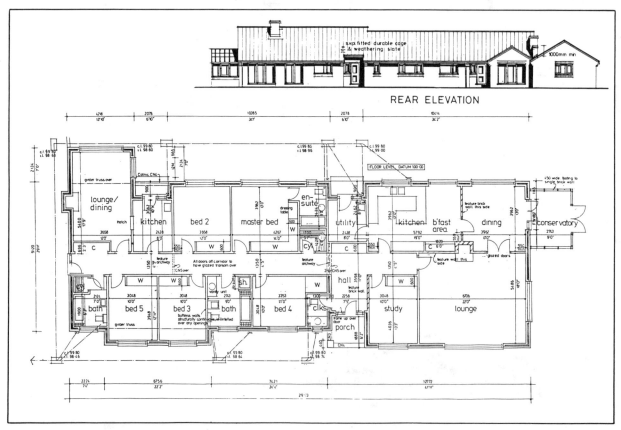

REAR ELEVATION

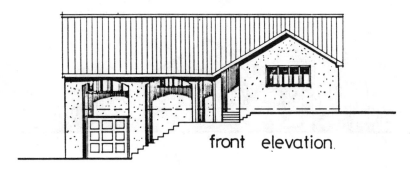

front elevation.

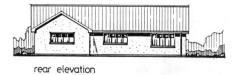

rear elevation

side elevations

national (assumed) levels only

There are two entrances into this split level bungalow: through the garage and up a flight of stairs, or up the feature steps to the front door at a higher level. In the layout illustrated the ground floor accommodation next to the garage is used as a laundry, but it could be a study, a bedroom with its own en-suite bathroom behind, or even a self-contained bed-sitter.

A glazed front door will be needed to light the hall, or an alternative is to move the kitchen door slightly to the left, when there will be room for a narrow window on either side of the door.

This bungalow was originally built in London with a rendered finish, but would look equally well in either brick or stone.

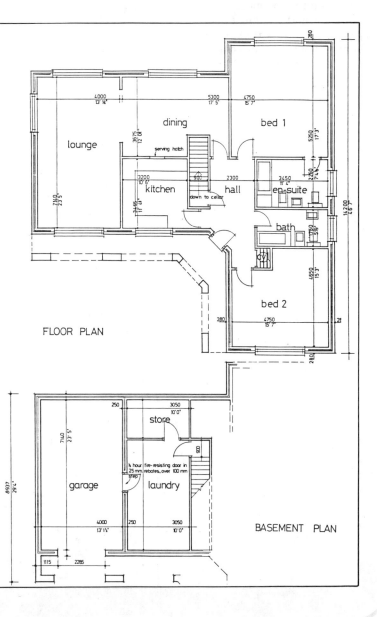

331

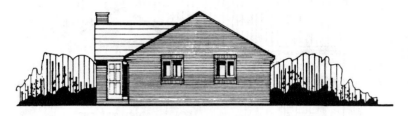

Front elevation

A bungalow on a site only thirty five feet wide, with three feet clearance from the boundary down one side and one foot at the other. A tight clearance at a boundary is a nuisance, but often inevitable with narrow plots. The provisions of the Building Regulations about how close you can build to a boundary are complex, and you must take professional advice before you commit yourself to any particular design if windows to the main living rooms or bedrooms are going to be close to a boundary.

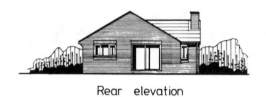

Rear elevation

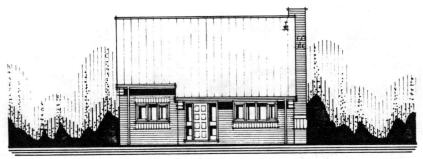

FRONT ELEVATION

SIDE ELEVATION

REAR ELEVATION

SIDE ELEVATION

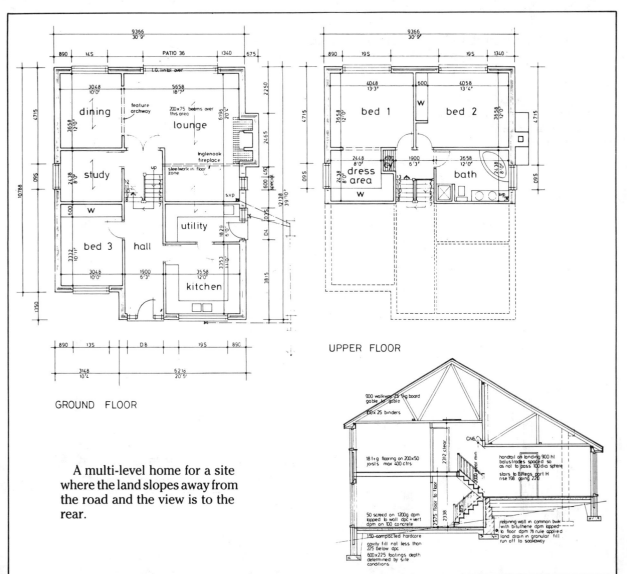

GROUND FLOOR

UPPER FLOOR

A multi-level home for a site where the land slopes away from the road and the view is to the rear.

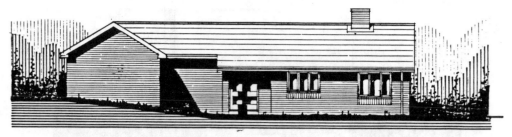

FRONT ELEVATION

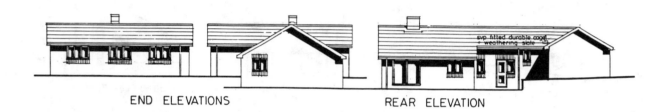

END ELEVATIONS

REAR ELEVATION

A bungalow on two levels with five steps in the hall linking the two halves. Note the big walk-in airing cupboard which has room for shelving to the ceiling all around the hot water cylinder. An airing cupboard like this is usually used for long term storage of household linen, and so it saves storage space elsewhere.

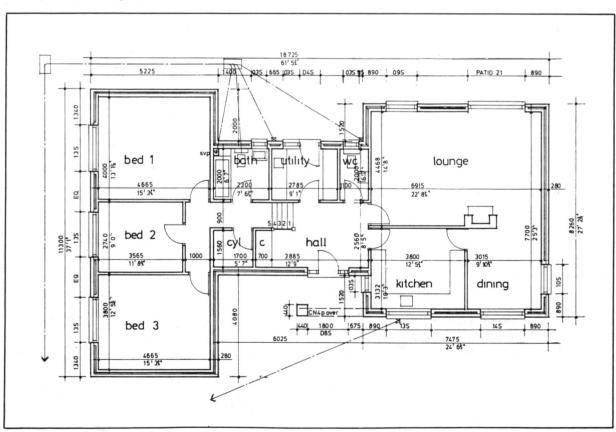

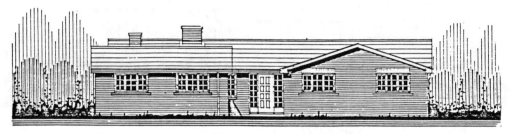

front elevation

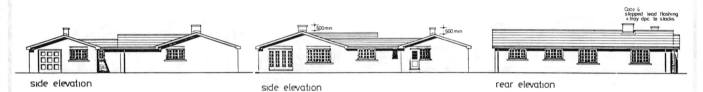

side elevation

side elevation

rear elevation

Code 4
stepped lead flashing
+ tray dpc to stacks

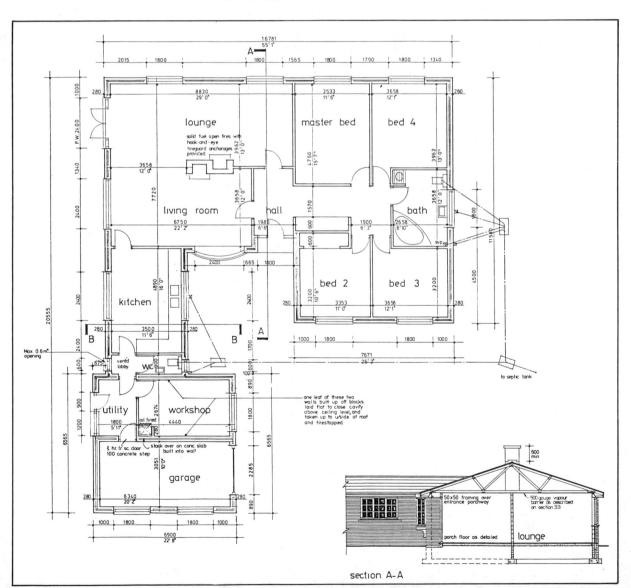

section A-A

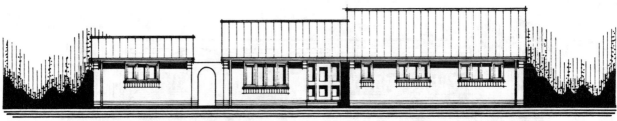

FRONT ELEVATION

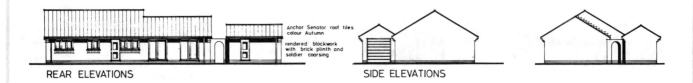

REAR ELEVATIONS

Anchor Senator roof tiles colour Autumn

rendered blockwork with brick plinth and soldier coarsing

SIDE ELEVATIONS

In many rural situations a narrow building is required to fit in with Victorian cottages that were often only one room deep. This three bedroom bungalow is ideal for this, and is shewn with a garage linked to it with an angled wall. The relationship between a garage and a house or bungalow is always important, and often does not receive sufficient consideration. A link wall with brickwork features, particularly a coping, has many advantages.

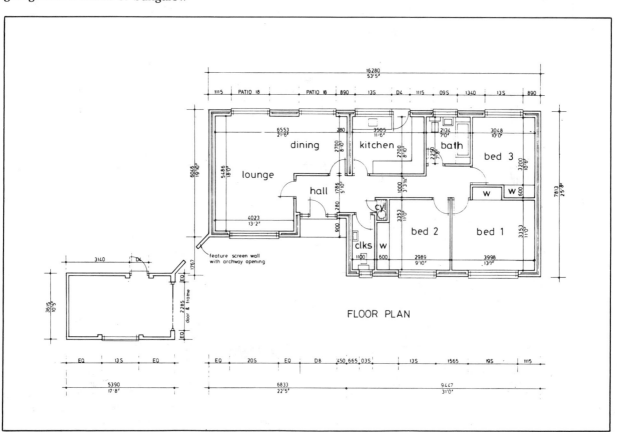

FLOOR PLAN

FRONT ELEVATION

ENTRANCE ELEVATION

Redland stonewold
colour slate grey

Desford old english multi
brickwork

Hardwood joinery

SIDE ELEVATION

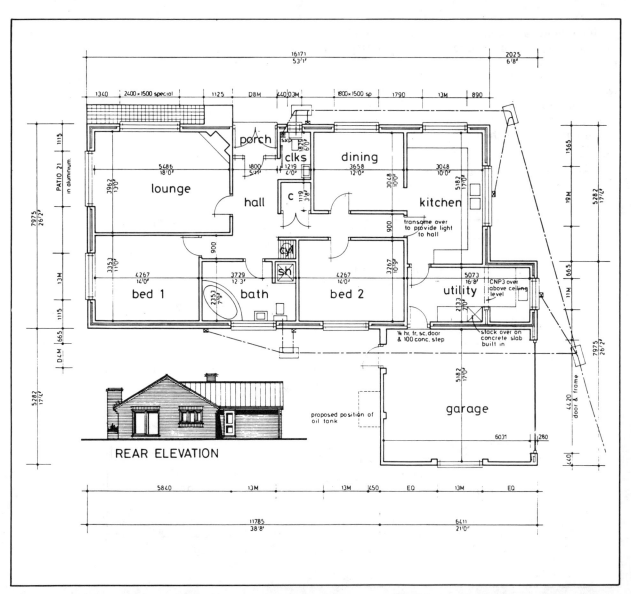

REAR ELEVATION

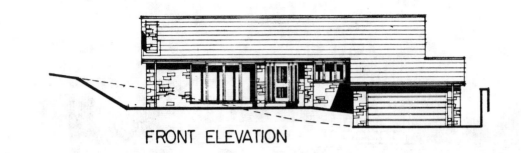

FRONT ELEVATION

SIDE ELEVATIONS   REAR ELEVATION

This preliminary study for a bungalow on a sloping site did not find favour with the planners for reasons that had nothing to do with the design itself.

The shower room can easily be rearranged to provide an en suite bathroom for one of the bedrooms, and the kitchen and dining room can change places if required.

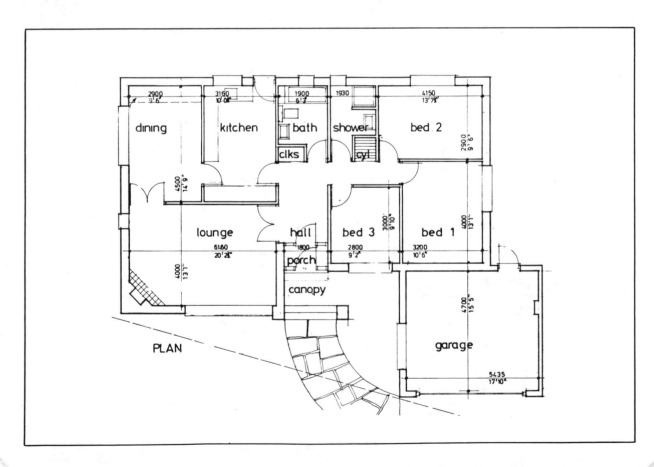

PLAN

FRONT ELEVATION

s.v.p. fitted durable cage
& weathering slate

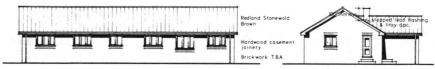

REAR ELEVATION

Redland Stonewold
Brown

Hardwood casement
joinery

Brickwork T.B.A.

SIDE ELEVATIONS

In most large homes the master bedroom suite is as far away from the living accommodation as possible, usually at the end of a bedroom corridor. In this five bedroom bungalow it is right in the centre of things. The choice is yours ... Note the outside store in the angle by the utility room window. This unusual feature was for a particular client, and most people interested in this design will want the boiler moved and the utility room rearranged to use this space in some other way.

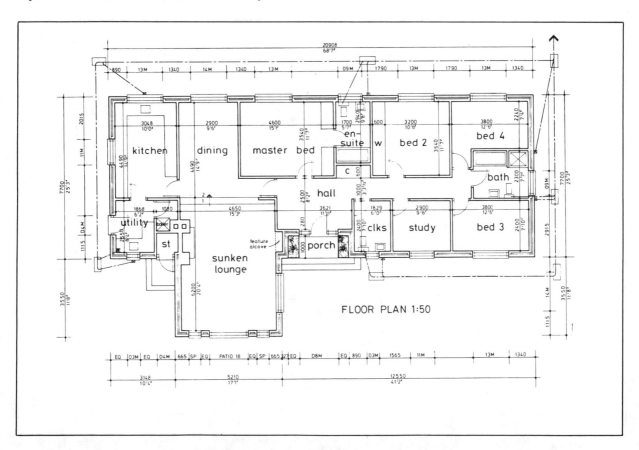

FLOOR PLAN 1:50

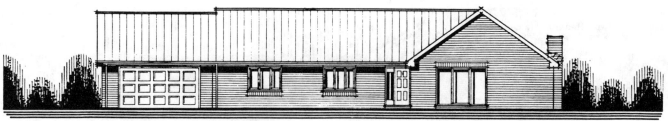

FRONT ELEVATION

REAR ELEVATION SIDE ELEVATIONS

Tilcon Wilnecot multi russett bricks under Grovebury farmhouse red pantiles were specified for this bungalow — a dark mottled tile over a light coloured mottled brick, looking very well together. As much time should be spent choosing the right materials for a new home as

you spend debating the design: all too often people settle for the first materials suggested to them. The choice is very wide these days, and shortages of building materials are generally a thing of the past. It is a buyers market: take advantage of it!

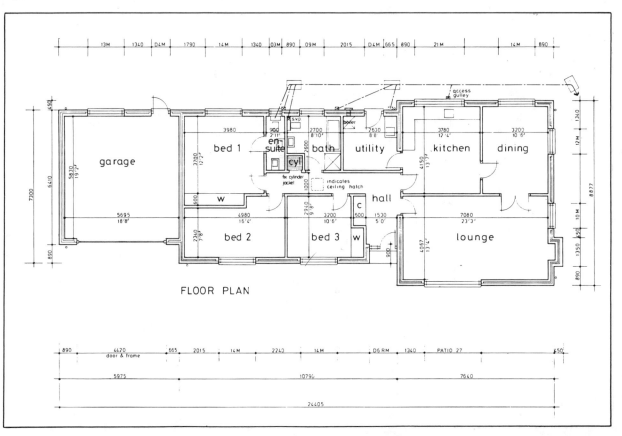

FLOOR PLAN

REAR ELEVATION   GABLE ELEVATIONS

600 min.

svp fitted durable cage weathering slate

stepped flashing + tray dpc

red bwk up gable

A conventional rectangular
bungalow given an unusual
appearance, and a lofty ceiling to
the lounge, by raising the roof to
part of the building. This gives a
very novel and attractive roof line
which is not shewn to advantage
in these strict elevation drawings.

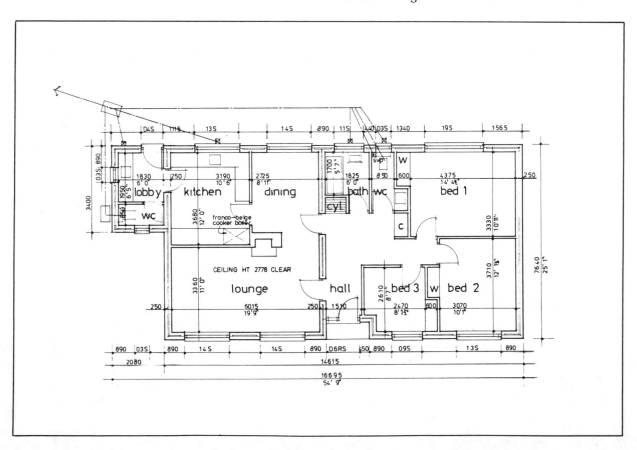

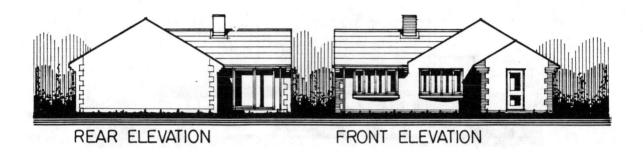

REAR ELEVATION   FRONT ELEVATION

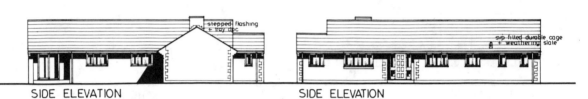

SIDE ELEVATION   SIDE ELEVATION

A bungalow with bow windows to the lounge, dining room and kitchen, because the client liked bow windows! When one thinks how fashions in windows change every few years, this is the best possible reason for choosing joinery in any particular style, providing that your choice is in sympathy with the joinery on adjacent properties.

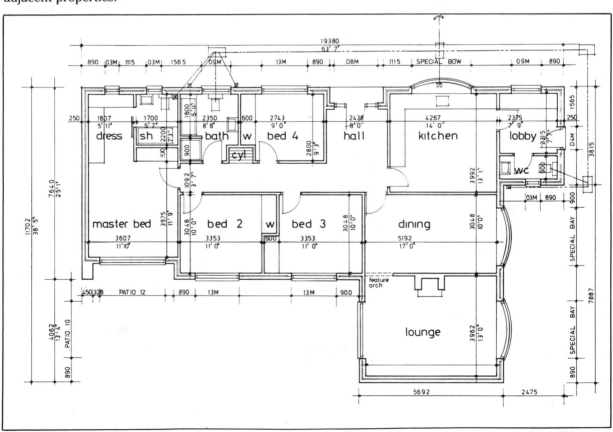

FRONT ELEVATION

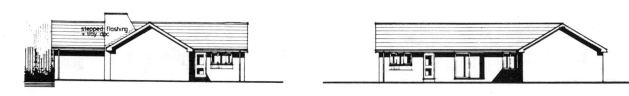

stepped flashing + tray dpc

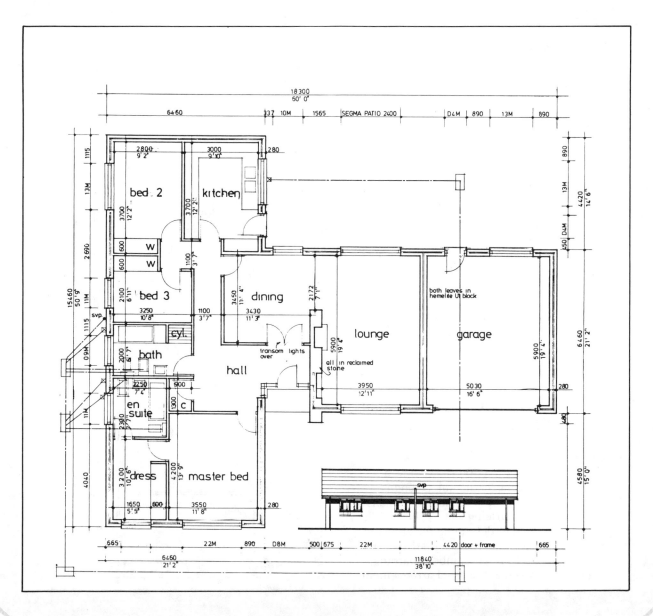

ENTRANCE ELEVATION

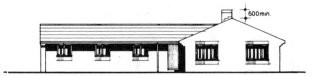

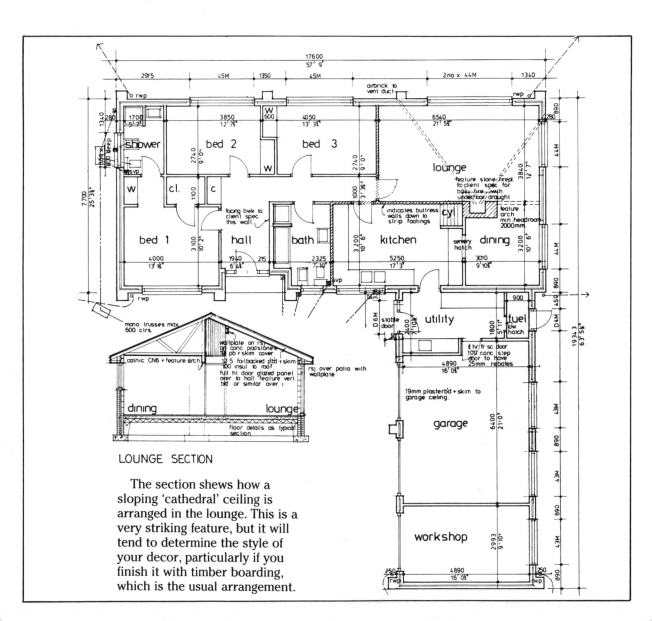

LOUNGE SECTION

The section shews how a
sloping 'cathedral' ceiling is
arranged in the lounge. This is a
very striking feature, but it will
tend to determine the style of
your decor, particularly if you
finish it with timber boarding,
which is the usual arrangement.

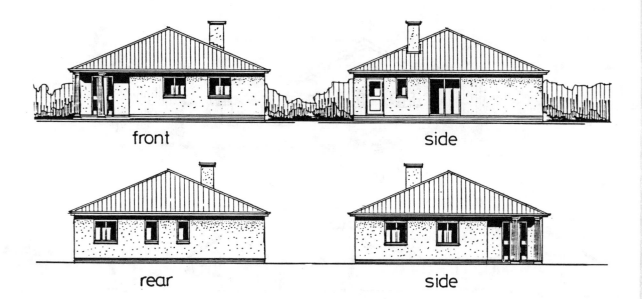

front

side

rear

side

Square bungalows were popular between the wars, and have not been built since. I wonder why? They are economical to build, to heat, and are very compact. At any rate, this example will suit an infill plot in a road of homes built fifty years ago and not look out of place in any way.

The sauna adjacent to the two bathrooms was specified by the client for whom this bungalow was designed. It is very imporant to give expert consideration to the ventilation of a sauna like this which is part of the structure of the building, and not simply free standing in the corner of a large bathroom.

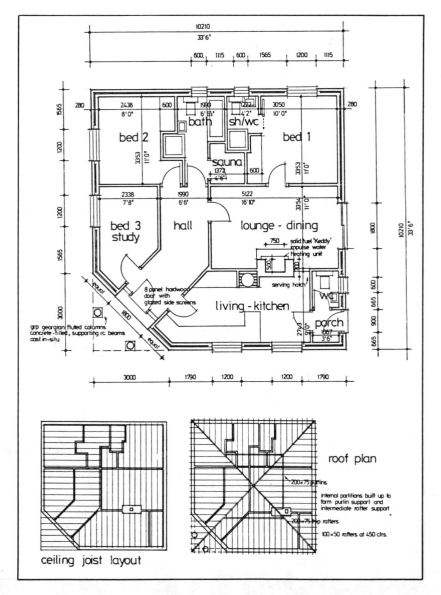

roof plan

ceiling joist layout

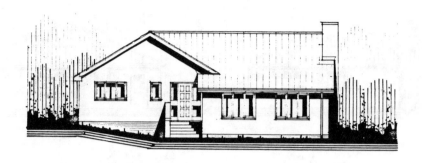

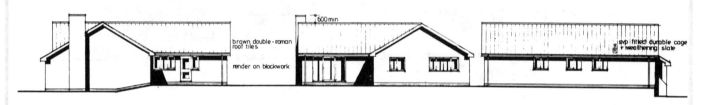

brown double-roman
roof tiles

render on blockwork

600 min

svp fitted durable cage
r weathering slate

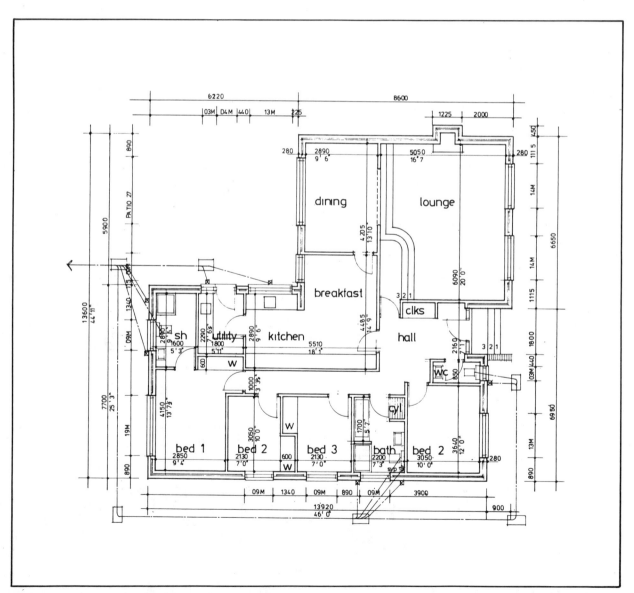

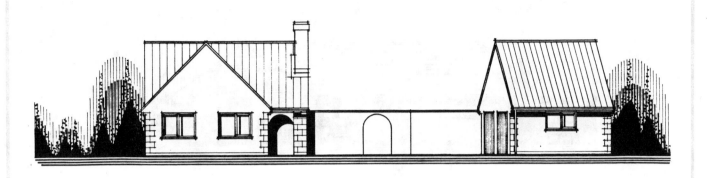

GARDEN ELEVATION　　　　　　　　　SIDE ELEVATION

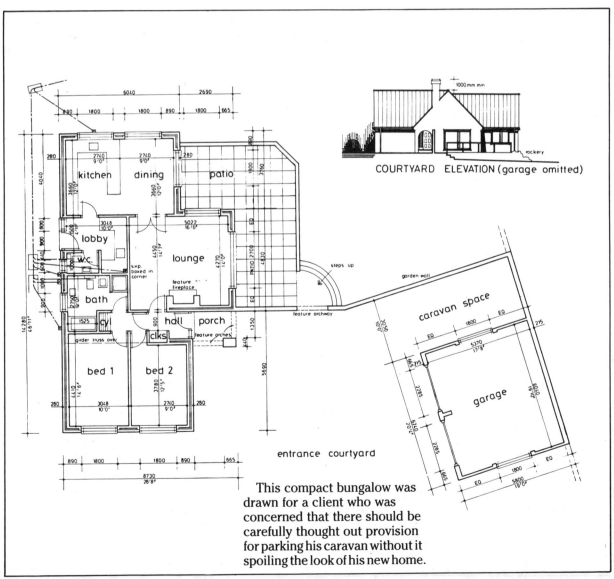

COURTYARD ELEVATION (garage omitted)

entrance courtyard

This compact bungalow was
drawn for a client who was
concerned that there should be
carefully thought out provision
for parking his caravan without it
spoiling the look of his new home.

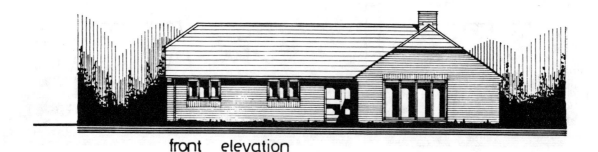

front elevation

gable elevations   rear elevation

The type of roof shewn on this bungalow is called a 'Hampshire hip' or 'half hip', and for centuries was the traditional roof style in some parts of East and Southern England. In recent years it has become very popular again, which is fine in the areas where it is traditional, but often less happy in other parts of the country. At any rate, this straight forward bungalow can be built with an ordinary gable roof if required, and this should give a cost saving.

The chimney breast has flues for both the fire in the lounge and also a solid fuel stove in the kitchen. Modern solid fuel stoves, which can often run the central heating, are gaining in popularity but if they are to share a chimney with the lounge fireplace it fixes their position in the kitchen and may not permit the layout of kitchen units which the housewife would prefer.

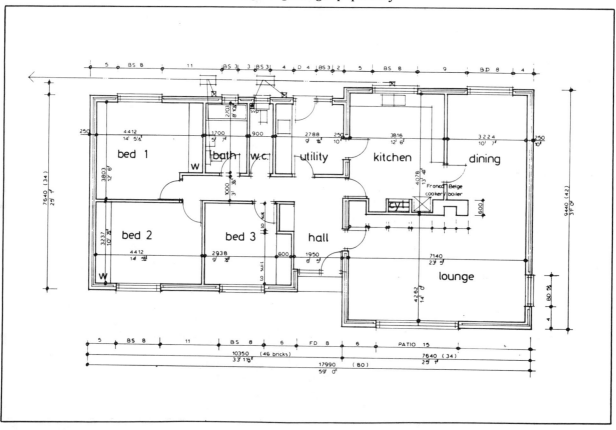

steppeu lead flashing
& tray d.p.c.

svp fitted durable cage
& weathering slate

Marley Mendip
Smooth grey tiles

L.B.C. Tudor
brickwork

A lot of rooms in this compact bungalow, and although the bedrooms are small the plans can be altered to make them bigger without altering the character. Note the sunken lounge, which need not be built in this way if it is not a feature that is required.

FLOOR PLAN

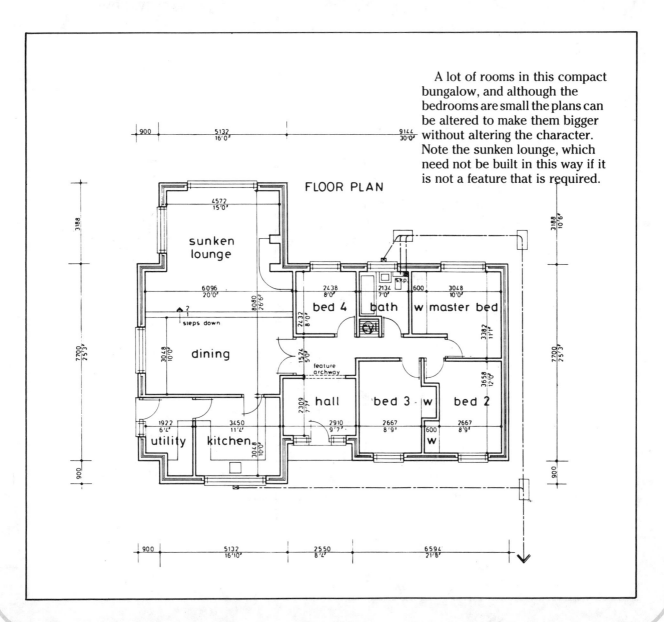

FRONT ELEVATION

REAR ELEVATION   SIDE ELEVATION   SIDE ELEVATION

breakfast area

PATIO 18   PATIO 21   PATIO 27

7700
25'3"

4242
13'11"

890   890   890

2240

155 obscure glass

1565

045

115

4265

13269
43'6"

kitchen
4092
13'5"

3658
12'0"

bedroom 1
3382
11'1"

4092
13'5"

190   190

lounge
3962
13'0"

7140
23'5"

190

B1
21N blockwork

ldr
900
3'0"

utility   cy   hall

1600
5'3"

5.v.p.
1879
6'2"

bath
190

feature brickwork

B2

21N blockwork   1000

2282
7'6"

clks

bed 2
3658
12'0"

bed 3
3382
11'1"

2134
7'0"

5529
14'10"

130   130   130   130   130   065   0455   890

7700
25'3"

5569

external

PURLIN A 100 × 300
         B 75 × 300
         C 75 × 250
B1·B2   203 × 203 × 46·u.c.
Padstone B1 400 long × 200 deep
         B2 300 long × 200 deep
Padstone 1:1½:3 conc. mix
21N blockwork 190 wide in 1:1:6 mortar

890   215   175   890   225   890

7700
25'3"

4242
13'11"

350

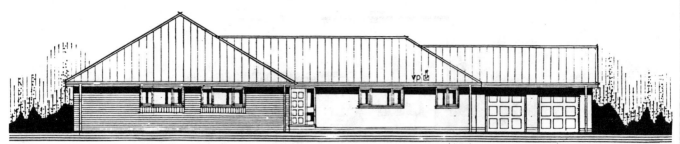

FRONT ELEVATION

vp fitted durable cape
+ weathering slate

facing brickwork

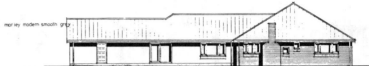

marley modern smooth grey

This large bungalow has some interesting features, and in particular look how much cupboard space has been provided. The angled fronts to the airing cupboard opposite the master bedroom, and the store in the kitchen, are unusual, and so are the two small windows at different levels adjacent to the fireplace in the lounge.

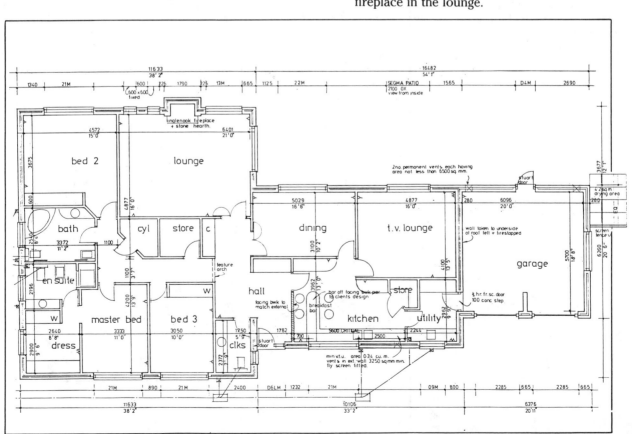

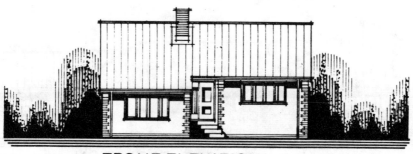

FRONT ELEVATION

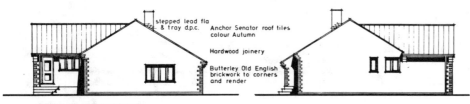

SIDE ELEVATIONS

REAR ELEVATION

The dropped floor to the lounge of this bungalow is matched by a dropped ceiling, so that the front wall of the lounge has a lower eaves line than the rest of the building. This is unusual: a dropped floor usually means a higher ceiling, and the way in which the change of ceiling heights is handled needs careful consideration.

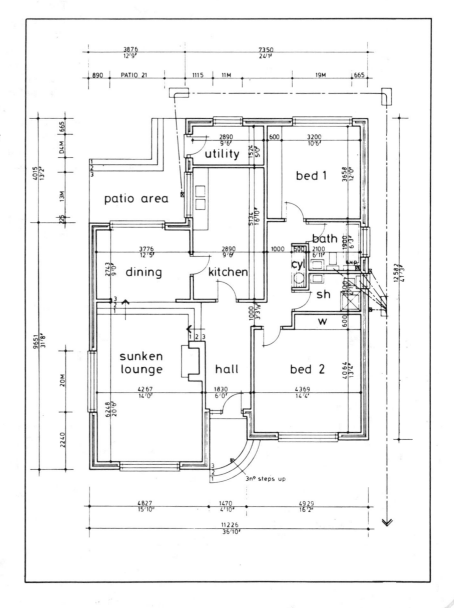

front elevation

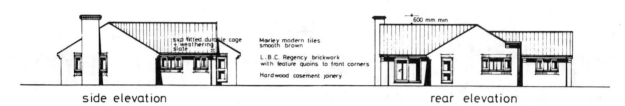

side elevation

svp fitted durable cage
+ weathering
slate

Marley modern tiles
smooth brown

L.B.C. Regency brickwork
with feature quoins to front corners

Hardwood casement joinery

600 mm min

rear elevation

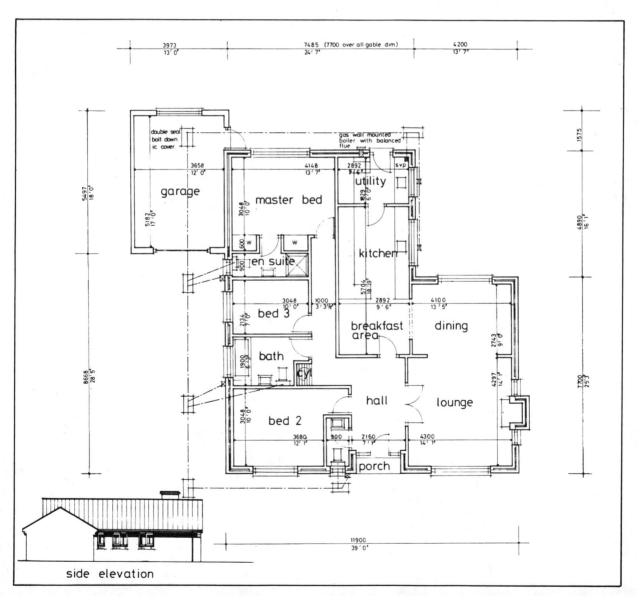

3973
13' 0"

7485 (7700 over all gable dim)
24' 7"

4200
13' 7"

1575

5497
18' 0"

double seal
bolt down
ic cover.

gas wall mounted
boiler with balanced
flue

3658
12' 0"

4148
13' 7"

2892
9' 6"

svp

garage

5182
17' 0"

master bed

3048
10' 0"

utility

1829
6' 0"

4890
16' 1"

w

w

600
900

en suite

kitchen

5704
18' 9"

3048
10' 0"

1000
3' 3½"

2892
9' 6"

4100
13' 5"

8668
28' 5"

2134
7' 0"

bed 3

breakfast
area

dining

2743
9' 0"

7700
25' 3"

1900
6' 3"

bath

cyl

4297
14' 1"

3048
10' 0"

bed 2

hall

lounge

3680
12' 1"

900

2160
7' 1"

4300
14' 1"

porch

11900
39' 0"

side elevation

FRONT ELEVATION

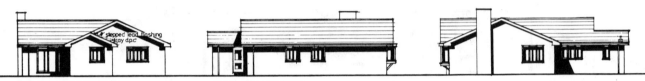

REAR ELEVATION   SIDE ELEVATIONS

A stone bungalow with box bay windows on the front elevation. These will dominate the appearance of the home from the front, and deserve special attention. Presumably they will be made in hardwood, and the corner timbers should be heavy enough to be chamfered or finished in some other decorative way. The gallows brackets below the windows should also be substantial and finished to match other features.

The angled wall at the door to the master bedroom is different, and helps to make the hall more interesting. Alternatively it can be straightened to give room in the hall for a telephone table.

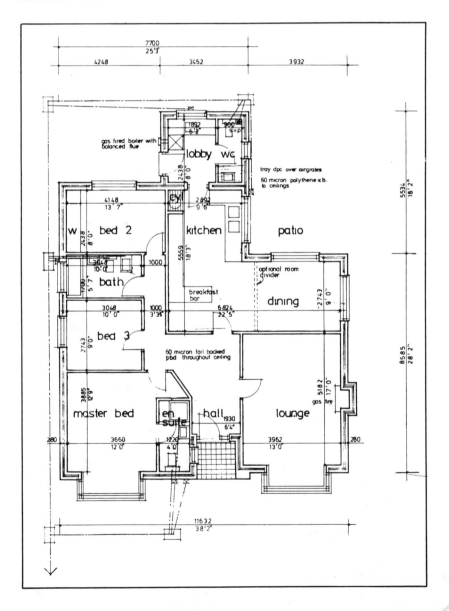

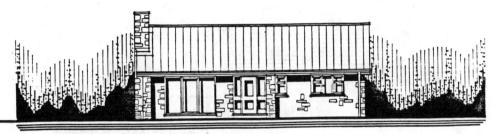

FRONT ELEVATION

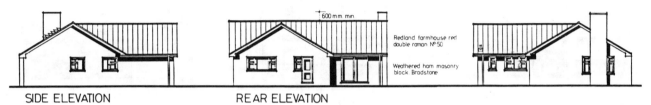

SIDE ELEVATION   REAR ELEVATION

600 m.m. min

Redland farmhouse red
double roman Nº 50

Weathered ham masonry
block. Bradstone

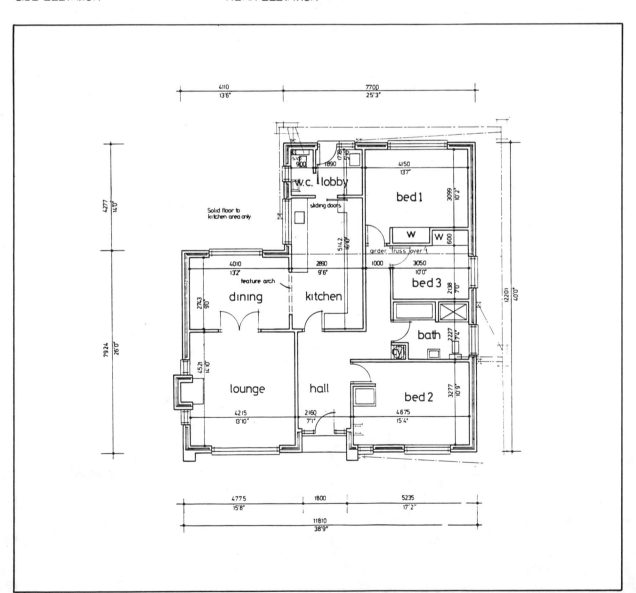

FRONT ELEVATION

REAR ELEVATION

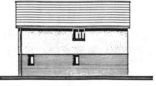

SIDE ELEVATION

SIDE ELEVATION

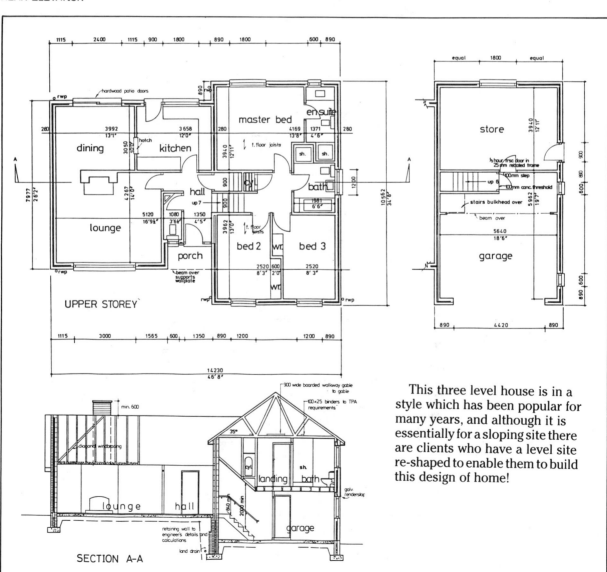

UPPER STOREY

SECTION A-A

This three level house is in a style which has been popular for many years, and although it is essentially for a sloping site there are clients who have a level site re-shaped to enable them to build this design of home!

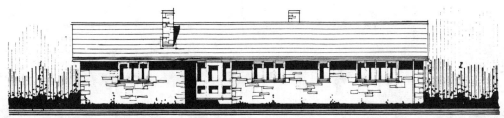

FRONT ELEVATION

SIDE ELEVATIONS

REAR ELEVATION

A three bedroom layout for a bungalow in a very popular style. The accommodation can easily be re-arranged to provide an extra bedroom, which can also double as a study.

A large patio window set centrally in a gable end as shown here always looks attractive when in the rear elevation, to be seen from the garden, but invariably looks awkward in the front of the building. I have never been able to understand why this is!

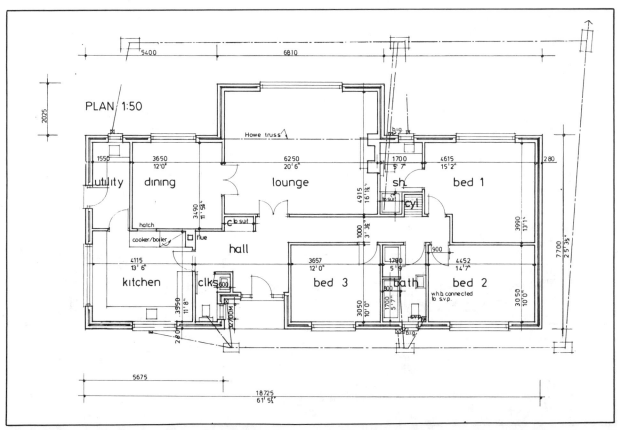

PLAN 1:50

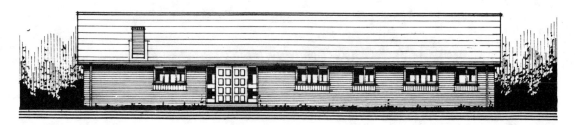

FRONT ELEVATION

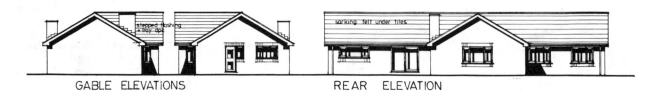

GABLE ELEVATIONS REAR ELEVATION

A big bungalow to a design originally drawn by D & M Ltd in 1974, and which has been built many times since in nearly every part of the UK. The deeply recessed front door helps the front elevation to escape the "railway carriage look" which is always a problem with a

bungalow that is over seventy feet long, but to look at its best this new home should be built on a plot of at least half an acre.

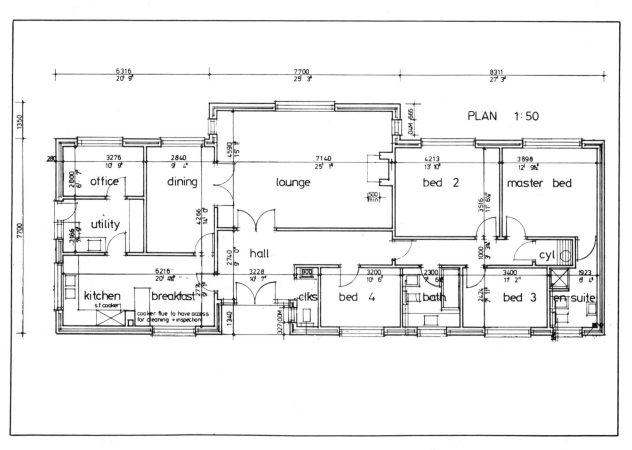

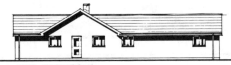

SIDE ELEVATIONS

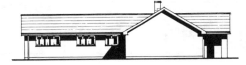

REAR ELEVATION

Another bungalow with an integral garage and easy access to the front door that will still fit on a forty five feet wide plot. The relationship between the living rooms is interesting, with a dining hall that is open-plan with the kitchen, and a separate utility room across the hall from the kitchen.

The master bedroom suite has a large en-suite bathroom, and the other bathroom is smaller and here shewn with a shower, basin and WC only. However, with some rearrangement of cupboards both bathrooms can have a bath if required.

The layout of the rooms makes it easy to arrange for a dropped floor in the lounge, with either one or two steps down from the dining hall. This gives a higher ceiling, and adds interest to the home, but make sure the steps will suit grandma if she is likely to come to stay!

No fireplace is shewn, but one is easily provided in the lounge gable end wall.

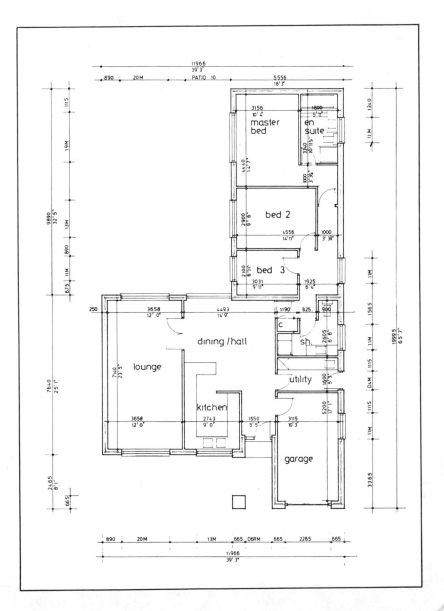

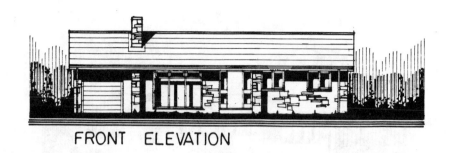

FRONT ELEVATION

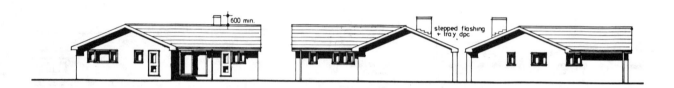

A four bedroom bungalow with an integral garage to fit on a narrow plot. The garage is over twenty three feet long, so there is plenty of room to divide it to fit a hobbies room or garden store into it at the back.

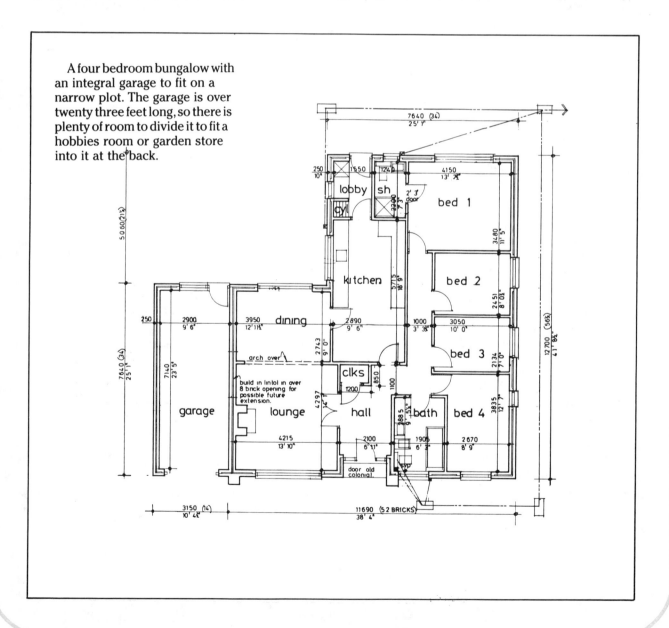

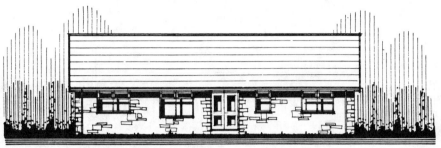

FRONT ELEVATION

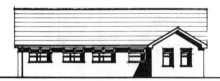

REAR ELEVATION

SIDE ELEVATIONS

Having a bar in the lounge is one way of keeping the boys at home, and this was certainly very important to the family for whom this bungalow was designed. There is a lot of room here, and the study can become a fifth bedroom if required.

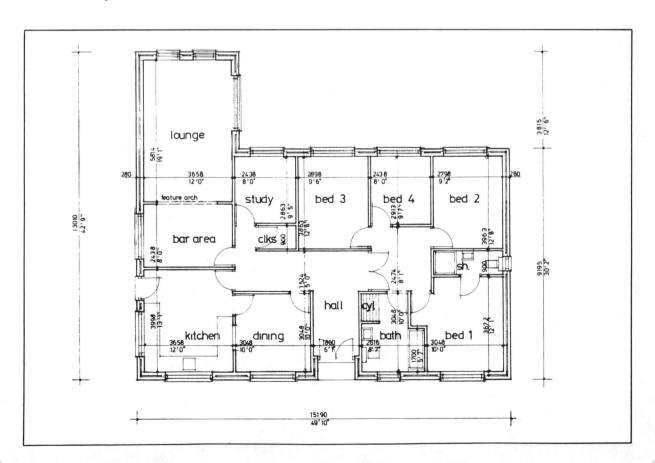

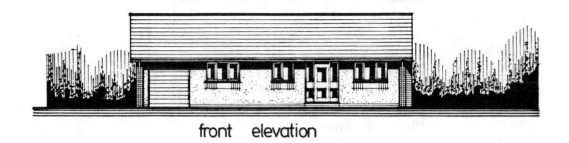

front elevation

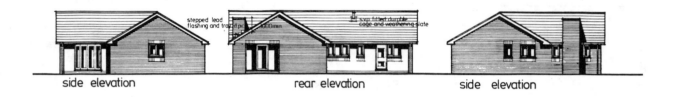

side elevation

rear elevation

side elevation

An unusual bungalow with all the bedrooms at the front and a roomy open-plan layout at the back.

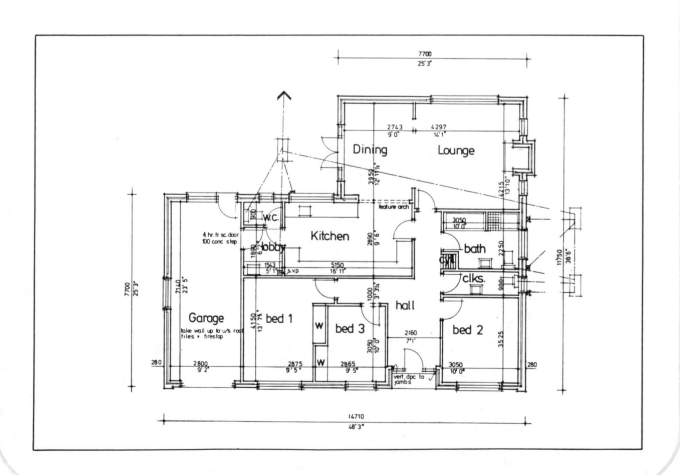

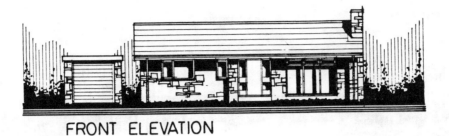

FRONT ELEVATION

GABLE ELEVATIONS

REAR ELEVATION

A compact bungalow to a very popular design concept, built together with a flat roofed garage. The garage is on the opposite side of the building to the back door, which is a disadvantage, but in this case was unavoidable because of the position of the access.

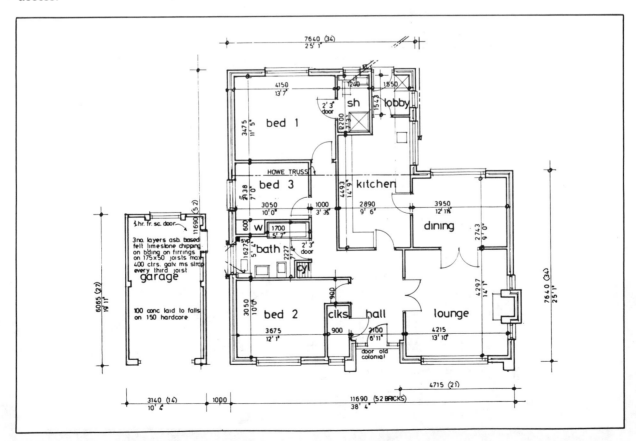

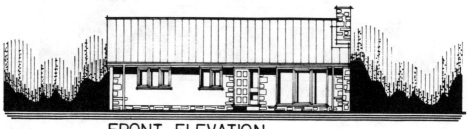

FRONT ELEVATION

600 mm min

Marley Modern
Smooth grey roof tiles

Pennant stone features
to quoins & plinth

stepped
& tray

REAR ELEVATION   SIDE ELEVATIONS

The feature archways between the lounge, dining room and kitchen are going to give an 'open-plan' feel to this compact bungalow. They can be replaced by doorways if required, and the dining room window can be moved into the rear wall, possible as a patio window if this suits the site.

This bungalow was built in Wales with the white render relieved with dark Pennant stone features — a combination that is very striking. Pennant stone is shiny, and always looks clean as if it was built only yesterday.

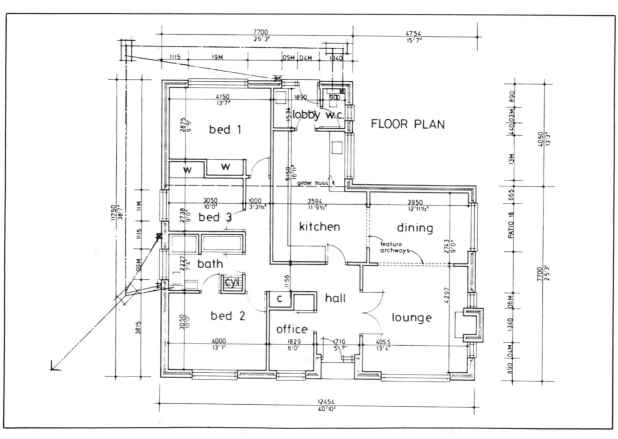

FLOOR PLAN

FRONT ELEVATION

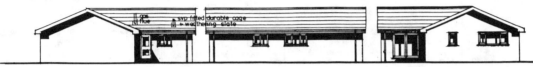

SIDE ELEVATIONS

REAR ELEVATION

A three bedroom bungalow which was developed from design W 893 with the overall dimensions stretched both ways to give larger rooms. If this plan interests you then it will be useful to compare these two plans, as each has its own distinctive features in the same design concept.

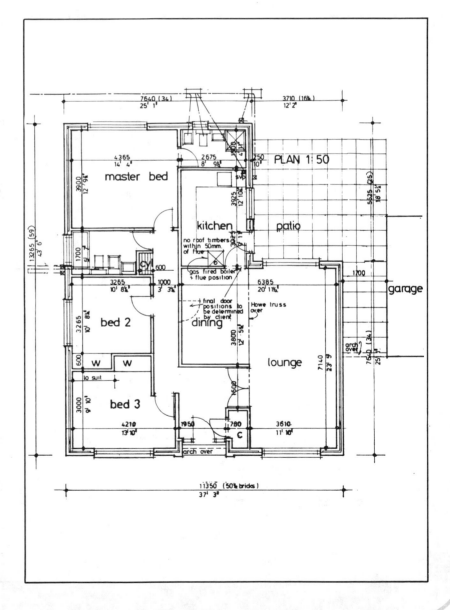

FRONT ELEVATION

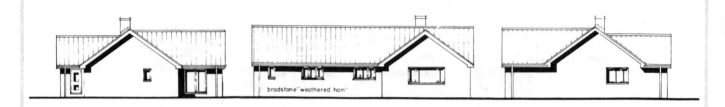

bradstone "weathered ham"

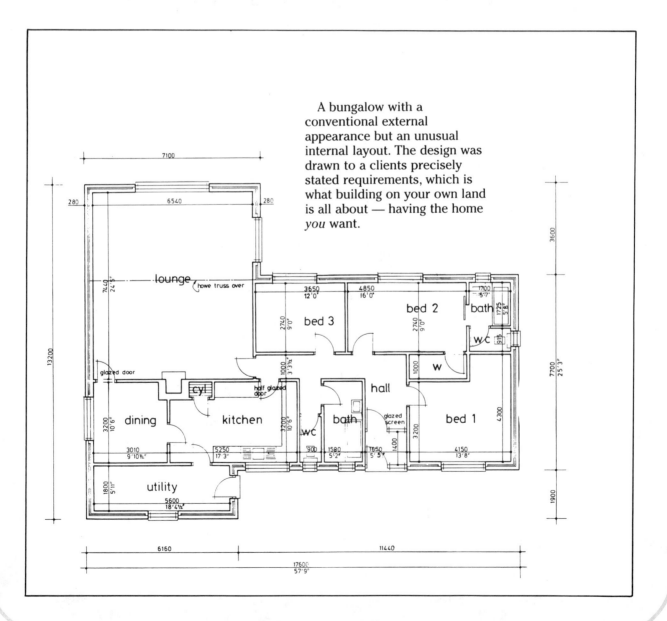

A bungalow with a
conventional external
appearance but an unusual
internal layout. The design was
drawn to a clients precisely
stated requirements, which is
what building on your own land
is all about — having the home
you want.

FRONT ELEVATION

REAR ELEVATION　　　　　　　SIDE ELEVATIONS

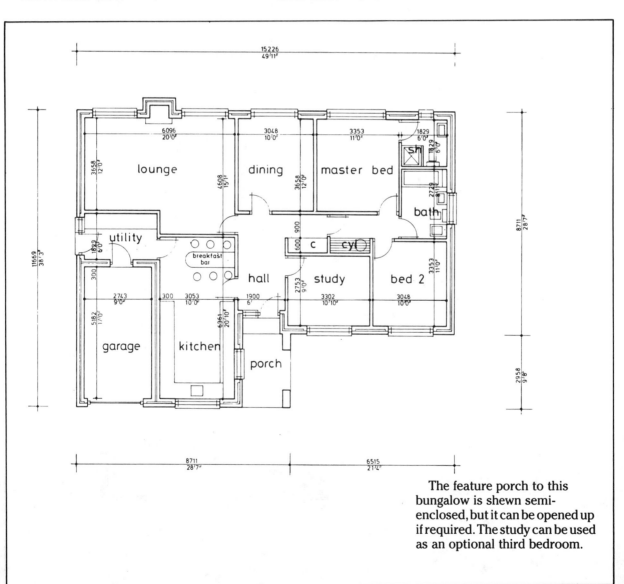

The feature porch to this
bungalow is shewn semi-
enclosed, but it can be opened up
if required. The study can be used
as an optional third bedroom.

367

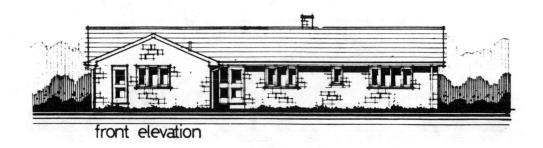

front elevation

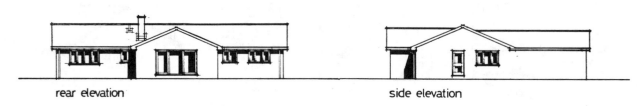

rear elevation

side elevation

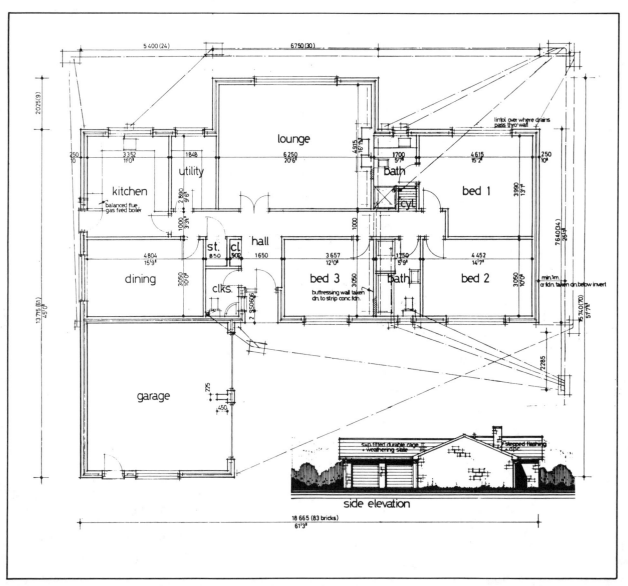

5 400 (24)   6 750 (30)

2025 (9)

lounge

250
10⁴   3 352
11'0⁴   1848   6 250
20'6⁴   4 915
16'1⁴   1700
5'7⁴   4 615
15'2⁴   250
10⁴

utility   bath

kitchen   2 890
9'6⁴   bed 1   3 990
13'1⁴

balanced flue,
gas fired boiler   1000
3'3⁴   cyl   7 640 (24)
25'1⁴

hall   lintol over where drains
pass thro' wall

st.   cl   1000

4 804
15'9⁴   850   502   1650   3 657
12'0⁴   1 750
5'9⁴   4 452
14'7⁴   min.1m
or fdn. taken dn.below invert

dining   3 050
10'0⁴   bed 3   3 050   bath   bed 2   3 050
10'0⁴

clks.   2 3050 06⁴   buttressing wall taken
dn. to strip conc fdn.

7 740 (70)
51'7⁴

2285

775

garage   450

side elevation

sup fitted durable cage II
+ weathering slate   stepped flashing
+ dpc

13 715 (61)
45'0⁴

18 665 (83 bricks)
61'3⁴

front elevation

rear elevation

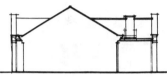

side elevation

side elevation

This stone bungalow, with tabling to the gable walls and chased corbel stones was built on a farm in the North East. Note the interesting arrangement for the hall, with an arch leading to the passage beyond, and the small window next to the lounge door to light the passage.

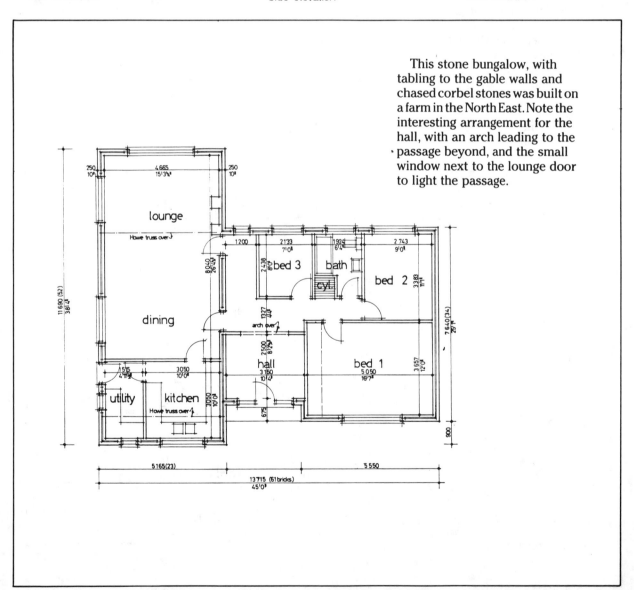

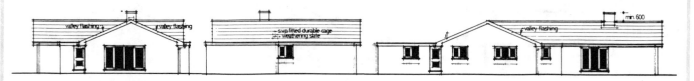

An angled fireplace in an L
shaped lounge like this looks very
striking, but does tend to limit the
number of possible furniture
arrangements. Any fireplace that
is directly under the ridge of the
roof in this way is cheaper and
less likely to give trouble than
one with a chimney in the side of
a roof, and it is always worth
keeping this in mind.

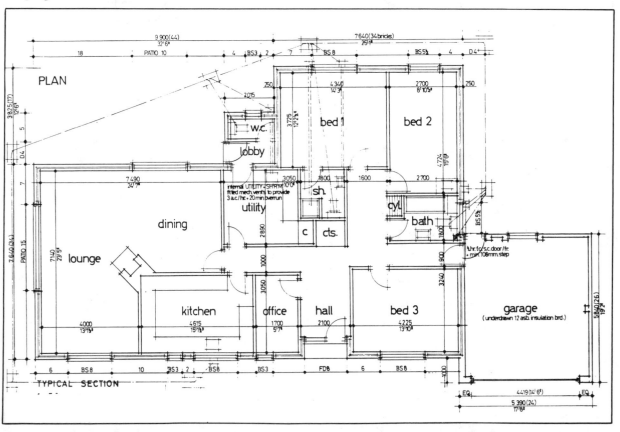

FRONT ELEVATION

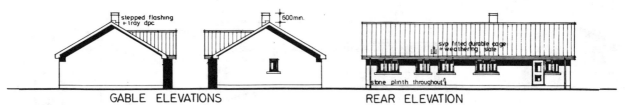

GABLE ELEVATIONS   REAR ELEVATION

This compact three bedroom bungalow has the garage door hidden away at the side of a projecting gable, which is the ideal arrangement for a garage door that has to be on the front of the building. By putting the lounge fireplace on the kitchen wall the chimney can be taken straight up through the roof ridge, avoiding the complicated work involved if it adjoins a valley in the roof. In this position it can also accommodate another flue from a solid fuel stove in the kitchen.

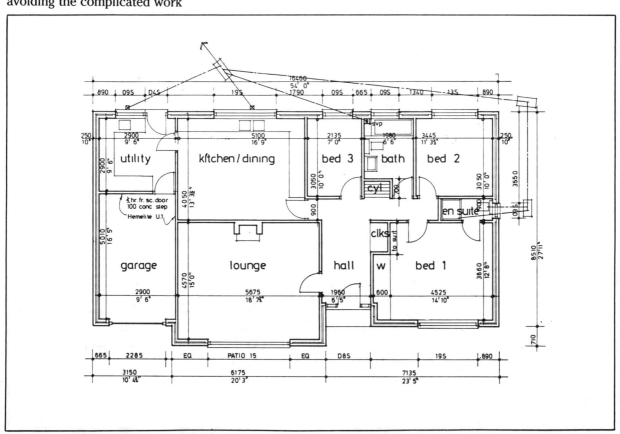

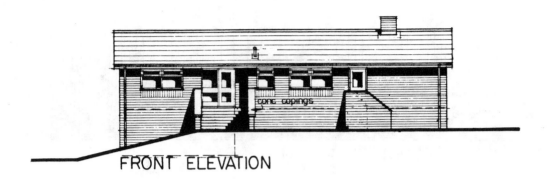

FRONT ELEVATION

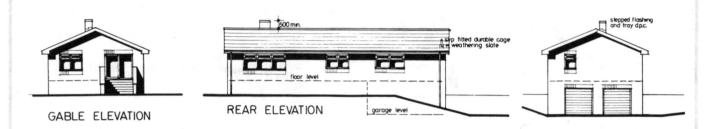

GABLE ELEVATION   REAR ELEVATION

This bungalow was designed for a sloping site on a river bank, and the planners required the high floor level which is shewn to keep it above any possible flood. The opportunity was taken to put the garage under one end of the building, and as the site was well wooded, with mature trees all around, the new home did not look as high out of the ground as it appears to be in these drawings.

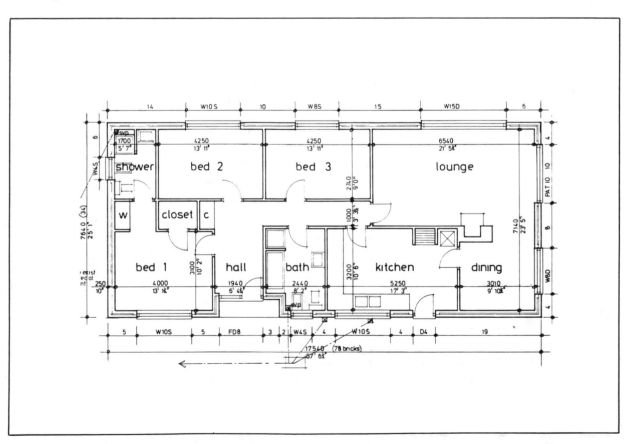

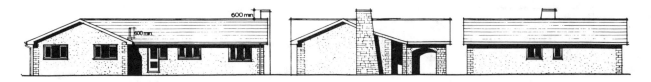

GABLE ELEVATION

SIDE ELEVATIONS

Bungalows with full length verandahs are very popular in Ireland and in parts of Wales, and have a very attractive period feel. The detail design of the pillars and of any arches that link them together is very important, and is shewn here in dark brickwork to set off the rendered walls.

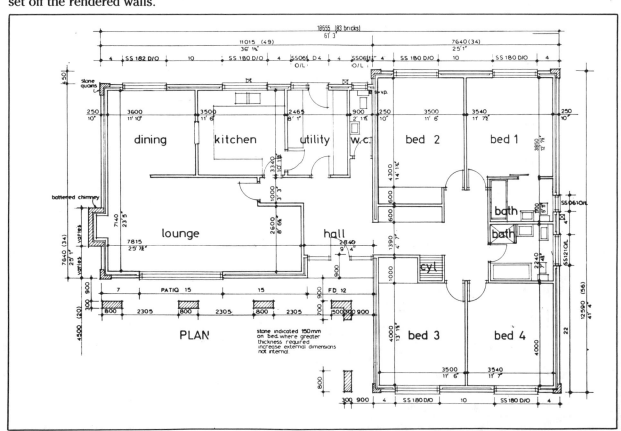

PLAN

FRONT ELEVATION

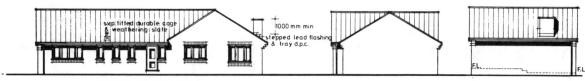

REAR ELEVATION

This bungalow with its attractive sunken lounge was originally designed for a site in Leicestershire where the views were to the front and back, so there are no side windows. The inset detail shews what is involved in dropping a floor level as in this case, and this is something that can only be arranged at the very start of the project, and cannot be dealt with as an afterthought.

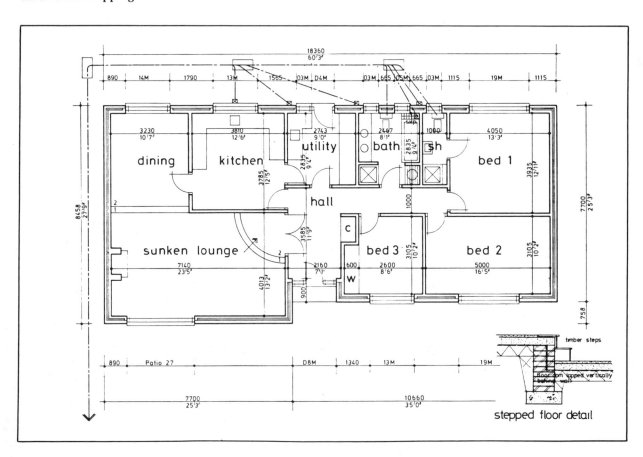

stepped floor detail

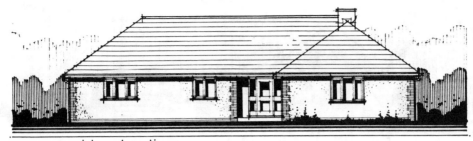

side elevation

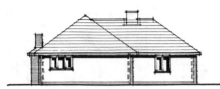

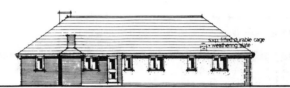

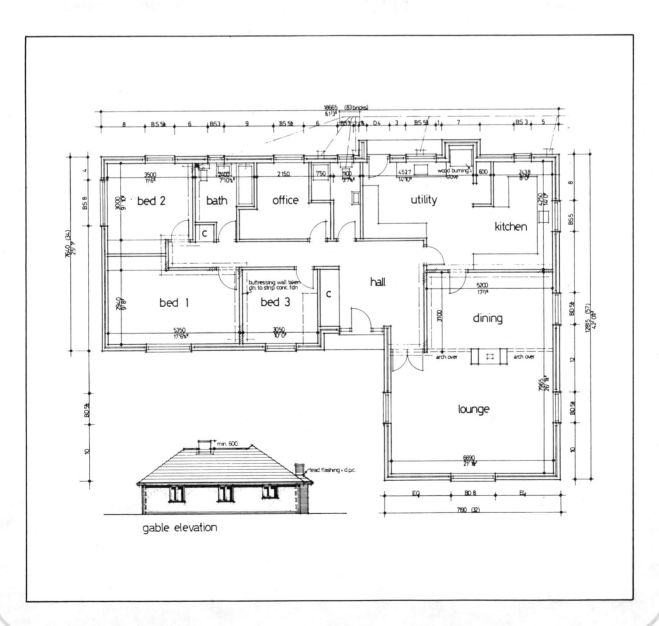

gable elevation

FRONT ELEVATION

s.v.p. fitted durable cope & weathering slate

Redland stonewold terracotta

Butterley thurcroft blenheim buff multi wirecut rustic 24

REAR ELEVATION

SIDE ELEVATION

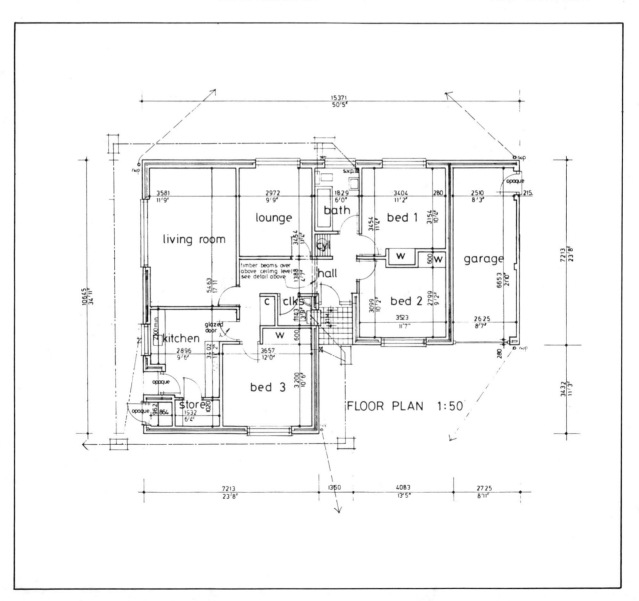

FLOOR PLAN 1:50

living room

lounge

bath

bed 1

garage

kitchen

hall

cyl

bed 2

c clk

w

bed 3

store

15371
50'5"

7213
23'8"

10645
34'11"

3581
11'9"

2972
9'9"

1829
6'0"

3404
11'2"

280

2510
8'3"

215

3657
12'0"

2896
9'6"

1932
6'4"

7213
23'8"

1350

4083
13'5"

2725
8'11"

3432
11'3"

6653
21'0"

2625
8'7"

3523
11'7"

3099
10'2"

2799
9'2"

5463
17'11"

timber beams over above ceiling level see detail above

glazed door

opaque

opaque

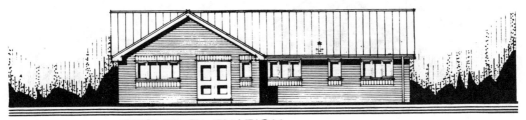

FRONT ELEVATION

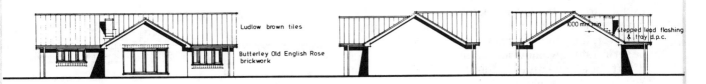

Ludlow brown tiles

Butterley Old English Rose brickwork

000 mm min   stepped lead flashing & tray d.p.c.

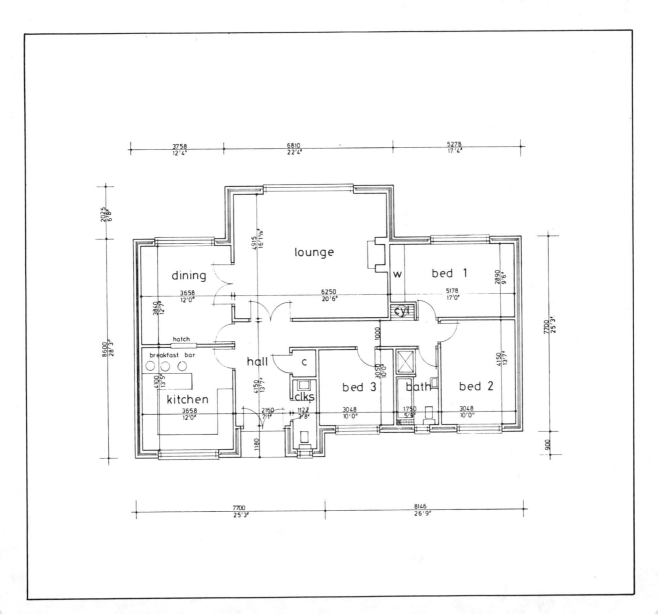

front elevation

An attractive home with an interesting layout. The round window to the front gable only lights the roof space, serving no useful purpose, but giving lots of character at minimal cost. However, the window itself must be set in a stone window surround if it is to be a key feature like this. You will find one listed in the Bradstone catalogue.

min. 600mm

Velux rooflights

rear elevation

roof tiles:- colour + type to be agreed

bradstone or similar artificial stone to front elevation with facing brick to remainder

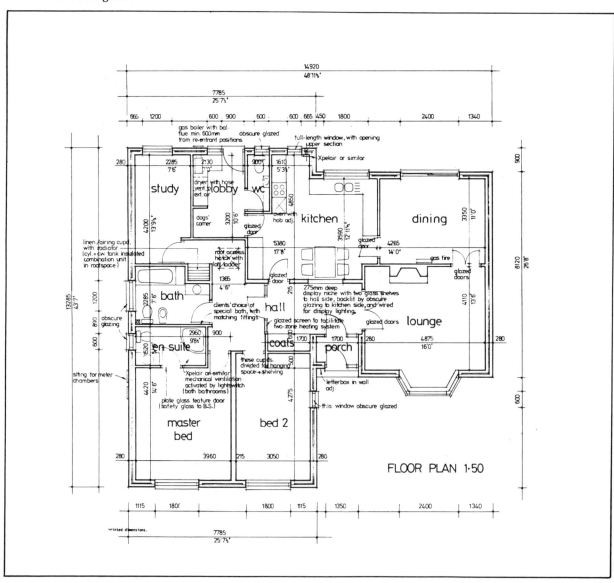

FLOOR PLAN 1·50

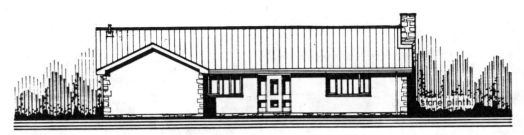

FRONT ELEVATION

SIDE ELEVATIONS   REAR ELEVATION

A four bedroom bungalow with storm porches at both front and back doors to keep the heat in and the weather out. If a home is occupied by a large busy family, with lots of coming and going, then storm porches like this will do a great deal to stop complaints when doors are constantly being opened and shut. However, in this case the appearance of the front elevation would be improved if it were possible to set the front door back a little, which has not been possible with this storm porch arrangment.

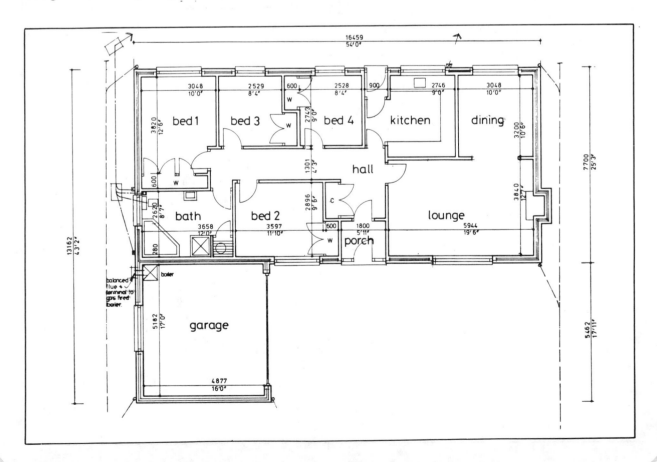

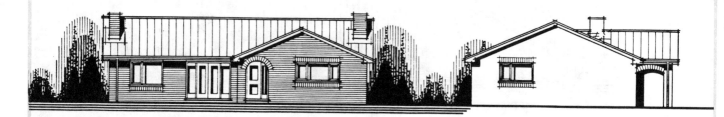

If the best view from a new home is to the front, why not have the kitchen at the front so that the housewife can enjoy it while washing up? After all, she is more likely to want to look out of the window while standing at the sink.

All internal doors are specified at 900mm wide — the width to suit a wheelchair.

SIDE ELEVATION

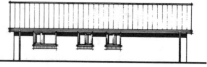

REAR ELEVATION

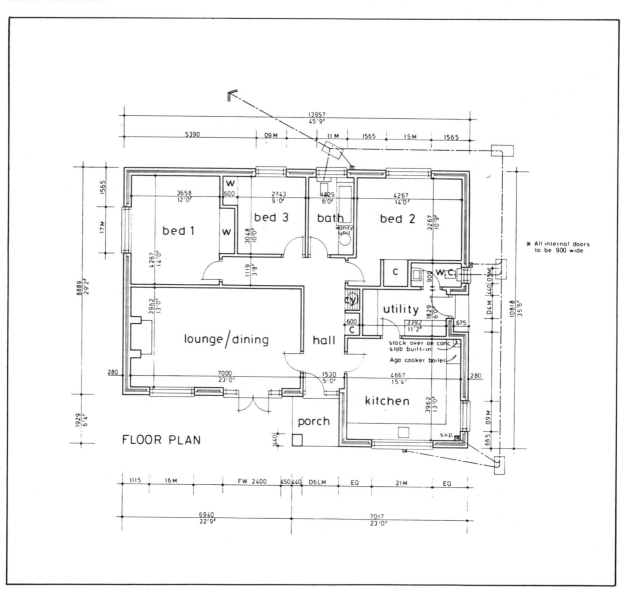

FLOOR PLAN

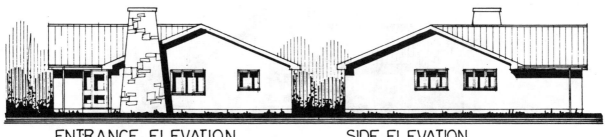

ENTRANCE ELEVATION   SIDE ELEVATION

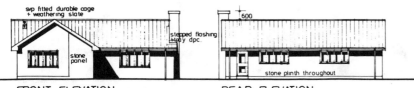

svp fitted durable cage
+ weathering slate

stepped flashing
+ d.p.c.

stone
panel

600

stone plinth throughout

FRONT ELEVATION   REAR ELEVATION

An interesting and attractive
home designed for a site in Wales
where these ranch style
bungalows are very popular.

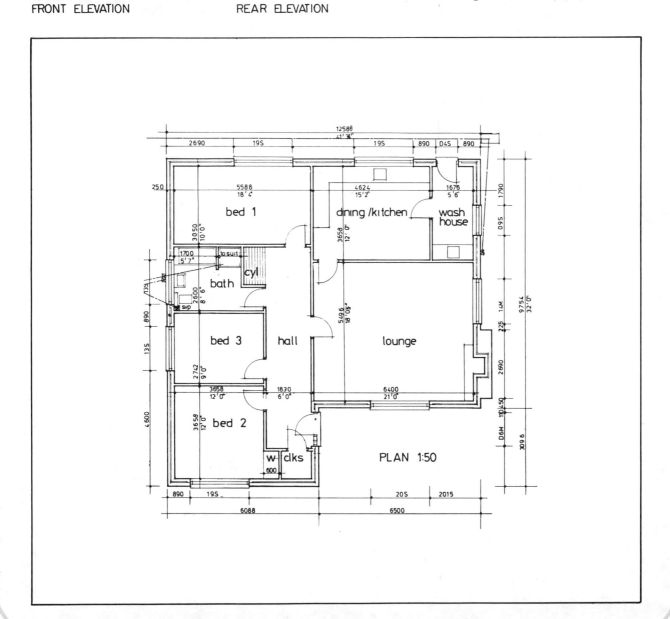

PLAN 1:50

FRONT ELEVATION

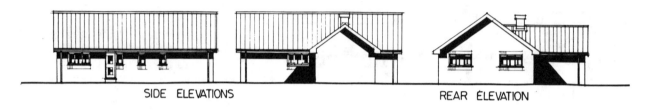

SIDE ELEVATIONS   REAR ELEVATION

A bungalow with a free standing fireplace and chimney breast in the middle of the open plan lounge and dining room. The double lines at the side of this fire indicate the position of a plant trough, but this sort of layout can be the basis of all sorts of imaginative interior design.

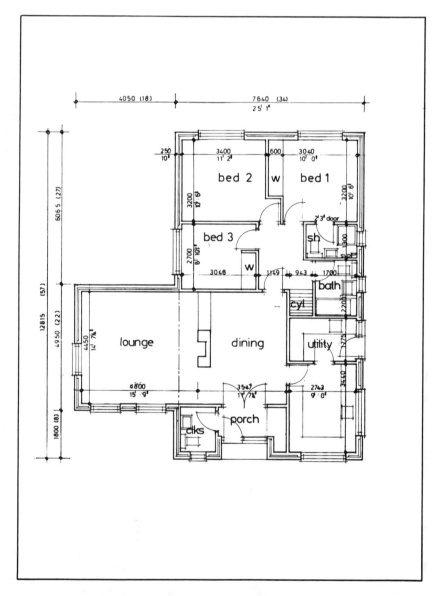

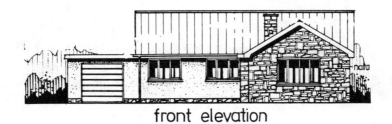

front elevation

side elevation　　　　　garage side elevation

A compact and attractive little bungalow with a flat roof to the garage. In most areas of the UK the planning officer will probably suggest that the tiled roof is extended over the garage, and this is easily arranged. The porch at the back door improves the appearance of the back of the building, and this is very convenient when the back door opens directly into a small kitchen.

The hall and corridor to the bedrooms will need to be lit by glazed screens over some of the internal doors.

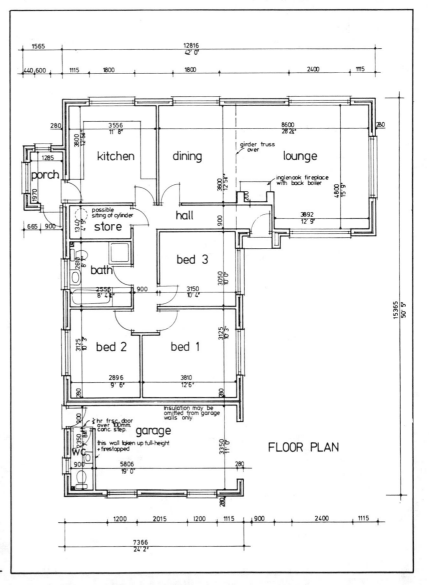

FLOOR PLAN

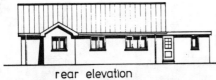

rear elevation

ENTRANCE ELEVATION

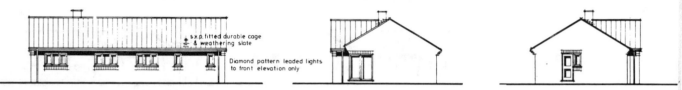

s.v.p. fitted durable cage & weathering slate

Diamond pattern leaded lights to front elevation only

A farm bungalow where the back door will be in constant use and the front entrance used only rarely. The bathroom is at the opposite end of the building from the main bedroom, which groups all the drainage at one end. It can easily be moved between any two of the bedrooms which will probably be thought to be more convenient.

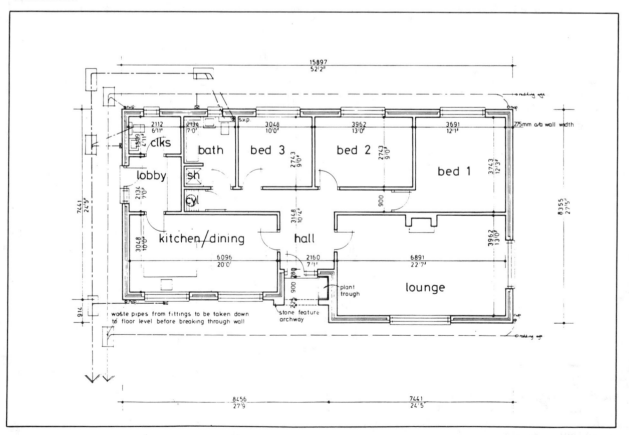

 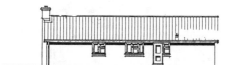 

A large bungalow suited to a retired couple who want the emphasis to be on their own accommodation, but who need three guest bedrooms for family occasions. The bungalow can be built without the garage, in which case a window should be built in the side wall of the second bedroom.

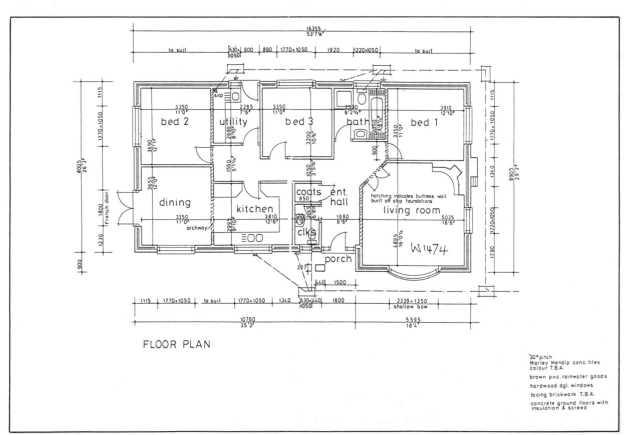

FLOOR PLAN

30° pitch
Marley Mendip conc. tiles
colour T.B.A.

brown p.v.c. rainwater goods

hardwood dgl. windows

facing brickwork T.B.A.

concrete ground floors with
insulation & screed

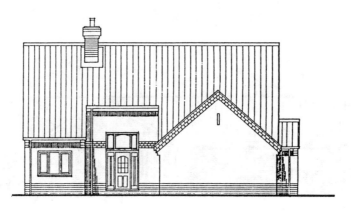

Planning consents sometimes read 'the building shall be of one storey' and this is a problem if you really want a two storey house. It is sometimes possible to get round this situation by persuading the planning authorities to accept a building that looks like a bungalow to the

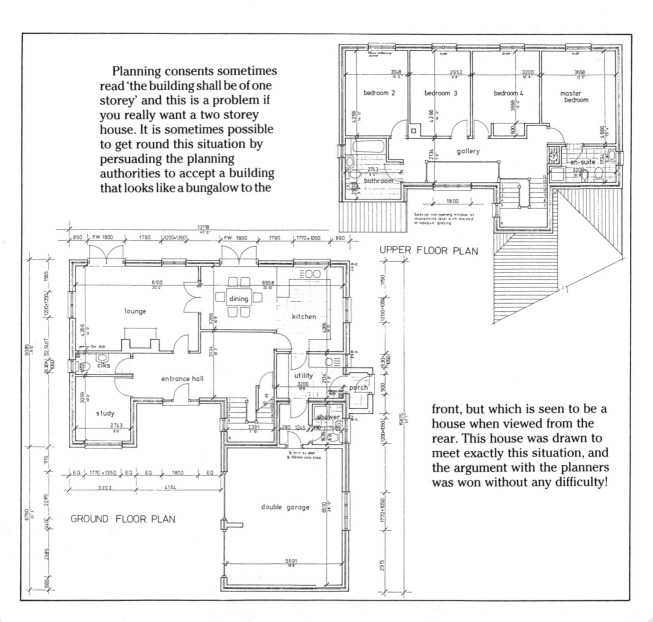

UPPER FLOOR PLAN

GROUND FLOOR PLAN

front, but which is seen to be a house when viewed from the rear. This house was drawn to meet exactly this situation, and the argument with the planners was won without any difficulty!

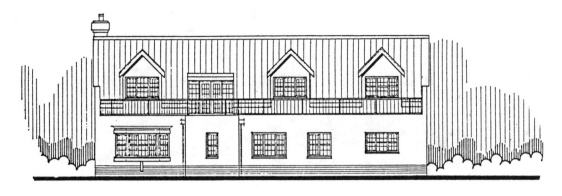

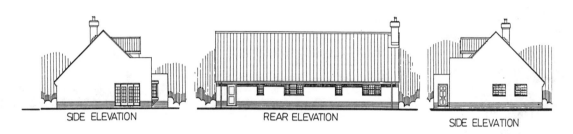

SIDE ELEVATION   REAR ELEVATION   SIDE ELEVATION

An unusual house designed to take advantage of a splendid view. A key requirement was the first floor balcony running the full length of the building, with the large gallery/sitting room. Not a particularly cheap home to build, but one which is very much in keeping with its surroundings in a south coast holiday resort.

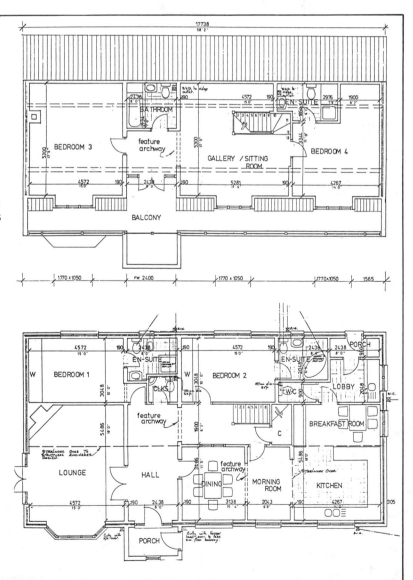

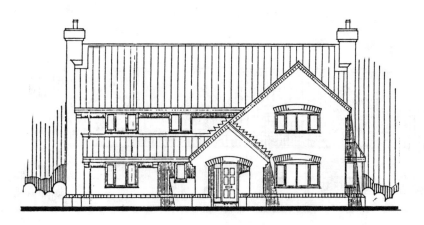

SIDE ELEVATION

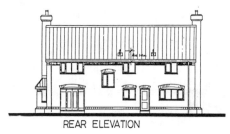

REAR ELEVATION

SIDE ELEVATION

A typical farmhouse for the
West Midlands, with fireplaces at
either end of the building and a
splendid farmhouse kitchen.
Many people building to this
design would want the back door
to open into the utility room, and
of course this is easily arranged.

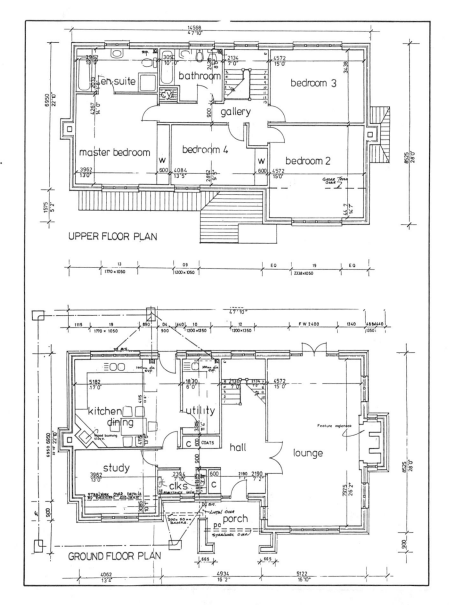

UPPER FLOOR PLAN

GROUND FLOOR PLAN

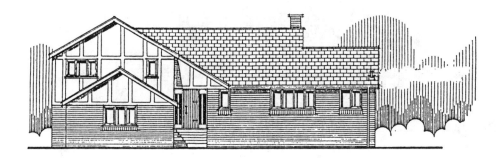

west elevation

north elevation

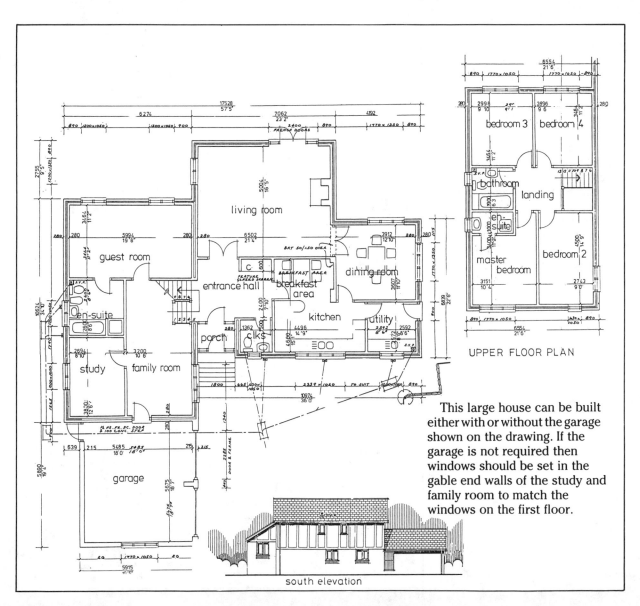

UPPER FLOOR PLAN

living room

guest room

entrance hall

breakfast area

dining room

kitchen

utility

en-suite

study

family room

porch

clks

garage

south elevation

bedroom 3

bedroom 4

bathroom

landing

en-suite

master bedroom

bedroom 2

This large house can be built either with or without the garage shown on the drawing. If the garage is not required then windows should be set in the gable end walls of the study and family room to match the windows on the first floor.

SIDE ELEVATION

REAR ELEVATION

SIDE ELEVATION

A large house with applied half timber features to the front elevation and a very interesting layout. The lounge/dining room/ drawing room arrangement will be popular with those who entertain on a large scale, while the kitchen linked with the breakfast room by a feature arch completes this design for open-plan living on the ground floor.

The upper floor has a large gallery lit by its own window, giving a very spacious feel to the whole property.

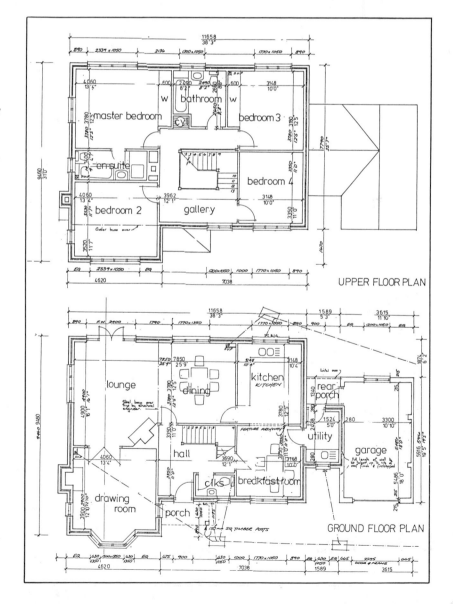

UPPER FLOOR PLAN

GROUND FLOOR PLAN

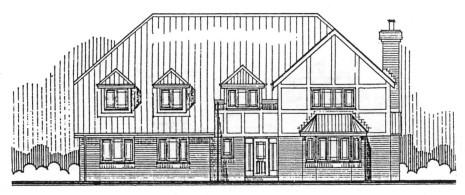

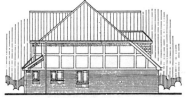

SIDE ELEVATION

REAR ELEVATION

SIDE ELEVATION

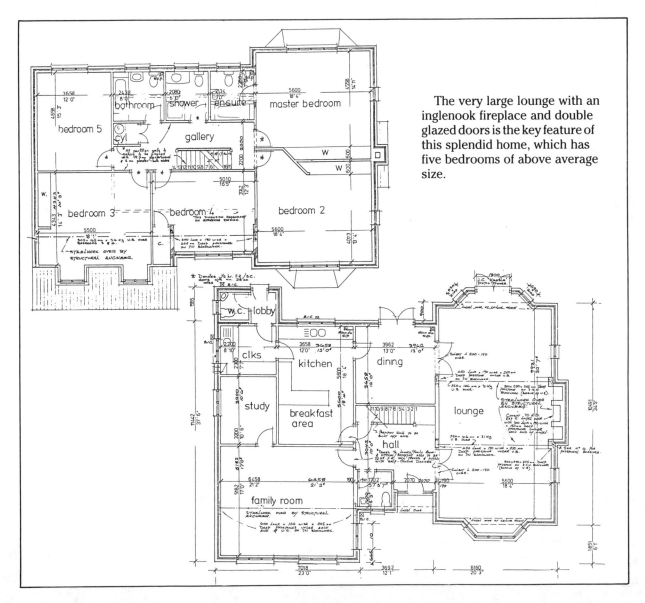

The very large lounge with an inglenook fireplace and double glazed doors is the key feature of this splendid home, which has five bedrooms of above average size.

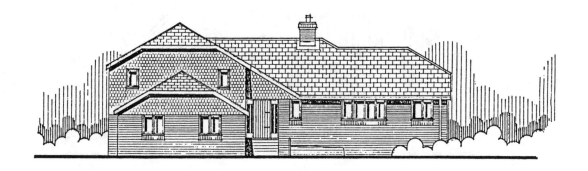

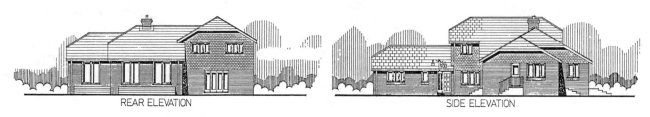

REAR ELEVATION

SIDE ELEVATION

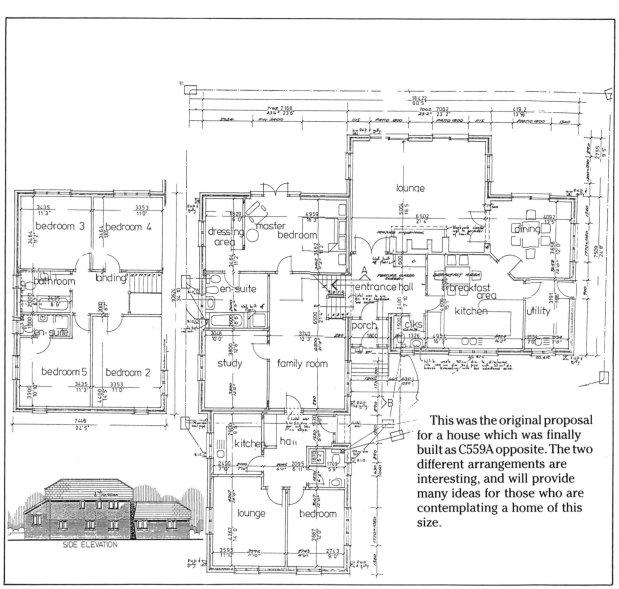

SIDE ELEVATION

This was the original proposal for a house which was finally built as C559A opposite. The two different arrangements are interesting, and will provide many ideas for those who are contemplating a home of this size.

SIDE ELEVATION   REAR ELEVATION   SIDE ELEVATION

This is the final version of the design opposite, and although in every way a large and imposing house in a regional style, the outline is essentially of a group of farm buildings. This is frequently a requirement in conservation areas.

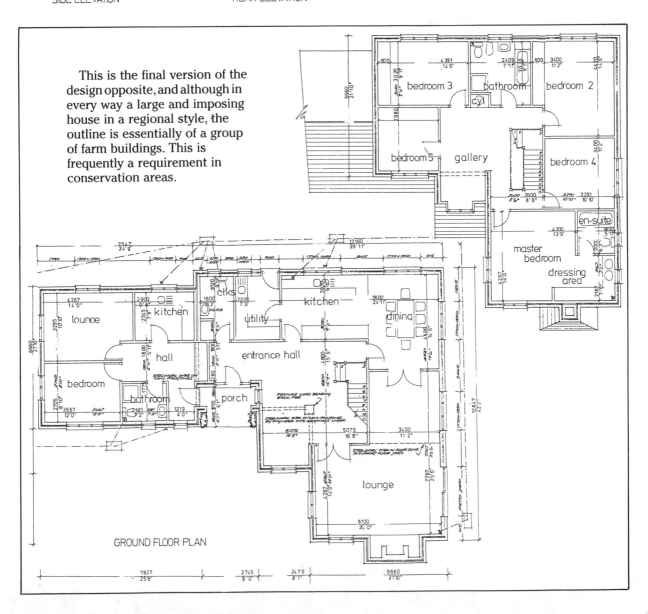

GROUND FLOOR PLAN

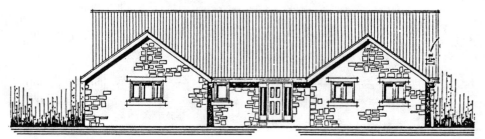

South Elevation

West Elevation

East Elevation

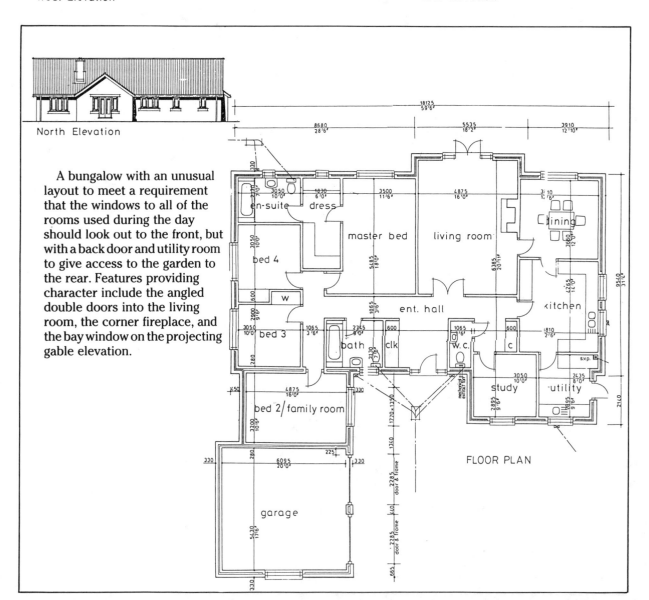

North Elevation

A bungalow with an unusual layout to meet a requirement that the windows to all of the rooms used during the day should look out to the front, but with a back door and utility room to give access to the garden to the rear. Features providing character include the angled double doors into the living room, the corner fireplace, and the bay window on the projecting gable elevation.

FLOOR PLAN

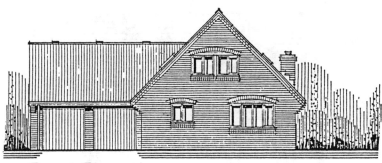

Front Elevation

Rear Elevation

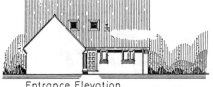

Entrance Elevation

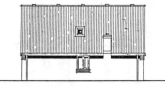

Side Elevation

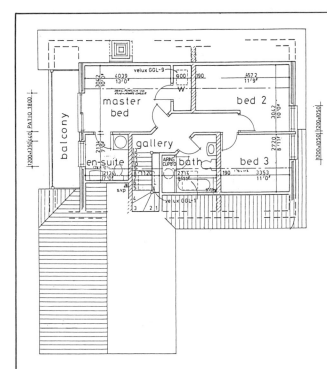

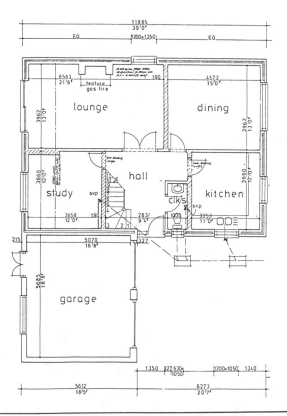

Another property where a first floor balcony was leading from the master bedroom was a key requirement. The layout of the living accommodation can be the basis of a much smaller, more compact and very cost effective bungalow if the garage is not required.

45° pitch
Marley Heritage
roofing tiles

Ockley Double Diamond
facing brickwork

Hardwood casement
joinery

This is really an example of a large house disguised as a cottage, which is sometimes necessary in order to get planning consent to build in a rural situation. By keeping the eaves level well below the sills to the first floor windows on all the elevations, and by keeping all continuous lengths of walling to a minimum, the overall effect is well suited to a village street site or other situation where a more imposing structure would not be acceptable. Two chimneys are required, for the inglenook fireplace and the AGA cooker, and with careful attention paid to the brick detailing the chimney stacks will add to the character of the property.

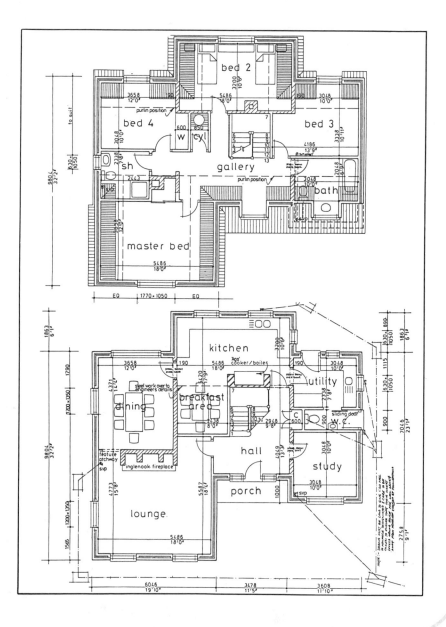

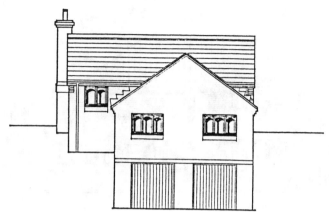

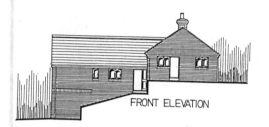

FRONT ELEVATION

ELEVATION FROM LOUNGE

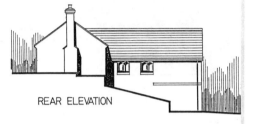

REAR ELEVATION

A bungalow built above a garage on a sloping site, with stairs from the garage up to the living accommodation.

Properties with this layout usually have the living accommodation to the front, but here it is to the back, with the french windows leading from the lounge.

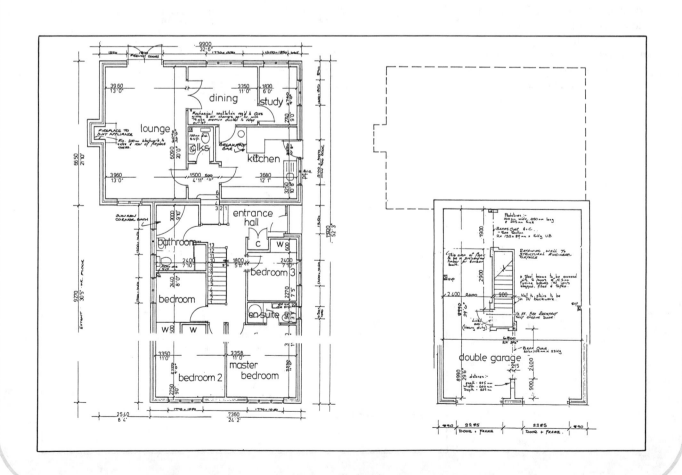

A large house with a large family room and a study of a useful size at the expense of the dining room which is integral with the kitchen. The unusual arrangement of the fireplace in the lounge was to suit a clients' particular requirements: it can be moved elsewhere if required, and indeed all the internal walling can be rearranged to provide a dining room if required.

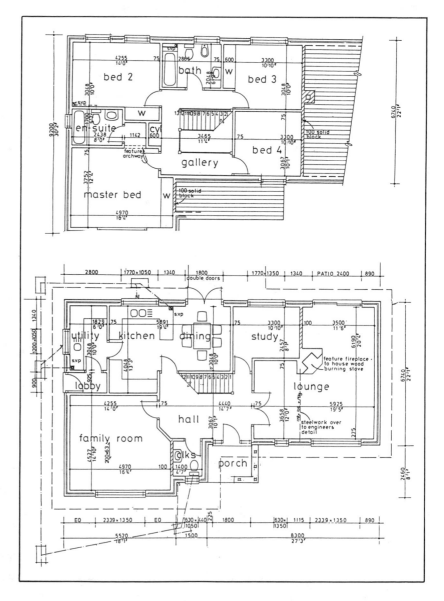

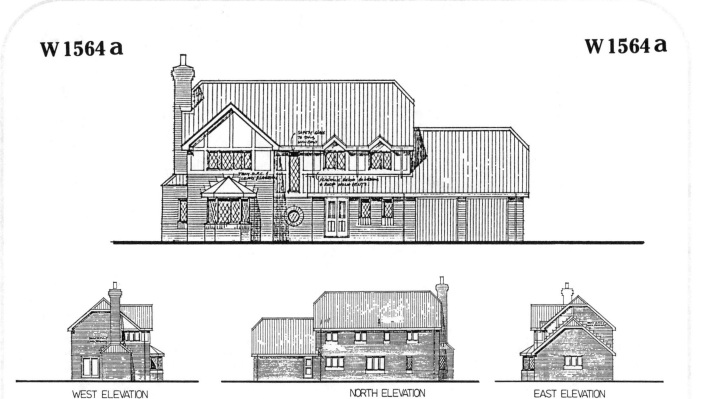

WEST ELEVATION   NORTH ELEVATION   EAST ELEVATION

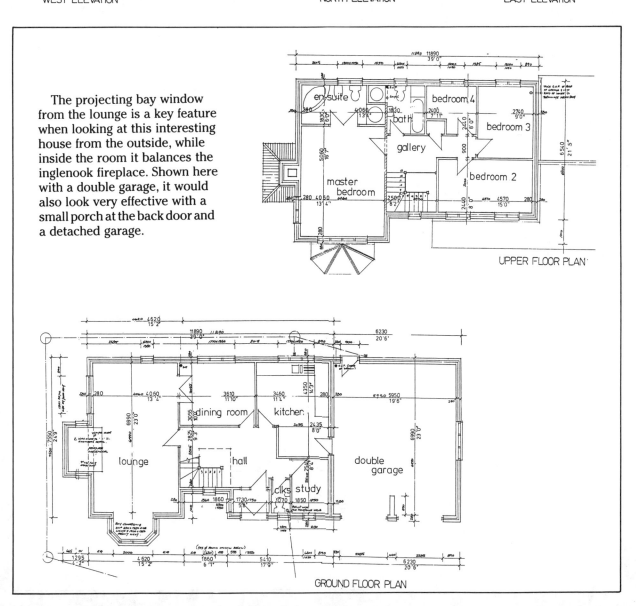

The projecting bay window from the lounge is a key feature when looking at this interesting house from the outside, while inside the room it balances the inglenook fireplace. Shown here with a double garage, it would also look very effective with a small porch at the back door and a detached garage.

UPPER FLOOR PLAN

en-suite   bedroom 4   bedroom 3   bath   gallery   master bedroom   bedroom 2

GROUND FLOOR PLAN

lounge   dining room   kitchen   hall   clks   study   double garage

399

FRONT ELEVATION

SIDE ELEVATION   REAR ELEVATION   SIDE ELEVATION

An interesting bungalow for a narrow site. The position of the corner fireplace enables the chimney to be taken out through the roof ridge, which is always the preferred way of doing this. A kitchen on the front elevation is a feature asked for by many housewives, and here there are two windows to add to the balance of the look of the property.

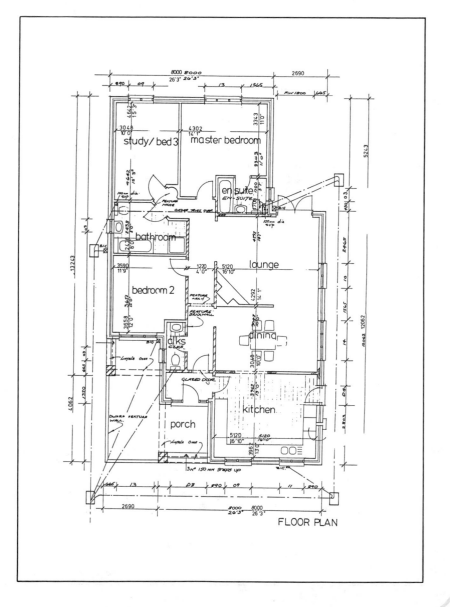

FLOOR PLAN

Coal Fires

Demand for Chimneys Goes Through The Roof!

There has rarely been a better time for the publication of the British Coal edition of *Plans for Dream Homes.*

Each year, tens of thousands of people are able to turn their dreams into reality by either building their own new homes or placing their scheme with an architect and/or builder.

Individual building plots are readily available and regularly snapped-up to become ideal locations for the new homes of Britain's growing army of self-builders.

British Coal sponsored its own nationwide survey to determine the public's view of traditional chimneys and real coal fires — and the results carry a strong message for British self-builders and architects.

The NOP survey of 1,200 people shows that sixty per cent of Britain's owner occupiers would want their next property to have a chimney.

Many people now understand the role played by chimneys and real coal fires in providing an excellent source of natural ventilation and in helping to reduce the difficult problem of condensation.

And at the base of the chimney, real coal or smokeless fuel fires are definitely making a comeback, with three out of four home owners in the survey convinced that a real fire is "unbeatable" as the traditional centrepiece of a living room.

Further market research, this time an RSGB Survey of 2,000 adults around Britain, showed 63 per cent of those questioned agreeing that "no matter how good an imitation fire is, it cannot be as satisfying as a real coal fire." This is the public's opinion, not British Coal's.

With more than 300 designs of solid fuel appliances on the British market today, the choice ranges from the practical to the impressive, from the traditional to the state-of-the art in solid fuel technology.

At the forefront of today's domestic real fire technology must be the Charnwood Fireflow — a coal fire that is controlled entirely automatically.

This remarkable appliance, which can be remotely controlled by a tv remote-type handset, is programmed to feed itself with solid fuel and even remove its own ashes. It is available to anyone who has a standard fireplace and a chimney on an outside wall, with a small amount of space outside for a hopper.

The open fire feeds itself day and night with Coalflow Pearls via an ingenious screw-feed arrangement which also removes the ash ready for collection by your dustman.

Traditional stalwarts of the real fire world would include the Charnwood Stove, which efficiently heats domestic hot water and up to eleven radiators, and the Rayburn Rembrandt, a black cast iron freestanding fire with an impressive canopy and brass finials.

The Parkray Traditional is a classic 16 inch inset open fire which is available with a high output back boiler, to heat hot water and up to six radiators, and the Baxi Burnall is an underfloor draught inset open fire which comes in a range of widths and finishes.

Choosing a complete central heating system, whether for your present home or a new one, is always a major decision and a key investment. It will add value to your property, boosting its eventual selling points, and it will add comfort to your life.

British Coal believes solid fuel central heating has many distinct advantages over its rivals, not least the fact that the fuel itself is very stable in price and boasts reserves in the UK — over three hundred years at the last count — which no other fuel can match.

There is also quite a variety of solid fuel central heating systems to choose from, according to the size of your home and your individual needs. Gravity feed or Coalflow boilers, such as the Trianco TRG or the new Hughes Edwards 65 respectively, are very efficient and economical to use. The higher output boilers can run up to 15 radiators, as well as meet all your hot water needs, while many models are designed to stoke and feed themselves from an in-built coal store.

One of the new generation of heating systems which gives you the best of both worlds is Link-Up. As the name implies, Link-Up actually links a central heating system powered by gas or oil to a real coal fire which is itself fitted with a back boiler.

The result is a system which has all the major benefits of a real fire plus the flexibility of switching to an alternative heat source and greater control over operating economy.

At its basic level, Link Up offers plenty of hot water — while more sophisticated systems can heat up to six radiators. Depending on the circumstances, it is possible to heat just one room with the fire while still having hot water, or the whole house using the central heating system.

Installation of any solid fuel appliance or central heating system is as easy as picking up the phone. All you have to do to be put in touch with a British Coal-approved Heating Engineer or Installer is Dial 0800 600 000. Alternatively contact your local British Coal Area Sales Office or Real Fire Heating shop.

One more important point remains to be made. Having chosen to install a real coal fire and/or solid fuel central heating system, new home self-builders should realise the problems which can be caused by burning cheap imported coal.

Contrary to popular belief, all coal is not the same. For example, imported petroleum coke, although cheap and easily lit, has a dangerous drawback. It burns at such high temperatures that it can melt firebars and badly damage roomheaters, cookers and boilers. Its high sulphur content can cause problems from chimney condensation and appliance manufacturers guarantees may not apply when this fuel is used.

Some imported coals contain up to 12 per cent ash and may have been from coal imported for industrial use, giving disappointing results when used in the home.

So the message is simple. Having invested in an efficient, economical solid fuel system, watch out for the unbranded, low quality imported coal. British Coal believes that Britain's 3.5 million solid fuel users can only be certain of the product they buy when it is Real British Coal, or one of the smokeless fuels made from it.

What is more there are over 100 varieties of housecoal and smokeless fuels produced in the UK, all of them tested for their fine burning characteristics, low ash, good general appearance and consistent size.

For further information about all aspects of real fire heating, either Dial 0800 600 000, or for specialist advice contact any of the organisations below.

National Fireplace Association, 8th Floor, Bridge House, Smallbrook, Queensway, Birmingham B5 4JP. Tel: 021 643 3377.

Solid Smokeless Fuels Federation, Devonshire House, Church Street, Sutton-in-Ashfield, Nottinghamshire, NG17 1AE. Tel: 0623 550411.

Association of British Solid Fuel Appliance Manufacturers — Fleming House, Renfrew Street, Glasgow, G3 6TG. Tel: 041 332 0826/8.

Designing for Energy Efficiency

The CES Heating Design Service

Choosing the right central heating system for your new house is one of the most important aspects of turning it into your dream home.

Like most other major items associated with your house, careful consideration needs to be given to the design of the heating system to ensure that you and your family are comfortable throughout the year.

A professionally designed central heating and hot water system will provide the comfort levels you are seeking and be both efficient and economic to run.

Coal and Energy Services, the consultancy arm of British Coal, offers a specialised heating design service which is tailored to meet your needs.

The service is ideally suited for use by anyone actively involved in domestic heating, from self-builders and DIY enthusiasts through to qualified architects and heating engineers.

Using the very latest Computer Aided Design technology, with software written specifically for CES, various levels of designs and specifications can be produced *regardless of the types of fuel being used to heat your home.*

The nationwide Heating Design Service offered by CES will produce full heat loss calculations, radiator/heat emitter schedules, pipework layout and sizes and recommend appliance/hot water storage cistern positions, with a schematic drawing detailing the appliance to cylinder connections — all invaluable information for the self-builder.

It's a flexible service which may use as its starting point either a simple plan drawing or Coal and Energy Service's own specially developed survey booklet — designed to provide all the necessary information for properties where no detailed drawings exist.

The survey booklet allows CES design staff to process the relevant details of any scheme, ensuring that customers' special heating requirements are met.

CES offers a number of set design options, depending on customers' needs, ranging from providing basic information on heat requirements of properties to full design drawings and parts listings.

These are the basic options available:

Option 1
Detailed heat loss calculations and radiator/emitter schedules.

Option 2
As above plus scale drawing, detailing pipework and sizes.

Option 3
As Options 1 and 2, plus schematic drawing detailing appliance to cylinder connections.

Option 4
All these options combined plus listing of all parts required for any particular scheme.

The CAD system can also be used to turn a basic architect's drawing into a complete presentation drawing, giving self-builders a detailed visual impression of the home they are building.

To take advantage of all or part of the CES Heating Design Service, you can write to Vincent Hale or Gary McMordie at Coal and Energy Services, British Coal, Hobart House, Grosvenor Place, London, SW1X 7AE, or telephone 071-235 2020.

The CES Heating Design Service

The CES Heating Design Service includes all the data and drawings required for the installation. The heating design here is for the design reference PM 514 illustrated on page 145.

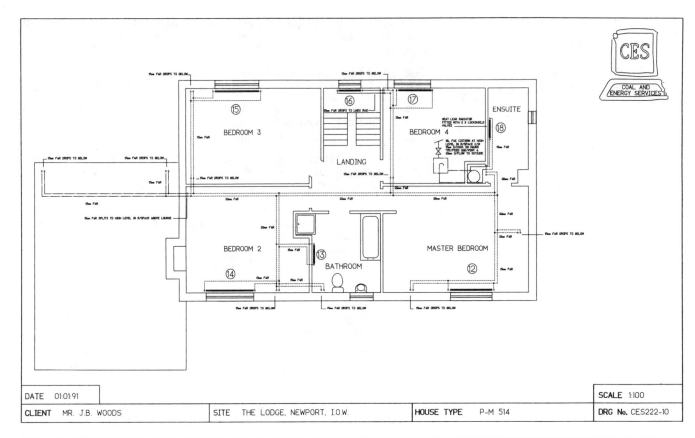

DATE 01·01·91			SCALE 1:100
CLIENT MR. J.B. WOODS	SITE THE LODGE, NEWPORT, I.O.W.	HOUSE TYPE P-M 514	DRG No. CES222-10

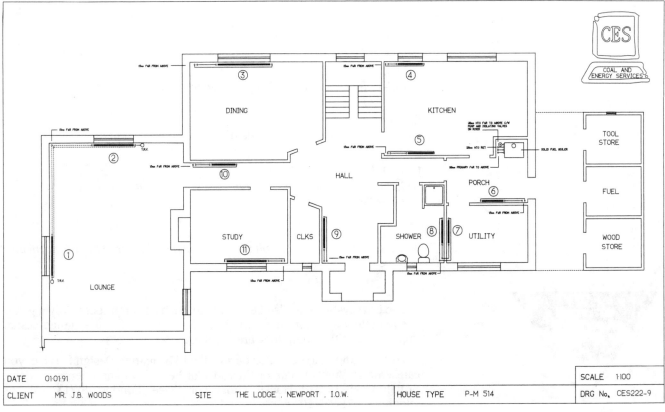

DATE 01·01·91			SCALE 1:100
CLIENT MR. J.B. WOODS	SITE THE LODGE, NEWPORT, I.O.W.	HOUSE TYPE P-M 514	DRG No. CES222-9

DOMESTIC HEATING DESIGN FROM COAL AND ENERGY SERVICES

— A typical example showing layout, cylinder to boiler connections, radiators schedules and parts lists.

For further information contact
GARY MCMORDIE
— Heating Design Manager

Tel No: 071 235 2020 Ext. 34281
Fax: 071 245 9842

EQUIPMENT SCHEDULE AND SYSTEM DRAWING LEGEND IDENTIFICATION

COAL AND ENERGY SERVICES

EQUIPMENT	DESCRIPTION
TYPE	TRIANCOMATIC 60
OUTPUT WATER	17.8kW
PROGRAMMER	SUNVIC SP50 OR EQUAL APPROVED
ROOM THERMOSTAT	SUNVIC TLX2222 OR EQUAL APPROVED
S	PEGLER TERRIER OR EQUAL APPROVED
RADIATOR	SUNVIC TRV4451 OR EQUAL APPROVED
	STELRAD ACCORD OR EQUAL APPROVED
ON CISTERN	SPECIFIERS CHOICE
VES	HONEYWELL 4043B OR EQUAL APPROVED

NOTES

E RESPONSIBILITY OF THE INSTALLER TO ENSURE THE ABOVE
T IS INSTALLED IN ACCORDANCE WITH THE DESIGN DRAWING(S)
49(1990),IEE ELECTRICAL REGULATIONS(15th EDITION),AND
EDITIONS OF WATER AND FIRE REGULATIONS

LEGENDS

OR LEVEL — — — — — — RED		D.F.A. = Drop From Above
VEL ———————— RED		R.T.A. = Rise To Above
LEVEL —·—·—·—·— RED		R.F.B. = Rise From Below
SPACE ———————— RED		D.T.B. = Drop To Below
ER ———————— BLUE		T.R.V. = Thermostatic Radiator Valve
R ———————— GREEN		R T = Room Thermostat

P-M 514	CLIENT	Mr J WOODS	TITLE	THE LODGE
01:01:90	SCALE		DRAWING No.	CES222-14

RADIATOR SCHEDULE

COAL AND ENERGY SERVICES

RAD No.	ROOM	HEAT LOSS W	CORRECTED HEAT LOSS W	RADIATORS	CONNECTIONS
1.	LOUNGE	1630	1630	600 x 1440 K1	15mm B.O.E.
2.	LOUNGE	1630	1630	600 x 1440 K1	15mm B.O.E.
3.	DINING	1914	1914	600 x 1760 K1	15mm B.O.E.
4.	KITCHEN	754	754	600 x 960 P1	15mm B.O.E.
5.	KITCHEN	754	754	600 x 960 P1	15mm B.O.E.
6.	PORCH	344	344	600 x 640 P1	15mm B.O.E.
7.	UTILITY	478	478	600 x 640 P1	15mm B.O.E.
8.	SHOWER	777	777	600 x 960 P1	15mm B.O.E.
9.	HALL	790	790	600 x 960 P1	15mm B.O.E.
10.	HALL	400	400	600 x 480 P1	15mm B.O.E.
11.	STUDY	1126	1126	600 x 1440 P1	15mm B.O.E.
12.	MASTER BEDROOM	849	849		
13.	BATHROOM	807	807	600 x 1120 P1	15mm B.O.E.
14.	BEDROOM 2	751	751	600 x 960 P1	15mm B.O.E.
15.	BEDROOM 3	.762	762	600 x 1120 P1	15mm B.O.E.
16.	LANDING	442	442	600 x 1120 P1	15mm B.O.E.
17.	BEDROOM 4	524	524	600 x 640 P1	15mm B.O.E.
18.	EN-SUITE	682	682	600 x 800 P1	15mm B.O.E.
				600 x 800 P1	15mm B.O.E.

DOMESTIC HOT WATER W	3000

SUGGESTED APPLIANCES
1. TRIANCOMATIC 60
2.
3.
4.

TOTAL HEAT REQUIRED W	18414

NOTES :
1. It is the responsibility of the installer to ensure that this system complies with the building regulations (1990). The current edition of BS5449 I.E.E. electrical regulations (15th edition), and current editions of water and fire regulations.

2. Radiators specified above are Stelrad Accord panel radiators. Other makes with similiar surface area may be installed.

3. The following temperatures have been used then calculating heat losses assuming an outside air temperature of -1 DEG C.
Living room 21 DEG C. Dining room 21 DEG C. Kitchen 18 DEG C. Kitchen/Dining 21 DEG C.
Hall/Landing 16 DEG C. Bedroom(s) 18 DEG C. Bathroom 22 DEG C. Bedsitting room 21 DEG C.

4. * Denotes backup radiator.

PROJECT	P-M 514				
DATE	01:01:90	CLIENT	mr J WOODS	TITLE	THE LODGE
		SCALE		DRAWING No.	CES222-14

405

The P.S.S. Service

P.S.S. PLANS

Plan Sales Services Ltd is a specialist company within the D & M group which handles sales of plans for houses and bungalows in the style of any of the designs in this book. The service which is offered covers the supply of plans, specification notes and books as detailed on pages 406 and 412.

To provide these plans and documents P.S.S. require specific information regarding the site and other details for the proposed building, and this is most conveniently provided by completing the order form on page 411.

ALTERATIONS TO PLANS

Many of the designs illustrated are standard plans for which drawings are immediately available. Such standard plans can be altered provided that the design concept is not changed. The cost of such alterations is quoted as an extra to the basic cost of the plans, and the procedure for preparing altered plans is for an order form to be sent to P.S.S. with the appropriate remittance for the cost of the standard plans. Two prints of the floor plans and elevation for the standard plans will be sent to the client, one copy of which should be returned marked up with the alterations required.

If the alterations are practicable the extra fee required for the altered drawings will be quoted, and if accepted the special drawings will be prepared and will normally be despatched within 15 working days.

SITE PLANS AND LOCATION PLANS

Planning applications require a site plan and a location plan. These are normally reproduced on a single sheet. The standard P.S.S. service can include drawing these plans from data supplied by clients, and responsibility for the accuracy of this data rests with the client.

Location plans are prepared from either any location plan which accompanied an application for an existing outline consent, or from a 1:2500 or similar large scale Ordnance Survey map, or from a deed plan or other map available. The original or photostats of such plan should be sent with the order and should have the boundary of the client's land clearly marked. The company holds a licence to reproduce Ordnance Survey plans in this way.

Site plans are best drawn from sketches prepared by clients, which must include adequate dimensions to allow them to be drawn to scale, and sufficient detail with regard to such features as existing drainage, trees on the site and other details required by the local authority. Delay will be unavoidable if these points are not covered.

We recognise that some clients prepare their own site and location plans.

Plans are individually prepared from master data, and are normally captioned with a general description such as "Proposed bungalow for Mr. H. Smith at High Lane, Sutton". They carry the client's name and address in the bottom right-hand corner. Except for a reference number they do not carry a P.S.S. or any other logo or name, except when they are timber frame plans for which

the design calculations are available from Prestoplan Homes Ltd.

Purchase of the plans conveys an automatic licence to build the dwelling to which they refer. They may not be used for the construction of further dwellings unless arrangements for this have been specially negotiated and confirmed in correspondence. Enquiries from builders and others for the use of designs on a repeat basis are welcomed.

FOUNDATION DETAILS

Most of our plans are drawn assuming a level site, but designs specifically advertised as suitable for sloping sites show standard details for notional slopes. All plans are normally supplied for solid ground floor construction with strip foundations, unless otherwise requested. Where a reinforced concrete raft is required, notional details will be shown, and further details may have to be provided by a Civil Engineer as explained below.

If the ground conditions are unusual, or if you are building on a steep slope, the Local Authority may require a site investigation and that foundations or retaining walls are specially designed. This information is only required to support Building Regulation applications, not Planning Applications. If an application to build on such sites is made using our standard drawings the Local Authority will reply advising whether any special data is required. Although we do not undertake the necessary site investigations and foundation design work for this ourselves, we can put clients in touch with Civil Engineers able to do this work.

If in doubt about this please telephone us and discuss your situation.

ALTERATION TO PLANS FOLLOWING NEGOTIATIONS WITH PLANNING AUTHORITIES

Negotiations with planners sometimes result in a request from the local authority for a new set of plans incorporating design changes. In this case the planning officer concerned should be invited to overdraw one of the original prints with his required alterations, and this should be sent to us. We will quote for preparing the revised drawings and supplying prints as appropriate.

QUERIES RAISED IN CONNECTION WITH BUILDING REGULATION APPLICATIONS

Queries relating to site conditions must be dealt with by the client. P.S.S. will deal with all queries which relate to the structure of the building raised by the local authority arising from building regulation applications. This is handled by sending P.S.S. the original or a photostat of the letter from the authority setting out the additional information required, and P.S.S. will return to the client three copies of amended drawings providing the relevant information or calculations — one for the client to retain and two to be sent to the authority. There is no charge for this if standard designs are involved.

If building regulation queries relate to an altered design, and arise from the alteration to the design, as

The P.S.S. Service

when roof design calculations are required after the span of a standard design has been increased, or special steelwork or timber joists are introduced, the cost of providing this information and any revised drawing will be quoted.

Information that is required regarding proprietary materials or products may have to be obtained from manufacturers. We advise on how this information is best obtained.

For obvious reasons it is preferable that clients check that no alterations are required by planning officers before dealing with building regulation queries.

Additional copies of plans required are available at a nominal charge to cover printing and postage.

P.S.S. are able to handle a limited number of planning and building regulation applications on behalf of clients. Fees for this are quoted individually. This work may be carried out by other companies within the D & M group, or by associates. The number of applications handled in this way is limited as all require individual attention. Normally, 95% of clients make their own submissions to the local authority.

TIMBER FRAME CONSTRUCTION

Clients who wish to build in the style of any of the designs in this book in timber frame can do so using the services of Prestoplan Homes Ltd. All the types of home shown in this book can be built using a timber frame and not just those from the Prestoplan standard range.

Plans can be supplied through P.S.S. if desired but it is preferable to contact Prestoplan direct if you wish to build in timber frame.

Prestoplan Homes Limited
Stanley Street
Preston
PR1 4AT.

DESIGN AND MATERIALS LTD.

P.S.S. is part of the same group of companies as Design & Materials Ltd., and if requested D & M will provide other services for those wishing to build to designs in styles shown in this book.

D & M offer an integrated architectural and material supply service for any house or bungalow in a style illustrated, and this will include a wide range of ancillary services including assistance in placing a contract with a builder. Other special services are provided for those who wish to manage the construction work themselves as self-builders. All D & M services are for traditional construction.

Clients who have purchased plans from P.S.S. can obtain a quotation from D & M for the supply of materials for the building entirely free of obligation.

Design & Materials Limited
Carlton Industrial Estate
Worksop
Notts S81 9LB.
Phone (0909) 730333

FEES FOR P.S.S. PLANS

Prices are quoted according to work involved. As a guide, 1990 average prices were as follows. If a set of PSS drawings leads to using the D & M service the cost of the drawings is refunded

Plans for homes to 1001 sq.ft.
£251.00 + £37.65 VAT = £288.65

Plans from 1002 to 1399 sq.ft.
£298.00 + £44.70 VAT = £342.70

Plans from 1400 to 1699 sq.ft.
£337.00 + £50.55 VAT = £387.50

Plans from 1700 to 2001 sq.ft.
£375.00 + £56.25 VAT = £431.25

Plans over 2001 sq.ft.
from £400.00 + £60.00 VAT = £460.00

Standard garages with plans
£25.00 + £3.75 VAT = £28.75

Standard garages without plans
£100.00 + £15.00 VAT = £115.00

Carsholme garage/flat
£175.00 + £26.25 = £201.25

The arrangements for altering plans and the fees involved are detailed elsewhere.

Extra copies of drawings required at any time are available at £1 per print.

All fees are subject to VAT.

Preliminary enquiries by telephone are welcome.

Plan Sales Services Ltd.,
Lawn Road, Carlton-in-Lindrick,
Worksop, Notts S81 9LB.
Phone Worksop (0909) 733927

Company Reg. No. 1625297

Note for 1991 edition.

Drawings for designs in the **Potton Collection** and the **D & M Collection** are not available from P.S.S., and are supplied as part of special services from the companies concerned. These designs are copyright of Potton Ltd and D & M Ltd.

P.S.S. SERVICE — DRAWINGS

A SET OF P.S.S. DRAWINGS COMPRISES:
* 12 copies of 1:50 floor plans, 1:100 elevations and 1.20 sections with full notes indicating compliance with Building Regulation Standards.
* 4 copies of a foundation plan.
* 4 copies of a floor joist plan.
* 12 copies of a site plan and location plan. Notes on submitting planning applications using P.S.S. drawings.

The P.S.S. Service - Ordering Plans

The P.S.S. Service is a **service**, and the company relies on its reputation for its continuing success. They aim to make ordering a set of plans as easy as possible, and are always ready to give advice to prospective purchasers before they commit themselves. The easiest way to get this advice is to telephone on 0909 733927 during office hours. One of the senior staff is usually on hand to discuss your requirements with you, but if the right person for you to speak to is not immediately available then someone will arrange to phone you back. If you prefer to write to P.S.S., they will send a reply back to you on the day that they get your letter.

The full details of the service are set out on pages 406 and 407, and explains how P.S.S. prepares drawings to your own requirements. They will draw your site plan, will provide a specification for the building, and much else. Please read these pages carefully, and if you have any queries telephone 0909 733927.

An order form is on the facing page. If possible please complete the part asking for your phone number, as we would like to be able to telephone you if there is any point regarding your order which we would like to check with you.

Ring P.S.S. on
0909 733927

Queries.

1/ Can we have a bigger porch at the front door?

2/ Must be able to get the piano in the study — can we move the door?

3/ Ask about the landing on the stairs.

4/ Can we have the drawings by the 25th for the Council?

Addresses

THE DESIGNERS

* Design & Materials Ltd, Carlton Industrial Estate, Worksop, Notts S81 9LB.
  Phone Worksop (0909) 730333

* Prestoplan Homes Ltd, Four Oaks Road, Walton Summit Centre, Preston PR5 9AS.
  Phone Preston (0772) 627373

* Potton Limited, The Old Foundry, Willow Road, Potton, Sandy, Beds. SG19 2PP
  Phone Potton (0767) 260348

* Plan Sales Services Ltd, Lawn Road, Carlton, Worksop, Notts S81 9LB.
  Phone Worksop (0909) 733927

* R.B.S. Ltd, Unit 29, Argyll Industrial Estate, Heol-Trelai, Ely, Cardiff CF5 5NJ.
  Phone Cardiff (0222) 596071

INSURANCES WHILE BUILDING

* DMS Services Ltd., Orchard House, Blyth, Worksop, Notts. Phone Worksop (0909) 591652

HEATING DESIGN

* C.E.S. Heating Design Service, Hobart House, Grosvenor Place, London SW1X 7AE.
  Phone 071 235 2020

BUILDING CENTRES PROVIDING INFORMATION SERVICES ONLY

* Building Materials Information Service, 22 Broadway, Peterborough PE1 1RU.

* The Building Centre, 6 Higham Place, Newcastle NE1 8AF.

INFORMATION ON ARCHITECTS

* The Royal Institute of British Architects, 66 Portland Place, London W1.

BUILDING WARRANTIES

* The National House Builders Council, 58 Portland Place, London W1.

* Municipal Mutual Insurance Limited, Building Guarantee Dept, P.O. Box 71, Farnborough, Hants. GU14 0NT
  Phone 0252 377474

ADVICE ON SELF BUILD GROUPS

* The National Federation of Housing Associations, 175 Grays Inn Road, London WC1X 8UP.

OTHER BOOKS IN THIS SERIES

* Ryton Books, 29 Ryton Street, Worksop, Notts S80 2AY. Phone Worksop (0909) 591652
  (see also order form at the back of this book)

Plans Order Form

P.S.S. Ltd.
Please supply a set of plans as in
Plans for Dream Homes. A cheque to cover fees is
enclosed.

I understand the basis on which plans are supplied, and am available to deal with queries by phone, when the most convenient time to ring is

a.m./p.m.

Are you placing this order following previous contact with P.S.S.? If so, please give some reference (eg date of telephone call, or details of correspondence).

Yes/No

Do you require plans for a design
generally as shown in the book?   ☐ tick

Or with alterations?   ☐ tick

Or an original design?   ☐ tick

Many plans in this book are of standard designs for which standard drawings are available. Others illustrate design styles in which new drawings can be prepared.

Which is the design that meets, or most nearly meets your requirements? (Give page number or design number)

Site Address ....

....

To which hand (ie as illustrated, or in mirror image)?

In what materials will you build?

Roofing ....

External Walling ....

Please indicate appropriate roof pitch (tick).

22½°   30°   35°

40°   other - please state

Name ....

Address ....

....

....

Daytime phone number ....

Evening phone number ....

> **Prices are quoted according to work involved. As a guide, 1990 average prices were as follows. If a set of PSS drawings leads to using the D & M service the cost of the drawings is refunded**
>
> Plans for homes to 1001 sq.ft.
> £251.00 + £37.65 VAT = £288.65
> Plans from 1002 to 1339 sq.ft.
> £298.00 + £44.70 VAT = £342.70
> Plans from 1400 to 1699 sq.ft.
> £337.00 + £50.55 VAT = £387.50
> Plans from 1700 to 2001 sq.ft.
> £375.00 + £56.25 VAT = £431.25
> Plans over 2001 sq.ft.
> from £400.00 + £60.00 VAT = £460.00
> Standard garages with plans
> £25.00 + £3.75 VAT = £28.75
> Standard garages without plans
> £100.00 + £15.00 VAT = £115.00
> Carsholme garage/flat
> £175.00 + £26.25 VAT = £201.25
> Amendments — minimum charge
> £50.00 + £7.50 VAT = £57.50
> Plan Sales Services Ltd.
> Lawn Road, Carlton-in-Lindrick, Worksop, Notts S81 9LB.
> Phone Worksop (0909) 733927

Is the roof to be shown with barge boards and fascia, or with pointed verge & corbells? Please tick appropriate sketch.

BARGE BOARD AND FASCIA   POINTED VERGE AND CORBELLS

Advise whether any french windows or patio doors shown in our design should be shown as french windows or as sliding patio doors (this does not count as an alteration to a standard design).

Should any fireplace and chimney shown in the drawings be retained or deleted? This does not count as an alteration.

Do you require the drawings to show a solid concrete ground floor, or a suspended timber ground floor? (delete)
Concrete/Timber

The attention of clients is drawn to the terms and conditions of sale printed on the reverse of this order form.

Terms and Conditions

TERMS AND CONDITIONS OF SALE

1. These terms and conditions are concerned with the sale by Plan Sales Services Ltd, of plans as advertised in the book Plans for Dream Homes. All sales of plans by the company unless expressly stated otherwise are in accordance with these terms and conditions of sale, and clients placing an order for these plans are deemed to do so on these conditions.

2. All contracts are for the sale of plans only, and do not imply the provision of an architectural service, advice on the use of plans or the construction of buildings or other services of any sort except where specifically arranged in writing.

3. All plans offered are fully detailed in accordance with current architectural practice, but no liability is accepted for any loss of any sort or additional expense incurred consequent on any failure, real or alleged, of the plans to meet the requirements of any body, statutory or otherwise, or of any loss of any sort or additional expense incurred due to any failure by the purchaser to submit the plans as and when required to any body, statutory or otherwise. All dimensions on drawings which relate to site dimensions, drainage, access, or other features of a development are deemed to have been checked and approved by clients. Clients purchasing plans are advised in writing to check all dimensions shown on drawings and to satisfy themselves that they are in every way correct. No responsibility can be accepted for any loss consequent on failure to do this.

4. All plans are supplied as being adequate to enable competent craftsmen, properly directed and working to the published recommendations of the National Housebuilders Registration Council to erect the building to which they relate, but no liability whatsoever is accepted for the building so erected. Contracts are established on the understanding that all plans and drawings supplied will be used by persons competent and experienced in the use of building plans and drawings, and no liability will be accepted for any expense incurred due to the failure of such persons to relate plans and drawings to site conditions, materials delivered, or other circumstances, or to take immediate action on discovering any anomaly in the drawings as detailed in sections 0500, 0530, 0540 and 0106 of the P.S.S. specification.

5. The company will alter drawings as detailed in the book Plans for Dream Homes, and in other advertising literature, but such alterations will only be made in accordance with specific and precise instructions.

6. The company will deal with technical queries dealing with the application of the Building Regulations and N.H.B.C. requirements to the structures shown in the drawings, but can only do this if provided with the original or a photostat of the query on the letterhead of the authority requiring this information. Information required regarding proprietary materials or components to be used may have to be obtained from manufacturers. We advise on how this information is best obtained.

7. The company is unable to deal with queries from statutory authorities relating to site conditions.

8. All orders for plans are dealt with immediately they are received. If plans are required urgently, as when drawings have to be submitted to a planning authority within a deadline, this should be advised to the company in writing and the work will be given every priority. However, no responsibility can be accepted for the consequences of any delay in delivery of plans.

9. Proof of posting of plans shall be proof of delivery. Any plans lost in the post will be replaced at "copy plan" cost.

10. Master negatives of plans supplied will be kept for a period of three years only.

11. No refunds can be made in respect of plans returned as no longer required, whether or not they have received Planning Consent or Building Regulation Approval.

12. Where clients are referred to Design & Materials Ltd, or any other company for special services beyond the scope of the P.S.S. service, any new contract is between the client and the company concerned, and P.S.S. Ltd will not be a party to any such contract.

13. The copyright of all plans is held by the company, and remains with the company on the supply of plans. The supply of a set of plans as advertised conveys a licence to build one dwelling to the plans supplied, and the erection of further dwellings is a breach of copyright unless this has been the subject of a separate written contract.

14. These terms and conditions define the nature of the contract, and attention is drawn to them in the book Plans for Dream Homes and other publications. They do not detract from the statutory rights of the client in the contract.

15. The description of the P.S.S. service as published in this 1991 edition of Plans for Dream Homes, replaces all previous descriptions, and all contracts made from the date of the publication of this 1991 edition are on these terms.

413

BUILDERS RISKS INSURANCES
FOR THOSE BUILDING ON THEIR OWN LAND

The Norwich Union is able to offer an insurance package for those who are building for their own occupation private dwellings of traditional construction with the help of labour only sub-contractors. It does not apply to the extension, alteration, repair or renovation of existing buildings. This affords Contract Works, Public Liability and Employers' Liability cover and automatically includes the interest of any Mortgagee. Cover will be provided in one policy document, summarised as follows. This description of insurance must be regarded only as an outline. The policy is a legal document and as such defines the insurance in precise terms. A specimen copy of the policy form is available on request.

CONTRACT WORKS

Cover   "All Risks" of loss or damage to:
- (a)   the new building whilst under construction and materials for incorporation therein
- (b)   plant, tools, equipment and temporary buildings (other than residential caravans).

Sum insured   The full rebuilding cost of the property, excluding the value of the land.
including
- (a)   your own and hired plant, tools and equipment used in connection with the work up to a total sum insured of £2000 (can be increased if required).
- (b)   Employees personal effects and tools whilst on the site up to a sum insured of £250 any one employee.
- (c)   Architects, Surveyors and other fees necessarily incurred in rebuilding following loss or damage.
- (d)   the cost of removing debris following any claim.

Excluding
- (a)   the first £50 of each and every claim for loss or damage to employees personal effects or tools.
- (b)   the first £250 of each and every other loss.

EMPLOYERS LIABILITY (compulsory by law)

Cover   Your legal liability for death or bodily injury to employees, including labour only sub-contractors, arising out of the building work.
Limit   Unlimited.
Including   Legal costs and expenses in defending any claim.
Note   A Certificate of Insurance will be provided, and must by law be displayed on site.

PUBLIC LIABILITY

Cover   Your legal liability to members of the public for death, bodily injury or damage to property, arising out of the building work.
Limit   £1,000,000 any one loss.
Including   Legal costs and expenses in defending any claim.
Excluding   The first £100 of any claim for damage to property.

PERIOD   From the commencement date you specify (which should be no earlier than the date you complete the proposal form) up to completion of the building work, subject to a maximum of 24 months. Extensions to this period are available on payment of an additional premium. There is no refund for early completion.

THE POLICY   Will be sent direct to you by the Insurance Company.

THE PREMIUM   £4.25 per £1,000 for traditional construction and £5.25 per £1,000 for timber frame construction on the rebuilding cost of the property. (Minimum Premium £150.) This is a total rate for all the cover set out above, subject to submission of the completed proposal form overleaf.

Declared value of new building (excluding land) up to £	Premium Std. £	Timber Frame £	Declared value of new building (excluding land) up to £	Premium Std. £	Timber Frame £	Declared value of new building (excluding land) up to £	Premium Std. £	Timber Frame £
35,000	150.00	183.70	75,000	318.75	393.70	130,000	552.50	682.50
40,000	170.00	210.00	80,000	340.00	420.00	140,000	595.00	735.00
45,000	191.25	236.20	85,000	361.25	446.20	150,000	637.50	787.50
50,000	212.50	262.50	90,000	382.50	472.50	160,000	680.00	840.00
55,000	233.75	288.70	95,000	403.75	498.70	170,000	722.50	892.50
60,000	255.00	315.00	100,000	425.00	525.00	180,000	765.00	945.00
65,000	276.25	341.20	110,000	467.50	577.50	190,000	807.50	997.50
70,000	297.50	367.50	120,000	510.00	630.00	200,000	850.00	1050.00

Over 200,000 @
£4.25 per £1000 (Std. Construction)
or
£5.25 per £1000 (Timber Frame)

IMPORTANT
The above terms only apply:
- (a)   up to 31st December 1991. Amended terms may be necessary for proposal forms completed after that date.
- (b)   to risks in Mainland Great Britain only. Proposals from N. Ireland are quoted individually. Phone 0909 591652 for a quotation
- (c)   where there is no history of flooding in the area.

THE AGENCY
The Agency is DMS Services Ltd., a company which provides specialised insurance services to those building on their own. The proposal form overleaf should be completed and sent to the agency with a cheque for the premium payable to the Norwich Union Insurance Fire Society Limited.

D.M.S. Services Ltd., Orchard House, Blyth, Worksop, Notts. S81 8HF. Phone 0909 591652

Agency: DMS Services Ltd   Agency Reference: 2GA479   Policy No.

Proposal - BUILDING OWN PRIVATE DWELLING
The Insurer: Norwich Union Fire Insurance Society Limited

Name of Proposer	Phone No.

Full Postal Address

....

Postcode

Address of property to be erected

....

Commencing date of insurance

Important - Please give a definite answer to each question (block letters) and tick appropriate boxes

	Yes	No	If "Yes" please give details

1. Have you made any other proposal for insurance in respect of the risk proposed? ☐ ☐

2. Has any company or underwriter declined your proposal? ☐ ☐

3. Have you ever been convicted of (or charged but not yet tried with) arson or any offence involving dishonesty of any kind (eg fraud, theft, handling stolen goods)? ☐ ☐

4. Will the property be

   (a) of standard brick, stone or concrete construction, roofed with slates, tiles, asphalt, concrete or metal? ☐ ☐

   (b) of timber frame construction? ☐ ☐

   (c) occupied as your permanent residence on completion? ☐ ☐   (If "No" please refer to DMS Services Ltd.) Phone 0909 591652

5. (a) Will the total value of plant, tools, equipment and temporary buildings used exceed £2,000 on site at any one time? ☐ ☐   Contractors plant hired in with operators, such as excavators, need not be included if proposers are wholly satisfied the hirers insurances cover all risks. However if cover is required on such machines phone DMS Services on 0909 591652

   (b) Will plant be hired-in for which you are responsible to insure? ☐ ☐

6. Is there any history of flooding in the area? ☐ ☐

7. Will all work be in accordance with drawings approved by the Local Authority and the instructions of their Building Inspector? ☐ ☐

8. State estimated value of building work on completion at builder price for reinstatement.   £   N.B. This will be the limit of indemnity for item (a) of the Contract Works Section.

9. Material facts — state any other material facts here. Failure to do so could invalidate the policy. A material fact is one which is likely to influence an insurer in the assessment and acceptance of the proposal. If you are in any doubt as to whether a fact is material it should be disclosed to the insurer.

Note: 1. You should keep a record (including copies of letters) of all information supplied to the insurer for the purpose of entering into the contract.
2. A copy of this proposal form will be supplied by the Insurer on request within three months of completion.
3. Please note that the details you are asked to supply may be used to provide you with information about other products and services which the Norwich Union Group can offer.

Declaration To be completed in all cases:

I desire to insure with the Insurer in the terms of the Policy used in this class of Insurance. I warrant that the above statements and particulars are true to the best of my knowledge and belief and that I have not withheld any material information. I agree to give immediate notice to the insurer of any alteration to the circumstances described herein and that this proposal shall form the basis of the contract between us.

Proposer's signature	Date

Send completed form to DMS Services Ltd., Orchard House, Blyth, Worksop, Notts. S81 8HF, together with a cheque made payable to the Norwich Union Fire Insurance Society Limited. Any queries to DMS Services, Phone 0909 591652.

Norwich Union Fire Insurance Society Limited. Registered in England No. 99122. Registered Office: Surrey Street, Norwich NR1 3NS. Member of the Association of British Insurers. Member of the Insurance Ombudsman Bureau.

HOME PLUS COVER
On completion cover for the building and contents is available under a Norwich Union Home Plus policy. For details tick this box — ☐